V. G. Maz'ja Sobolev Spaces

Vladimir G. Maz'ja

Sobolev Spaces

Translated from the Russian by
T. O. Šapošnikova

With 25 Figures

Springer-Verlag
Berlin Heidelberg New York Tokyo

Professor Vladimir G. Maz'ja

Leningrad University
Faculty of Mathematics and Mechanics
198904 Leningrad, USSR

This volume is part of the *Springer Series in Soviet Mathematics*
Advisers: L. D. Faddeev (Leningrad), R. V. Gamkrelidze (Moscow)

Mathematics Subject Classification (1980):
46E35, 35J, 35P, 31B15, 26B

ISBN 3-540-13589-8 Springer-Verlag Berlin Heidelberg New York Tokyo
ISBN 0-387-13589-8 Springer-Verlag New York Heidelberg Berlin Tokyo

Printed in Germany

Typesetting: K+V Fotosatz GmbH, Beerfelden. Offsetprinting: Mercedes-Druck, Berlin
Bookbinding: Lüderitz & Bauer, Berlin

2141/3020-543210

To Tatyana

Preface

The Sobolev spaces, i.e. the classes of functions with derivatives in L_p, occupy an outstanding place in analysis. During the last two decades a substantial contribution to the study of these spaces has been made; so now solutions to many important problems connected with them are known.

In the present monograph we consider various aspects of Sobolev space theory. Attention is paid mainly to the so called imbedding theorems. Such theorems, originally established by S. L. Sobolev in the 1930s, proved to be a useful tool in functional analysis and in the theory of linear and nonlinear partial differential equations.

We list some questions considered in this book.

1. What are the requirements on the measure μ for the inequality

$$(\int |u|^q d\mu)^{1/q} \leqslant C \| u \|_{S_p^l},$$

where S_p^l is the Sobolev space or its generalization, to hold?

2. What are the minimal assumptions on the domain for the Sobolev imbedding theorem to remain valid? How do these theorems vary under the degeneration of the boundaries? How does the class of admissible domains depend on additional requirements placed upon the behavior of a function near the boundary?

3. How "massive" must a subset e of the domain Ω be in order that "the Friedrichs inequality"

$$\| u \|_{L_q(\Omega)} \leqslant C \| \nabla_l u \|_{L_p(\Omega)}$$

hold for all smooth functions that vanish in a neighborhood of e?

The investigation of these and similar problems is not only of interest in its own right. By virtue of well-known general considerations it leads to conditions for the solvability of boundary value problems for elliptic equations and to theorems on the structure of the spectrum of the corresponding operators. Such applications are also included.

The selection of topics was mainly influenced by my involvement in their study, so a considerable part of the text is a report of my work in the field.

The book has no essential intersection with the monographs by S. M. Nikol'skiĭ [202], Besov, Il'in, Nikol'skiĭ [27], R. A. Adams [12], Peetre [210] and Triebel [244, 245], which were published during the last decade and are also devoted to spaces of differentiable functions.

Each of the twelve chapters of the book is divided into sections and most of the latter consist of subsections. The sections and subsections are numbered by two and three numbers, respectively (3.1 is Section 1 in Chapter 3, 1.4.3 is Subsection 3 in Section 4 in Chapter 1). Inside subsections we use an independent numbering of theorems, lemmas, propositions, corollaries, remarks, etc. If a subsection contains only one theorem or lemma then this theorem or lemma has no number. In references to the material from another section or subsection we first indicate the number of this section or subsection. For example, Theorem 1.2.1/1 means Theorem 1 in Subsection 1.2.1, (2.7/2) denotes formula (2) in Section 2.7.

The reader can obtain a general idea of the contents of the book from the Introduction. Most of the references to the literature are collected in Comments. The list of notation is given at the end of the book.

A part of this monograph was published in German in three volumes of Teubner-Texte zur Mathematik, Leipzig (Einbettungssätze für Sobolewsche Räume, Teil 1, 1979; Teil 2, 1980; Zur Theorie Sobolewscher Räume, 1981). In the present volume the material is essentially expanded and revised.

Acknowledgements

I gratefully remember my talented pupil A. L. Rosin who perished in 1976 in a mountain ascent and with whom I repeatedly discussed the project of this book.

I wish to express my gratitude to Ju. D. Burago who in spite of being busy with writing his own book found time for the joint work on Chapter 6.

I take pleasure in acknowledging the friendly help of S. P. Preobraženskiĭ and S. V. Poborčiĭ for their contributions to the improvement of the text.

My cordial thanks are due Leo F. Boron who kindly agreed to prepare the manuscript for publication and reduced the quantity of obscurities and slips.

It is my pleasant duty to thank Springer-Verlag for the excellent quality of this edition.

The dedication of this book to its translator and my wife Dr. T. O. Šapošnikova is a weak expression of my gratitude for her infinite patience, useful advice and constant assistance.

Leningrad, autumn 1985 V. G. Maz'ja

Contents

Introduction

In [229 – 231] Sobolev proved general integral inequalities for differentiable functions of several variables and applied them to a number of problems of mathematical physics. Sobolev introduced a notion of the generalized derivative and considered the Banach space $W_p^l(\Omega)$ of functions in $L_p(\Omega)$, $p \geqslant 1$, with generalized derivatives of order l summable of order p. In particular, using his theorems on the potential type integrals as well as an integral representation of functions and the properties of mollifications, Sobolev established the imbedding of $W_p^l(\Omega)$ into $L_q(\Omega)$ or $C(\Omega)$ under certain conditions on the exponents p, l, q.

Later the Sobolev theorems were generalized and refined in various ways (Kondrašov, Il'in, Gagliardo, Nirenberg etc.). In these studies the domains of functions possess the so-called cone property (each point of a domain is the vertex of a spherical cone with fixed height and angle which is situated inside the domain). Simple examples show that this condition is precise, e.g. if the boundary contains an outward "cusp" then a function in $W_p^1(\Omega)$ is not in general summable with power $pn/(n-p)$, $n > p$, contrary to the Sobolev inequality. On the other hand, looking at Fig. 1, the reader can easily see that

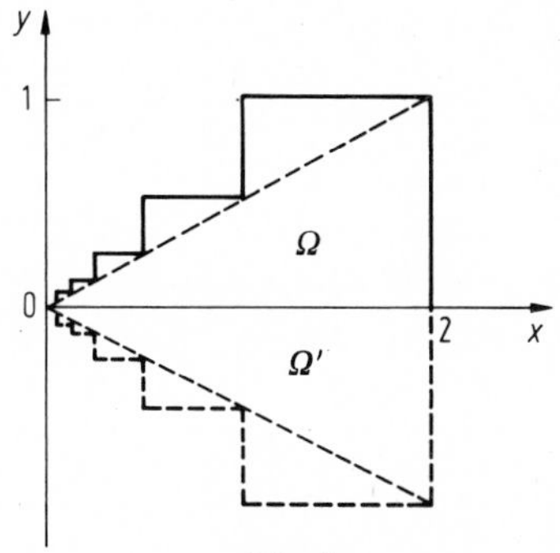

Fig. 1

the cone property is unnecessary for the imbedding $W_p^1(\Omega) \subset L_{2p/(2-p)}(\Omega)$, $2 > p$. Indeed, by unifying Ω with its mirror image, we obtain a new domain with the cone property for which the above imbedding is true by the Sobolev theorem. Consequently, the same is valid for the initial domain although it does not have the cone property.

Now we note that even before the Sobolev results it was known that certain integral inequalities hold under fairly weak requirements on the domain. For instance, the Friedrichs inequality ([68], 1927)

$$\int_{\Omega} u^2 dx \leqslant K\left(\int_{\Omega} (\operatorname{grad} u)^2 dx + \int_{\partial\Omega} u^2 ds\right)$$

was established under the sole assumption that Ω is a bounded domain for which the Gauss-Green formula holds. In 1933 Nikodým [199] gave an example of a domain Ω such that the square summability of the gradient does not imply the square summability of the function defined in Ω. The monograph of Courant and Hilbert [47] contains sufficient conditions for the validity of the Poincaré inequality

$$\int_{\Omega} u^2 dx \leqslant K \int_{\Omega} (\operatorname{grad} u)^2 dx + \frac{1}{m_n \Omega}\left(\int_{\Omega} u\, dx\right)^2$$

and of the Rellich lemma on the compactness in $L_2(\Omega)$ of a set bounded in the metric

$$\int_{\Omega} [(\operatorname{grad} u)^2 + u^2]\, dx\,.$$

The above exposition naturally suggests the problem of describing the properties of domains which are equivalent to various properties of imbedding operators. In the author's papers, the first of which was published in 1960, necessary and sufficient as well as simple sufficient conditions for the validity of certain imbedding theorems were obtained for the space $W_p^1(\Omega)$.

For $p=1$ these conditions coincide with "isoperimetric inequalities" connecting the volume and the area of a part of the boundary of an arbitrary subset of the domain. The proofs were based on certain representations of integrals in terms of level sets and subsequent estimates of these integrals by isoperimetric inequalities. Concurrently and independently of the author the same device was used by Federer and Fleming [63], 1960, for the proof of the Gagliardo inequality

$$\| u \|_{L_{n/(n-1)}(R^n)} \leqslant c \,\| \operatorname{grad} u \|_{L_1(R^n)}\,, \qquad u \in C_0^\infty(R^n)\,,$$

with the best constant.

For $p>1$, geometric functionals such as volume and area are insufficient for an adequate description of the properties of domains. Here the isoperimetric inequalities between the volume and the p-capacity or the p-conductivity arise [141–144, 146, 149–152].

The material of the present book is concentrated around similar results although they do not exhaust it even conceptually.

The book is devoted to numerous aspects of the theory of Sobolev spaces. However, attention is mainly paid to the study of imbedding operators.

The most extensive Chapter 1 represents a modern introduction to the theory. Along with classical facts this chapter contains certain new results.

In § 1.3 a complete study of the one-dimensional Hardy inequality with two weights is presented. § 1.4 contains the generalizations of the Sobolev theorems on necessary and sufficient conditions for the L_q-summability with respect to an arbitrary measure of functions in $W_p^l(\Omega)$. These results are due to D. R. Adams [1, 2] and the author [163]. Here, as in Sobolev's papers, it is assumed that the domain is "good", for instance, it possesses the cone property. In general, in requirements on a domain in Chapter 1 we follow the "all or nothing" principle.

The exceptional § 1.5 concerns the class preserving extension of functions in Sobolev spaces. This problem was paid much attention recently [77, 78, 107]. In particular, we consider an example of a domain for which the extension operator exists and which is not a quasicircle.

In § 1.6 the integral representation of functions in $W_p^l(\Omega)$ that vanish on $\partial\Omega$ along with all their derivatives up to the order $k-1$, $2k \geqslant l$, is obtained. This representation entails the imbedding theorems of Sobolev type for any bounded domain Ω. In the case $2k < l$ it is shown by example that some requirements on $\partial\Omega$ are necessary.

The idea of the equivalence of isoperimetric inequalities and imbedding theorems is crucial for many subsequent chapters of the book.

Most of Chapter 2 deals with necessary and sufficient conditions for the validity of integral inequalities for gradients of functions that vanish at the boundary. Of special importance for applications are multi-dimensional inequalities of Hardy-Sobolev type proved in § 2.1. The basic results of Chapter 2 are applied to the spectral theory of the Schrödinger operator in § 2.5.

The space $L_p^1(\Omega)$ of functions with gradients in $L_p(\Omega)$ is studied in Chapters 3–5. Chapter 3 deals with the case $p=1$. Here, necessary and sufficient conditions for the validity of imbedding theorems, stated in terms of the classes $\mathscr{J}_\alpha$, are found. We also check whether some concrete domains belong to this class. In Chapters 4 and 5 we extend the presentation to the case $p>1$. Here the criteria are formulated in terms of the p-conductivity. In Chapter 4 we discuss theorems on imbeddings into $L_q(\Omega)$ and $L_q(\partial\Omega)$. Chapter 5 concerns imbeddings into $L_\infty(\Omega) \cap C(\Omega)$. In particular, we present necessary and sufficient conditions for the validity of the above mentioned Friedrichs and Poincaré inequalities and of the Rellich lemma. Throughout the book and especially in Chapters 3–5 we include numerous examples of domains which illustrate possible pathologies of imbedding operators. For instance, in § 1.1 we show that the square summability of second derivatives and of the function do not imply the square summability of first derivatives. In § 5.5 we consider the domain for which the imbedding operator of $W_p^1(\Omega)$ into $L_\infty(\Omega) \cap C(\Omega)$ is continuous without being compact. This is impossible for domains with "good" boundaries. The results of Chapters 3–5 show that not only the classes of domains determine the parameters p, q, etc. in imbedding theorems but that a feedback takes place. The criteria for the validity of integral inequalities are applied in Chapter 4 to the theory of elliptic boundary value problems. The exhaustive results on imbedding operators can be restated as necessary and sufficient conditions for the unique solvability and for the discreteness of the spectrum of boundary value problems, in particular, of the Neumann problem.

Chapter 6, written together with Ju. D. Burago, is devoted to the study of the space $BV(\Omega)$ consisting of the functions whose gradients are vector charges. Here we present a necessary and sufficient condition for the existence of a bounded nonlinear extension operator $BV(\Omega)\to BV(R^n)$. We find necessary and sufficient conditions for the validity of imbedding theorems for the space $BV(\Omega)$ which are similar to those obtained for $L_1^1(\Omega)$ in Chapter 3. In some integral inequalities we obtain best constants. The results of §§ 6.5, 6.6 on traces of functions in $BV(\Omega)$ make it possible to discuss boundary values of "bad" functions defined on "bad" domains. Along with results due to Burago and the author in Chapter 6 we present the De Giorgi-Federer theorem on conditions for the validity of the Gauss-Green formula.

Chapters 2–6 mainly concern functions with *first* derivatives in L_p or in C^*. This restriction is essential since the proofs are based on the truncation of functions along their level surfaces. The next six chapters deal with functions that have derivatives of any integer, and sometimes of fractional, order.

Chapter 7 is auxiliary. Here we collect (mainly without proofs) the well-known properties of Bessel and Riesz potential spaces and of Besov spaces in R^n. In Chapter 7 we also present a review of results of the theory of (p, l)-capacities and of nonlinear potentials.

In Chapter 8 we investigate necessary and sufficient conditions for the validity of the inequality

$$\|u\|_{L_q(\mu)} \leqslant C\|u\|_{S_p^l}, \quad u\in C_0^\infty(R^n), \tag{1}$$

where $L_q(\mu)$ is the space with the norm $(\int |u|^q d\mu)^{1/q}$, μ is a measure and S_p^l is one of the spaces just mentioned. For $q\geqslant p$ (1) is equivalent to the isoperimetric inequality connecting the measure μ and the capacity generated by the space S_p^l. This result is of the same type as the theorems in Chapters 2–6. It immediately follows from the inequality

$$\int_0^\infty \operatorname{cap}(\mathcal{N}_t; S_p^l)\, t^{p-1} dt \leqslant C\|u\|_{S_p^l}^p,$$

where $\mathcal{N}_t=\{x: |u(x)|\geqslant t\}$. Inequalities of this type, initially found by the author for the spaces $L_p^1(\Omega)$ and $\mathring{L}_p^2(R^n)$ [152], have proven to be useful in a number of problems of function theory. Recently they were intensively studied by D. R. Adams [5], Dahlberg [48], Hansson [87, 88], the author [160, 168], and others. The transition to derivatives of an arbitrary order turned out to be nontrivial and up to now has been performed only for functions defined on the whole space.

For $q > p \geqslant 1$ the criteria for the validity of (1) do not contain a capacity. In this case the measure of any ball is estimated by a certain function of the radius. Results of this kind, also presented in Chapter 8, are due to the author and Preobraženskiĭ [176] and to the author [163]. They are related to the theorem of D. R. Adams [1, 2] proved in § 1.4.

Further, in Chapter 9 we introduce and study a certain kind of capacity. In comparison with the capacities defined in Chapter 7 here the class of admissible functions is restricted, they equal the unity in a neighborhood of a compactum. (In the case of capacities in Chapter 7 the admissible functions majorize the unity on a compactum.) If the order, l, of the derivatives in the norm of the space equals 1, then the two capacities coincide. For $l \neq 1$ they are equivalent which is proved in § 9.3.

The capacity introduced in Chapter 9 is applied in all subsequent chapters to prove various imbedding theorems. An inequality of the Friedrichs type for functions on a cube is studied in detail in Chapter 10. This inequality is used to study conditions for the imbedding of $\mathring{L}_p^l(\Omega)$ into different function spaces in Chapter 11. By $\mathring{L}_p^l(\Omega)$ we mean the completion of the space $C_0^\infty(\Omega)$ with respect to the metric $\| \nabla_l u \|_{L_p(\Omega)}$. It is known that this completion is not imbedded, in general, into the distribution space $\mathscr{D}'$. In Chapter 11 we present necessary and sufficient conditions for the imbeddings of $\mathring{L}_p^l(\Omega)$ into $\mathscr{D}'$, $L_q(\Omega, \mathrm{loc})$, $L_q(\Omega)$. For $p = 2$ these results can be interpreted as necessary and sufficient conditions for the solvability of the Dirichlet problem for the polyharmonic equation in unbounded domains provided the right-hand side is contained in $\mathscr{D}'$ or in $L_q(\Omega)$. Finally, in Chapter 12 we find criteria for the boundedness and the compactness of the imbedding operator of the space $\mathring{L}_p^l(\Omega, \nu)$ into $W_q^r(\Omega)$, where ν is a measure and $\mathring{L}_p^l(\Omega, \nu)$ is the completion of $C_0^\infty(\Omega)$ with respect to the norm

$$\left(\int_\Omega | \nabla_l u |^p dx + \int_\Omega | u |^p d\mu \right)^{1/p} .$$

The results of this chapter are mostly borrowed from the papers by the author [156] and the author and Otelbaev [175]. They represent an extension of the well-known criterion for the discreteness of the spectrum of the Schrödinger operator due to Molčanov [189].

Chapter 1. Basic Properties of Sobolev Spaces

§ 1.1. The Spaces $L_p^l(\Omega)$, $V_p^l(\Omega)$ and $W_p^l(\Omega)$

1.1.1. Notation

Let Ω be an open subset of n-dimensional Euclidean space $R^n = \{x\}$.

Let $C^\infty(\Omega)$ denote the space of infinitely differentiable functions on Ω; by $C^\infty(\bar{\Omega})$ we mean the space of restrictions to Ω of functions in $C^\infty(R^n)$.

In what follows $\mathscr{D}(\Omega)$ or $C_0^\infty(\Omega)$ is the space of functions in $C^\infty(R^n)$ with compact supports in Ω.

The classes $C^k(\Omega)$, $C^k(\bar{\Omega})$, $C_0^k(\Omega)$ of functions with continuous derivatives of order k and the classes $C^{k,\alpha}(\Omega)$, $C^{k,\alpha}(\bar{\Omega})$, $C_0^{k,\alpha}(\bar{\Omega})$ of functions for which the derivatives of order k satisfy a Hölder condition with exponent $\alpha \in (0,1]$ are defined in an analogous way.

Let $\mathscr{D}'(\Omega)$ be the space of distributions dual to $\mathscr{D}(\Omega)$ (cf. Schwartz [224], Gel'fand and Šilov [72]).

Let $L_p(\Omega)$, $1 \leqslant p \leqslant \infty$, denote the space of Lebesgue measurable functions, defined on Ω, for which

$$\|f\|_{L_p(\Omega)} = \left(\int_\Omega |f|^p dx \right)^{1/p} < \infty ;$$

by $L_p(\Omega, \text{loc})$ we mean the space of functions locally summable of order p in Ω. The space $L_p(\Omega, \text{loc})$ can be naturally equipped with a countable system of seminorms $\|u\|_{L_p(\omega_k)}$, where $\{\omega_k\}_{k \geqslant 1}$ is a sequence of domains with compact closures $\bar{\omega}_k$, $\bar{\omega}_k \subset \omega_{k+1} \subset \Omega$, $\bigcup_k \omega_k = \Omega$. Then $L_p(\Omega, \text{loc})$ becomes a complete metrizable space.

If $\Omega = R^n$ we shall often omit Ω in notations of spaces and norms. Integration without indication of limits extends over R^n.

Further let $\operatorname{supp} f$ be the support of a function f and let $\operatorname{dist}(F, E)$ denote the distance between the sets F and E. Let $B(x, \varrho)$ or $B_\varrho(x)$ denote an open ball with center x and radius ϱ, $B_\varrho = B_\varrho(0)$. We shall use the notation m_n for n-dimensional Lebesgue measure in R^n and v_n for $m_n(B_1)$.

Let $c, c_1, c_2, \ldots$ denote positive constants that depend only on "dimensionless" parameters n, p, l, and the like. We call the quantities a and b equivalent and write $a \sim b$ if $c_1 a \leqslant b \leqslant c_2 a$.

If α is a multi-index $(\alpha_1, \ldots, \alpha_n)$, then, as usual, $|\alpha| = \sum_j \alpha_j$, $\alpha! = \alpha_1! \ldots \alpha_n!$, $D^\alpha = D_{x_1}^{\alpha_1} \ldots D_{x_n}^{\alpha_n}$, where $D_{x_i} = \partial/\partial x_i$, $x^\alpha = x_1^{\alpha_1} \ldots x_n^{\alpha_n}$. The inequality $\beta \geqslant \alpha$ means that $\beta_i \geqslant \alpha_i$ for $i = 1, \ldots, n$. Finally, $\nabla_l = \{D^\alpha\}$, where $|\alpha| = l$ and $\nabla = \nabla_1$.

1.1.2. Local Properties of Elements in the Space $L_p^l(\Omega)$

Let $L_p^l(\Omega)$ denote the space of distributions on Ω with derivatives of order l in the space $L_p(\Omega)$. We equip $L_p^l(\Omega)$ with the seminorm

$$\| \nabla_l u \|_{L_p(\Omega)} = \left(\int_\Omega \left(\sum_{|\alpha| = l} |D^\alpha u(x)|^2 \right)^{p/2} \right)^{1/p}.$$

Theorem. *Any element of $L_p^l(\Omega)$ is in $L_p(\Omega, \mathrm{loc})$.*

Proof. Let ω and g be bounded open subsets of R^n such that $\omega \subset g \subset \Omega$. Moreover, we assume that the sets ω and g are contained in g and Ω along with their ε-neighborhoods. We introduce $\varphi \in \mathscr{D}(\Omega)$ with $\varphi = 1$ on g, take an arbitrary $u \in L_p^l(\Omega)$ and set $T = \varphi u$. Further, let $\eta \in \mathscr{D}$ be such that $\eta = 1$ in a neighborhood of the origin and $\operatorname{supp} \eta \subset B_\varepsilon$.

It is well known that the fundamental solution of the polyharmonic operator Δ^l is

$$\Gamma(x) = \begin{cases} c_{n,l} |x|^{2l-n}, & \text{for } 2l < n \text{ or for odd } n \leqslant 2l; \\ c_{n,l} |x|^{2l-n} \log |x|, & \text{for even } n \leqslant 2l. \end{cases}$$

Here the constant $c_{n,l}$ is chosen so that $\Delta^l \Gamma = \delta(x)$ holds.

It is easy to see that $\Delta^l(\eta\Gamma) = \zeta + \delta$ with $\zeta \in \mathscr{D}(R^n)$. Therefore,

$$T + \zeta * T = \sum_{|\alpha| = l} \frac{l!}{\alpha!} D^\alpha(\eta\Gamma) * D^\alpha T,$$

where the star denotes convolution. We note that $\zeta * T \in C^\infty(R^n)$. So, we have to examine the expression $D^\alpha(\eta\Gamma) * D^\alpha T$.

Using the formula

$$D^\alpha(\varphi u) = \sum_{\alpha \geqslant \beta} \frac{\alpha!}{\beta!\,(\alpha - \beta)!} D^\alpha \varphi D^{\alpha - \beta} u,$$

we obtain

$$D^\alpha T = D^\alpha(\varphi u) = \varphi D^\alpha u$$

in g. Hence,

$$D^\alpha(\eta\Gamma) * D^\alpha T = D^\alpha(\eta\Gamma) * \varphi D^\alpha u$$

in ω. To conclude the proof, we observe that the integral operator with a weak singularity, applied to $\varphi D^\alpha u$, is continuous in $L_p(\omega)$.

Corollary. *Let* $u \in L_p^l(\Omega)$. *Then all distributional derivatives* $D^\alpha u$ *with* $|\alpha| = 0, 1, \ldots, l-1$ *belong to the space* $L_p(\Omega, \mathrm{loc})$.

The proof follows immediately from the inclusion $D^\alpha u \in L_p^{l-|\alpha|}(\Omega)$ and the above theorem.

Remark. By making use of results in 1.4.5 we can refine Theorem to obtain more information on elements in $L_p^l(\Omega)$.

1.1.3. Absolute Continuity of Functions in $L_p^1(\Omega)$

Here we shall discuss a well-known property of $L_p^1(\Omega)$, $p \geqslant 1$.

A function defined on Ω is said to be absolutely continuous on the straight line l if this function is absolutely continuous on any segment of l, contained in Ω.

Theorem 1. *Any function in* $L_p^1(\Omega)$ *(possibly modified on a set of zero measure* m_n*) is absolutely continuous on almost all straight lines which are parallel to coordinate axes. The distributional gradient of a function in* $L_p^1(\Omega)$ *coincides with the usual gradient almost everywhere.*

In the proof of this assertion we use the following simple lemma.

Lemma. *Let* $g \in L_1(0,1)$ *and let* η *be an arbitrary function in* $\mathscr{D}(0,1)$. *If* $\int_0^1 g(t)\eta'(t)\,dt = 0$ *then* $g(t) = \mathrm{const}$ *for almost all* $t \in (0,1)$.

Proof. Let Φ and α be functions in $\mathscr{D}(0,1)$, $\int_0^1 \alpha(\tau)\,d\tau = 1$. It is clear that $\Phi - \alpha \int_0^1 \Phi(\tau)\,d\tau$ is the derivative of a function in $\mathscr{D}(0,1)$. Hence

$$0 = \int_0^1 g(t)\left(\Phi(t) - \alpha(t)\int_0^1 \Phi(\tau)\,d\tau\right)dt = \int_0^1 \left(g(t) - \int_0^1 g(\tau)\,\alpha(\tau)\,d\tau\right)\Phi(t)\,dt\,.$$

Since $\Phi \in \mathscr{D}(0,1)$ is arbitrary, then

$$g(t) = \int_0^1 g(\tau)\,\alpha(\tau)\,d\tau \qquad \text{a.e. on } (0,1)\,.$$

For *the proof of Theorem 1* it suffices to assume that $\Omega = \{x\colon 0 < x_i < 1, 1 \leqslant i \leqslant n\}$. Let $x' = (x_1, \ldots, x_{n-1})$ be a point of the $(n-1)$-dimensional cube $\omega = \{x'\colon 0 < x_i < 1, 1 \leqslant i \leqslant n-1\}$. By Fubini's theorem

$$\int_0^1 \left|\frac{\partial u}{\partial t}(x', t)\right| dt < \infty \qquad \text{for almost all } x' \in \omega\,,$$

where $\partial u/\partial t$ is the distributional derivative. Therefore, the function

$$x_n \to v(x) = \int_0^{x_n} \frac{\partial u}{\partial t}(x',t)\,dt$$

is absolutely continuous on the segment $[0,1]$ for almost all $x' \in \omega$ and its classical derivative coincides with $\partial u/\partial x_n$ for almost all $x_n \in (0,1)$.

Let $\zeta \in \mathscr{D}(\omega)$ and let $\eta \in \mathscr{D}(0,1)$. After integration by parts we obtain

$$\int_0^1 v(x',t)\,\eta'(t)\,dt = -\int_0^1 \eta(t)\,\frac{\partial v}{\partial t}(x',t)\,dt\,.$$

Multiplying both sides of the preceding equation by $\zeta(x')$ and integrating over ω, we obtain

$$\int_\Omega v(x)\,\eta'(x_n)\,\zeta(x')\,dx = -\int_\Omega \eta(x_n)\,\zeta(x')\,\frac{\partial v}{\partial x_n}\,dx\,.$$

By the definition of distributional derivative,

$$\int_\Omega u(x)\,\eta'(x_n)\,\zeta(x')\,dx = -\int_\Omega \eta(x_n)\,\zeta(x')\,\frac{\partial v}{\partial x_n}\,dx\,.$$

Hence the left sides of the two last identities are equal. Since the function $\zeta \in \mathscr{D}(\omega)$ is arbitrary, we obtain

$$\int_0^1 [u(x',x_n) - v(x',x_n)]\,\eta'(x_n)\,dx_n = 0$$

for almost all $x' \in \omega$. By Lemma the difference $u(x',x_n) - v(x',x_n)$ does not depend on x_n a.e. on ω. In other words, for almost any fixed x'

$$u(x) = \int_0^{x_n} \frac{\partial u}{\partial t}(x',t)\,dt + \text{const}\,.$$

This concludes the proof.

The converse assertion is contained in the following theorem.

Theorem 2. *If a function u defined on Ω is absolutely continuous on almost all straight lines that are parallel to coordinate axes and the first classical derivatives of u belong to $L_p(\Omega)$, then these derivatives coincide with the corresponding distributional derivatives, and hence $u \in L_p^1(\Omega)$.*

Proof. Let v_j be the classical derivative of u with respect to x_j and let $\eta \in \mathscr{D}(\Omega)$. After integration by parts we obtain

$$\int_\Omega \eta\, v_j\, dx = -\int_\Omega \frac{\partial \eta}{\partial x_j}\, u\, dx$$

which shows that v_j is the distributional derivative of u with respect to x_j.

1.1.4. The Spaces $W_p^l(\Omega)$ and $V_p^l(\Omega)$

We introduce the spaces $W_p^l(\Omega) = L_p^l(\Omega) \cap L_p(\Omega)$ and $V_p^l(\Omega) = \bigcap_{k=0}^{l} L_p^k(\Omega)$, equipped with the norms

$$\|u\|_{W_p^l(\Omega)} = \|\nabla_l u\|_{L_p(\Omega)} + \|u\|_{L_p(\Omega)},$$

$$\|u\|_{V_p^l(\Omega)} = \sum_{k=0}^{l} \|\nabla_k u\|_{L_p(\Omega)}.$$

We present here two examples of domains which show that in general $L_p^l(\Omega) \neq W_p^l(\Omega) \neq V_p^l(\Omega)$.

In his paper of 1933 Nikodým [199] studied functions with finite Dirichlet integral. There he gave an example of a domain for which $W_2^1(\Omega) \neq L_2^1(\Omega)$.

Example 1. The domain Ω considered by Nikodým is the union of the rectangles (cf. Fig. 2)

$$A_m = \{(x,y): 2^{1-m} - 2^{-1-m} < x < 2^{1-m},\quad 2/3 < y < 1\},$$

$$B_m = \{(x,y): 2^{1-m} - \varepsilon_m < x < 2^{1-m},\quad 1/3 \leqslant y \leqslant 2/3\},$$

$$C = \{(x,y): 0 < x < 1,\quad 0 < y < 1/3\},$$

where $\varepsilon_m \in (0, 2^{-m-1})$ and $m = 1, 2, \ldots$.

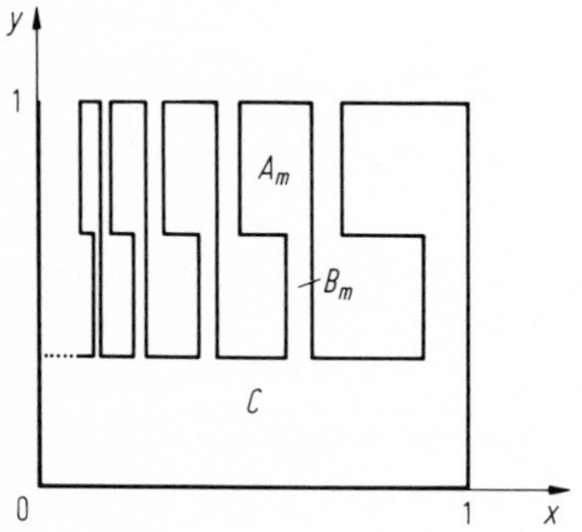

Fig. 2

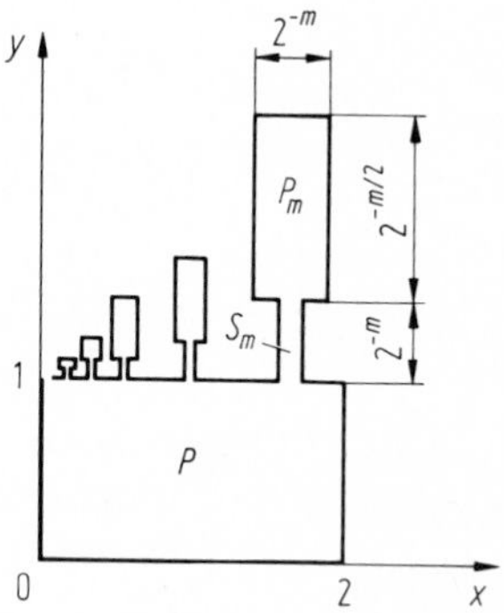

Fig. 3

Positive numbers α_m are chosen so that the series

$$\sum_{k=1}^{\infty} \alpha_m^2 m_2(A_m) \tag{1}$$

diverges. Let u be a continuous function on Ω that is equal to α_m on A_m, zero on C and linear on B_m. Since the series (1) diverges, u does not belong to

$L_2(\Omega)$. On the other hand, the numbers ε_k can be chosen so small that the Dirichlet integral

$$\sum_{k=1}^{\infty} \iint_{B_k} \left(\frac{\partial u}{\partial y}\right)^2 dx\,dy$$

converges.

Example 2. The spaces $W_2^2(\Omega)$ and $V_2^2(\Omega)$ do not coincide for the domain Ω shown in Fig. 3. Let

$$u(x,y) = \begin{cases} 0 & \text{on } P, \\ 4^m(y-1)^2 & \text{on } S_m \quad (m=1,2,\ldots), \\ 2^{m+1}(y-1)-1 & \text{on } P_m \quad (m=1,2,\ldots). \end{cases}$$

We can easily check that

$$\iint_{S_m} (\nabla_2 u)^2 dx\,dy = 2^{2-m},$$

$$\iint_{S_m} u^2 dx\,dy = 2^{-5m},$$

$$\iint_{P_m} u^2 dx\,dy \sim 2^{-m/2},$$

$$\iint_{S_m} (\nabla u)^2 dx\,dy \sim 2^{-3m},$$

$$\iint_{P_m} (\nabla u)^2 dx\,dy \sim 2^{m/2}.$$

Therefore, $\| \nabla u \|_{L_2(\Omega)} = \infty$ whereas $\| u \|_{W_2^2(\Omega)} < \infty$.

1.1.5. Approximation of Functions in Sobolev Spaces by Smooth Functions on Ω

Let $\varphi \in \mathscr{D}$, $\varphi \geqslant 0$, $\operatorname{supp} \varphi \subset B_1$ and $\int \varphi(x)\,dx = 1$.

With any $u \in L(\Omega)$ that vanishes on $R^n \backslash \Omega$, we associate the family of its *mollifications*

$$(\mathscr{M}_\varepsilon u)(x) = \varepsilon^{-n} \int \varphi\left(\frac{x-y}{\varepsilon}\right) u(y)\,dy.$$

The function φ is called a *mollifier* and ε is called *a radius of mollification.*

We formulate some almost obvious properties of a mollification:

1) $\mathscr{M}_\varepsilon u \in C^\infty(\Omega)$;
2) If $u \in L_p(\Omega)$, then $\mathscr{M}_\varepsilon u \to u$ in $L_p(\Omega)$ and $\| \mathscr{M}_\varepsilon u \|_{L_p(R^n)} \leqslant \| u \|_{L_p(\Omega)}$;
3) If ω is a bounded domain, $\bar{\omega} \subset \Omega$, then for sufficiently small ε

$$D^\alpha \mathscr{M}_\varepsilon u = \mathscr{M}_\varepsilon D^\alpha u$$

in ω. So for $u \in L_p^l(\Omega)$

$$D^\alpha \mathscr{M}_\varepsilon u \to D^\alpha u \quad \text{in } L_p(\omega) .$$

The properties of a mollification enable us to prove easily that $\| \nabla_l u \|_{L_p(\Omega)} = 0$ is equivalent to asserting that u is a polynomial of degree not higher than $l-1$.

The following two theorems show the possibility of approximating any function in $L_p^l(\Omega)$ and $W_p^l(\Omega)$ by smooth functions on Ω.

Theorem 1. *The space $L_p^l(\Omega) \cap C^\infty(\Omega)$ is dense in $L_p^l(\Omega)$.*

Proof. Let $\{\mathscr{B}_k\}_{k \geqslant 1}$ be a locally finite covering of Ω by open balls $\mathscr{B}_k$ with radii r_k, $\bar{\mathscr{B}}_k \subset \Omega$, and let $\{\varphi_k\}_{k \geqslant 1}$ be a partition of unity subordinate to this covering. Let $u \in L_p^l(\Omega)$ and let $\{\varrho_k\}$ be a sequence of positive numbers which monotonically tends to zero so that the sequence of balls $\{(1+\varrho_k)\,\mathscr{B}_k\}$ has the same properties as $\{\mathscr{B}_k\}$. If $\mathscr{B}_k = B_\varrho(x)$, then by definition we put $c\,\mathscr{B}_k = B_{c\varrho}(x)$. Let w_k denote the mollification of $u_k = \varphi_k u$ with radius $\varrho_k r_k$. Clearly, $w = \sum w_k$ belongs to $C^\infty(\Omega)$. We take $\varepsilon \in (0, 1/2)$ and choose ϱ_k to satisfy

$$\| u_k - w_k \|_{L_p^l(\Omega)} \leqslant \varepsilon^k .$$

On any bounded open set ω, $\bar{\omega} \subset \Omega$, we have

$$u = \sum u_k$$

where the sum contains a finite number of terms. Hence,

$$\| u - w \|_{L_p^l(\omega)} \leqslant \sum \| u_k - w_k \|_{L_p^l(\omega)} \leqslant \varepsilon (1-\varepsilon)^{-1} .$$

Therefore, $w \in L_p^l(\Omega) \cap C^\infty(\Omega)$ and

$$\| u - w \|_{L_p^l(\Omega)} \leqslant 2\varepsilon .$$

The theorem is proved.

The next theorem is proved similarly.

Theorem 2. *The space $W_p^l(\Omega) \cap C^\infty(\Omega)$ is dense in $W_p^l(\Omega)$ and the space $V_p^l(\Omega) \cap C^\infty(\Omega)$ is dense in $V_p^l(\Omega)$.*

Remark. It follows from the proof of Theorem 1 that the space $L_p^l(\Omega) \cap C^\infty(\Omega) \cap C(\bar{\Omega})$ is dense in $L_p^l(\Omega) \cap C(\bar{\Omega})$ if Ω has a compact closure. The same is true if L_p^l is replaced by W_p^l or by V_p^l.

In fact, let ϱ_k be such that

$$\|u_k - w_k\|_{C(\bar{\Omega})} \leqslant \varepsilon^k .$$

We put

$$\mathscr{V}_N = \sum_{k=1}^{N} w_k + \sum_{k=N+1}^{\infty} u_k .$$

Then

$$\sup_{x\in\Omega} |w(x) - \mathscr{V}_N(x)| \leqslant \sum_{k=N+1}^{\infty} \|u_k - w_k\|_{C(\bar{\Omega})} \leqslant 2\varepsilon^{N+1}$$

and hence $w \in C(\bar{\Omega})$, since w is the limit of a sequence in $C(\bar{\Omega})$. On the other hand,

$$\|u - w\|_{C(\bar{\Omega})} \leqslant \sum_{k=1}^{\infty} \|u_k - w_k\|_{C(\bar{\Omega})} \leqslant 2\varepsilon ,$$

which completes the proof.

1.1.6. Approximation of Functions in Sobolev Spaces by Functions in $C^\infty(\bar{\Omega})$

We consider a domain $\Omega \subset R^2$ for which $C^\infty(\Omega)$ can not be replaced by $C^\infty(\bar{\Omega})$ in Theorems 1.1.5/1 and 1.1.5/2.

We introduce polar coordinates (ϱ, θ) with $0 \leqslant \theta < 2\pi$. The boundary of the domain $\Omega = \{(\varrho, \theta)\colon 1 < \varrho < 2, 0 < \theta < 2\pi\}$ consists of the two circles $\varrho = 1$, $\varrho = 2$ and the interval $\{(\varrho, \theta)\colon 1 < \varrho < 2, \ \theta = 0\}$. The function $u = \theta$ is summable on Ω along with all its derivatives, but it is not absolutely continuous on segments of straight lines $x = \text{const} > 0$, which intersect Ω. According to Theorem 1.1.3/1 the function u does not belong to $L_p^l(\Omega_1)$, where Ω_1 is the annulus $\{(\varrho, \theta)\colon 1 < \varrho < 2, 0 \leqslant \theta < 2\pi\}$. Hence, the derivatives of this function can not be approximated in the mean by functions in $C^\infty(\bar{\Omega})$.

A necessary and sufficient condition for the density of $C^\infty(\bar{\Omega})$ in Sobolev spaces is unknown. The following two theorems contain simple sufficient conditions.

Definition. A domain $\Omega \subset R^n$ is called *starshaped with respect to a point 0* if any ray with origin 0 has a unique common point with $\partial\Omega$.

Theorem 1. *If Ω is a bounded domain, starshaped with respect to a point, then $C^\infty(\bar{\Omega})$ is dense in $W_p^l(\Omega)$, $V_p^l(\Omega)$ and $L_p^l(\Omega)$.*

Proof. Let $u \in W_p^l(\Omega)$. We may assume that Ω is starshaped with respect to the origin. We introduce the notation $u_\tau(x) = u(\tau x)$ for $\tau \in (0, 1)$. We can easily see that $\|u - u_\tau\|_{L_p(\Omega)} \to 0$ as $\tau \to 1$.

From the definition of the distributional derivative it follows that $D^\alpha(u_\tau) = \tau^l (D^\alpha u)_\tau$, $|\alpha| = l$. So, $u_\tau \in W_p^l(\tau^{-1}\Omega)$ and

$$\|D^\alpha(u - u_\tau)\|_{L_p(\Omega)} \leqslant (1 - \tau^l)\, \|D^\alpha u\|_{L_p(\Omega)} + \|D^\alpha u - (D^\alpha u)_\tau\|_{L_p(\Omega)} .$$

The right-hand side tends to zero as $\tau \to 1$. Therefore, $u_\tau \to u$ in $W_p^l(\Omega)$.

Since $\bar{\Omega} \subset \tau^{-1}\Omega$, the sequence of mollifications of u_τ converges to u_τ in $W_p^l(\Omega)$. Now, using the diagonalization process, we can construct a sequence of functions in $C^\infty(\bar{\Omega})$ which approximates u in $W_p^l(\Omega)$.

Thus we proved the density of $C^\infty(\bar{\Omega})$ in $W_p^l(\Omega)$. The spaces $L_p^l(\Omega)$ and $V_p^l(\Omega)$ can be considered in an analogous manner.

Theorem 2. *Let Ω be a domain with compact closure of the class C. This means that every $x \in \partial\Omega$ has a neighborhood $\mathscr{U}$ such that $\Omega \cap \mathscr{U}$ has the representation $x_n < f(x_1, \dots, x_{n-1})$ in some system of Cartesian coordinates with a continuous function f. Then $C^\infty(\bar{\Omega})$ is dense in $W_p^l(\Omega)$, $V_p^l(\Omega)$ and $L_p^l(\Omega)$.*

Proof. We limit consideration to the space $V_p^l(\Omega)$. By Theorem 1.1.5/2 we may assume that $u \in C^\infty(\Omega) \cap V_p^l(\Omega)$.

Let $\{\mathscr{U}\}$ be a small covering of $\partial\Omega$ such that $\mathscr{U} \cap \partial\Omega$ has an explicit representation in Cartesian coordinates and let $\{\eta\}$ be a smooth partition of unity subordinate to this covering. It is sufficient to construct the required approximation for $u\eta$.

We may specify Ω by

$$\Omega = \{x = (x', x_n) \colon x' \in G,\, 0 < x_n < f(x')\}$$

where $G \subset R^{n-1}$ and $f \in C(\bar{G})$, $f > 0$ on G. Also we may assume that u has a compact support in $\Omega \cup \{x \colon x' \in G,\, x_n = f(x')\}$.

Let ε denote any sufficiently small positive number. Obviously, $u_\varepsilon(x) = u(x', x_n - \varepsilon)$ is smooth on $\bar{\Omega}$. It is also clear that for any multi-index α, $0 \leqslant |\alpha| \leqslant l$,

$$\|D^\alpha(u_\varepsilon - u)\|_{L_p(\Omega)} = \|(D^\alpha u)_\varepsilon - D^\alpha u\|_{L_p(\Omega)} \to 0$$

as $\varepsilon \to +0$. The result follows.

Remark. The domain Ω, considered at the beginning of this section, for which $C^\infty(\bar{\Omega})$ is not dense in Sobolev spaces, has the property $\partial\Omega \neq \partial\bar{\Omega}$. We might be tempted to suppose that the equality $\partial\Omega = \partial\bar{\Omega}$ provides the density of $C^\infty(\bar{\Omega})$ in $L_p^l(\Omega)$. The following example shows that this conjecture is not true.

Example (Kolsrud [113]). We shall prove the existence of a bounded domain $\Omega \subset R^n$ such that $\partial\Omega = \partial\bar{\Omega}$ and $L_p^1(\Omega) \cap C(\bar{\Omega})$ is not dense in $L_p^1(\Omega)$.

We start with the case $n = 2$. Let K be a closed nowhere dense subset of the segment $[-1, 1]$ and let $\{B_i\}$ be a sequence of open disks constructed on adjacent intervals of K taken as their diameters. Let B be the disk $x^2 + y^2 < 4$ and let $\Omega = B \backslash \overline{\cup B_i}$. We can choose K so that the linear measure of $\Gamma = \{x \in K \colon |x| < 1/2\}$ is positive. Consider the characteristic function θ of the upper half-plane $y > 0$ and a function $\eta \in C_0^\infty(-1, 1)$ which is equal to unity on $(-1/2, 1/2)$.

The function U, defined by

$$U(x,y) = \eta(x)\,\theta(x,y)\ ,$$

belongs to the space $L_p^1(B)$ for all $p \geqslant 1$. Suppose that $u_j \to U$ in $L_p^1(\Omega)$, where $\{u_j\}_{j\geqslant 1}$ is a sequence of functions in $C(\bar{\Omega}) \cap L_p^1(\Omega)$. According to our assumption, for almost all $x \in \Gamma$ and for all $\delta \in (0, 1/2)$,

$$u_j(x,\delta) - u_j(x,-\delta) = \int_{-\delta}^{\delta} \frac{\partial u_j(x,y)}{\partial y}\, dy\ .$$

Hence

$$\int_{\Gamma} |u_j(x,\delta) - u_j(x,-\delta)|\, dx \leqslant \iint_{\Gamma(\delta)} |\operatorname{grad} u_j(x,y)|\, dx\, dy$$

where $\Gamma(\delta) = \Gamma \times (-\delta, \delta)$.

Since $u_j \to U$ in L_1^1, the integrals

$$\iint_{\Gamma(\delta)} |\operatorname{grad} u_j(x,y)|\, dx\, dy\ , \qquad j \geqslant 1\ ,$$

are uniformly small. Therefore, for each $\varepsilon > 0$ there exists a $\delta_0 > 0$ such that for all $\delta \in (0, \delta_0)$

$$\int_{\Gamma} |u_j(x,\delta) - u_j(x,-\delta)|\, dx < \varepsilon\ .$$

Applying Fubini's theorem we obtain that the left-hand side converges to

$$\int_{\Gamma} |U(x,\delta) - U(x,-\delta)|\, dx = m_1(\Gamma)$$

as $j \to \infty$ for almost all small δ. Hence $m_1(\Gamma) \leqslant \varepsilon$ which contradicts the positiveness of $m_1(\Gamma)$.

Since $\partial\Omega = \partial\bar{\Omega}$ the required counterexample has been constructed for $n = 2$.

In case $n > 2$, let Ω_2 denote the plane domain considered above, put $\Omega = \Omega_2 \times (0,1)^{n-2}$ and duplicate the above argument.

1.1.7. Transformation of Coordinates in Norms of Sobolev Spaces

Let H and G be domains in R^n and let

$$T\colon\ y \to x(y) = (x_1(y), \ldots, x_n(y))$$

be a homeomorphic map of H onto G.

We say that T is a *quasi-isometric map,* if for any $y_0 \in H$, $x_0 \in G$,

$$\limsup_{y \to y_0} \frac{|x(y) - x(y_0)|}{|y - y_0|} \leqslant L \,, \quad \limsup_{x \to x_0} \frac{|y(x) - y(x_0)|}{|x - x_0|} \leqslant L \tag{1}$$

and the Jacobian $\det x'(y)$ preserves its sign in H.

We can check that the estimates (1) are equivalent to

$$\|x'(y)\| \leqslant L \text{ a.e. on } H \,, \quad \|y'(x)\| \leqslant L \text{ a.e. on } G \,,$$

where x', y' are the Jacobi matrices of the mappings $y \to x(y)$, $x \to y(x)$ and $\|\cdot\|$ is the norm of a matrix. This immediately implies that the quasi-isometric map satisfies the inequalities

$$L^{-n} \leqslant |\det x'(y)| \leqslant L^n \,. \tag{2}$$

By definition, the map T belongs to the class $C^{l-1,1}(\bar{H})$, $l \geqslant 1$, if the functions $y \to x_i(y)$ belong to the class $C^{l-1,1}(\bar{H})$.

It is easy to show that if T is a quasi-isometric map of the class $C^{l-1,1}(\bar{H})$, then T^{-1} is of the class $C^{l-1,1}(\bar{G})$.

Theorem. *Let T be a quasi-isometric map of the class $C^{l-1,1}(\bar{H})$, $l \geqslant 1$, that maps H onto G. Let $u \in V_p^l(G)$ and $v(y) = u(x(y))$. Then $v \in V_p^l(H)$ and for almost all $y \in H$ the derivatives $D^\alpha v(y)$, $|\alpha| \leqslant l$, exist and are expressed by the classical formula*

$$D^\alpha v(y) = \sum_{1 \leqslant |\beta| \leqslant |\alpha|} \varphi_\beta^\alpha(y) (D^\beta u)(x(y)) \,. \tag{3}$$

Here

$$\varphi_\beta^\alpha(y) = \sum_s c_s \prod_{i=1}^n \prod_j (D^{s_{ij}} x_i)(y)$$

and the summation is taken over all multi-indices $s = (s_{ij})$ satisfying the conditions

$$\sum_{i,j} s_{ij} = \alpha \,, \quad |s_{ij}| \geqslant 1 \,, \quad \sum_{i,j} (|s_{ij}| - 1) = |\alpha| - |\beta| \,.$$

Moreover, the norms $\|v\|_{V_p^l(H)}$ and $\|u\|_{V_p^l(G)}$ are equivalent.

Proof. Let $u \in C^\infty(G) \cap V_p^1(G)$. Then v is absolutely continuous on almost all straight lines which are parallel to coordinate axes. The first partial derivatives of v are expressed by the formula

$$\frac{\partial v(y)}{\partial y_m} = \sum_{i=1}^n \frac{\partial x_i(y)}{\partial y_m} \left(\frac{\partial u}{\partial x_i} \right) (x(y)) \tag{4}$$

for almost all y. Since

$$\| \nabla v \|_{L_p(H)} \leqslant c \| \nabla u \|_{L_p(G)}$$

then by Theorem 1.1.3/2, $v \in V_p^1(H)$. After the approximation of an arbitrary $u \in V_p^l(G)$ by functions in $C^\infty(G) \cap V_p^1(G)$ (cf. Theorem 1.1.5/2) the result follows in the case $l = 1$.

For $l > 1$ we use induction. Let (3) hold for $|\alpha| = l-1$. Since $D^\beta u \in V_p^1(G)$, the functions $y \to (D^\beta u)(x(y))$ belong to the space $V_p^1(H)$. This and $\varphi_\beta^\alpha \in C^{0,1}(\bar{H})$ imply that each summand in the right-hand side of (2) with $|\alpha| = l-1$ belongs to $V_p^1(H)$. Applying (4) to (3) with $|\alpha| = l$ we obtain

$$\| \nabla_l v \|_{L_p(H)} \leqslant c \| u \|_{V_p^l(G)} \cdot$$

The result follows.

1.1.8. Domains Starshaped with Respect to a Ball

Definition. Ω is *starshaped with respect to a ball* contained in Ω if Ω is starshaped with respect to each point of this ball.

Lemma. *Let Ω be a bounded domain starshaped with respect to a ball B_ϱ with radius ϱ and with center at the origin of spherical coordinates (r, ω). If $\partial\Omega$ has a representation $r = r(\omega)$, then $r(\omega)$ satisfies a Lipschitz condition.*

Proof. We shall show that for all $x, y \in \partial\Omega$ with

$$(1) \qquad |\omega_x - \omega_y| < 1$$

the inequality

$$|x - y| \leqslant 2D^2 \varrho^{-1} |\omega_x - \omega_y|$$

holds, where D is the diameter of Ω.

The inequality (1) means that the angle φ between the vectors x and y is less than $\pi/3$. We shall show that the straight line l, passing through the points x, y, can not intersect the ball $B_{\varrho/2}$.

In fact, if there exists a point $z \in l \cap B_{\varrho/2}$, then z belongs to the segment xy since Ω is starshaped with respect to z. Consider the triangles Oxz, Oyz. The inequalities $|x| \geqslant \varrho$, $|y| \geqslant \varrho$, $|z| \leqslant \varrho/2$ imply $|z| \leqslant |y-z|$, $|z| \leqslant |x-z|$. Hence $\measuredangle Oxz \leqslant \pi/3$, $\measuredangle Oyz \leqslant \pi/3$ and $\varphi = \pi - \measuredangle Oxz - \measuredangle Oyz \geqslant \pi/3$, which contradicts (1).

The distance from the origin O to the line l is $|x||y||x-y|^{-1} \sin\varphi$ which is less than $\varrho/2$ since $l \cap B_{\varrho/2} \neq \varnothing$. Therefore

$$|x - y| \leqslant 2\varrho^{-1} |x||y| \sin\varphi \leqslant 4\varrho^{-1} D^2 \sin(\varphi/2) = 2\varrho^{-1} D^2 |\omega_x - \omega_y|$$

and the result follows.

Remark. It is easy to see that the converse assertion also holds. Namely, if Ω is a bounded domain and $\partial\Omega$ has a representation $r = r(\omega)$ in spherical coordinates with $r(\omega)$ satisfying a Lipschitz condition, then Ω is starshaped with respect to a ball with center at the origin.

1.1.9. Domains of the Class $C^{0,1}$ or Domains Having the Cone Property

Definition 1. We say that a bounded domain Ω belongs to *the class* $C^{0,1}$ if each point $x \in \partial\Omega$ has a neighborhood $\mathscr{U}$ such that the set $\mathscr{U} \cap \Omega$ is represented by the inequality $x_n < f(x_1, \ldots, x_{n-1})$ in some Cartesian coordinate system with function f satisfying a Lipschitz condition.

By Lemma 1.1.8 any bounded domain starshaped with respect to a ball belongs to the class $C^{0,1}$.

Definition 2. A domain Ω possesses *the cone property* if each point of Ω is the vertex of a cone contained in Ω along with its closure, the cone being represented by the inequalities $x_1^2 + \cdots + x_{n-1}^2 < b x_n^2$, $0 < x_n < a$ in some Cartesian coordinate system, $a, b = \text{const}$.

Remark 1. It is easy to show that bounded domains of the class $C^{0,1}$ have the cone property. The example of a ball with deleted center shows that the converse assertion is not true.

Lemma 1. *Let Ω be a bounded domain having the cone property. Then Ω is a union of a finite number of domains starshaped with respect to a ball.*

Since a domain having the cone property is a union of congruent cones and hence it is a union of domains starshaped with respect to balls of a fixed radius, then Lemma 1 follows immediately from the next lemma.

Lemma 2. *If a bounded domain Ω is a union of an infinite number of domains G_α starshaped with respect to balls $\mathscr{B}_\alpha \subset G_\alpha$ of a fixed radius $R > 0$, then for each $r < R$ there exists a finite number of domains Ω_k $(1 \leqslant k \leqslant N)$ starshaped with respect to balls of radius r, contained in Ω_k, and such that $\bigcup_k \Omega_k = \Omega$.*

Proof. Let G_1 be a domain in the collection $\{G_\alpha\}$. Consider the domain $\Omega_1 = \bigcup_\beta G_\beta$, where the union is taken over all domains G_β for which the distance between the centers of the balls $\mathscr{B}_\beta$ and $\mathscr{B}_1$ is $\varrho \leqslant R - r$. Obviously, any of the balls $\mathscr{B}_\beta$ contains the ball C_1 of radius r concentric with $\mathscr{B}_1$. Since any G_β is starshaped with respect to C_1, then Ω_1 is starshaped with respect to C_1.

We define G_2 to be any one of the domains G_α such that $G_\alpha \cap \Omega_1 = \varnothing$. Repeating the preceding construction, we define a domain Ω_2 starshaped with respect to a ball C_2 of radius r with center situated at a distance $d > R - r$ from the center of the ball C_1. Analogously, we construct a domain Ω_3 starshaped with respect to a ball C_3 of radius r with center situated at a distance $d > R - r$ from the centers of the balls C_1 and C_2, etc.

Clearly, this process will stop after a finite number of steps since the centers of the balls $C_1, C_2, \ldots$ are contained in a bounded domain and the distance between centers is more than $R - r > 0$. The result follows.

Remark 2. Domains of the class $C^{0,1}$ are sometimes called domains having *the strong Lipschitz property* whereas *Lipschitz domains* are defined as follows.

Definition 3. A bounded domain Ω is called *a Lipschitz domain* if each point of its boundary has a neighborhood $\mathscr{U} \subset R^n$ such that a quasi-isometric transformation maps $\mathscr{U} \cap \Omega$ onto a cube.

Clearly, domains of the class $C^{0,1}$ are Lipschitz domains. The following example shows that the converse is not true, i.e. a Lipschitz domain may not have the strong Lipschitz property. What is more, the Lipschitz domain considered in the next example fails to have the cone property (cf. Remark 1).

Example. Let $\Omega \subset R^2$ be the union of the rectangles $P_k = \{x: |x_1 - 2^{-k}| < 2^{-k-2},\ 0 \leqslant x_2 < 2^{-k-2}\}$, $k = 1, 2, \ldots$ and the square $Q = \{x: 0 < x_1 < 1,\ -1 < x_2 < 0\}$. Obviously, Ω does not have the cone property. We shall show that Ω can be mapped onto the square Q by a quasi-isometric map.

We can easily check that the mapping T_0: $x \to y = (y_1, y_2)$, being the identity on Q and defined on P_k by

$$y_1 = (x_1 - 2^{-k})(1 - 2^k x_2) + 2^{-k}, \quad y_2 = x_2,$$

is quasi-isometric. The image $T_0\Omega$ is the union of the square $T_0 Q$ and the set $\{y: 0 < y_1 < 1,\ 0 \leqslant y_2 < f(y_1)\}$ with f satisfying a Lipschitz condition with the constant 4 and $0 \leqslant f(y_1) \leqslant 1/8$ (cf. Fig. 4).

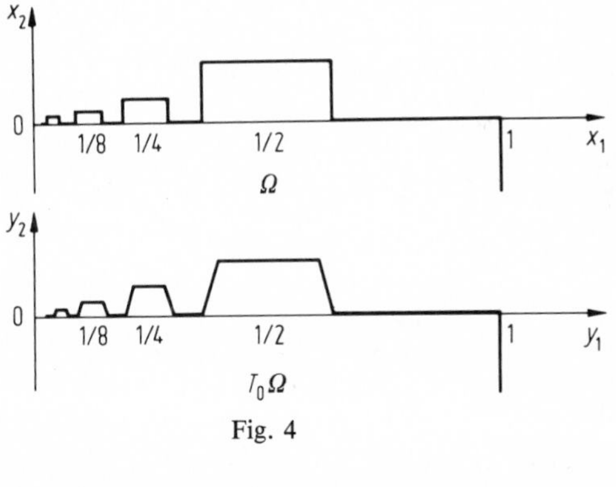

Fig. 4

Let η be a piecewise linear function, $\eta = 1$ for $y > 0$ and $\eta = 0$ for $y < -1$. The Lipschitz transformation T_1: $y \to z$, defined by

$$z_1 = y_1, \quad z_2 = y_2 - f(y_1)\,\eta(y_2),$$

maps $T_0\Omega$ onto the square $\{z: 0 < z_1 < 1,\ -1 < z_2 < 0\}$. The Jacobian of T_1 is more than 1/2; therefore T_1 is a quasi-isometric mapping.

Thus, Ω is mapped onto Q by the quasi-isometric mapping $T_0 T_1$.

1.1.10. The Sobolev Integral Representation

Theorem 1. *Let Ω be a bounded domain starshaped with respect to a ball B_δ, $B_\delta \subset \Omega$, and let $u \in L_p^l(\Omega)$. Then for almost all $x \in \Omega$*

(1)
$$u(x) = \delta^{-n} \sum_{|\beta|<l} \left(\frac{x}{\delta}\right)^\beta \int_{B_\delta} \varphi_\beta\left(\frac{y}{\delta}\right) u(y)\,dy + \sum_{|\alpha|=l} \int_\Omega \frac{f_\alpha(x;r,\theta)}{r^{n-l}} D^\alpha u(y)\,dy$$

where $r = |y-x|$, $\theta = (y-x)r^{-1}$, $\varphi_\beta \in \mathscr{D}(B_1)$, f_α are infinitely differentiable functions such that

$$|f_\alpha| \leqslant c(D/\delta)^{n-1},$$

where c is a constant that is independent of Ω and D is the diameter of Ω.

Proof. It suffices to put $\delta = 1$. Let $\omega \in \mathscr{D}(B_1)$ and

(2)
$$\int_{B_1} \omega(y)\,dy = 1\,.$$

We first assume that $u \in C^l(\bar{\Omega})$ and introduce two functions:

$$\psi(x;r,\theta) = -\frac{r^{l-1}}{(l-1)!} \int_r^\infty \omega(x+t\theta)\,t^{n-1}\,dt\,;$$

(3)
$$\mathscr{U}(x;r,\theta) = \sum_{k=0}^{l-1} (-1)^k \frac{\partial^k}{\partial r^k} u(x+r\theta) \frac{\partial^{l-1-k}}{\partial r^{l-1-k}} \psi(x;r,\theta)$$

if $y \in \Omega$ and $\mathscr{U}(x;r,\theta) = 0$ if $y \bar{\in} \Omega$.

First of all we note that

$$\mathscr{U}(x;0,\theta) = -u(x) \int_0^\infty \omega(x+t\theta)\,t^{n-1}\,dt\,.$$

Differentiating (3), we obtain

$$\frac{\partial \mathscr{U}}{\partial r} = u\,\frac{\partial^l \psi}{\partial r^l} + (-1)^l \psi\,\frac{\partial^l u}{\partial r^l}$$

which together with (3) yields

$$u(x) \int_0^\infty \omega(x+t\theta)\,t^{n-1}\,dt = \int_0^\infty u(x+r\theta) \frac{\partial^l \psi}{\partial r^l}(x;r,\theta)\,dr$$
$$+ (-1)^{l-1} \int_0^\infty \psi(x;r,\theta) \frac{\partial^l}{\partial r^l} u(x+r\theta)\,dr\,.$$

Integrating this identity over the sphere $\{\theta: |\theta| = 1\}$ and using (2), we arrive at

$$(4)\qquad u(x)=\int_\Omega u(y)\frac{\partial^l}{\partial r^l}\psi(x;r,\theta)\frac{dy}{r^{n-1}}+(-1)^{l-1}\int_\Omega \psi(x;r,\theta)\frac{\partial^l}{\partial r^l}u(y)\frac{dy}{r^{n-1}}\,.$$

We can easily check that

$$\frac{1}{r^{n-1}}\frac{\partial^l}{\partial r^l}\psi(x;r,\theta)=\sum_{k=0}^{l-1}\frac{(n+l-1)!}{(n+k)!\,(l-k-1)\,!\,k!}r^k\frac{\partial^k}{\partial r^k}\omega(x+r\theta)\,.$$

Since

$$r^k\frac{\partial^k}{\partial r^k}\omega(x+r\theta)=\sum_{|\beta|=k}\frac{k!}{\beta!}(y-x)^\beta D^\beta\omega(y)\,,$$

then

$$\frac{1}{r^{n-1}}\frac{\partial^l}{\partial r^l}\psi(x;r,\theta)=\sum_{|\beta|<l}x^\beta\varphi_\beta(y)\,,$$

where $\varphi_\beta\in\mathscr{D}(B_1)$. Therefore, the first summand in (4) is a polynomial in x of degree $l-1$,

$$\sum_{|\beta|<l}x^\beta\int_{B_1}\varphi_\beta(y)\,u(y)\,dy\,.$$

Consider the second summand in (4). We have

$$\frac{\partial^l}{\partial r^l}u(x+r\theta)=\sum_{|\alpha|=l}\frac{l!}{\alpha!}\theta^\alpha D^\alpha u(y)\,,$$

where $\theta_i=(y_i-x_i)\,r^{-1}$. Hence

$$(-1)^{l-1}\frac{1}{r^{n-1}}\psi(x;r,\theta)\frac{\partial^l}{\partial r^l}u(x+r\theta)$$

$$=\frac{(-1)^l l}{r^{n-l}}\sum_{|\alpha|=l}\frac{\theta^\alpha}{\alpha!}D^\alpha u(y)\int_r^\infty\omega(x+t\theta)\,t^{n-1}dt$$

and we obtain (1) with

$$(5)\qquad f_\alpha(x;r,\theta)=\frac{(-1)^l l}{\alpha!}\theta^\alpha\int_r^\infty\omega(x+t\theta)\,t^{n-1}dt\,.$$

The estimate $|f_\alpha|\leqslant cD^{n-1}$ is obvious. We proved (1) for $u\in C^l(\bar\Omega)$. Suppose $u\in L_p^l(\Omega)$. We note that the family of functions u_τ constructed in Theorem 1.1.6/1 is such that $u_\tau\to u$ as $\tau\to 1$ in $L_p(\Omega,\mathrm{loc})$ and in $L_p^l(\Omega)$. Passing to the limit in (1) for u_τ and using the continuity of the integral operator with a weak singularity in $L_p(\Omega)$, we arrive at (1) in the general case.

For $\Omega=R^n$ we obtain a simpler integral representation of $u\in\mathscr{D}$.

Theorem 2. *If* $u \in \mathscr{D}$, *then*

(6) $$u(x)=\frac{(-1)^l l}{n v_n}\sum_{|\alpha|=l}\int_{R^n}\frac{\theta^\alpha}{\alpha!}D^\alpha u(y)\frac{dy}{r^{n-l}}$$

where, as in Theorem 1, $r=|y-x|$, $\theta=(y-x)r^{-1}$.

To derive (6) we must duplicate the preceding proof with the function $\psi(x;r,\theta)$ replaced by $\psi(r)=r^{l-1}/(l-1)!$.

1.1.11. Generalized Poincaré Inequality

The following assertion, based on Lemma 1.1.9/1 and Theorem 1.1.10/1, will be used in 1.1.13.

Lemma. *Let* Ω *be a bounded domain having the cone property and let* ω *be an arbitrary open set,* $\bar{\omega}\subset\Omega$. *Then for any* $u\in L_p^l(\Omega)$, $p\geqslant 1$, *there exists a polynomial*

(1) $$\Pi(x)=\sum_{|\alpha|\leqslant l-1}(u,\varphi_\alpha)x^\alpha$$

such that

(2) $$\sum_{k=0}^{l-1}\|\nabla_k(u-\Pi)\|_{L_p(\Omega)}\leqslant C\|\nabla_l u\|_{L_p(\Omega)}\,.$$

Here $\varphi_\alpha\in\mathscr{D}(\omega)$ *and* C *is a constant that is independent of* u.

Proof. Clearly, we may assume that ω is a ball.

Let G be any subdomain of Ω starshaped with respect to a ball referred to in Lemma 1.1.9/1 and let $\mathscr{B}$ be the corresponding ball. We construct a finite family of balls $\{\mathscr{B}_i\}_{i=0}^M$ such that $\mathscr{B}_0=\mathscr{B}$, $\mathscr{B}_i\cap\mathscr{B}_{i+1}\neq\varnothing$, $\mathscr{B}_M=\omega$. Since G is starshaped with respect to any ball contained in $\mathscr{B}_0\cap\mathscr{B}_1$, then by the integral representation (1.1.10/1) and by continuity of the integral operator with the kernel $|x-y|^{l-k-n}$ in $L_p(G)$ we obtain

(3) $$\|\nabla_k u\|_{L_p(G)}\leqslant C(\|\nabla_l u\|_{L_p(G)}+\|u\|_{L_p(\mathscr{B}_0\cap\mathscr{B}_1)})\,,\qquad 0\leqslant k<l\,.$$

Also, for $i=1,\dots,M-1$,

$$\|u\|_{L_p(\mathscr{B}_i)}\leqslant C(\|\nabla_l u\|_{L_p(\mathscr{B}_i)}+\|u\|_{L_p(\mathscr{B}_i\cap\mathscr{B}_{i+1})})\,.$$

Therefore,

$$\|\nabla_k u\|_{L_p(G)}\leqslant C(\|\nabla_l u\|_{L_p(\Omega)}+\|u\|_{L_p(\omega)})\,.$$

Summing over all G, we obtain

(4) $$\|\nabla_k u\|_{L_p(\Omega)}\leqslant C(\|\nabla_l u\|_{L_p(\Omega)}+\|u\|_{L_p(\omega)})\,.$$

From the integral representation (1.1.10/1) for a function on ω it follows that

$$\|u-\Pi\|_{L_p(\omega)} \leqslant C\|\nabla_l u\|_{L_p(\omega)},$$

where

$$\Pi(x)=\sum_{|\beta|<l} x^\beta \int_\omega \varphi_\beta(y)u(y)\,dy\,, \qquad \varphi_\beta\in\mathscr{D}(\omega)\,.$$

It remains to replace u by $u-\Pi$ in (4). The lemma is proved.

The Lemma implies the following obvious corollary.

Corollary. *The spaces $V_p^l(\Omega)$, $W_p^l(\Omega)$ and $L_p^l(\Omega)$ coincide for Ω having the cone property.*

Remark. In this subsection we deliberately do not give a general formulation of Lemma for functions on domains that have the cone property. Such a formulation follows immediately from Lemma combined with Theorem 1.4.5, which will appear later.

On the other hand, the class of domains, considered in Lemma, is also not maximal. The statements of Lemma and of Corollary are true for any bounded domain which is a union of domains of the class C, defined in Theorem 1.1.6/2. The proof is essentially the same, but we must use the following simple property of domains of the class C instead of (3).

Let

$$\Omega=\{x\colon x_1^2+\cdots+x_{n-1}^2<\varrho^2,\ 0<x_n<f(x_1,\ldots,x_{n-1})\}$$

with a continuous function f defined on the ball $x_1^2+\cdots+x_{n-1}^2\leqslant\varrho^2$. Let G denote the "base" of Ω, i.e. the cylinder

$$\{x\colon x_1^2+\cdots+x_{n-1}^2<\varrho^2,\ 0<x_n<\min f(x_1,\ldots,x_{n-1})\}\,.$$

Then for all $u\in C^1(\bar\Omega)$

$$\|u\|_{L_p(\Omega)}\leqslant C(\|\nabla u\|_{L_p(\Omega)}+\|u\|_{L_p(G)})\,.$$

The preceding inequality follows from the elementary inequality

$$\int_0^a |f(t)|^p dt\leqslant c\left(a^p\int_0^a |f'(t)|^p dt+\frac{a}{b}\int_0^b |f(t)|^p dt\right), \tag{5}$$

where $f\in C^1[0,a]$, $0<b<a$ and c depends only on p.

The proof of (5) runs as follows. Let

$$\Phi_a=\left(a^{-1}\int_0^a |f(t)|^p dt\right)^{1/p}$$

be the value of $|f|$ at some point of $(0, a)$. We have

$$|\Phi_a - \Phi_b| \leqslant \int_0^a |f'(t)|\,dt \leqslant a^{1/p'} \|f'\|_{L_p(0,a)}$$

and (5) follows.

Example. Considering the domain

$$\Omega = \{(x,y) \in R^2 : |y| < \exp(-1/x),\ 0 < x < 1\}$$

and the function $u(x,y) = x^{2l}\exp(1/px)$, we may easily check that in general the space $L_p(\Omega)$ in the left-hand side of (2) can not be replaced by any of the spaces $L_q(\Omega)$, $q > p$, for domains of the class C.

1.1.12. Completeness of $W_p^l(\Omega)$ and $V_p^l(\Omega)$

In the following theorem Ω is an arbitrary open subset of R^n.

Theorem. *The spaces $W_p^l(\Omega)$ and $V_p^l(\Omega)$ are complete.*

Proof. Let $\{u_k\}_{k\geqslant 1}$ be a Cauchy sequence in $W_p^l(\Omega)$. Let $u_k \to u$ in $L_p(\Omega)$ and let $D^\alpha u_k \to v_\alpha$, $|\alpha| = l$, in $L_p(\Omega)$. For any $\varphi \in \mathscr{D}(\Omega)$ we have

$$\int_\Omega u D^\alpha \varphi\,dx = \lim_{k\to\infty} \int_\Omega u_k D^\alpha \varphi\,dx = (-1)^l \lim_{k\to\infty} \int_\Omega \varphi D^\alpha u_k\,dx = (-1)^l \int_\Omega v_\alpha \varphi\,dx\,.$$

Thus, $v_\alpha = D^\alpha u$ and the sequence $\{u_k\}$ converges to $u \in W_p^l(\Omega)$. The result follows for the space $W_p^l(\Omega)$. The case of $V_p^l(\Omega)$ can be considered in the same way.

1.1.13. The Space $\dot{L}_p^l(\Omega)$ and its Completeness

Let Ω be a domain.

Definition. $\dot{L}_p^l(\Omega)$ is the factor space $L_p^l(\Omega)/\mathscr{P}_{l-1}$, where $\mathscr{P}_k$ is the subspace of polynomials of degree not higher than k.

We equip $\dot{L}_p^l(\Omega)$ with the norm $\|\nabla_l u\|_{L_p(\Omega)}$. The elements of $\dot{L}_p^l(\Omega)$ are classes $\dot{u} = \{u + \Pi\}$ where $\Pi \in \mathscr{P}_{l-1}$, $u \in L_p^l(\Omega)$.

Theorem 1. *The space $\dot{L}_p^l(\Omega)$ is complete.*

Proof. Let $\{\dot{u}_k\}_{k\geqslant 1}$ be a Cauchy sequence in $\dot{L}_p^l(\Omega)$. This means that for any u_k in the class $\dot{u}_k$ and any multi-index α, $|\alpha| = l$, $D^\alpha u_k \to T_\alpha$ in $L_p(\Omega)$. We shall show that there exists a $u \in L_p^l(\Omega)$ such that $D^\alpha u = T_\alpha$.

Let B be an open ball, $\bar{B} \subset \Omega$, and let $\{\omega_j\}_{j\geqslant 0}$ be a sequence of domains with compact closures and smooth boundaries such that

$$\bar{B} \subset \omega_0\,, \qquad \bar{\omega}_j \subset \omega_{j+1}\,, \qquad \bigcup_j \omega_j = \Omega\,.$$

Let Π_k be a polynomial specified by the set $\omega = B$ and by the function u_k in Lemma 1.1.11. Since u_k is in the class $\dot{u}_k$, then

$$v_k = u_k - \Pi_k$$

is in the same class. By Lemma 1.1.11, $\{v_k\}$ is a Cauchy sequence in $L_p(\omega_j)$ for any j.

We denote the limit function by u. Clearly, for any $\varphi \in \mathscr{D}(\Omega)$ and any multi-index α, $|\alpha| = l$,

$$(u, D^\alpha \varphi) = \lim_{k\to\infty} (v_k, D^\alpha \varphi) = \lim_{k\to\infty} (-1)^l (D^\alpha u_k, \varphi) = (-1)^l (T_\alpha, \varphi) .$$

The result follows.

The proof of Theorem 1 also contains the following assertion.

Theorem 2. *Let $\{u_k\}$ be a sequence of functions in $L_p^l(\Omega)$ such that*

$$\| \nabla_l (u_k - u) \|_{L_p(\Omega)} \xrightarrow[k\to\infty]{} 0$$

for some $u \in L_p^l(\Omega)$. Then there exists a sequence of polynomials $\Pi_k \in \mathscr{P}_{l-1}$ with $u_k - \Pi_k \to u$ in $L_p(\Omega, \mathrm{loc})$.

1.1.14. Dual of a Sobolev Space

Theorem 1. *Let $1 \leqslant p < \infty$. Any linear functional on $L_p^l(\Omega)$ can be expressed as*

$$f(u) = \int_\Omega \sum_{|\alpha|=l} g_\alpha(x) D^\alpha u(x)\, dx , \tag{1}$$

where $g_\alpha \in L_{p'}(\Omega)$, $pp' = p + p'$, and

$$\|f\| = \inf \left\| \left(\sum_{|\alpha|=l} g_\alpha^2 \right)^{1/2} \right\|_{L_{p'}(\Omega)} . \tag{2}$$

Here the infimum is taken over all collections $\{g_\alpha\}_{|\alpha|=l}$, for which (1) holds with any $u \in L_p^l(\Omega)$.

Proof. Obviously, the right-hand side of (1) is a linear functional on $L_p^l(\Omega)$ and

$$\|f\| \leqslant \left\| \left(\sum_{|\alpha|=l} g_\alpha^2 \right)^{1/2} \right\|_{L_{p'}(\Omega)} .$$

In order to express $f(u)$ as (1), consider the space $L_p(\Omega)$ of vectors $v = \{v_\alpha\}_{|\alpha|=l}$ with components in $L_p(\Omega)$, equipped with the norm

$$\left\| \left(\sum_{|\alpha|=l} v_\alpha^2 \right)^{1/2} \right\|_{L_p(\Omega)} .$$

Since the space $L_p^l(\Omega)$ is complete, the range of the operator ∇_l: $L_p^l(\Omega) \to \boldsymbol{L}_p(\Omega)$ is a closed subspace of $\boldsymbol{L}_p(\Omega)$. For any vector $\boldsymbol{v} = \nabla_l u$ we define $\Phi(\boldsymbol{v}) = f(u)$. Then

$$\|\Phi\| = \|f\|$$

and by the Hahn-Banach theorem Φ has a norm-preserving extension to $\boldsymbol{L}_p(\Omega)$. The proof is complete.

As before, let $W_p^l(\Omega) = L_p^l(\Omega) \cap L_p(\Omega)$. Let $\mathring{W}_p^l(\Omega)$ denote the completion of $\mathscr{D}(\Omega)$ with respect to the norm in $W_p^l(\Omega)$.

The following assertion is proved in the same manner as Theorem 1.

Theorem 2. *Any linear functional on $W_p^l(\Omega)$ (or on $\mathring{W}_p^l(\Omega)$) has the form*

$$f(u) = \int_\Omega \left(\sum_{|\alpha|=l} g_\alpha(x) D^\alpha u(x) + g(x) u(x) \right) dx, \tag{3}$$

where $g_\alpha \in L_{p'}(\Omega)$, $g \in L_{p'}(\Omega)$, and

$$\|f\| = \inf \left\| \left(\sum_{|\alpha|=l} g_\alpha^2 + g^2 \right)^{1/2} \right\|_{L_p(\Omega)} . \tag{4}$$

Here the infimum is taken over all collections of functions g_α, $g \in L_{p'}(\Omega)$ for which (3) *holds with any $u \in W_p^l(\Omega)$ (or $u \in \mathring{W}_p^l(\Omega)$).*

The following simpler characterization of the space of linear functionals on $\mathring{W}_p^l(\Omega)$ is a corollary of Theorem 2.

Corollary. *Any linear functional on $\mathring{W}_p^l(\Omega)$ can be identified with a generalized function $f \in \mathscr{D}'(\Omega)$ given by*

$$f = \sum_{|\alpha|=l} (-1)^l D^\alpha g_\alpha + g, \tag{5}$$

where g_α, $g \in L_{p'}(\Omega)$. The norm of this functional is equal to the right-hand side of (4), *where the infimum is taken over all collections of functions g_α, g, entering the expression* (5).

1.1.15. Equivalent Norms in $W_p^l(\Omega)$

The following theorem describes a wide class of equivalent norms in $W_p^l(\Omega)$.

Theorem. *Let Ω be a bounded domain such that $L_p^l(\Omega) \subset L_p(\Omega)$ (for example, Ω has the cone property). Let $\mathscr{F}(u)$ be a continuous functional in $W_p^l(\Omega)$, $\mathscr{F}(\Pi_{l-1}) \neq 0$ for any nonzero polynomial Π_{l-1} of degree not higher than $l-1$. Then the norm*

$$\| \nabla_l u \|_{L_p(\Omega)} + \mathscr{F}(u) \tag{1}$$

is equivalent to the norm in $W_p^l(\Omega)$.

Proof. Let $\mathscr{I}$ be the identity mapping of $W_p^l(\Omega)$ into the space $B(\Omega)$ obtained by the completion of $W_p^l(\Omega)$ with respect to the norm (1). This mapping is one-to-one, linear and continuous. By Theorem 1.1.13 on the completeness of $\dot{L}_p^l(\Omega)$ it follows that $B(\Omega) \subset L_p^l(\Omega)$. Since $L_p^l(\Omega) = W_p^l(\Omega)$, then $\mathscr{I}$ maps $W_p^l(\Omega)$ onto $B(\Omega)$. By the Banach theorem (cf. Bourbaki [34], Ch. I, § 3, Sect. 3) $\mathscr{I}$ is an isomorphism. The result follows.

Remark. The functional

$$\mathscr{F}(u) = \sum_{0 \leqslant |\alpha| < l} |f_\alpha(u)| ,$$

where the f_α are linear functionals in $W_p^l(\Omega)$ such that

$$\det(f_\alpha(x^\beta)) \neq 0 , \qquad |\alpha|, |\beta| \leqslant l-1 ,$$

satisfies the conditions of Theorem. For example, we can put

$$f_\alpha(u) = \int_\Omega u D^\alpha \varphi dx$$

where $\varphi \in \mathscr{D}(\Omega)$, $\int_\Omega \varphi(x)dx \neq 0$.

Let $\mathfrak{P}$ be a projector of $W_p^l(\Omega)$ onto the subspace $\mathscr{P}_{l-1}$, i.e. a linear continuous mapping of $W_p^l(\Omega)$ onto $\mathscr{P}_{l-1}$ such that $\mathfrak{P}^2 = \mathfrak{P}$. Then we may take $|\mathfrak{P}(u)|$ as $\mathscr{F}(u)$.

Since $\mathfrak{P}(u - \mathfrak{P}(u)) = 0$, by Theorem we have the equivalence of the seminorms $\| \nabla_l u \|_{L_p(\Omega)}$ and $\|u - \mathfrak{P}(u)\|_{W_p^l(\Omega)}$ (cf. Lemma 1.1.11).

1.1.16. Extension of Functions in $V_p^l(\Omega)$ onto R^n

In this subsection we discuss space-preserving extensions of functions in $V_p^l(\Omega)$ onto the exterior of Ω. We begin with the well-known procedure of "finite-order reflection".

We introduce the notation. Let $x = (x', x_n)$, where $x' = (x_1, \dots, x_{n-1})$, let π be an n-dimensional parallelepiped, $P = \pi \times (-a/(l+1), a)$, $P_+ = \pi \times (0, a)$, $P_- = P \backslash P_+$.

Theorem. *For any integer $l \geqslant 0$ there exists a linear mapping*

$$C^\infty(\bar{P}_+) \ni u \to u^* \in C^l(\bar{P})$$

such that $u^* = u$ *on* P_+. *It can be uniquely extended to a continuous mapping* $L_p^k(P_+) \to L_p^k(P)$, $p \geqslant 1$, *for* $k = 0, 1, \ldots, l$.

The extension $u \to u^*$ *can be defined on the space* $C^{k,1}(\bar{P}_+)$, $k = 0, 1, \ldots l-1$. *It is a continuous mapping into* $C^{k,1}(\bar{P})$.

This mapping has the following property: if dist (supp $u, F) > 0$, *where F is a compactum in* $\bar{P}_+$, *then* $u^* = 0$ *in a neighborhood of F.*

Proof. Let $u \in C^\infty(\bar{P}_+)$. We set $u^* = u$ in P_+ and

$$u^*(x) = \sum_{j=1}^{l+1} c_j u(x', -jx_n) \quad \text{in} \quad P_- ,$$

where the coefficients c_j satisfy the system

$$\sum_{j=1}^{l+1} (-j)^k c_j = 1 , \qquad k = 0, \ldots, l .$$

The determinant of this system (the Vandermonde determinant) does not vanish.

Obviously, $u^* \in C^l(\bar{P})$. It is also clear that

$$\| \nabla_k u^* \|_{L_p(P)} \leqslant c \| \nabla_k u \|_{L_p(P_+)} .$$

Since $C^\infty(\bar{P}_+)$ is dense in $L_p^k(P_+)$ by Theorem 1.1.6/1, the mapping $u^* \to u$ admits a unique extension to a continuous mapping $L_p^k(P_+) \to L_p^k(P)$. The continuity of the mapping $C^{k,1}(\bar{P}_+) \ni u \to u^* \in C^{k,1}(\bar{P})$ can be checked directly.

Let dist (supp $u, F) > 0$. We denote an arbitrary point of $F \cap \pi$ by x and introduce a small positive number δ such that $(l+1)\delta <$ dist (supp u, F). Since $u = 0$ on $\{x \in \bar{P}_+ : |x'| < (l+1)x_n\}$, then $u^* = 0$ on $\{x \in P_- : |x'|^2 + (l+1)^2 x_n^2 < (l+1)^2 \delta^2\}$. So $u^* = 0$ if $|x| < \delta$. This completes the proof.

Let Ω be a domain in R^n with compact closure $\bar{\Omega}$ and with sufficiently smooth boundary $\partial\Omega$. Using the described extension procedure along with a partition of unity and a local mapping of Ω onto halfspace, it is possible to construct a linear continuous operator $\mathscr{E}: V_p^l(\Omega) \to V_p^l(R^n)$ such that $\mathscr{E}u|_\Omega = u$ for all $u \in V_p^l(\Omega)$.

If such an operator exists for a domain then, by definition, this domain belongs to *the class* EV_p^l.

Thus, domains with smooth boundaries are contained in EV_p^l. The bounded domains of the class $C^{0,1}$ turn out to have the same property. The last assertion is proved in Stein [237], § 3, Ch. VI (cf. also Comments to the present section).

In § 1.5 we shall return to the problem of the description of domains in EV_p^l.

1.1.17. Comments to § 1.1

The space $W_p^l(\Omega)$ was introduced and studied in detail by S. L. Sobolev [229–231]. The definitions of the spaces $L_p^l(\Omega)$ and $\dot{L}_p^l(\Omega)$ are borrowed from the paper by Deny and Lions [51]. The proofs of Theorems 1.1.2, 1.1.5/1, 1.1.12, 1.1.13/1, 1.1.13/2 follow the arguments of this paper where similar results are obtained for $l=1$. Theorem 1.1.5/1 was also proved by Meyers and Serrin [185]. Concerning the contents of subsection 1.1.3 we note that the property of absolute continuity on almost all straight lines parallel to coordinate axes was used as a foundation for the definition of spaces similar to L_p^1 in papers by Levi [128], Nikodým [199], Morrey [190], etc. The example of a domain for which $W_2^2(\Omega) \neq V_2^2(\Omega)$ (see subsection 1.1.4) is due to the author. The example considered at the beginning of 1.1.6 is borrowed from the paper by Gagliardo [70]. Remark 1.16 and the subsequent example are taken from the paper by Kolsrud [113]. Theorem 1.1.6/1 is proved in the textbook by Smirnov [227] and Theorem 1.1.6/2 is proved in the above-mentioned paper by Gagliardo. In connection with subsection 1.17 see the books by Morrey [191], Rešetnjak [218] and the paper by the author and Šapošnikova [180].

The condition of being starshaped with respect to a ball and having the cone property were introduced into the theory of W_p^l-spaces by Sobolev [229–231]. Lemma 1.1.8 is undoubtedly known, but the author cannot give the exact reference. Lemma 1.1.9/2 was proved by Gluško [76]. The example given in 1.1.9 is due to the author; another example of a Lipschitz domain which does not belong to $C^{0,1}$ can be found in the book by Morrey [191].

Integral representations (1.1.10/1) and (1.1.10/6) were obtained by Sobolev [230, 231] and used in his proof of imbedding theorems. Various generalizations of such representations are due to Il'in [105, 106], Smith [228] (see also the book by Besov, Il'in, Nikol'skiĭ [27]) and to Rešetnjak [217].

The Poincaré inequality for bounded domains which are the unions of domains of the class C is proved in Courant and Hilbert [47]. The properties of functions in $L_p^l(\Omega)$ for a wider class of domains were studied by Lions [131].

Theorem 1.1.15 on equivalent norms in $W_p^l(\Omega)$ is due to Sobolev [231, 232].

The extension procedure described at the beginning of 1.1.16 was proposed by Hestenes [97] for the space $C^k(\bar{\Omega})$ (see also Lichtenstein [130]). The same method was used by Nikol'skiĭ [201] and Babič [20] for $W_p^l(\Omega)$. The fact that a space-preserving extension for functions in $W_p^l(\Omega)$ $(1<p<\infty)$ onto R^n is possible for domains of the class $C^{0,1}$ was discovered by Calderon [41]. His proof is based on the integral representation (1.1.10/1) along with the theorem on the continuity of the singular integral operator in L_p. A method that is appropriate for $p=1$ and $p=\infty$ as well was given by Stein [237]. The main part of his proof is based on the extension of functions defined in a neighborhood of a boundary point. Then, using a partition of unity, he constructs a global extension. For the simple domain

$$\Omega=\{x=(x',x_n):\ x'\in R^{n-1},\ x_n>f(x')\}\,,$$

where f is a function on R^{n-1} satisfying a Lipschitz condition, the extension of u is defined by

$$u^*(x',x_n)=\int_1^\infty u(x',x_n+\lambda\delta(x',x_n))\,\psi(\lambda)\,d\lambda\,,\qquad x_n<f(x')\,.$$

Here δ is an infinitely differentiable function, equivalent to the distance to $\partial\Omega$. The function ψ is defined and continuous on $[1,\infty)$, decreases as $\lambda\to\infty$ more rapidly than any power of λ^{-1}, and satisfies the conditions

$$\int_1^\infty \psi(\lambda)\,d\lambda=1\,,\qquad \int_1^\infty \lambda^k\psi(\lambda)\,d\lambda=0\,,\qquad k=1,2,\ldots\,.$$

§ 1.2. Some Facts from Set Theory and Function Theory

In this section we collect some known facts from set theory and function theory that will be used later.

1.2.1. Two Theorems on Coverings

Theorem 1. *Let $\mathscr{S}$ be a bounded set in R^n. With each point $x\in\mathscr{S}$ we associate the ball $B_{r(x)}(x)$, $r(x)>0$, and denote the collection of these balls by $\mathfrak{B}$. Then we can choose a sequence of balls $\{\mathscr{B}_m\}$ in $\mathfrak{B}$ such that:*

1) $\mathscr{S}\subset\bigcup_m \mathscr{B}_m$;

2) *there exists a number M, depending on the dimension of the space only, such that every point of R^n belongs to at most M balls in $\{\mathscr{B}_m\}$;*

3) *the balls* $(1/3)\,\mathscr{B}_m$ *are disjoint;*

4) $\bigcup_{B\in\mathfrak{B}} B\subset\bigcup_m 4\,\mathscr{B}_m$.

Proof. We put $a_1=\sup_{x\in\mathscr{S}} r(x)$. If $a_1=\infty$, then the result follows. If $a_1<\infty$, then we choose a point $x_1\in\mathscr{S}$ such that $r(x_1)>(3/4)\,a_1$ and define $\mathscr{B}_1=B_{r(x_1)}(x_1)$. Suppose points $x_1, x_2,\ldots,x_m$ have been chosen in $\mathscr{S}$. We define $a_{m+1}=\sup\{r(x):\ x\in\mathscr{S}\setminus\bigcup_{j=1}^m\mathscr{B}_j\}$ and take $x_{m+1}\in\mathscr{S}\setminus\bigcup_{j=1}^m\mathscr{B}_j$ to satisfy $r(x_{m+1})>(3/4)\,a_{m+1}$. We shall show that $\{\mathscr{B}_m\}$ is the required sequence.

If the construction of this sequence stops in a finite number of steps, then, obviously, $\mathscr{S}\subset\bigcup_m\mathscr{B}_m$ and 2) holds. The assertion 3) follows from $r(x_i)\leqslant a_i\leqslant a_j<(4/3)\,r(x_j)$ for $i>j\geqslant 1$. In fact, let r_{ij} be the distance between the centers of $\mathscr{B}_i$ and $\mathscr{B}_j$ for $i>j$ and let r_i be the radius of $\mathscr{B}_i$. By construction, the center x_i of $\mathscr{B}_i$ is not in $\mathscr{B}_j$, so

(1) $$r_{ij} > r_j .$$

Suppose the balls $(1/3)\mathscr{B}_i$ and $(1/3)\mathscr{B}_j$ intersect and $y \in (1/3)\mathscr{B}_i \cap (1/3)\mathscr{B}_j$. Then $r_{ij} \leqslant |x_i - y| + |y - x_j| \leqslant (1/3) r_i + (1/3) r_j \leqslant (7/9) r_j$ which contradicts (1). So, the property 3) holds even in case the number of balls $\mathscr{B}_m$ is infinite.

Now, we prove that $r_m \to 0$ as $m \to \infty$ if $\{\mathscr{B}_m\}$ is an infinite sequence. In fact, as we already showed, the balls $(1/3)\mathscr{B}_m$ do not intersect and therefore, if r_m does not tend to zero, then infinitely many disjoint balls with the same radius are contained in a bounded set (in an a_1-neighborhood of $\mathscr{S}$), which is impossible. Suppose $s \in \mathscr{S} \setminus \bigcup_{m=1}^{\infty} \mathscr{B}_m$. Since $r(s) > 0$, then s was missed when $\{x_m\}$ was constructed. Thus $\mathscr{S} \subset \bigcup_{m=1}^{\infty} \mathscr{B}_m$ and 1) follows.

Now, we proceed to the proof of 2). Let x_k and x_m be the centers of $\mathscr{B}_k$ and $\mathscr{B}_m$. By the construction of $\{\mathscr{B}_m\}$, either (i) $x_k \bar{\in} \mathscr{B}_m$ and $x_m \bar{\in} \mathscr{B}_k$, or (ii) only one of the centers is contained in the ball with another index, for instance, $x_k \in \mathscr{B}_m$. If $y \in \mathscr{B}_k \cap \mathscr{B}_m$ and (i) holds, then the angle between the vectors $\boldsymbol{yx_k}$ and $\boldsymbol{yx_m}$ exceeds $\pi/3$. In the case (ii) the lower bound for this angle can be derived if $y \bar{\in} (2/5)\mathscr{B}_k$. We note that the balls $(2/5)\mathscr{B}_k$, like the balls $(1/3)\mathscr{B}_k$, are mutually disjoint. An elementary calculation shows that the angle between $\boldsymbol{yx_k}$ and $\boldsymbol{yx_m}$ exceeds some positive number independent of k and m. We can take this number to be $\alpha = \arccos(11/12)$. Now let

(2) $$y \in \bigcap_{m=1}^{N} \mathscr{B}_{k_m} .$$

If y belongs to some ball in the collection $\{(2/5)\mathscr{B}_{k_m}\}$, for instance, $y \in (2/5)\mathscr{B}_{k_N}$, then we omit the corresponding index in (2) and write

$$y \in \bigcap_{m=1}^{N-1} \mathscr{B}_{k_m} .$$

So the above estimates for the angle are applicable for any pair $\mathscr{B}_{k_i}$, $\mathscr{B}_{k_j}$ in this intersection. The angle between the vectors $\boldsymbol{yx_{k_i}}$ and $\boldsymbol{yx_{k_j}}$ exceeds a positive number α independent of k. The maximal number of vectors $\boldsymbol{yx_k}$, emanating from the same point y, depends only on α and on the dimension of the space. Consequently, the number N does not depend on y and 2) is proved.

Now, we proceed to 4). Let $\mathscr{B} \in \mathfrak{B}$ be disjoint with $\mathscr{B}_1, \ldots, \mathscr{B}_{k-1}$ and let it intersect $\mathscr{B}_k$. Then we show that $\mathscr{B} \subset 4\mathscr{B}_k$. First of all, since the center of $\mathscr{B}$ does not belong to $\mathscr{S} \setminus \bigcup_{j=1}^{k-1} \mathscr{B}_j$ then

$$r \leqslant a_k < (4/3) r(x_k) .$$

We take $x \in \mathscr{B}$, $y \in \mathscr{B} \cap \mathscr{B}_k$ and write

$$|x - x_k| \leqslant |x - y| + |y - x_k| = 2r + r_k < (8/3) r_k + r_k < 4 r_k .$$

Therefore any $x \in \mathcal{B}$ is in $4\,\mathcal{B}_k$.

It remains to show that every $x \in \bigcup_{\mathcal{B} \in \mathfrak{B}} \mathcal{B}$ belongs to a ball which intersects some ball in the constructed sequence.

If the sequence $\{\mathcal{B}_m\}$ is finite and the number of its elements is k_0, then any $\mathcal{B} \in \mathfrak{B}$ intersects one of the balls in $\{\mathcal{B}_m\}_{m \geqslant 1}^{k_0}$.

If the sequence $\{\mathcal{B}_m\}$ is infinite then the sequence of their radii converges to zero. But if $\mathcal{B}$ is disjoint with $\mathcal{B}_1, \mathcal{B}_2, \dots, \mathcal{B}_{k-1}$, then its radius r satisfies the inequality

$$r < (4/3)\, r_k .$$

Since $r_k \to 0$ and $r > 0$ then $\mathcal{B}$ intersects some $\mathcal{B}_m$. The theorem is proved.

Remark 1. Theorem 1 remains valid if balls are replaced by cubes with edges parallel to coordinate planes, and can be proved in the same way. This result follows from the paper by Morse [193]. It also follows from this paper that balls and cubes can be replaced by other bodies.

The set $\mathcal{S}$ can be unbounded if the conditions of the theorem are complemented with the following two assumptions:

α) the radii of balls in $\mathfrak{B}$ are totally bounded,

β) the sequence of radii of any disjoint sequence of balls in $\mathfrak{B}$ tends to zero.

Lemma. *Let g be an open subset of R^n with smooth boundary and let $2m_n(B_r \cap g) = m_n(B_r)$. Then*

$$s(B_r \cap \partial g) \geqslant c_n r^{n-1} ,$$

where c_n is a positive constant that depends only on n, and s is the $(n-1)$-dimensional area.

Proof. Let χ and ψ be the characteristic functions of the sets $g \cap B_r$ and $B_r \backslash g$. For any vector $z \neq 0$ we introduce a projection mapping P_z onto the $(n-1)$-dimensional subspace orthogonal to z. By Fubini's theorem,

$$(1/4)\, v_n^2 r^{2n} = m_n(g \cap B_r)\, m_n(B_r \backslash g) = \int_{R^n} \int_{R^n} \chi(x)\, \psi(y)\, dx\, dy$$

$$= \int_{R^n} \int_{R^n} \chi(x)\, \psi(x+z)\, dz\, dx = \int_{|z| \leqslant 2r} m_n(\{x \colon x \in B_r \cap g,\ x+z \in B_r \backslash g\})\, dz .$$

Since every interval connecting $x \in g \cap B_r$ with $(x+z) \in B_r \backslash g$ intersects $B_r \cap \partial g$, the last integral does not exceed

$$2r \int_{|z| \leqslant 2r} m_{n-1}[P_z(B_r \cap \partial g)] \leqslant (2r)^{n+1} v_n s(B_r \cap \partial g) .$$

The lemma is proved.

Remark 2. The best value of c_n equals the volume of the $(n-1)$-dimensional unit ball (cf. Lemma 3.2.1/1).

Theorem 2. *Let g be a bounded open subset of R^n with smooth boundary. There exists a covering of g by a sequence of balls with radii ϱ_i, $i = 1, 2, \ldots$, such that*

$$\sum_j \varrho_j^{n-1} \leqslant cs(\partial g) , \tag{3}$$

where c is a constant that depends only on n.

Proof. Each point $x \in g$ is the center of a ball $B_r(x)$ for which

$$\frac{m_n(B_r(x) \cap g)}{m_n(B_r(x))} = \frac{1}{2} . \tag{4}$$

(This ratio is a continuous function of r, which is equal to 1 for small values of r and converges to zero as $r \to \infty$.) By Lemma there exists a sequence of disjoint balls $B_{r_j}(x_j)$ such that

$$g \in \bigcup_{j=1}^{\infty} B_{3r_j}(x_j) .$$

(Here we actually use a weaker variant of Theorem 1 (cf. Dunford and Schwartz [54], III.12.1).)

Lemma together with (4) implies

$$s(B_{r_j}(x_j) \cap \partial g) \geqslant c_n r_j^{n-1}.$$

Therefore,

$$s(\partial g) \geqslant \sum_j s(B_{r_j}(x_j) \cap \partial g) \geqslant 3^{1-n} c_n \sum_j (3r_j)^{n-1} .$$

Thus, $\{B_{3r_j}(x_j)\}$ is the required covering.

1.2.2. Theorem on Level Sets of a Smooth Function

We recall the Vitali covering theorem (see [54], III.12.2).

Let $E \subset R^1$ and let $\mathscr{M}$ be a collection of intervals. We say that $\mathscr{M}$ forms a covering of E in the sense of Vitali if for each $t \in E$ and any $\varepsilon > 0$ there exists an interval $i \in \mathscr{M}$ such that $t \in i$, $m_1(i) < \varepsilon$.

Theorem 1. *If E is covered by a collection $\mathscr{M}$ of intervals in the sense of Vitali, then we can select a countable or finite set of intervals $\{i_k\}$ such that $i_k \cap i_l = \varnothing$ for $k \neq l$, $m_1(E \backslash \bigcup_k i_k) = 0$.*

Consider a function f:

$$\Omega \ni x \to f(x) = t \in R^1 .$$

The set

$$K_1 = \{x \colon \nabla f(x) = 0\}$$

is called critical.

If $E \subset \Omega$ then $f(E)$ is the image of E under the mapping f. If $A \subset R^1$ then $f^{-1}(A)$ is the preimage of A in Ω. We shall briefly denote $f^{-1}(t)$ by $\mathscr{E}_t$.

Theorem 2. *Let Ω be an open set in R^n and $f \in C^\infty(\Omega)$. Then*

$$m_1[f(K_1)] = 0 .$$

Proof. It is sufficient to assume that Ω is a bounded set.

1. We introduce the notation

$$K_n = \{x\colon (\nabla f)(x) = 0, \ldots, (\nabla_n f)(x) = 0\} .$$

First we show that

$$m_1[f(K_n)] = 0 .$$

For any $\varepsilon > 0$ and each $x \in K_n$ we choose a number $r_x > 0$ such that $B(x, r_x) \subset \Omega$ and

$$\operatorname*{osc}_{B(x,r_x)} f < \varepsilon r_x^n .$$

We fix a point $t \in f(K_n)$ and consider any point

$$x(t) \in \mathscr{E}_t \cap K_n .$$

Then we cover t by intervals $(t-\delta, t+\delta)$ with

$$\delta < \varepsilon r_{x(t)}^n . \tag{1}$$

The collection of all these intervals forms a covering of $f(K_n)$ in the sense of Vitali. We choose a countable system of disjoint intervals $i_1, i_2, \ldots$ which covers $f(K_n)$ up to a set of linear measure zero.

Let

$$i_m = (t_m - \delta_m, t_m + \delta_m)$$

and $x_m \in \mathscr{E}_{t_m} \cap K_n$. By (1), $\delta_m < \varepsilon r_{x_m}^n$. So

$$f^{-1}(i_m) \supset B(x_m, (\delta_m/\varepsilon)^{1/n})$$

and therefore,

$$m_n[f^{-1}(i_m)] \geqslant v_n \frac{\delta_m}{\varepsilon} .$$

Since the i_m are mutually disjoint, their preimages have the same property.

Thus,

$$\sum \delta_m \leqslant \frac{\varepsilon}{v_n} \sum_{m=1}^{\infty} m_n[f^{-1}(i_m)] \leqslant m_n(\Omega) ,$$

i.e. $m_1[f(K_n)] \leqslant c\varepsilon m_n(\Omega)$, $m_1[f(K_n)] = 0$.

2. Now we use induction on n. The theorem holds for $n=1$. Assume it holds for $n-1$.

Consider the set $K_1 \setminus K_n$. For any $x \in K_1 \setminus K_n$ there exists a multi-index α, $|\alpha| < n$, and an integer $i \leqslant n$ such that

$$(D^\alpha f)(x) = 0\,, \quad \left(\frac{\partial}{\partial x_i} D^\alpha f\right)(x) \neq 0\,. \tag{2}$$

Let H be a set of points for which (2) holds. This set obviously is defined by the pairs (α, i). We show that

$$m_1[f(H)] = 0\,.$$

Without loss of generality we may assume $i = n$. With the notation $g = D^\alpha f$, we have

$$g(x) = 0\,, \quad \frac{\partial g}{\partial x_n} \neq 0 \quad \text{for } x \in H\,.$$

By the implicit function theorem, for any $x_0 \in H$ there exists a neighborhood $\mathscr{U}$ such that

$$\mathscr{U} \cap \{x \colon g(x) = 0\} \subset \{x \colon x_n = \varphi(X)\}\,,$$

where $X = (x_1, \ldots, x_{n-1})$ and φ is an infinitely differentiable function in some domain $G \subset R^{n-1}$. Since we can select a countable covering from any covering of H, it is sufficient to prove that

$$m_1[f(H \cap \mathscr{U})] = 0\,.$$

If $x \in H \cap \mathscr{U}$, then

$$f(x) = f(X, \varphi(X)) \stackrel{\text{def}}{=} h(X)$$

where $X \in G$. Let P denote the projection of $H \cap \mathscr{U}$ onto the plane $x_n = 0$. Since $\nabla h = 0$ for $X \in P$, then by the induction hypothesis,

$$m_1[h(P)] = 0\,.$$

Taking into account that $h(P) = f(H \cap \mathscr{U})$, we complete the proof.

From Theorem 2 and the implicit function theorem we immediately obtain the following corollary.

Corollary. *If $f \in C^\infty(\Omega)$ $(f \in \mathscr{D}(\Omega))$, then for almost all t the sets $\mathscr{E}_t = \{x \colon f(x) = t\}$ are C^∞-manifolds (C^∞-compact manifolds).*

1.2.3. Representation of the Lebesgue Integral as a Riemann Integral along a Halfaxis

Theorem. *Let $(X, \mathfrak{B}, \mu)$ be a space with a (nonnegative) measure and let $u: X \to R^1$ be a μ-measurable nonnegative function. Then*

$$\int_X u(x)\mu(dx) = \int_0^\infty \mu(\mathcal{M}_t)\,dt = \int_0^\infty \mu(\mathcal{L}_t)\,dt\,, \tag{1}$$

where

$$\mathcal{M}_t = \{x \in X: u(x) \geqslant t\}, \quad \mathcal{L}_t = \{x \in X: u(x) > t\}\,.$$

Proof. Let $u(x) \leqslant A < \infty$. We subdivide the range of u by points $\{t_k\}_{k=0}^m$ such that $0 = t_0 < t_1 < \dots < t_m = A$. Then

$$X = \mathcal{M}_{t_m} \cup \left(\bigcup_{k=0}^{m-1} (\mathcal{M}_{t_k} \backslash \mathcal{M}_{t_{k+1}})\right)$$

and

$$\int_X u(x)\mu(dx) = \sum_{k=0}^{m-1} \int_{\mathcal{M}_{t_k} \backslash \mathcal{M}_{t_{k+1}}} u(x)\mu(dx) + \int_{\mathcal{M}_{t_m}} u(x)\mu(dx)\,.$$

Hence,

$$\sum_{k=0}^{m-1} t_k \mu_k(\mathcal{M}_{t_k} \backslash \mathcal{M}_{t_{k+1}}) + t_m\,\mu(\mathcal{M}_{t_m}) \leqslant \int_X u(x)\mu(dx)$$

$$\leqslant \sum_{k=0}^{m-1} t_{k+1}\mu(\mathcal{M}_{t_k} \backslash \mathcal{M}_{t_{k+1}}) + t_m \mu(\mathcal{M}_{t_m})\,.$$

Since

$$\sum_{k=0}^{m-1} a_k(b_k - b_{k+1}) = a_0 b_0 - a_{m-1} b_m + \sum_{k=1}^{m-1} (a_k - a_{k-1}) b_k\,,$$

then, putting $a_k = t_k$, $b_k = \mu(\mathcal{M}_{t_k})$, we obtain

$$\sum_{k=1}^{m} (t_k - t_{k-1})\mu(\mathcal{M}_{t_k}) = \sum_{k=1}^{m-1} (t_k - t_{k-1})\mu(\mathcal{M}_{t_k}) + (t_m - t_{m-1})\mu(\mathcal{M}_{t_m})$$

$$\leqslant \int_X u(x)\mu(dx) \leqslant \sum_{k=0}^{m-1} (t_{k+1} - t_k)\mu(\mathcal{M}_{t_k})\,.$$

Refining the partition and passing to the limit, we arrive at the first equality (1).

Now let u be an unbounded function. Setting $u_k(x) = \min\{u(x), k\}$, we obtain the nondecreasing sequence $\{u_k(x)\}_{k \geqslant 1}$, which converges in measure to $u(x)$. Hence, by Beppo Levi's theorem,

$$\lim_{k \to \infty} \int_X u_k(x)\mu(dx) = \int_X u(x)\mu(dx)\,.$$

Taking into account that

$$\int_X u_k(x)\,\mu(dx) = \int_0^k \mu(\mathcal{M}_t)\,dt$$

and

$$\lim_{k\to\infty} \int_0^k \mu(\mathcal{M}_t)\,dt = \int_0^\infty \mu(\mathcal{M}_t)\,dt\,,$$

we arrive at the first equality (1). The second equality can be obtained in the same way. The theorem is proved.

Remark. We can easily derive a generalization of (1) for the integral

$$\int_X u(x)\,\mu(dx)\,,$$

where μ is a charge and u is not necessarily of a definite sign and

$$\int_X |u(x)|\,|\mu|(dx) < \infty\,.$$

1.2.4. A Formula for the Integral of the Modulus of the Gradient

In order to formulate the following theorem we need the definition of d-dimensional Hausdorff measure. Let E be a set in R^n. Consider various coverings of E by balls of radii $\leqslant \varepsilon$. We put $\sigma(\varepsilon) = v_d \inf \sum_i r_i^d$, where r_i is the radius of the i-th ball, v_d is the volume of the unit ball in R^d and the infimum is taken over all such coverings. The limit value of $\sigma(\varepsilon)$ as $\varepsilon \to 0$ is called d-dimensional Hausdorff measure. Obviously, this limit, infinite or finite, exists by virtue of the monotonicity of σ.

Theorem. *Let Φ be a Borel measurable nonnegative function on Ω and let $u \in C^{0,1}(\Omega)$, where Ω is an open subset of R^n. Then*

$$\int_\Omega \Phi(x)\,|\nabla u(x)|\,dx = \int_0^{+\infty} dt \int_{\mathscr{E}_t} \Phi(x)\,ds(x)\,, \tag{1}$$

where s is $(n-1)$-dimensional Hausdorff measure, $\mathscr{E}_t = \{x \in \Omega : |u(x)| = t\}$.

We shall derive (1) in the following weaker formulation, which will be used in this chapter.

If $\Phi \in C(\Omega)$, $\Phi \geqslant 0$, and $u \in C^\infty(\Omega)$, then (1) *holds.*

(Here we may assume s to be $(n-1)$-dimensional Lebesgue measure, since by Corollary 1.2.2 *the $\mathscr{E}_t$ are smooth manifolds.)*

Proof. Let $\boldsymbol{w}$ be an n-tuple vector-function in $\mathscr{D}(\Omega)$. Using integration by parts and applying Theorem 1.2.3, we obtain

$$\int_\Omega \boldsymbol{w}\,\nabla u\,dx = -\int_\Omega u \operatorname{div} \boldsymbol{w}\,dx = -\int_0^\infty dt \int_{u \geqslant t} \operatorname{div} \boldsymbol{w}\,dx + \int_{-\infty}^0 dt \int_{u \leqslant t} \operatorname{div} \boldsymbol{w}\,dx\,.$$

Since $u \in C^\infty(\Omega)$, then for almost all t the sets $\{x: u(x) = t\}$ are infinitely differentiable manifolds. Therefore for almost all $t > 0$

$$\int_{u>t} \operatorname{div} w \, dx = -\int_{u=t} w \nu \, ds = -\int_{u=t} \frac{w \nabla u}{|\nabla u|} ds ,$$

where $\nu(x)$ is the normal to $\{x: u(x) = t\}$ directed into the set $\{x: u(x) \geqslant t\}$. The integral

$$\int_{u \leqslant t} \operatorname{div} w \, dx$$

must be treated analogously. Consequently,

$$\int_\Omega w \nabla u \, dx = \int_0^\infty dt \int_{\mathscr{E}_t} \frac{w \nabla u}{|\nabla u|} dx .$$

Setting

$$w = \Phi \frac{\nabla u}{(|\nabla u|^2 + \varepsilon)^{1/2}} ,$$

where $\Phi \in \mathscr{D}(\Omega)$ and ε is a positive number, we obtain

$$\int_\Omega \Phi \frac{(\nabla u)^2}{((\nabla u)^2 + \varepsilon)^{1/2}} dx = \int_0^\infty dt \int_{\mathscr{E}_t} \frac{w \nabla u}{|\nabla u|} ds .$$

Passing to the limit as $\varepsilon \downarrow 0$ and making use of Beppo Levi's monotone convergence theorem we obtain (1) for all $\Phi \in \mathscr{D}(\Omega)$.

Let $\Phi \in C(\Omega)$, supp $\Phi \subset \Omega$ and let $\mathscr{M}_h \Phi$ be a mollification of Φ with radius h. Since supp $\mathscr{M}_h \Phi \subset \Omega$ for small values of h, then

$$\int_\Omega (\mathscr{M}_h \Phi)(\nabla u) \, dx = \int_0^\infty dt \int_{\mathscr{E}_t} \mathscr{M}_h \Phi \, ds . \tag{2}$$

Obviously, there exists a constant $C = C(\Phi)$ such that

$$\int_{\mathscr{E}_t} \mathscr{M}_h \Phi \, ds \leqslant C \int_{\mathscr{E}_t} \alpha \, ds , \tag{3}$$

where $\alpha \in \mathscr{D}(\Omega)$, $\alpha = 1$ on $\bigcup_h \operatorname{supp} \mathscr{M}_h \Phi$, $\alpha \geqslant 0$. By (1), applied to $\Phi = \alpha$, the integral in the right-hand side of (3) is a summable function on $(0, +\infty)$. Since $\mathscr{M}_h \Phi \to \Phi$ uniformly and since $s(\mathscr{E}_t \cap \operatorname{supp} \alpha) < \infty$ for almost all t, then also

$$\int_{\mathscr{E}_t} \mathscr{M}_h \Phi \, ds \underset{h \to 0}{\longrightarrow} \int_{\mathscr{E}_t} \Phi \, ds$$

for almost all t. Now, Lebesgue's theorem ensures the possibility of passing to the limit as $h \to 0$ in (2).

Further, we remove the restriction $\operatorname{supp}\Phi \subset \Omega$. Let $\Phi \in C(\Omega)$, $\Phi \geqslant 0$ and let α_m be a sequence of nonnegative functions in $\mathscr{D}(\Omega)$ such that $\bigcup_m \operatorname{supp}\alpha_m = \Omega$, $0 \leqslant \alpha_m \leqslant 1$ and $\alpha_m(x) = 1$ for $x \in \operatorname{supp}\alpha_{m-1}$. Then $\operatorname{supp}(\alpha_m \Phi) \subset \Omega$ and

$$\int_\Omega \alpha_m \Phi |\nabla u| dx = \int_0^\infty dt \int_{\mathscr{E}_t} \alpha_m \Phi ds .$$

Since the sequence $\alpha_m \Phi$ does not decrease, then by Beppo Levi's theorem we may pass to the limit as $m \to \infty$ (see [196]). This completes the proof.

1.2.5. Comments to § 1.2

In § 1.2 we collected auxiliary material most of which will be used in this chapter.

Theorem 1.2.1/1 is due to Besicovitch [24] (see also Guzman [84]) and Theorem 1.2.1/2 is due to Gustin [83]. Here we presented a simple proof of Theorem 1.2.1/2 given by Federer [60].

Theorem 1.2.2/2 was proved by Morse [192] for functions in C^n. Here we followed the proof presented in the book by Landis [123] Ch. II, § 2. Whitney showed that there exist functions $f \in C^{n-1}$ for which Theorem 1.2.2/2 fails.

Theorem 1.2.3 is contained in the paper by Faddeev [57]. The equality (1.2.4/1) was established by Kronrod [120] in the two-dimensional case for asymptotically differentiable functions. Federer proved a generalization of Theorem 1.2.4 for Lipschitz mappings $R^n \to R^m$, [59].

§ 1.3. Some Inequalities for Functions of One Variable

Most of this section is concerned with a generalization of the following Hardy inequality (cf. Hardy, Littlewood and Pólya [91], Sect. 9.9).

If $f(x) \geqslant 0$, then

$$\int_0^\infty x^{-r} F(x)^p dx \leqslant \left(\frac{p}{|r-1|} \right)^p \int_0^\infty x^{-r} (x f(x))^p dx ,$$

where $p > 1$, $r \neq 1$ and

$$F(x) = \int_0^x f(t) dt \qquad \text{for } r > 1 ,$$

$$F(x) = \int_x^\infty f(t) dt \qquad \text{for } r < 1 .$$

1.3.1. The Case $p \leqslant q$

Theorem 1. *Let μ and ν be nonnegative Borel measures on $(0, \infty)$ and let ν^* be the absolutely continuous part of ν. The inequality*

$$\left[\int_0^\infty \left|\int_0^x f(t)\,dt\right|^q d\mu(x)\right]^{1/q} \leqslant C\left[\int_0^\infty |f(x)|^p d\nu(x)\right]^{1/p} \tag{1}$$

holds for all Borel functions f and $1 \leqslant p \leqslant q \leqslant \infty$ if and only if

$$B = \sup_{r>0}[\mu([r,\infty))]^{1/q}\left[\int_0^r \left(\frac{d\nu^*}{dx}\right)^{-1/(p-1)} dx\right]^{(p-1)/p} < \infty . \tag{2}$$

Moreover, if C is the best constant in (1), *then*

$$B \leqslant C \leqslant B\left(\frac{q}{q-1}\right)^{(p-1)/p} q^{1/q} . \tag{3}$$

If $p=1$ or $q=\infty$, then $B=C$.

In the case $q=\infty$ the condition (2) *means that*

$$B = \sup\{r>0 \colon \mu([r,\infty)) > 0\} < \infty$$

and $\dfrac{d\nu^*}{dx} > 0$ for almost all $x \in [0, B]$.

We begin with the proof of the following less general theorem on absolutely continuous measures μ and ν.

Theorem 2. *Let $1 \leqslant p \leqslant q \leqslant \infty$. In order that there exists a constant C, independent of f, such that*

$$\left[\int_0^\infty \left|w(x)\int_0^x f(t)\,dt\right|^q dx\right]^{1/q} \leqslant C\left[\int_0^\infty |v(x)f(x)|^p dx\right]^{1/p}, \tag{4}$$

it is necessary and sufficient that

$$B = \sup_{r>0}\left(\int_r^\infty |w(x)|^q dx\right)^{1/q}\left(\int_0^r |v(x)|^{-p'} dx\right)^{1/p'} < \infty, \tag{5}$$

where $p' = p/(p-1)$. Moreover, if C is the best constant in (4) *and B is defined by* (5), *then* (3) *holds. If $p=1$ or $p=\infty$, then $B=C$.*

Proof. The case $1 < p \leqslant q < \infty$. *Necessity.* If $f \geqslant 0$ and $\operatorname{supp} f \subset [0, r]$, then from (4) it follows that

$$\left(\int_r^\infty |w(x)|^q dx\right)^{1/q} \int_0^r f(t)\,dt \leqslant C\left(\int_0^r |v(x) f(x)|^p dx\right)^{1/p}.$$

Let

$$\int_0^r |v(x)|^{-p/(p-1)} dx < \infty .$$

We set $f(x) = |v(x)|^{-p'}$ for $x<r$ and $f(x)=0$ for $x>r$. Then

(6) $$\left[\int_r^\infty |w(x)|^q dx\right]^{1/q} \left[\int_0^r |v(x)|^{-p'} dx\right]^{1/p'} \leqslant C .$$

If $\int_0^r |v(x)|^{-p'} dx = \infty$, then we arrive at the same result, replacing $v(x)$ by $v(x)+\varepsilon \operatorname{sgn} v(x)$ with $\varepsilon>0$ in (4) and passing to the limit as $\varepsilon \to 0$.

Sufficiency. We put

$$h(x) = \left(\int_0^x |v(t)|^{-p'} dt\right)^{1/qp'} .$$

By Hölder's inequality,

(7) $$\left(\int_0^\infty \left| w(x) \int_0^x f(t)\,dt\right|^q dx\right)^{p/q}$$

$$\leqslant \left\{\int_0^\infty |w(x)|^q \left(\int_0^x |f(t) h(t) v(t)|^p dt\right)^{q/p} \left(\int_0^x |h(t) v(t)|^{-p'} dt\right)^{q/p'} dx\right\}^{p/q} .$$

Now we prove that

(8) $$\left(\int_0^\infty \varphi(x) \left(\int_0^x f(y)\,dy\right)^r dx\right)^{1/r} \leqslant \int_0^\infty f(y) \left(\int_y^\infty \varphi(x)\,dx\right)^{1/r} dy$$

provided $\varphi, f \geqslant 0$ and $r \geqslant 1$. In fact, the left-hand side in (8) is equal to

$$\left(\int_0^\infty \left(\int_0^\infty \varphi(x)^{1/r} f(y) \chi_{[y,\infty)}(x)\,dy\right)^r dx\right)^{1/r},$$

where $\chi_{[y,\infty)}$ is the characteristic function of the halfaxis $[y,\infty)$. By Minkowski's inequality the last expression does not exceed

$$\int_0^\infty \left(\int_0^\infty [\varphi(x)^{1/r} f(y) \chi_{[y,\infty)}(x)]^r dx\right)^{1/r} dy = \int_0^\infty f(y) \left(\int_y^\infty \varphi(x)\,dx\right)^{1/r} dy .$$

According to (8) the right-hand side in (7) is majorized by

$$(9)\qquad \int_0^\infty |f(t)h(t)v(t)|^p\left(\int_t^\infty |w(x)|^q\left(\int_0^x |h(y)v(y)|^{-p'}dy\right)^{q/p'}dx\right)^{p/q}dt\,.$$

Using here the expression for h, we rewrite the integral in x as

$$(10)\qquad \int_t^\infty |w(x)|^q\left(\int_0^x |v(y)|^{-p'}\left(\int_0^y |v(z)|^{-p'}dz\right)^{-1/q}dy\right)^{q/p'}dx\,.$$

Since

$$\int_0^x |v(y)|^{-p'}\left(\int_0^y |v(z)|^{-p'}dz\right)^{-1/q}dy = q'\left(\int_0^x |v(y)|^{-p'}dy\right)^{1/q'},$$

then (10) is equal to

$$(q')^{q/p'}\int_t^\infty |w(x)|^q\left(\int_0^x |v(y)|^{-p'}dy\right)^{q/(p'q')}dx\,.$$

By the definition of B this expression is majorized by

$$(11)\qquad B^{q/q'}(q')^{q/p'}\int_t^\infty |w(x)|^q\left(\int_x^\infty |w(y)|^q dy\right)^{-1/q'}dx$$

$$= B^{q-1}(q')^{q/p'}q\left(\int_t^\infty |w(x)|^q dx\right)^{1/q} \leqslant B^q(q')^{q/p'}q\left(\int_0^t |v(x)|^{-p'}dx\right)^{-1/p'}$$

$$= B^q(q')^{q/p'}q\,h(t)^{-q}\,.$$

The preceding along with (9) yields the following majorant for (7)

$$\int_0^\infty |f(t)v(t)h(t)|^p(B^q(q')^{q/p'}q\,h(t)^{-q})^{p/q}dt$$

$$= B^p(q')^{p/p'}q^{p/q}\int_0^\infty |v(t)f(t)|^p dt\,.$$

Hence, (4) holds with the constant $B(q')^{(p-1)/p}q^{1/q}$.

Now we consider the limit cases.

If $p=\infty$ then $q=\infty$ and (4) follows from the obvious estimate

$$\operatorname*{ess\,sup}_{0<x<\infty}\left|w(x)\int_0^x f(t)\,dt\right|$$

$$\leqslant \operatorname*{ess\,sup}_{0<x<\infty}|w(x)|\int_0^x\frac{dt}{|v(t)|}\operatorname*{ess\,sup}_{0<t<x}|v(t)f(t)|\,.$$

If $p=1$, $q<\infty$, then from (8) it follows that

$$\left(\int_0^\infty \left| w(x)\int_0^x f(t)\,dt\right|^q dx\right)^{1/q}$$

$$\leqslant \int_0^\infty |f(t)| \left(\int_t^\infty |w(x)|^q dx\right)^{1/q} \frac{1}{|v(t)|} |v(t)|\,dt \leqslant B\int_0^\infty |v(t)f(t)|\,dt\,.$$

Let $q=\infty$, $p=1$. Then

$$\operatorname*{ess\,sup}_{0<x<\infty} \left| w(x)\int_0^x f(t)\,dt\right|$$

$$\leqslant \operatorname*{ess\,sup}_{0<x<\infty}\left(|w(x)|\operatorname*{ess\,sup}_{0<t<x}\frac{1}{|w(t)|}\int_0^x |v(t)f(t)|\,dt\right) \leqslant B\int_0^\infty |v(t)f(t)|\,dt\,.$$

If $p>1$, then

$$\operatorname*{ess\,sup}_{0<x<\infty} \left| w(x)\int_0^x f(t)\,dt\right|$$

$$\leqslant \operatorname*{ess\,sup}_{0<x<\infty}\left[\operatorname*{ess\,sup}_{x<t\leqslant\infty}|w(x)|\left(\int_0^x |v(t)|^{-p'}dt\right)^{1/p'}\left(\int_0^x |v(t)f(t)|^p dt\right)^{1/p}\right]$$

$$\leqslant B\left(\int_0^x |v(t)f(t)|^p dt\right)^{1/p}.$$

This concludes the proof of Theorem 2.

Proof of Theorem 1. Setting $f=0$ on the support of the singular part of the measure ν, we obtain that (1) is equivalent to

$$\left[\int_0^\infty \left|\int_0^x f(t)\,dt\right|^q d\mu(x)\right]^{1/q} \leqslant C\left[\int_0^x |f(x)|^p \frac{d\nu^*}{dx}\,dx\right]^{1/p}.$$

The estimate $B\leqslant C$ can be derived in the same way as in the proof of Theorem 2, if $|v(x)|^p$ is replaced by $d\nu^*/dx$ and $\int_r^\infty |w(x)|^q dx$ by $\mu([r,\infty))$.

Now we establish the upper bound for C. We may assume $f\geqslant 0$. Let $\{g_n\}$ be a sequence of decreasing absolutely continuous functions on $[0,\infty)$ satisfying

$$0\leqslant g_n(x)\leqslant g_{n+1}(x)\leqslant \mu([x,\infty))\,,$$

$$\lim_{n\to\infty} g_n(x) = \mu([x,\infty))$$

for almost all x.

We have

$$\left[\int_0^\infty \left(\int_0^x f(t)\,dt\right)^q d\mu(x)\right]^{1/q} = \left[\int_0^\infty \mu([x,\infty))\,d\left(\int_0^x f(t)\,dt\right)^q\right]^{1/q}.$$

By the monotone convergence theorem the right-hand side is equal to

$$\sup_n \left[\int_0^\infty g_n(x)\,d\left(\int_0^x f(t)\,dt\right)^q\right]^{1/q} \tag{12}$$

$$= \sup_n \left[\int_0^\infty \left(\int_0^x f(t)\,dt\right)^q [-g_n'(x)]\,dx\right]^{1/q}.$$

The definition of the constant B and of the sequence $\{g_n\}$ imply

$$\left[\int_r^\infty [-g_n'(x)]\,dx\right]^{1/q} \left[\int_0^r \left(\frac{d\nu^*}{dx}\right)^{-p'/p} dx\right]^{1/p'} \leqslant B.$$

From this and Theorem 2 we conclude that the right-hand side in (12) is not more than

$$B(q')^{(p-1)/p} q^{1/q} \left(\int_0^\infty (f(x))^p \frac{d\nu^*}{dx}\,dx\right)^{1/p},$$

which completes the proof.

Replacing x by x^{-1} we derive the following assertion from Theorem 1.

Theorem 3. *Let* $1 \leqslant p \leqslant q \leqslant \infty$. *In order that there exist a constant* C, *independent of* f *and such that*

$$\left[\int_0^\infty \left|\int_0^\infty f(t)\,dt\right|^q d\mu(x)\right]^{1/q} \leqslant C\left[\int_0^\infty |f(x)|^p\,d\nu(x)\right]^{1/p}, \tag{13}$$

it is necessary and sufficient that the value

$$B = \sup_{r>0}\,[\mu((0,r])]^{1/q} \left[\int_r^\infty \left(\frac{d\nu^*}{dx}\right)^{-1/(p-1)} dx\right]^{(p-1)/p}$$

be finite. The best constant in (13) *satisfies the same inequalities as in Theorem* 1.

Analogously, by the change of variable

$$(0,\infty) \ni x \to y = x - x^{-1} \in (-\infty, +\infty),$$

from Theorem 1 we obtain the next assertion.

Theorem 4. *Let $1 \leqslant p \leqslant q \leqslant \infty$. In order that there exist a constant C, independent of f and such that*

$$\left[\int_{-\infty}^{+\infty}\left|\int_{x}^{\infty} f(t)\,dt\right|^{q} d\mu(x)\right]^{1/q} \leqslant C\left[\int_{-\infty}^{+\infty} |f(x)|^{p}\,d\nu(x)\right]^{1/p}, \tag{14}$$

it is necessary and sufficient that the value

$$B = \sup_{r\in(-\infty,\infty)} [\mu((-\infty,r))]^{1/q}\left[\int_{r}^{\infty}\left(\frac{d\nu^*}{dx}\right)^{-1/(p-1)} dx\right]^{(p-1)/p}$$

be finite. The constants B and C are related in the same way as in Theorem 1.

1.3.2. The Case $p > q$

Lemma. *Let $1 \leqslant q < p \leqslant \infty$ and let ω be a nonnegative Borel function on $(0, b)$, where $b \in (0, \infty]$. In order that there exist a constant C, independent of ψ and such that*

$$\left(\int_0^b \omega(t)\left|\int_0^t \psi(\tau)\,d\tau\right|^q dt\right)^{1/q} \leqslant C\left(\int_0^b |\psi(t)|^p\,dt\right)^{1/p}, \tag{1}$$

it is necessary and sufficient that

$$B = \left(\int_0^b \left(\int_t^b \omega(\tau)\,d\tau\right)^{p/(p-q)} t^{(q-1)p/(p-q)}\,dt\right)^{(p-q)/pq} < \infty. \tag{2}$$

If C is the best constant in (2), *then*

$$\left(\frac{p-q}{p-1}\right)^{(q-1)/q} q^{1/q} B \leqslant C \leqslant \left(\frac{p}{p-1}\right)^{(q-1)/q} q^{1/q} B \quad \textit{for } q > 1$$

and $B = C$ for $q = 1$.

Proof. Sufficiency. First consider the case $q > 1$. We may assume $\psi(t) \geqslant 0$. Integrating by parts in the left-hand side of (1) and using Hölder's inequality with exponents $p/(p-q)$, $p/(q-1)$ and p, we obtain

$$\left(\int_0^b \omega(t)\left(\int_0^t \psi(\tau)\,d\tau\right)^q dt\right)^{1/q} \tag{3}$$

$$= q^{1/q}\left(\int_0^b\int_t^b \omega(\tau)\,d\tau\,\psi(t)\left(\int_0^t \psi(\tau)\,d\tau\right)^{q-1} dt\right)^{1/q} \leqslant$$

$$\leqslant q^{1/q}\left[\left(\int_0^b \psi(t)^p dt\right)^{1/p}\left(\int_0^b\left(\int_0^t \psi(\tau)\,d\tau\right)^p t^{-p}dt\right)^{(q-1)/p}\right.$$

$$\left.\times\left(\int_0^b t^{(q-1)p/(p-q)}\left(\int_t^b \omega(\tau)\,d\tau\right)^{p/(p-q)}dt\right)^{(p-q)/p}\right]^{1/q}.$$

From (2) and Hardy's inequality, formulated just before 1.3.1, it follows that (3) is majorized by

$$B\left(\frac{p}{p-1}\right)^{(q-1)/q}\cdot\ q^{1/q}\left(\int_0^b \psi(t)^p dt\right)^{1/p}.$$

Necessity. Consider, for example, the case $b=\infty$. The proof is similar for $b<\infty$.

If (1) holds for the weight ω with the constant C, then it holds for the weight $\omega_N=\omega\chi_{[0,N]}$, where $\chi_{[0,N]}$ is the characteristic function of the segment $[0,N]$, with the same constant. We put

$$f_N(x)=\left(\int_x^\infty \omega_N(t)\,dt\right)^{1/(p-q)} x^{(q-1)/(p-q)},$$

$$B_N=\left(\int_0^\infty\left(\int_t^\infty \omega_N(\tau)\,d\tau\right)^{p/(p-q)} t^{(q-1)p/(p-q)}dt\right)^{(p-q)/p}.$$

From (1) we have

$$\text{(4)}\qquad CB_N^{q/(p-q)}=C\left(\int_0^\infty f_N(x)^p dx\right)^{1/p}\geqslant\left(\int_0^\infty \omega_N(t)\left(\int_0^t f_N(\tau)\,d\tau\right)^q dt\right)^{1/q}.$$

Integrating by parts, we find that the right-hand side in (4) is equal to

$$\text{(5)}\qquad \left(q\int_0^\infty f_N(t)\int_t^\infty \omega_N(\tau)\,d\tau\left(\int_0^t f_N(\tau)\,d\tau\right)^{q-1}dt\right)^{1/q}.$$

Since

$$\left(\int_0^t f_N(\tau)\,d\tau\right)^{q-1}=\left(\int_0^t x^{(q-1)/(p-q)}\left(\int_x^\infty \omega_N(\tau)\,d\tau\right)^{1/(p-q)}dx\right)^{q-1}$$

$$\geqslant\left(\int_t^\infty \omega_N(\tau)\,d\tau\right)^{(q-1)/(p-q)} t^{(p-1)(q-1)/(p-q)}\left(\frac{p-1}{p-q}\right)^{1-q},$$

then (5) is not less than

$$q^{1/q}\left(\frac{p-1}{p-q}\right)^{(1-q)/q}\left(\int_0^\infty\left(\int_t^\infty \omega_N(\tau)\,d\tau\right)^{p/(p-q)} t^{(q-1)p/(p-q)}\,dt\right)^{1/q}$$

$$=q^{1/q}\left(\frac{p-1}{p-q}\right)^{(1-q)/q} B_N^{p/(p-q)}\,.$$

Therefore,

$$B_N\leqslant q^{-1/q}\left(\frac{p-q}{p-1}\right)^{(1-q)/q} C\,,$$

and the same estimate is valid for B.

In the case $q=1$ the condition (2) becomes especially simple:

$$B=\left(\int_0^b\left(\int_t^b \omega(\tau)\,d\tau\right)^{p'} dt\right)^{1/p'}<\infty\,.$$

To prove that in this case $C\leqslant B$ we integrate by parts in the left-hand side of (1) and apply Hölder's inequality with exponents p and p' (cf. (3)). Then the right-hand side of (1) has the upper bound

$$\left(\int_0^b\left(\int_t^\infty \omega(\tau)\,d\tau\right)^{p'} dt\right)^{1/p'}\left(\int_0^b |\psi(t)|^p\,dt\right)^{1/p}.$$

Thus, we proved that $C\leqslant B$.

To derive the inequality $B\leqslant C$ we substitute

$$f_N(x)=\left(\int_x^\infty \omega_N(t)\,dt\right)^{1/(p-1)}$$

into (5). This yields $B_N\leqslant C$ and hence $B\leqslant C$. The lemma is proved.

Theorem 1. *Let* $1\leqslant q<p\leqslant\infty$. *Inequality* (1.3.1/4) *holds if and only if*

$$\text{(6)}\qquad B=\left(\int_0^\infty\left[\left(\int_0^x |v(y)|^{-p'}dy\right)^{q-1}\int_x^\infty |w(y)|^q dy\right]^{p/(p-q)}\frac{dx}{|v(x)|^{p'}}\right)^{(p-q)/pq}<\infty\,.$$

If C is the best constant in (1.3.1/4), *then*

$$\left(\frac{p-q}{p-1}\right)^{(q-1)/q} q^{1/q}B\leqslant C\leqslant\left(\frac{p}{p-1}\right)^{(q-1)/q} q^{1/q}B\quad \textit{for } 1<q<p\leqslant\infty$$

and $B=C$ for $q=1$, $1<p\leqslant\infty$.

Proof. We may assume that $f\geqslant 0$, since the right-hand side in (1.3.1/4) does not change and the left-hand side increases if f is replaced by $|f|$.

We may as well assume $f(x)=0$ for sufficiently large values of x. Let us put

$$t(x)=\int_0^x |v(y)|^{-p'}dy\,.$$

Then (1.3.1/4) becomes

$$\left(\int_0^b |\tilde{w}(t)|^q|\tilde{v}(t)|^{p'}|\varphi(t)|^q dt\right)^{1/q}\leqslant C\left(\int_0^b |\varphi'(t)|^p dt\right)^{1/p},$$

where $\tilde{w}(t(x))=w(x)$, $\tilde{v}(t(x))=v(x)$,

$$\varphi(t(x))=\int_0^x f(y)\,dy\,,\qquad b=\int_0^\infty |v(y)|^{-p'}dy\,.$$

Now, in the case $1\leqslant q<p<\infty$ the result follows from Lemma.

Let $p=\infty$. Then

$$B=\left(\int_0^\infty\left(\int_0^x |v(y)|^{-1}dy\right)^{q-1}\int_x^\infty |w(y)|^q dy\frac{dx}{|v(x)|}\right)^{1/q}$$

$$=q^{-1/q}\left(\int_0^\infty |w(x)|^q\left(\int_0^x\frac{dy}{|v(y)|}\right)^q dx\right)^{1/q}.$$

Hence

$$\left(\int_0^\infty\left|w(x)\int_0^x f(t)\,dt\right|^q dx\right)^{1/q}\leqslant Bq^{1/q}\operatorname*{ess\,sup}_{0<x<\infty}|vf|\,.$$

To prove the necessity we note that v does not vanish on a set of positive measure and put $f=1/v$. The theorem is proved.

The following more general assertion can be derived from Theorem 1 in the same way as Theorem 1.3.1/1 was derived from Theorem 1.3.1/2.

Theorem 2. *Let μ and ν be nonnegative Borel measures on* $(0,\infty)$ *and let ν^* be the absolutely continuous part of ν. Inequality* (1.3.1/4) *with* $1\leqslant q<p\leqslant\infty$ *holds for all Borel functions f if and only if*

$$B=\left(\int_0^\infty\left[\mu([x,\infty))\left(\int_0^x\left(\frac{d\nu^*}{dy}\right)^{-p'}dy\right)^{q-1}\right]^{p/(p-q)}\left(\frac{d\nu^*}{dx}\right)^{-p'}dx\right)^{(p-q)/pq}<\infty\,.$$

The best constant C in (1.3.1/13) *is related with B in the same manner as in Theorem* 1.

The change of variable $(0,\infty)\ni x\to y=x-x^{-1}\in(-\infty,+\infty)$ leads to the following *necessary and sufficient condition for the validity of* (1.3.1/14):

$$\int_{-\infty}^{+\infty}\left[\mu((-\infty,x])\left(\int_x^{\infty}\left(\frac{dv^*}{dy}\right)^{-p'}dy\right)^{q-1}\right]^{p/(p-q)}\left(\frac{dv^*}{dx}\right)^{-p'}dx<\infty,$$

where $1\leqslant q<p\leqslant\infty$.

1.3.3. Three Inequalities for Functions on $(0,\infty)$

Lemma 1. *If f is a nonnegative nonincreasing function on* $(0,\infty)$ *and* $p\geqslant 1$, *then*

$$\int_0^{\infty}[f(x)]^p d(x^p)\leqslant\left(\int_0^{\infty}f(x)\,dx\right)^p. \tag{1}$$

Proof. Obviously,

$$p\int_0^{\infty}[xf(x)]^{p-1}f(x)\,dx\leqslant p\int_0^{\infty}\left[\int_0^x f(t)\,dt\right]^{p-1}f(x)\,dx$$

$$=\left(\int_0^{\infty}f(x)\,dx\right)^p.$$

The result follows.

Lemma 2. *If* $f(x)\geqslant 0$, *then*

$$\left[\int_0^{\infty}f(x)\,dx\right]^{a\mu+b\lambda}\leqslant c(a,b,\lambda,\mu)\left[\int_0^{\infty}x^{a-1-\lambda}f(x)^a dx\right]^{\mu}\left[\int_0^{\infty}x^{b-1+\mu}f(x)^b dx\right]^{\lambda},$$

where $a>1$, $b>1$, $0<\lambda<a$, $0<\mu<b$.

Proof. Obviously,

$$\int_0^{\infty}f(x)\,dx=\int_0^{\infty}x^{(a-1-\lambda)/a}f(x)\,\frac{dx}{x^{(a-1-\lambda)/a}(1+x)}$$

$$+\int_0^{\infty}x^{(b-1+\mu)/b}f(x)\,\frac{dx}{x^{(b-1+\mu)/b}(1+x^{-1})}.$$

By Hölder's inequality

$$\int_0^{\infty}x^{(a-1-\lambda)/a}f(x)\,\frac{dx}{x^{(a-1-\lambda)/a}(1+x)}\leqslant L\left(\int_0^{\infty}x^{a-1-\lambda}f(x)^a dx\right)^{1/a},$$

$$\int_0^{\infty}x^{(b-1+\mu)/b}f(x)\,\frac{dx}{x^{(b-1+\mu)/b}(1+x^{-1})}\leqslant M\left(\int_0^{\infty}x^{b-1+\mu}f(x)^b dx\right)^{1/b},$$

where

$$L=\left(\int_0^{\infty}\frac{dx}{x^{(a-1-\lambda)/(a-1)}(1+x)^{a/(a-1)}}\right)^{(a-1)/a},$$

$$M=\left(\int_0^\infty \frac{dx}{x^{(b-1+\mu)/(b-1)}(1+x^{-1})^{b/(b-1)}}\right)^{(b-1)/b}.$$

Hence

$$\int_0^\infty f(x)\,dx\leqslant L\left(\int_0^\infty x^{a-1-\lambda}f(x)^a dx\right)^{1/a}+M\left(\int_0^\infty x^{b-1+\mu}f(x)^b dx\right)^{1/b}.$$

Replacing $f(x)$ by $f(z/\varrho)$, where $\varrho>0$, and setting $z=\varrho x$, we obtain

$$\varrho^{-1}\int_0^\infty f(z/\varrho)\,dz\leqslant L\varrho^{(\lambda-a)/a}\left(\int_0^\infty z^{a-1-\lambda}f(z/\varrho)^a dz\right)^{1/a}$$
$$+M\varrho^{-(\mu+b)/b}\left(\int_0^\infty z^{b-1+\mu}f(z/\varrho)^b dz\right)^{1/b}.$$

Thus, for all measurable nonnegative functions on $(0,\infty)$ and for any $\varrho>0$,

$$\int_0^\infty \varphi(z)\,dz\leqslant L\varrho^{\lambda/a}\left(\int_0^\infty z^{a-1-\lambda}\varphi(z)^a dz\right)^{1/a}$$
$$+M\varrho^{-\mu/b}\left(\int_0^\infty z^{b+\mu-1}\varphi(z)^b dz\right)^{1/b}.$$

Taking the minimum of the right-hand side over ϱ, we obtain (2).

Lemma 3. *If f is a nonnegative nonincreasing function on $(0,\infty)$ and $p\geqslant 1$, then*

$$\frac{(p-1)^{p-1}}{p^p}\sup_x x^p f(x)\leqslant \sup_x x^{p-1}\int_x^\infty f(t)\,dt. \tag{3}$$

The characteristic function of the interval $(0,1)$ turns (3) into an equality.

Proof. Let c be an arbitrary positive number. Since f does not increase, then

$$f\left(\frac{p}{p-1}c\right)^{1/p}\leqslant\frac{p-1}{c}\int_c^{cp/(p-1)} f(t)^{1/p}dt.$$

By Hölder's inequality

$$f\left(\frac{p}{p-1}c\right)^{1/p}\leqslant\frac{(p-1)^{1/p}}{c^{1/p}}\left(\int_c^{cp/(p-1)} f(t)\,dt\right)^{1/p}.$$

Hence

$$\left(\frac{p}{p-1}c\right)^p f\left(\frac{p}{p-1}c\right)\leqslant\frac{p^p}{(p-1)^{p-1}}c^{p-1}\int_c^{cp/(p-1)} f(t)\,dt$$
$$\leqslant\frac{p^p}{(p-1)^{p-1}}\sup_y y^{p-1}\int_y^\infty f(t)\,dt.$$

Setting $x = \dfrac{p}{p-1}c$, we arrive at (3).

If f is equal to unity for $0<x<1$ and to zero for $x \geqslant 1$ then

$$\sup_x x^{p-1} \int_x^\infty f(t)\,dt = \sup_{0 \leqslant x \leqslant 1} x^{p-1}(1-x) = \frac{(p-1)^{p-1}}{p^p} = \frac{(p-1)^{p-1}}{p^p} \sup_x x^p f(x)\,.$$

The lemma is proved.

Remark. If f is an arbitrary nonnegative measurable function on $(0, \infty)$, then the inequality, opposite to (3), is valid:

$$\sup_x x^{p-1} \int_x^\infty f(t)\,dt \leqslant \frac{1}{p-1} \sup_x x^p f(x)\,, \tag{4}$$

the equality being attained for $f(x) = x^{-p}$.

In fact,

$$x^{p-1} \int_x^\infty f(t)\,dt \leqslant x^{p-1} \int_x^\infty \frac{dt}{t^p} \sup_x x^p f(x) = \frac{1}{p-1} \sup_x x^p f(x)\,.$$

1.3.4. Comments to § 1.3

There are a number of papers where particular cases of the theorems in subsections 1.3.1, 1.3.2 are used. For $p = q$ Theorems 1.3.1/1 and 1.3.1/2 are due to Muckenhoupt [194]. The generalizations for $p \neq q$ presented in subsections 1.3.1, 1.3.2 were obtained by Rosin and the author (see Maz'ja [165]). The case $p < q$ was independently investigated by Kokilašvili [112].

Inequality (1.3.3/1) is proved in the paper by Hardy, Littlewood and Pólya [90] and (1.3.3/2) is presented in the book [91] by the same authors. The best constant in (1.3.3/2) was found by Levin [129]. Lemma 1.3.3/3 was published in the author's book [165].

§ 1.4. Imbedding Theorems of Sobolev Type

This section deals with a generalization of the Sobolev imbedding theorem. The heart of this result will be obtained as a corollary of estimates, in which the norms in the space of functions, summable with power p with respect to an arbitrary measure, are majorized by norms in Sobolev spaces. First we shall consider functions defined on R^n and then we shall proceed to the case of a bounded domain.

1.4.1. D.R. Adams' Theorem on Riesz Potentials

Let μ be a measure in R^n, i.e. a nonnegative countably additive set function, defined on a Borel σ-algebra of R^n. Let $L_q(R^n, \mu) = L_q(\mu)$ denote the space of functions on R^n, which are summable with power q with respect to μ. We put

$$\|u\|_{L_p(\mu)} = (\int |u|^q d\mu)^{1/q}.$$

The space $L_q(\Omega, \mu)$, where μ is a measure on an open set Ω, is defined in an analogous manner.

In order to prove the basic result of this subsection, we need the classical *Marcinkiewicz interpolation theorem*, which is presented here without proof (cf., for example, Stein's book [237]).

Suppose p_0, p_1, q_0, q_1 are real numbers, $1 \leqslant p_i \leqslant q_i < \infty$, $p_0 < p_1$ and $q_0 \neq q_1$. Let μ be a measure in R^n and let T be an additive operator defined on $\mathscr{D}$, its values being μ-measurable functions.

The operator T is said to be of weak type (p_i, q_i) if there exists a constant $\mathscr{A}_i$ such that for any $f \in \mathscr{D}$, $\alpha > 0$,

$$\mu(\{x: |(Tf)(x)| > \alpha\}) \leqslant (\alpha^{-1} \mathscr{A}_i \|f\|_{L_{p_i}})^{q_i}.$$

Theorem 1. *Let T be an operator of the weak types (p_0, q_0) and (p_1, q_1). If $0 < \theta < 1$ and*

$$\frac{1}{p} = \frac{1-\theta}{p_0} + \frac{\theta}{p_1}, \qquad \frac{1}{q} = \frac{1-\theta}{q_0} + \frac{\theta}{q_1},$$

then for all $f \in \mathscr{D}$

$$\|Tf\|_{L_q(\mu)} \leqslant c \mathscr{A}_0^{1-\theta} \mathscr{A}_1^{\theta} \|f\|_{L_p},$$

and, hence, T can be extended onto $L_p(R^n)$ as a continuous operator: $L_p \to L_q(\mu)$. Here $c = c(p_1, p_2, q_1, q_2, \theta)$ is a constant independent of μ, T and f.

Now, we proceed to the statement and proof of the basic theorem of this subsection.

Theorem 2. *Let $l > 0$, $1 < p < q < \infty$, $lp < n$. The Riesz potential*

$$(I_l f)(x) = \int_{R^n} |x-y|^{l-n} f(y)\, dy$$

maps L_p continuously into $L_q(\mu)$ if and only if the function

$$\mathscr{M}(x) = \sup_{\varrho > 0} \varrho^{-s} \mu(B(x, \varrho)),$$

where $s = q\left(\dfrac{n}{p} - l\right)$, is bounded.

Proof. Sufficiency. We show that

$$t\mu(\mathscr{L}_t)^{1/q} \leqslant v_n^{1/p'} \frac{pq}{(n-pl)(q-p)} \sup \mathscr{M}(x)^{1/q} \|f\|_{L_p}, \tag{1}$$

where

$$p' = \frac{p}{p-1}, \qquad \mathcal{L}_t = \{y\colon (I_l|f|)(y) > t\}, \qquad t > 0.$$

Let μ_t be the restriction of μ to $\mathcal{L}_t$ and let r be a positive number, which will be specified later. Clearly,

$$\begin{aligned} t\mu(\mathcal{L}_t) &\leqslant \int_{R^n} |f(x)| \int |x-y|^{l-n} d\mu_t(y)\, dx \\ &= (n-l) \int_0^\infty \int_{R^n} |f(x)|\, \mu_t(B(x,\varrho))\, dx\, \varrho^{l-n-1} d\varrho \\ &= (n-l) \int_0^r (\ldots)\, \varrho^{l-n-1} d\varrho + \int_r^\infty (\ldots)\, \varrho^{l-n-1} d\varrho = A_1 + A_2. \end{aligned}$$

Using the obvious inequality

$$\mu_t(B(x,\varrho)) \leqslant (\mu_t(B(x,\varrho)))^{1/p'} \mathcal{M}(x)^{1/p} \varrho^{s/p},$$

we obtain

$$A_1 \leqslant (n-l) \sup \mathcal{M}(x)^{1/p} \|f\|_{L_p} \int_0^r \left(\int_{R^n} \mu_t(B(x,\varrho))\, dx \right)^{1/p'} \varrho^{l-n-1+s/p} d\varrho.$$

Since

$$\int_{R^n} \mu_t(B(x,\varrho))\, dx = v_n \varrho^n \mu(\mathcal{L}_t),$$

then

$$A_1 \leqslant \frac{p(n-l)}{pl-n+s} v_n^{1/p'} \sup \mathcal{M}(x)^{1/p} \|f\|_{L_p} \mu(\mathcal{L}_t)^{1/p'} r^{l-(n-s)/p}.$$

Similarly,

$$\begin{aligned} A_2 &\leqslant (n-l) \|f\|_{L_p} \mu(\mathcal{L}_t)^{1/p} \int_r^\infty \left(\int_{R^n} \mu_t(B(x,\varrho))\, dx \right)^{1/p'} \varrho^{l-n-1} d\varrho \\ &= \frac{p(n-l)}{n-pl} v_n^{1/p'} \|f\|_{L_p} \mu(\mathcal{L}_t) r^{l-n/p}. \end{aligned}$$

Hence,

$$t\mu(\mathcal{L}_t)^{1/p} \leqslant \|f\|_{L_p} v_n^{1/p'} (n-l) p \left(\frac{\sup \mathcal{M}(x)^{1/p}}{pl-n+s} r^{l-(n-s)/p} + \frac{\mu(\mathcal{L}_t)^{1/p}}{n-pl} r^{l-n/p} \right).$$

The right-hand side attains its minimum value at

$$r^s = \mu(\mathcal{L}_t)/\sup \mathcal{M}(x)$$

and is equal to

$$\frac{p(n-l)s}{(n-pl)(pl-n+s)} v_n^{1/p'} \|f\|_{L_p} \sup \mathcal{M}(x)^{1/q} \mu(\mathcal{L}_t)^{1/p-1/q}.$$

Thus, (1) is proved.

Applying interpolation Theorem 1, we find that the operator $I_l: L_p \to L_q(\mu)$ is continuous and

(2) $$\| I_l f \|_{L_p(\mu)} \leqslant c \sup \mathscr{M}(x)^{1/q} \| f \|_{L_p} .$$

Necessity. Let

(3) $$\| I_l f \|_{L_q(\mu)} \leqslant C \| f \|_{L_p} .$$

Let f denote the characteristic function of the ball $B(x, \varrho)$. Then, for $z \in B(x, \varrho)$,

$$(I_l f)(z) \geqslant (2\varrho)^{l-n} \int_{B(x,\varrho)} dy = v_n 2^{l-n} \varrho^l .$$

This and (3) imply

$$(\mu(B(x,\varrho)))^{1/q} \leqslant 2^{n-l} v_n^{-1/p'} C \varrho^{-l+n/p} .$$

The theorem is proved.

From Theorem 2 and the integral representation (1.1.10/6) we obtain the following corollary.

Corollary. *Let* $1 < p < q < \infty$, $n > pl$.

1) *For all* $u \in \mathscr{D}$

(4) $$\| u \|_{L_q(\mu)} \leqslant C \| \nabla_l u \|_{L_p} ,$$

where

$$C^q \leqslant c_1 \sup_{x;\varrho} \varrho^{(l-n/p)q} \mu[B(x,\varrho)] .$$

2) *If* (4) *holds for all* $u \in \mathscr{D}$, *then*

$$C^q \geqslant c_2 \sup_{x;\varrho} \varrho^{(l-n/p)q} \mu[B(x,\varrho)] .$$

1.4.2. An Estimate for the Norm in $L_q(R^n, \mu)$ by the Integral of the Modulus of the Gradient

Theorem 1. 1) *Let*

(1) $$\sup_{\{g\}} \frac{\mu(g)^{1/q}}{s(\partial g)} < \infty ,$$

where $q \geqslant 1$ *and* $\{g\}$ *is a collection of subsets of an open set* Ω, $\bar{g} \subset \Omega$, *with compact closures and bounded by* C^∞*-manifolds. Then for all* $u \in \mathscr{D}(\Omega)$

(2) $$\| u \|_{L_q(\Omega,\mu)} \leqslant C \| \nabla u \|_{L_1(\Omega)} ,$$

where

(3) $$C \leqslant \sup_{\{g\}} \frac{\mu(g)^{1/q}}{s(\partial g)} .$$

2) *Suppose that for all* $u \in \mathscr{D}(\Omega)$ *the inequality* (2) *holds. Then*

(4) $$C \geqslant \sup_{\{g\}} \frac{\mu(g)^{1/q}}{s(\partial g)} .$$

Proof. 1) By Theorem 1.2.3

$$\|u\|_{L_q(\Omega,\mu)} = \left(\int_0^\infty \mu(\mathscr{L}_t)\, d(t^q) \right)^{1/q},$$

where $\mathscr{L}_t = \{x\colon |u(x)| > t\}$. Since $\mu(\mathscr{L}_t)$ does not increase, then applying (1.3.3/1) we obtain

$$\|u\|_{L_q(\Omega,\mu)} \leqslant \int_0^\infty \mu(\mathscr{L}_t)^{1/q} dt \leqslant \sup_{\{g\}} \frac{\mu(g)^{1/q}}{s(\partial g)} \int_0^\infty s(\partial \mathscr{L}_t)\, dt .$$

Here we used Corollary 1.2.2, according to which almost all sets $\mathscr{L}_t$ are bounded by smooth manifolds. By Theorem 1.2.4, the last integral coincides with $\|\nabla u\|_{L_1(\Omega)}$.

2) Let g be an arbitrary set in $\{g\}$ and let $d(x) = \operatorname{dist}(x, g)$, $g_t = \{x\colon d(x) < t\}$. Into (1) we substitute the function $u_\varepsilon(x) = \alpha[d(x)]$, where $\alpha(d)$ is a non-decreasing C^∞-function on $[0,1]$, equal to unity for $d = 0$ and to zero for $d > \varepsilon$, $\varepsilon > 0$. According to Theorem 1.2.4,

$$\int_\Omega |\nabla u_\varepsilon|\, dx = \int_0^\varepsilon \alpha'(t)\, s(\partial g_t)\, dt .$$

Since $s(\partial g_t) \to s(\partial g)$ as $t \to 0$, then

(5) $$\int_\Omega |\nabla u_\varepsilon|\, dx \to s(\partial g) .$$

On the other hand,

(6) $$\|u_\varepsilon\|_{L_q(\Omega,\mu)} \geqslant \mu(g)^{1/q} .$$

Combining (5) and (6) with (2), we obtain

$$\mu(g)^{1/q} \leqslant C s(\partial g) ,$$

which completes the proof.

From Theorem 1 and the classical isoperimetric inequality

(7) $$m_n(g)^{(n-1)/n} \leqslant n^{-1} v_n^{-1/n} s(\partial g)$$

(cf. Ljusternik [140], Schmidt [223], Hadwiger [85], and others), it follows that *for all* $u \in \mathscr{D}(\Omega)$

$$(8)\qquad \|u\|_{L_{n/(n-1)}} \leqslant n^{-1} v_n^{-1/n} \|\nabla u\|_{L_1}$$

with the best constant.

In the case $n > p \geqslant 1$ we replace u by $|u|^{p(n-1)/(n-p)}$ in (8) and then estimate the right-hand side by Hölder's inequality. We have

$$\|u\|_{L_{pn/(n-p)}}^{p(n-1)/(n-p)} \leqslant \frac{p(n-1)}{n(n-p)} v_n^{-1/n} \| |u|^{n(p-1)/(n-p)} \nabla u \|_{L_1}$$

$$\leqslant \frac{p(n-1)}{n(n-p)} v_n^{-1/n} \|u\|_{L_{pn/(n-p)}}^{n(p-1)/(n-p)} \|\nabla u\|_{L_p} .$$

Consequently,

$$\|u\|_{L_{pn/(n-p)}} \leqslant \frac{p(n-1)}{n(n-p)} v_n^{-1/n} \|\nabla u\|_{L_p} .$$

This along with

$$|\nabla|\nabla_{l-k} u|| \leqslant n^{1/2} |\nabla_{l-k+1} u|, \qquad k = 1, \ldots, l-1$$

yields

$$(9)\qquad \|\nabla_{l-k} u\|_{L_{pn/(n-kp)}} \leqslant \frac{p(n-1)n^{-1/2}}{n-kp} v_n^{-1/n} \|\nabla_{l-k+1} u\|_{L_{pn/(n-(k-1)p)}},$$

where $kp < n$. Putting $k = 1, 2, \ldots, l-1$ in (9) and then multiplying all inequalities obtained, we arrive at the next corollary.

Corollary. *If $n > lp$, $p \geqslant 1$, then for all $u \in \mathscr{D}$*

$$(10)\qquad \|u\|_{L_{pn/(n-lp)}} \leqslant n^{-(l+1)/2} \left(\frac{n-1}{v_n^{1/n}} \right)^l \frac{\Gamma(n/p-l)}{\Gamma(n/p)} \|\nabla_l u\|_{L_p} .$$

Thus we obtained the Sobolev ($p > 1$)-Gagliardo ($p = 1$) inequality with an explicit (but not the best possible for $p > 1$, $l \geqslant 1$ or for $p \geqslant 1$, $l > 1$) constant. In the case $l = 1$ the best constant is known (cf. 2.3.1).

The following theorem shows that in the case $\Omega = R^n$ the condition (1) can be replaced by the equivalent one:

$$(11)\qquad \sup_{x;\varrho} \varrho^{(1-n)q} \mu(B_\varrho(x)) < \infty .$$

Theorem 2. 1) *If* (11) *holds, then* (2) *holds for all $u \in \mathscr{D}(R^n)$ with $q \geqslant 1$ and*

$$(12)\qquad C^q \leqslant c^q \sup_{x;\varrho} \varrho^{(1-n)q} \mu(B_\varrho(x)) ,$$

where c depends only on n.

2) *If* (2) *holds for all* $u \in \mathscr{D}(R^n)$, *then*

$$C^q \geqslant (n v_n)^{-q} \sup_{x;\varrho} \varrho^{(1-n)q} \mu(B_\varrho(x)) . \tag{13}$$

Proof. Let $\{B(x_j, \varrho_j)\}$ be the covering of g constructed in Theorem 1.2.1/2. By the obvious inequality $(\sum_j a_j)^{1/q} \leqslant \sum_j a_j^{1/q}$, where $a_j \geqslant 0$, $q \geqslant 1$, we have

$$\mu(g) \leqslant \sum_j \mu(B(x_j, \varrho_j)) \leqslant [\sum_j \mu(B(x_j, \varrho_j))^{1/q}]^q$$

$$\leqslant \sup_{x;\varrho} \varrho^{(1-n)q} \mu(B(x, \varrho)) (\sum_j \varrho_j^{n-1})^q .$$

This and (1.2.1/3) imply

$$\mu(g) \leqslant c^q \sup_{x;\varrho} \varrho^{(1-n)q} \mu(B(x, \varrho)) s(\partial g)$$

which along with Theorem 1 yields (2).

The inequality (13) is an obvious corollary of (4). The theorem is proved.

1.4.3. An Estimate for the Norm in $L_q(R^n, \mu)$ by the Integral of the Modulus of the l-th Order Gradient

Lemma. *Let* μ *be a measure on* R^n, $n > l$, $1 \leqslant q < (n-l+1)(n-l)^{-1}$ *and* $\tau^{-1} = 1 - n^{-1}(q-1)(n-l)$. *Further, let*

$$(I_1 \mu)(x) = \int_{R^n} |x-y|^{1-n} d\mu(y) .$$

Then for all $x \in R^n$ *and* $\varrho > 0$

$$\varrho^{l-1-n} \| I_1 \mu \|_{L_\tau(B(x,\varrho))} \leqslant c \sup_{x \in R^n, r>0} r^{(l-n)q} \mu(B(x, r)) .$$

Proof. Without loss of generality we may put $x = 0$. By Minkowski's inequality,

$$\left(\int_{|x| \leqslant \varrho} \left(\int_{|y| < 2\varrho} \frac{d\mu(y)}{|x-y|^{n-1}} \right)^\tau dx \right)^{1/\tau} \leqslant \int_{|y| < 2\varrho} \left(\int_{|x| \leqslant \varrho} \frac{dx}{|x-y|^{(n-1)\tau}} \right)^{1/\tau} d\mu(y) . \tag{1}$$

Since $(n-1)\tau < n$, then

$$\int_{|x| \leqslant \varrho} \frac{dx}{|x-y|^{(n-1)\tau}} \leqslant c \varrho^{n-\tau(n-1)} .$$

Hence the right-hand side in (1) does not exceed $c \varrho^{n\tau^{-1}-n+1} \mu(B(2\varrho))$. Consequently,

$$\varrho^{l-n-1}\left(\int_{|x|\leqslant\varrho}\left(\int_{|y|<2\varrho}\frac{d\mu(y)}{|x-y|^{n-1}}\right)^{\tau}dx\right)^{1/\tau}\leqslant c\varrho^{(l-n)q}\mu(B(2\varrho)).$$

On the other hand,

$$\left(\int_{|x|<\varrho}\left(\int_{|y|\geqslant 2\varrho}\frac{d\mu(y)}{|x-y|^{n-1}}\right)^{\tau}dx\right)^{1/\tau}\leqslant c\varrho^{n/\tau}\int_{|y|\geqslant 2\varrho}\frac{d\mu(y)}{|y|^{n-1}}.$$

The last integral is equal to

$$(n-1)\int_{2\varrho}^{\infty}\mu(B(r)\backslash B(2\varrho))r^{-n}dr$$

and therefore it is majorized by

$$c\varrho^{q(n-l)-n+1}\sup_{0<r<\infty}r^{(l-n)q}\mu(B(r)).$$

The result follows.

Theorem. *Let μ be a measure on R^n and let $l\leqslant n$, $q\geqslant 1$. The inequality*

(2)
$$\|u\|_{L_q(\mu)}\leqslant C\|\nabla_l u\|_{L_1},\quad u\in\mathscr{D},$$

holds if and only if

(3)
$$\mathscr{K}=\sup_{x\in R^n,\varrho>0}\varrho^{l-n}\mu(B(x,\varrho))^{1/q}<\infty.$$

Moreover, $\mathscr{K}$ is equivalent to the best constant C in (2).

Proof. The estimate $C\geqslant c\mathscr{K}$ is obvious. We prove the opposite one. In the case $l=n$ it follows from the identity

(4)
$$u(x)=\int_{-\infty}^{x_1}\dots\int_{-\infty}^{x_n}\frac{\partial^n u}{\partial x_1\dots\partial x_n}dx_1\dots dx_n,\quad u\in\mathscr{D}.$$

Let $l<n$. For $l=1$ the result follows by Theorem 1.4.2/2. First consider the case $l>1$, $q>n/(n-1)$. By Corollary 1.4.1

$$\|u\|_{L_q(\mu)}\leqslant c\mathscr{K}\|\nabla_{l-1}u\|_{L_{n/(n-1)}}.$$

Applying (1.4.2/8), we obtain that the right-hand side does not exceed $c\mathscr{K}\|\nabla_l u\|_{L_1}$.

Now let $l>1$, $q\leqslant n/(n-1)$. We use induction on the number of derivatives. Suppose the assertion holds for derivatives of orders $2,\dots,l-1$. By virtue of the integral representation (1.1.10/6),

$$\int |u|^q d\mu(x) \leqslant c_0 \int \left| \int \frac{(\xi - x)\, \nabla_\xi |u(\xi)|^q}{|\xi - x|^n} d\xi \right| d\mu(x) \leqslant c_0 q \int |\nabla u| |u|^{q-1} I_1 \mu d\xi .$$

So

$$\int |u|^q d\mu(x) \leqslant c \| u \|^{q-1}_{L_{n/(n-l)}} \| |\nabla u| I_1 \mu \|_{L_\tau},$$

where $\tau^{-1} = 1 - (q-1)(n-l)n^{-1}$. By (1.4.2/10) the first norm in the right-hand side is majorized by $c \| \nabla_l u \|_{L_1}$. The second norm is majorized by

$$c \sup_{x \in R^n, \varrho > 0} \varrho^{l-1-n} \| I_1 \mu \|_{L_\tau(B(x,\varrho))} \| \nabla_l u \|_{L_1},$$

which follows by the induction hypothesis. Since $q \leqslant n(n-1)^{-1}$ then $q < (n-l+1)(n-l)^{-1}$ and we may use Lemma. Thus, the sufficiency of the condition (3) as well as the estimate $C \leqslant c \mathscr{K}$ are proved. The necessity of (3) and the estimate $C \geqslant c \mathscr{K}$ follow by insertion of the test function

$$y \to \eta \left(\frac{y - x}{\varrho} \right),$$

where $\eta \in \mathscr{D}(B_2)$, $\eta = 1$ on B_1, into (2). This completes the proof.

1.4.4. Corollaries of Previous Results

The following assertion combines and complements Corollary 1.4.1 and Theorem 1.4.3.

Theorem 1. *Let either $k < l$, $p(l-k) < n$, $1 \leqslant p < q < \infty$ or $l - k = n$, $p = 1 \leqslant q \leqslant \infty$. The best constant in*

(1) $$\| \nabla_k u \|_{L_q(\mu)} \leqslant C \| \nabla_l u \|_{L_p}, \qquad u \in \mathscr{D}(R^n),$$

is equivalent to

$$\mathscr{K} = \sup_{x, \varrho} \varrho^{l-k-np^{-1}} [\mu(B(x, \varrho))]^{1/q} .$$

Proof. The estimate $C \leqslant c \mathscr{K}$ is proved in Corollary 1.4.1 and in Theorem 1.4.3. Inserting

$$u(y) = (x_1 - y_1)^k \eta \left(\frac{x - y}{\varrho} \right),$$

where $\varrho > 0$, $\eta \in \mathscr{D}(B_2)$, $\eta = 1$ on B_1, into (1), we obtain the lower bound for C.

The next assertion is the analog of Theorem 1 for the space V_p^l.

Theorem 2. *Let the conditions of Theorem 1 relating the values of p, q, l, k, n hold. The best constant in*

$$\| \nabla_k u \|_{L_q(\mu)} \leqslant C \| u \|_{V_p^l}, \quad u \in \mathscr{D},$$

is equivalent to

(2) $$\mathscr{K}_1 = \sup_{x;\, \varrho \in (0,1)} \varrho^{l-k-np^{-1}} [\mu(B(x, \varrho))]^{1/q}.$$

Proof. First we derive the upper bound for C. Let the cubes $\mathscr{Q}_j$ form the coordinate net in R^n with step 1 and let $2\mathscr{Q}_j$ be concentric homothetic cubes with edge length 2. By $\{\eta_j\}$ we denote a partition of unity subordinate to the covering $\{2\mathscr{Q}_j\}$ and such that $|\nabla_m \eta_j| \leqslant c(m)$ for all j. Here $c(m)$ is a positive number and m is any integer. Since the multiplicity of the covering $\{2\mathscr{Q}_j\}$ is finite and depends on n only, then

$$\int |\nabla_k u|^q d\mu \leqslant \int \Big(\sum_j |\nabla_k(\eta_j u)| \Big)^q d\mu \leqslant c \sum_j \int |\nabla_k(\eta_j u)|^q d\mu.$$

Applying Theorem 1 to each summand of the last sum, we obtain

$$\| \nabla_k(\eta_j u) \|_{L_q(\mu)} \leqslant c \sup_{x;\varrho} \varrho^{l-k-np^{-1}} [\mu(2\mathscr{Q}_j \cap B(x, \varrho))]^{1/q} \| \nabla_l(\eta_j u) \|_{L_p}.$$

Consequently,

$$\| \nabla_k u \|_{L_p(\mu)} \leqslant c \mathscr{K} \| u \|_{V_p^l},$$

where $\mathscr{K}$ is the constant defined by (2).

The lower bound for C can be obtained in the same way as in Theorem 1.

1.4.5. Generalized Sobolev Theorem

Theorem. *Let Ω be a domain in R^n with compact closure and let it be the union of a finite number of domains of the class EV_p^l. (In particular, according to subsection* 1.1.9 *and the Stein extension theorem, mentioned in* 1.1.16, *this assumption holds if Ω has the cone property.)*

Further, let μ be a measure on Ω satisfying

(1) $$\sup_{x \in R^n,\, \varrho > 0} \varrho^{-s} \mu(\Omega \cap B(x, \varrho)) < \infty,$$

where $s > 0$ (for example, if s is an integer, then μ can be s-dimensional Lebesgue measure on $\Omega \cap R^s$).

Then for any $u \in C^\infty(\Omega) \cap V_p^l(\Omega)$

(2) $$\sum_{j=0}^{k} \| \nabla_j u \|_{L_q(\Omega, \mu)} \leqslant C \| u \|_{V_p^l(\Omega)},$$

where C is a constant that is independent of u, and the parameters q, s, p, l, k satisfy the inequalities:

(*a*) $p>1,\ 0<n-p(l-k)<s\leqslant n,\ q\leqslant sp(n-p(l-k))^{-1}$;
(*b*) $p=1,\ 0<n-l+k\leqslant s\leqslant n,\ q\leqslant s(n-l+k)^{-1}$;
(*c*) $p>1,\ n=p(l-k),\ s\leqslant n$, *q is any positive number.*
If either one of the conditions holds:
(*d*) $p>1,\ n<p(l-k)$;
(*e*) $p=1,\ n\leqslant l-k$,
then

$$\sum_{j=0}^{k}\sup_{\Omega}|\nabla_j u|\leqslant C\|u\|_{V_p^l(\Omega)}. \tag{3}$$

If Ω belongs to the class EV_p^l (for example, Ω is in $C^{0,1}$), then in the case (d) Theorem can be refined as follows.

(*f*) *If $p\geqslant 1$, $(l-k-1)p<n<(l-k)p$ and $\lambda=l-k-n/p$, then for all $u\in V_p^l(\Omega)$*

$$\sup_{\substack{x,y\in\Omega\\ x\neq y}}\frac{|\nabla_k u(x)-\nabla_k u(y)|}{|x-y|^{\lambda}}\leqslant C\|u\|_{V_p^l(\Omega)}. \tag{4}$$

(*g*) *If $(l-k-1)p=n$, then inequality* (4) *holds for all $0<\lambda<1$ and $u\in V_p^l(\Omega)$.*

Proof. First we note that in cases (*c*) and (*g*) the result follows from (*e*) and (*f*), respectively, since $V_{p_1}^l(\Omega)\subset V_{p_2}^l(\Omega)$ for $p_1>p_2$.

It is sufficient to prove (2) and (3) for domains of the class EV_p^l. Since for such a domain there exists an extension operator $V_p^l(\Omega)\to V_p^l(R^n)$, we can limit ourselves to consideration of the case $\Omega=R^n$. In order to obtain (2) in cases (*a*) and (*b*) we refer to Theorem 1.4.4/2.

Let (*d*) holds. It is sufficient to prove (3) for functions in $V_p^l(R^n)$ with supports in some ball. Then (3) results from the integral representation (1.1.10/6) and Hölder's inequality.

In the case (*e*) the estimate (3) follows immediately from (1.4.3/4).

Let (*f*) hold. Clearly, it is sufficient to assume that $k=0$. Since $\Omega\in EV_p^l$, then, as before, we may put $\Omega=R^n$. By (1.1.10/6)

$$u(x)=\sum_{|\alpha|=l}\int_{R^n}K_\alpha(x-y)D^\alpha u(y)\,dy,$$

where $|K_\alpha(z)|\leqslant c|z|^{l-n}$ and

$$|K_\alpha(z+h)-K_\alpha(z)|\leqslant c|h||z|^{l-1-n}\quad\text{for } |z|\geqslant 3|h|.$$

Therefore,

$$|u(x+h)-u(x)|\leqslant c\int_{|x-y|\leqslant 4|h|}\frac{|\nabla_l u(y)|}{|x-y|^{n-l}}dy+c|h|\int_{|x-y|\geqslant 4|h|}\frac{|\nabla_l u(y)|}{|x-y|^{n-l+1}}dy.$$

It remains to apply Hölder's inequality to both integrals in the right-hand side. The theorem is proved.

Remark 1. All the relations between n, p, l, k, λ in $(d)-(g)$ of Theorem are the best possible. This fact can be verified using examples of functions $x_1^k \log|\log|x||$, $|x|^\alpha$.

Remark 2. From Theorem it follows that $V_p^l(\Omega)$ is continuously imbedded into $V_q^k(\Omega)$, $q = np(n-p(l-k))^{-1}$ for $n > p(l-k)$, $p \geqslant 1$, if Ω is bounded and has the cone property. In the case $n = p(l-k)$ the same holds for any $q < \infty$. In the cases $p(l-k) > n$ and $p = 1$, $l-k \geqslant n$ the space $V_p^l(\Omega)$ is continuously imbedded into $C^k(\Omega)$.

If $\Omega \in C^{0,1}$, then under the conditions (f), (g) the space $V_p^l(\Omega)$ is imbedded into the space $\tilde{C}^{k,\lambda}(\bar{\Omega})$, obtained by the completion of $C^{k+1}(\bar{\Omega})$ with respect to the norm

$$\sum_{j=0}^{k} \| \nabla_j u \|_{L_\infty(\Omega)} + \sup_{\substack{x,y \in \Omega, \\ x \neq y}} \frac{|\nabla_k u(x) - \nabla_k u(y)|}{|x-y|^\lambda}.$$

From (a), (b), (c) it follows that for integer s the restriction operator

$$C^\infty(\Omega) \cap V_p^l(\Omega) \ni u \to u|_{R^s \cap \Omega} \tag{5}$$

can be uniquely extended to a linear operator $V_p^l(\Omega) \to V_q^k(R^s \cap \Omega)$.

Using Lemma 1.1.11 we may rewrite (2) as

$$\sum_{j=0}^{k} \| \nabla_j (u - \Pi) \|_{L_q(\Omega, \mu)} \leqslant C \| \nabla_l u \|_{L_p(\Omega)},$$

where Π is the polynomial (1.1.11/1). This enables us to introduce a continuous restriction operator $\dot{L}_p^l \to V_q^k(R^s \cap \Omega)/\mathscr{P}_{l-1}$ to $R^s \cap \Omega$ for $\mu = m_s$. Analogously, we may establish that in cases (d), (e) or (f), (g) the space $\dot{L}_p^l(\Omega)$ is continuously imbedded into $C^k(\bar{\Omega})/\mathscr{P}_{l-1}$ or into $C^{k,\lambda}(\bar{\Omega})/\mathscr{P}_{l-1}$, respectively.

In conclusion we note that Theorem of the present subsection refines Theorem 1.1.2 on local properties of functions in $L_p^l(\Omega)$, where Ω is an arbitrary open subset of R^n.

1.4.6. Compactness Theorems

The imbedding and restriction operators mentioned in Remark 1.4.5/2, which are continuous by Theorem 1.4.5, turn out to be compact for certain values of p, l, q, n, s. This result will be proved at the end of the present subsection.

Lemma. *Any bounded subset of the space $V_p^l(R^n)$ is compact in $V_p^{l-1}(\Omega)$, where Ω is a bounded domain.*

Proof. It suffices to limit consideration to the case $l = 1$. Let f be a summable nonnegative function on $[0, a+\delta]$, where $a > 0$, $\delta > 0$. Then

$$\int_0^a dt \int_t^{t+\delta} f(\tau)\, d\tau \leqslant \delta \int_0^{a+\delta} f(t)\, dt. \tag{1}$$

In fact, the integral in the left-hand side is

$$\int_0^a dt \int_0^\delta f(\tau+t)\,d\tau = \int_0^\delta d\tau \int_\tau^{a+\tau} f(t)\,dt \leqslant \delta \int_0^{a+\delta} f(t)\,dt\,.$$

Now let $u \in C_0^\infty(R^n)$. Obviously, for all $h \in R^n$

$$\int_\Omega |u(x+h)-u(x)|^p dx \leqslant \int_\Omega \left(\int_{\sigma_{x,h}} |\nabla u|\,dl \right)^p dx\,,$$

where $\sigma_{x,h} = [x, x+h]$. Hence

$$\int_\Omega |u(x+h)-u(x)|^p dx \leqslant |h|^{p-1} \int_\Omega \int_{\sigma_{x,h}} |\nabla u|^p dl\,dx\,.$$

Applying (1) with $\delta = |h|$ to the last integral, we obtain

$$\left(\int_\Omega |u(x+h)-u(x)|^p dx \right)^{1/p} \leqslant |h| \|\nabla u\|_{L_p(R^n)}\,.$$

It remains to note that by M. Riesz's theorem, a set of functions, defined on a bounded open domain Ω, is compact in $L_p(\Omega)$, if it is bounded in $L_p(\Omega)$ and

$$\int_\Omega |u(x+h)-u(x)|^p dx \to 0$$

uniformly as $|h| \to 0$, where h is an arbitrary vector in R^n. This completes the proof.

Theorem 1. *Let a bounded domain $\Omega \subset R^n$ be the union of a finite number of domains in EV_p^l (for example, Ω has the cone property). Let μ be a non-negative measure in R^n with support in Ω. Further, let either $k < l$, $p(l-k) < n$, $1 \leqslant p < q < \infty$ or $k \leqslant l-1$, $1 = p \leqslant q$.*

Then any subset of the space $C^\infty(\bar{\Omega})$, bounded in $V_p^l(\Omega)$, is relatively compact in the metric

(2) $$\sum_{j=0}^{k} \|\nabla_j u\|_{L_q(\bar{\Omega}, \mu)}$$

if and only if

(3) $$\lim_{\varrho \to 0} \sup_{x \in R^n} \varrho^{q(l-k-n/p)} \mu(B(x, \varrho)) = 0\,.$$

Proof. Sufficiency. We may assume from the very beginning that $\Omega \in EV_p^l$. Then it suffices to prove that any bounded subset of the space $C^\infty(R^n) \cap W_p^l(R^n)$ is relatively compact in the metric (2).

According to (3), given any $\varepsilon > 0$ there exists a number δ such that

$$\varrho^{q(l-k-n/p)} \sup_x \mu(B(x,\varrho)) < \varepsilon$$

for $\varrho \leqslant \delta$.

We construct a covering $\{\mathscr{B}_i\}$ of $\bar{\Omega}$ by balls with diameter $\delta \leqslant 1$, the multiplicity of the covering being not more than a constant that depends only on n. Let μ_i be the restriction of μ to $\mathscr{B}_i$ and let $\{\eta_i\}$ be a partition of unity subordinate to the covering $\{\mathscr{B}_i\}$. Using Theorem 1.4.4/1, we obtain

$$\int_{\mathscr{B}_i} \sum_{j=0}^{k} |\nabla_j(u\eta_i)|^q d\mu_i \leqslant c \sup_{\varrho;x} \varrho^{q(l-k-n/p)} \mu_i(B(x,\varrho)) \|u\eta_i\|^q_{V_p^l(\mathscr{B}_i)}$$

$$\leqslant c\varepsilon \sum_{j=0}^{l} \left(\delta^{p(j-l)} \int_{\mathscr{B}_i} |\nabla_j u|^p dx \right)^{q/p}.$$

Summing over i, we arrive at

$$\int_{\bar{\Omega}} \sum_{j=0}^{k} |\nabla_j u|^q d\mu \leqslant c\varepsilon \|\nabla_l u\|^q_{L_p(R^n)} + C(\varepsilon) \|u\|^q_{V_p^{l-1}(\bigcup_i \mathscr{B}_i)}.$$

It remains to note that, by Lemma, any bounded set in $V_p^l(R^n)$ is compact in $V_p^{l-1}(\bigcup_i \mathscr{B}_i)$.

Necessity. Let us take the origin of Cartesian coordinates to be an arbitrary point $0 \in R^n$. Let η denote a function in $\mathscr{D}(B_{2\varrho})$ that is equal to unity on B_ϱ, $\varrho < 1$, and such that $|\nabla_j \eta| \leqslant c\varrho^{-j}$, $j = 1, 2, \ldots$.

From the relative compactness of the set $\{u \in C^\infty(\bar{\Omega}): \|u\|_{V_p^l(R^n)} \leqslant 1\}$ in the metric (2) it follows that given any $\varepsilon > 0$, any function of this set and any point 0 we have

$$\int_{B_{2\varrho}} |\nabla_k u|^q d\mu \leqslant \varepsilon$$

for some ϱ. Inserting the function

$$u(x) = \frac{x_1^k \eta(x)}{\|x_1^k \eta\|_{V_p^l(R^n)}}$$

into the last inequality, we obtain

$$\mu(B_\varrho) \leqslant \varepsilon \|x_1^k \eta\|^q_{V_p^l(B_{2\varrho})} \leqslant c\varepsilon \varrho^{q(n/p-l+k)}.$$

The result follows.

Theorem 2. *Let a bounded domain $\Omega \subset R^n$ be the union of a finite number of domains in EV_p^l. Then for $l > k \geqslant 0$, $p \geqslant 1$ we have:*

(*a*) *If s is a positive integer and $n > (l-k)p$, then the restriction operator (1.4.5/5) is compact as an operator, mapping $V_p^l(\Omega)$ into $V_q^k(\Omega \cap R^s)$ for $n-(l-k)p < s \leqslant n$ and $q < sp(n-(l-k)p)^{-1}$.*

(*b*) *If s is a positive integer and $n = (l-k)p$, then the operator (1.4.5/5) is compact as an operator, mapping $V_p^l(\Omega)$ into $V_q^k(\Omega \cap R^s)$ for any $q \geqslant 1$, $s \leqslant n$.*

(c) *If* $n<(l-k)p$, *then the imbedding of* $V_p^l(\Omega)$ *into the space* $C^k(\Omega)$ *equipped with the norm*

$$\sum_{j=0}^{k} \sup_{\Omega} |\nabla_j u|$$

is compact.

Proof. Since $V_{p_1}^l(\Omega) \subset V_{p_2}^l(\Omega)$ for $p_1 > p_2$, then (*b*) follows from (*a*). In turn, (*a*) is a corollary of Theorem 1.

In order to obtain (c) it suffices to prove the compactness of the unit ball in $V_p^l(R^n)$ with respect to the metric of the space $C^k(G)$, where $(l-k)p>n$ and G is any bounded domain. Let $x \in \bar{G}$ and $\varrho>0$. By (1.4.5/3)

$$\sum_{j=0}^{k} \sup_{B(x,1)} |\nabla_j u| \leqslant C \|u\|_{V_p^l(B(x,1))} .$$

Applying a dilation with coefficient ϱ, we obtain

$$\sum_{j=0}^{k} \varrho^j \sup_{B(x,\varrho)} |\nabla_j u| \leqslant c \sum_{i=0}^{l} \varrho^{i-n/p} \|\nabla_i u\|_{L_p(B(x,\varrho))} .$$

Therefore, for $j=0,\ldots,k$,

$$\sup_{B(x,\varrho)} |\nabla_j u| \leqslant c\varrho^{l-j-n/p} \|\nabla_l u\|_{L_p(B(x,\varrho))} + C(\varrho) \|u\|_{V_p^{l-1}(B(x,\varrho))}$$

and so

$$\sum_{j=0}^{k} \sup_{G} |\nabla_j u| \leqslant c\varrho^{l-k-n/p} \|u\|_{V_p^l(R^n)} + C(\varrho) \|u\|_{V_p^{l-1}(G_\varrho)} ,$$

where G_ϱ is the ϱ-neighborhood of $\bar{G}$. Since ϱ is an arbitrarily small number, then by Lemma the unit ball in $V_p^l(R^n)$ is compact in $V_p^{l-1}(G_\varrho)$. Thus (c) is proved.

1.4.7. A Multiplicative Inequality

This subsection deals with a necessary and sufficient condition for the validity of the inequality

(1) $$\|\nabla_k u\|_{L_q(\mu)} \leqslant C \|\nabla_l u\|_{L_p}^{\tau} \|u\|_{L_p}^{1-\tau} .$$

Lemma. *Let* μ *be a measure in* R^n *with support in* $B_\varrho = \{x\colon |x|<\varrho\}$ *and such that*

(2) $$K = \sup_{x;r} r^{-s} \mu(B(x,r)) < \infty$$

for some $s \in [0,n]$. *Further, let* $p \geqslant 1$, *let* k *and* l *be integers,* $k<l$, *and let* $s>n-p(l-k)$ *if* $p>1$, $s \geqslant n-l+k$ *if* $p=1$.

Then for all $v \in C(\bar{B}_\varrho)$ *and for* q *satisfying the inequalities* $l-k-n/p+s/q>0$, $q \geqslant p$, *we have*

$$\text{(3)} \qquad \| \nabla_k v \|_{L_q(\mu, B_\varrho)} \leqslant c K^{1/q} \varrho^{s/q-n/p-k} (\varrho^l \| \nabla_l v \|_{L_p(B_\varrho)} + \| v \|_{L_p(B_\varrho)}) .$$

Proof. According to subsection 1.1.16 any function $w \in C^\infty(\bar{B}_1)$ can be extended to a function $w \in C_0^l(B_2)$ satisfying the inequality

$$\| \nabla_l w \|_{L_p(B_2)} \leqslant c \| w \|_{V_p^l(B_1)} .$$

Since $V_p^l(B_1) = W_p^l(B_1)$ (see Corollary 1.1.11), the last estimate is equivalent to

$$\| \nabla_l w \|_{L_p(B_2)} \leqslant c(\| \nabla_l w \|_{L_p(B_1)} + \| w \|_{L_p(B_1)}) .$$

Thus, applying a dilation, we obtain that the function v, mentioned in the statement of Lemma, admits an extension $v \in C_0^l(B_{2\varrho})$ such that

$$\text{(4)} \qquad \| \nabla_l v \|_{L_p(B_{2\varrho})} \leqslant c(\| \nabla_l v \|_{L_p(B_\varrho)} + \varrho^{-l} \| v \|_{L_p(B_\varrho)}) .$$

Let $(l-k)p<n$, $p>1$ or $l-k \leqslant n$, $p=1$. By Theorem 1.4.4/1 we obtain

$$\text{(5)} \qquad \| \nabla_k v \|_{L_t(\mu, B_{2\varrho})} \leqslant c K^{1/t} \| \nabla_l v \|_{L_p(B_{2\varrho})} ,$$

where $t = ps/(n-p(l-k))$.

In the case $(l-k)p=n$, $p>1$, we let p_1 denote a number in $[1,p)$, that is sufficiently close to p. We put $t = p_1 s/(n-p_1(l-k))$. Then by Corollary 1.4.1

$$\text{(6)} \quad \| \nabla_k v \|_{L_t(\mu, B_{2\varrho})} \leqslant c K^{1/t} \| \nabla_l v \|_{L_{p_1}(B_{2\varrho})} \leqslant c K^{1/t} \varrho^{n/p_1 - n/p} \| \nabla_l v \|_{L_p(B_{2\varrho})} .$$

In the case $(l-k)p>n$, $p \geqslant 1$ we put $t=\infty$. Then by Sobolev's theorem

$$\text{(7)} \qquad \| \nabla_k v \|_{L_t(\mu, B_{2\varrho})} \leqslant c \varrho^{l-k-n/p} \| \nabla_l v \|_{L_p(B_{2\varrho})} .$$

Combining (5) – (7), we obtain

$$\text{(8)} \qquad \| \nabla_k v \|_{L_t(\mu, B_{2\varrho})} \leqslant c K^{1/t} \varrho^{l-k-n/p+s/t} \| \nabla_l v \|_{L_p(B_{2\varrho})} .$$

By Hölder's inequality

$$\| \nabla_k v \|_{L_q(\mu, B_\varrho)} \leqslant [\mu(B_\varrho)]^{1/q-1/t} \| \nabla_k v \|_{L_t(\mu, B_\varrho)} \leqslant K^{1/q-1/t} \varrho^{s(1/q-1/t)} \| \nabla_k v \|_{L_t(\mu, B_\varrho)} ,$$

which along with (8) gives

$$\| \nabla_k v \|_{L_t(\mu, B_{2\varrho})} \leqslant c K^{1/q} \varrho^{s/q+l-k-n/p} \| \nabla_l v \|_{L_p(B_{2\varrho})} .$$

Using (4), we complete the proof.

Theorem. 1) *Let μ be a measure in R^n that satisfies the condition* (2) *for some $s \in [0,n]$. Let $p \geqslant 1$ and let k, l be integers, $0 \leqslant k \leqslant l-1$; $s > n-p(l-k)$ if $p>1$ and $s \geqslant n-l+k$ if $p=1$. Then for all $u \in \mathscr{D}$ the estimate* (1) *holds, where $C \leqslant cK^{1/q}$, $n/p-l+k<s/q$, $q \geqslant p$ and $\tau=(k-s/q+n/p)/l$.*

2) *If* (1) *is valid for all $u \in \mathscr{D}$, then $C \geqslant cK^{1/q}$.*

Proof. According to Lemma, for all $x \in R^n$ and $\varrho>0$,

$$(9) \qquad \|\nabla_k u\|_{L_q(\mu, B(x,\varrho))} \leqslant cK^{1/q}\varrho^{s/q-n/p-k}(\varrho^l\|\nabla_l u\|_{L_p(B(x,\varrho))}+\|u\|_{L_p(B(x,\varrho))}).$$

We fix an arbitrary $\varrho_0>0$. If the first summand in the right-hand side of (9) exceeds the second for $\varrho=\varrho_0$, then we cover a point $x \in \operatorname{supp}\mu$ by the ball $B(x,\varrho)$. Otherwise we increase ϱ until the first summand becomes equal to the second. Then the point x is covered by the ball $B(x,\varrho)$, where

$$\varrho = \|u\|^{1/l}_{L_p(B(x,\varrho))}\|\nabla_l u\|^{-1/l}_{L_p(B(x,\varrho))}.$$

In both cases

$$(10) \qquad \|\nabla_k u\|^q_{L_q(\mu,B(x,\varrho))} \leqslant cK(\varrho_0^{s-q(n/p-l+k)}\|\nabla_l u\|^q_{L_p(B(x,\varrho))} + \|\nabla_l u\|^{q\tau}_{L_p(B(x,\varrho))}\|u\|^{q(1-\tau)}_{L_p(B(x,\varrho))}).$$

According to Theorem 1.2.1/1, we can select a subcovering $\{\mathscr{B}^{(i)}\}_{i\geqslant 1}$ of finite multiplicity, depending only on n, from the covering $\{B(x,\varrho)\}$ of $\operatorname{supp}\mu$. Summing (10) over all balls $\mathscr{B}^{(i)}$ and noting that

$$\sum_i a_i^\alpha b_i^\beta \leqslant (\sum_i a_i^{\alpha+\beta})^{\alpha/(\alpha+\beta)}(\sum_i b_i^{\alpha+\beta})^{\beta/(\alpha+\beta)} \leqslant (\sum_i a_i)^\alpha(\sum_i b_i)^\beta,$$

where a_i, b_i, α, β are positive numbers, $\alpha+\beta \geqslant 1$, we arrive at

$$\|\nabla_k v\|^q_{L_q(\mu)} \leqslant cK(\varrho_0^{q(n/p-l+k)}(\sum_i \|\nabla_l u\|^p_{L_p(\mathscr{B}^{(i)})})^{q/p} + (\sum_i \|\nabla_l u\|^p_{L_p(\mathscr{B}^{(i)})})^{\tau q/p}(\sum_i \|u\|^p_{L_p(\mathscr{B}^{(i)})})^{(1-\tau)q/p}.$$

Since the multiplicity of the covering $\{\mathscr{B}^{(i)}\}$ depends only on n, the right-hand side is majorized by

$$cK(\varrho_0^{s-q(n/p-l+k)}\|\nabla_l u\|^q_{L_p} + \|\nabla_l u\|^{\tau q}_{L_p}\|u\|^{(1-\tau)q}_{L_p}).$$

Passing to the limit as $\varrho_0 \to 0$, we complete the proof of 1).

To prove 2) it is sufficient to insert the function $u_\varrho(x)=(y_1-x_1)^k \times \varphi(\varrho^{-1}(x-y))$, where $\varphi \in \mathscr{D}(B_2)$, $\varphi=1$ on B_1, into (1). The result follows.

Corollary 1. 1) *Let μ be a measure in R^n such that*

(11) $$K_1 = \sup_{x\in R^n,\, r\in(0,1)} r^{-s}\mu(B(x,r)) < \infty$$

for some $s\in[0,n]$. Further let $p\geqslant 1$, let k and l be integers, $0\leqslant k\leqslant l-1$; $s>n-p(l-k)$ if $p>1$ and $s\geqslant n-l+k$ if $p=1$. Then for all $u\in\mathscr{D}$

(12) $$\|\nabla_k u\|_{L_q(\mu)}\leqslant C_1\|u\|^{\tau}_{V^l_p}\|u\|^{1-\tau}_{L_p},$$

where $C_1\leqslant cK_1^{1/q}$, $n/p-l+k<s/q$, $q\geqslant p$ and $\tau=(k-s/q+n/p)/l$.

2) *If* (12) *is valid for all $u\in\mathscr{D}$, then $C_1\geqslant cK_1^{1/q}$.*

Proof. Let $\{\mathscr{Q}^{(i)}\}$ denote a sequence of closed cubes with edge length 1 which form a coordinate grid in R^n. Let $\mathscr{O}^{(i)}$ be the center of the cube $\mathscr{Q}^{(i)}$, $\mathscr{O}^{(0)}=0$ and let $2\mathscr{Q}^{(i)}$ be the concentric homothetic cube with edge length 2. We put $\eta_i(x)=\eta(x-\mathscr{O}^{(i)})$, where $\eta\in C_0^\infty(2\mathscr{Q}^{(0)})$, $\eta=1$ on $\mathscr{Q}^{(0)}$.

Applying Theorem of the present subsection to the function $u\eta_i$ and to the measure $e\to\mu(e\cap\mathscr{Q}^{(i)})$, we obtain

$$\|\nabla_k(u\eta_i)\|^p_{L_q(\mu)}\leqslant cK_1^{p/q}\|\nabla_l(u\eta_i)\|^{p\tau}_{L_p}\|u\eta_i\|^{p(1-\tau)}_{L_p}.$$

Summing over i and using the inequality $(\sum a_i)^{p/q}\leqslant\sum a_i^{p/q}$, where $a_i\geqslant 0$, we arrive at (12).

The second assertion follows by insertion of the function u_ϱ, defined at the end of the proof of Theorem, into (12).

The next assertion follows immediately from Corollary 1.

Corollary 2. 1) *Suppose there exists an extension operator which maps $V^l_p(\Omega)$ continuously into $V^l_p(R^n)$ and $L_p(\Omega)$ into $L_p(R^n)$ (for instance, Ω is a bounded domain of the class $C^{0,1}$). Further, let μ be a measure in $\bar\Omega$ satisfying* (11), *where s is a number subject to the same inequalities as in Corollary* 1. *Then for all $u\in C^l(\Omega)$*

(13) $$\|\nabla_k u\|_{L_q(\mu,\bar\Omega)}\leqslant C\|u\|^{\tau}_{V^l_p(\Omega)}\|u\|^{1-\tau}_{L_p(\Omega)},$$

where $n/p-l+k<s/q$, $q\geqslant p\geqslant 1$ and $\tau=(k-s/q+n/p)/l$.

2) *If for all $u\in C^l(\bar\Omega)$ the estimate* (13) *holds, then the measure μ with support in $\bar\Omega$ satisfies* (11).

1.4.8. Comments to § 1.4

Theorem 1.4.1/2 is due to D. R. Adams [1, 2]. The proof given above is borrowed from the paper by D. R. Adams [2]. For $\mu=m_s$, i.e. for s-dimensional Lebesgue measure in R^s, inequality (1.4.1/4) was proved by Sobolev [230] in the case $s=n$ and by Il'in [103] in the case $s<n$. They used the integral representation (1.1.10/6) and the multidimensional generalization of the following Hardy-Littlewood theorem (cf. Hardy, Littlewood and Pólya [91]).

If $1<p<q<\infty$ *and* $\mu=1-p^{-1}+q^{-1}$, *then the operator* $|x|^{-\mu}*f$ *with* $f: R^1\to R^1$ *maps* $L_p(R^1)$ *continuously into* $L_q(R^1)$.

Theorems 1.4.2/1 and 1.4.2/2 are due to the author [152, 160]. Inequality (1.4.2/8) (without the best constant and derived by a different approach) was obtained by Gagliardo [70]. The proof, ensuring the best possible constant, was simultaneously and independently proposed by Federer and Fleming [63] and the author [141].

Although the constant in (1.4.2/8) is best possible it can be improved by constriction of the class of admissible functions in this inequality. For example, since for any N-gon $\Omega_N\subset R^2$ the isoperimetric inequality

$$[s(\partial\Omega_N)]^2\geqslant(4/N)\tan(\pi/N)\,m_2(\Omega_N)$$

is valid (see [232]) then duplicating the proof of Theorem 1.4.2/1 we obtain the following assertion.

Let u_N *be a function on* R^2 *with compact support, whose graph is a polygon with N sides. Then*

$$(4/N)\tan(\pi/N)\int_{R^2}|u_N|^2dx\leqslant\left(\int_{R^2}|\nabla u_N|\,dx\right)^2.$$

Lemma 1.4.3 is a special case of a result due to D. R. Adams [1]. Theorem 1.4.3 was proved by the author [163].

Theorem 1.4.5 for $\mu=m_s$ is the classical Sobolev theorem (see Sobolev [230, 231]) with supplements due to Il'in [103], Gagliardo [70] and Morrey [190]. Here we stated this theorem in the form presented by Gagliardo [70].

The continuity of functions in $W_p^1(\Omega)$ for $p>2$, $n=2$, was proved by Tonelli [243].

The estimate (1.4.6/1) is contained in the paper by Morrey [190]. Lemma 1.4.6 is the classical lemma due to Rellich [215]. Theorem 1.4.6/2 was proved by Kondrašov [114] for $p>1$ and by Gagliardo [70] for $p=1$.

In connection with the estimate (1.4.7/1) we note that multiplicative inequalities of the form

$$\|\nabla_j u\|_{L_q}\leqslant c\,\|\nabla_l u\|_{L_p}^{\tau}\,\|u\|_{L_r}^{1-\tau}$$

and their modifications are well known (see Il'in [102] and Ehrling [56]). Their general form is due to Gagliardo [71] and Nirenberg [203] (see also Solonnikov [234]). The papers of Gagliardo [71] and Nirenberg [203] contain the following theorem.

Theorem 1. *Let* Ω *be a bounded domain having the cone property and let*

$$\langle u\rangle_\sigma=\left(\int_\Omega|u|^\sigma dx\right)^{1/\sigma}$$

for $\sigma>0$. *Then*

(1) $$\langle \nabla_j u \rangle_q \leqslant c(\langle \nabla_l u \rangle_p + \langle u \rangle_r)^\tau \langle u \rangle_r^{1-\tau},$$

where $p \geqslant 1$, $1/q = j/n + \tau(1/p - l/n) + (1-\tau)/r$ *for all* $\tau \in [j/l, 1]$ *unless* $1 < p < \infty$ *and* $l - j - n/p$ *is a nonnegative integer when* (1) *holds for* $\tau \in [j/l, 1)$.

In the paper by Nirenberg [204] the stated result is supplemented by the following assertion.

Theorem 2. *Let* $\sigma < 0$, $s = [-n/\sigma]$, $-\alpha = s + n/\sigma$ *and let*

$$\langle u \rangle_\sigma = \sup |\nabla_s u| \quad \text{for } \alpha = 0, \ \langle u \rangle_s = [\nabla_s u]_\alpha \quad \text{for } \alpha > 0,$$

where $[f]_\alpha = \sup\limits_{x \neq y} |x-y|^{-\alpha} |f(x) - f(y)|$. *Further, let* $1/r = -\beta/n$, $\beta > 0$. *Then* (1) *is valid for* $\beta \leqslant j < l$ *and for all* $\tau \in [(j-\beta)/(l-\beta), 1]$, *except the case mentioned in Theorem* 1.

The proof is reduced to derivation of the inequality

$$\int_{\mathscr{I}} |u^{(j)}|^q dx \leqslant c\left(\int_{\mathscr{I}} |u^{(l)}|^p dx + [u]_\beta^p\right) [u]_\beta^{q-p}$$

for functions of the variable x on a unit interval $\mathscr{I}$.

§ 1.5. More on Extension of Functions in Sobolev Spaces

1.5.1. Survey of Results and Examples of Domains

In 1.1.16, we introduced the class EV_p^l of domains in R^n for which there exists a linear continuous extension operator $\mathscr{E}$: $V_p^l(\Omega) \to V_p^l(R^n)$. There we noted that the class EV_p^l contains strong Lipschitz domains.

Vodopjanov, Gol'dsteĭn and Latphulin [249] proved that a simply connected plane domain belongs to the class EV_2^1 if and only if its boundary is a quasicircle, i.e. the image of a circle under a quasiconformal mapping of the plane onto itself. By Ahlfors' theorem [13] (see also Rickman [219]) the last condition is equivalent to the inequality

(1) $$|x - z| \leqslant c|x - y|, \qquad c = \text{const},$$

where x, y are arbitrary points of $\partial\Omega$ and z is an arbitrary point on that subarc of $\partial\Omega$ which joins x and y and has the smaller diameter.

We give an example of a quasicircle of infinite length.

Example 1. Let Q be the square $\{(x_1, x_2): 0 < x_i < 1, i = 1, 2\}$. We divide the sides of the square Q into three equal parts and construct the squares Q_{i_1}, $i_1 = 1, \dots, 4$, $Q_{i_1} \cap Q = \varnothing$, on the middle segments. Proceeding in the same manner with each Q_{i_1}, we obtain the squares Q_{i_1, i_2}, $i_2 = 1, \dots, 4$ with edge length 3^{-2}. Repeating the procedure, we construct a sequence of squares $\{Q_{i_1, i_2, \dots, i_k}\}$ ($k = 1, 2, \dots; i_k = 1, \dots, 4$), whose union with Q is denoted by Ω (see Fig. 5). Clearly,

$$m_1(\partial\Omega) = 4 \sum_{k=1}^{\infty} 3^{k-1}(2/3)^k = \infty .$$

Let $x, y \in \partial\Omega$. It suffices to consider the case $x \in \partial Q_{i_1,\ldots,i_k}$ and $y \in \partial Q_{j_1,\ldots,j_m}$ where $i_1 = j_1, \ldots, i_l = j_l$, $i_{l+1} \neq j_{l+1}$. Then $|x-y| \geqslant c_1 3^{-l}$ and any point z in (1) satisfies the inequality $|x-y| \leqslant c_2 3^{-l}$. Thus, $\partial\Omega$ is a quasicircle.

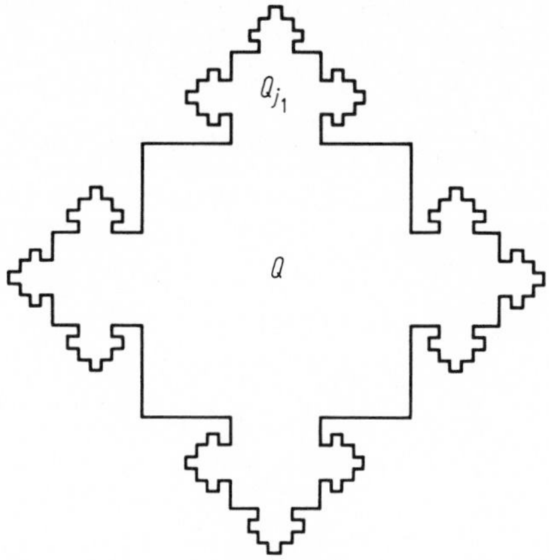

Fig. 5

A domain in R^2 that is bounded by a quasicircle belongs to the class EV_p^l for all $p \in [1, \infty)$, $l = 1, 2, \ldots$ (cf. Gol'dsteĭn, Vodopjanov [78] for $l = 1$, Jones [107] for $l \geqslant 1$). In the paper by Jones just mentioned a class of n-dimensional domains in EV_p^l is described. It is larger than $C^{0,1}$ and coincides with the class of quasidisks for $n = 2$.

Gol'dsteĭn [77] showed that the simultaneous inclusion of a plane simply connected domain Ω and the domain $R^2 \backslash \Omega$ in EV_p^l implies that $\partial\Omega$ is a quasicircle.

Is the last property true under the single condition $\Omega \in EV_p^1$ for some $p \neq 2$? In other words, are quasidisks the only plane simply connected domains contained in EV_p^1, $p \neq 2$? This question is discussed in the present subsection.

We give two examples which speak in favor of an affirmative answer. The first shows that "cusps" directed into the exterior of a domain do not allow us to construct an extension operator.

Example 2. Let $\Omega = \{(x_1, x_2): 0 < x_1 < 1, 0 < x_2 < x_1^\alpha\}$ where $\alpha > 1$. Suppose $\Omega \in EV_p^l$. Then $V_p^l(\Omega) \subset V_q^{l-1}(\Omega)$ for $1 \leqslant p < 2$, $q = 2p/(2-p)$; $V_2^l(\Omega) \subset V_q^{l-1}(\Omega)$ for any $q < \infty$ and $V_p^l(\Omega) \subset C^{l-1,1-2/p}(\bar{\Omega})$ for $p > 2$. Let $u(x) = x_1^{l-\beta}$. If $\beta < (\alpha+1)/p$, then $u \in V_p^l(\Omega)$. Under the additional condition that β is close to $(\alpha+1)/p$ the function u does not belong to $V_q^{l-1}(\Omega)$ ($p < 2$, $q = 2p/(2-p)$ or $p = 2$, q is a large number) and does not belong to $C^{l-1,1-1/p}(\bar{\Omega})$ ($p > 2$). Thus, $\Omega \bar{\in} EV_p^l$.

The following example excludes domains with inward cusps at the boundary from EV_p^l, $p>1$. It shows, incidentally, that the union of two domains in EV_p^l is not always in the same class.

Example 3. Let Ω be the domain considered above. We shall prove that $R^2\backslash\bar{\Omega}\notin EV_p^l$. We introduce polar coordinates (r,θ) with origin $x=0$ so that the ray $\theta=0$ is directed along the halfaxis $x_1>0$, $x_2=0$. We put $u(x)=r^{l-\beta}\psi(\theta)\eta(x)$. Here, β satisfies the inequality $\beta<2/p$ and is close to $2/p$; $\eta\in C_0^\infty(R^2)$, $\eta(x)=1$ for $r<1$ and ψ is a smooth function on $(0,2\pi]$, $\psi(\theta)=1$ for small values of $\theta>0$ and $\psi(\theta)=0$ for $\theta\in[\pi,2\pi]$. Let $v\in V_p^l(R^2)$ be an extension of $u\in V_p^l(R^2\backslash\bar{\Omega})$. Since for small positive values of x_1

$$\frac{\partial^{l-1}v}{\partial x_1^{l-1}}(x_1,x_1^\alpha)\geqslant cx_1^{1-\beta}\,,\qquad \frac{\partial^{l-1}v}{\partial x_1^{l-1}}(x_1,0)=0\,,$$

then

$$\int_\Omega\left|\frac{\partial^l v}{\partial x_1^{l-1}\partial x_2}\right|^p dx\geqslant\int_0^\delta\left(\int_0^{x_1^\alpha}\left|\frac{\partial^l v}{\partial x_1^{l-1}\partial x_2}\right|dx_2\right)^p\frac{dx_1}{x_1^{\alpha(p-1)}}$$

$$\geqslant\int_0^\delta\left|\frac{\partial^{l-1}v}{\partial x_1^{l-1}}(x_1,x_1^\alpha)\right|^p\frac{dx_1}{x_1^{\alpha(p-1)}}$$

$$\geqslant c\int_0^\delta x_1^{1-p\beta-(\alpha-1)(p-1)}dx_1=\infty$$

if $p>1$. The latter contradicts the inclusion $v\in EV_p^l(\Omega)$. Thus $R^2\backslash\bar{\Omega}\notin EV_p^l$ for $p>1$.

Nevertheless, we shall show that $R^2\backslash\bar{\Omega}\in V_1^1$. Let $u\in V_1^1(R^2\backslash\bar{\Omega})$. Suppose for a moment that $u=0$ for $x_1>1/2$.

We put $u^-(x)=u(x_1,-x_2)$, $u^+(x)=u(x_1,2x_1^\alpha-x_2)$ for $x\in\Omega$. It is clear that

$$\|u^-\|_{V_1^1(\Omega)}+\|u^+\|_{V_1^1(\Omega)}\leqslant c\|u\|_{V_1^1(R^2\backslash\bar{\Omega})}\,.$$

The function v defined in R^2 by

$$v(x)=\begin{cases}u(x)\,, & x\notin\Omega\,,\\ u^-(x)+x_2x_1^{-\alpha}(u^+(x)-u^-(x))\,, & x\in\Omega\,,\end{cases}$$

is absolutely continuous on almost all straight lines parallel to coordinate axes. Besides,

$$\|\nabla v\|_{L_1(\Omega)}\leqslant\|\nabla u^-\|_{L_1(\Omega)}+\|\nabla u^+\|_{L_1(\Omega)}+c\|x_1^{-\alpha}(u^+-u^-)\|_{L_1(\Omega)}\,.$$

Since

$$|u^+(x)-u^-(x)| \leqslant |u^+(x)-u(x_1,x_1^\alpha)|+|u(x_1,x_1^\alpha)-u(x_1,0)| + |u(x_1,0)-u^-(x)|\,,$$

then

$$\|x_1^{-\alpha}(u^+-u^-)\|_{L_1(\Omega)} \leqslant \Big\|x_1^{-\alpha}\int_0^{x_1^\alpha}|u_t^+(x_1,t)|\,dt\Big\|_{L_1(\Omega)}+\|x_1^{-\alpha}(u(x_1,x_1^\alpha) - u(x_1,0))\|_{L_1(\Omega)}+\Big\|x_1^{-\alpha}\int_0^{x_1^\alpha}|u_t^-(x_1,t)|\,dt\Big\|_{L_1(\Omega)}$$
$$\leqslant \|u^+\|_{V_1^1(\Omega)}+\|u^-\|_{V_1^1(\Omega)}+\int_0^1|u(x_1,x_1^\alpha)-u(x_1,0)|\,dx_1\,.$$

Clearly, the latter integral does not exceed $c\|u\|_{V_1^1(R^2\backslash\bar\Omega)}$. We put $\mathscr{E}_0u=v$. Thus we have

$$\|\mathscr{E}_0u\|_{V_1^1(R^2)} \leqslant c\,\|u\|_{V_1^1(R^2\backslash\bar\Omega)}\,.$$

In the general case we introduce a truncating function $\eta\in C^\infty(R^1)$ equal to unity on $(-\infty,1/3]$ and to zero on $[1/2,+\infty)$. Further, let $\Omega_1=\Omega\cap\{1/3<x_1<1\}$. The required extension operator $\mathscr{E}$: $V_1^1(R^2\backslash\bar\Omega)\to V_1^1(R^2)$ is defined by

$$\mathscr{E}u=\mathscr{E}_0(\eta u)+\mathscr{E}_1((1-\eta)u)\,,$$

where $\mathscr{E}_1$: $V_1^1(R^2\backslash\bar\Omega_1)\to V_1^1(R^2)$ is a linear continuous extension operator.

In general, for $p\in[1,\infty)$, $l=1,2,\ldots$, S. V. Poborčiĭ and the author proved the existence of a linear bounded extension operator mapping $V_p^l(R^2\backslash\bar\Omega)$ into the space $V_p^l(R^2;\sigma)$ with the weighted norm

$$\left(\int_{R^2}\sum_{s=0}^{l}|\nabla_s u|^p\sigma\,dx\right)^{1/p}, \qquad 1\leqslant p<\infty\,,$$

where σ is a function that is equal to unity outside Ω and coincides with $x_1^{(\alpha-1)(lp-1)}$ on Ω. Moreover, if there exists an extension operator: $V_p^l(R^2\backslash\bar\Omega)\to V_p^l(R^2;\sigma)$ and the weight σ is nonnegative, depends only on x_1 on Ω and increases then

$$\sigma(x)\leqslant c x_1^{(\alpha-1)(lp-1)}, \qquad c=\text{const}\,,$$

for $x\in\Omega$ and for small enough x_1.

1.5.2. Domains in EV_p^1 which are not Quasidisks

The examples in 1.5.1 suggest that the class of Jordan curves that bound domains in EV_p^l consists of quasicircles only. However, we shall show that this conjecture is false.

Theorem. *There exists a domain $\Omega\subset R^2$ with compact closure and Jordan boundary such that:*

(α) *$\partial\Omega$ is not a quasicircle.*

(β) *$\partial\Omega$ is of finite length and Lipschitz in a neighborhood of all but one of its points.*

(γ) *Ω belongs to EV_p^1 for $p\in[1,2)$.*

(δ) *$R^2\backslash\bar{\Omega}$ belongs to EV_p^1 for $p>2$.*

(From the aforementioned theorem by Gol'dsteĭn [77] and from the conditions (α), (γ), (δ) we obtain in addition that $\Omega\bar{\in}EV_p^1$ for $p\geqslant 2$ and $R^2\backslash\bar{\Omega}\bar{\in}EV_p^1$ for $p\in[1,2]$.)

Before we prove this theorem we recall a well-known inequality which will be used later.

Lemma 1. *Let Ω be a sector defined in polar coordinates by the inequalities $0<\theta<\alpha$, $0<r<a$. Let $u\in W_p^1(\Omega)$, $u|_{r=a}=0$ for $p<2$ and $u(0)=0$ for $p>2$. Then*

$$\left\| \frac{u}{r} \right\|_{L_p(\Omega)} \leqslant \frac{p}{|2-p|} \| \nabla u \|_{L_p(\Omega)} .$$

This estimate is an immediate corollary of the following particular case of Hardy's inequality:

$$\int_0^a |u|^p r^{1-p} dr \leqslant \frac{p^p}{|2-p|^p} \int_0^a |u'|^p r dr$$

(cf. § 1.3).

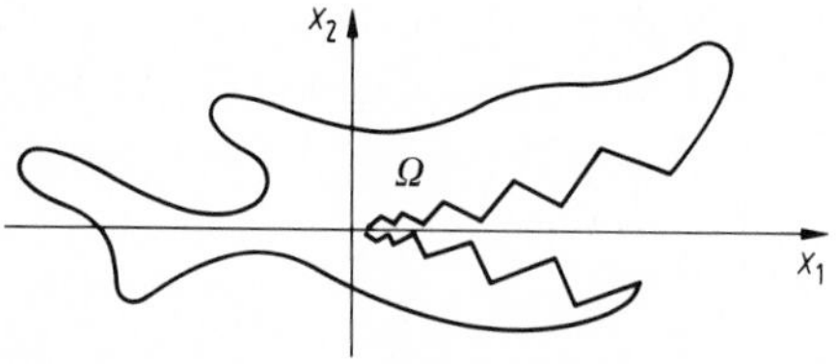

Fig. 6

Proof of Theorem. Figure 6 presents a domain Ω satisfying the conditions (α) – (δ). The corresponding upper and lower "teeth" come close so rapidly that (1.5.1/1) does not hold. So $\partial\Omega$ is not a quasicircle. The "teeth" almost do not change their form and decrease in geometric progression, so (β) holds.

Now we verify (γ). Let G be the difference of the rectangle $R=\{-1/3<x_1<1, 0<x_2<1/3\}$ and the union T of the sequence of isosceles right triangles $\{t_k\}_{k\geqslant 0}$ (cf. Fig. 7). The hypotenuse of t_k is the segment $[2^{-k-1}, 2^{-k}]$.

Lemma 2. *There exists a linear continuous extension operator $\mathscr{E}_1$: $V_p^1(G) \to V_p^1(R)$, $1\leqslant p<2$, such that $\mathscr{E}_1 u=0$ almost everywhere on the interval $x_2=0$, $0<x_1<1$.*

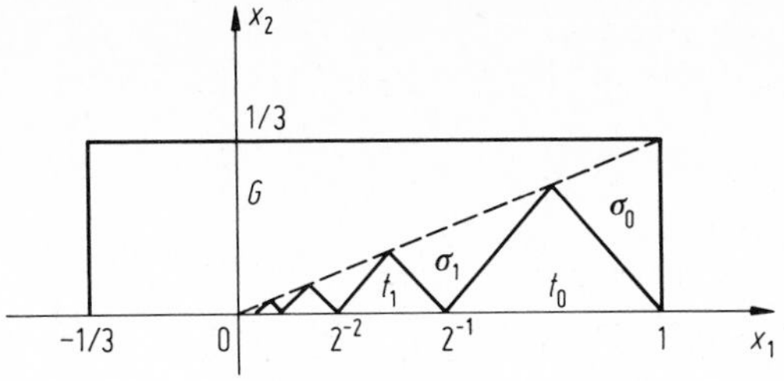

Fig. 7

Proof. Since "the saw" $\{x \in \partial T, x_2 > 0\}$ is a curve of the class $C^{0,1}$ there exists a linear continuous extension operator $V_p^1(G) \to V_p^1(R)$. Let v be an extension of $u \in V_p^1(G)$. We introduce a truncating function θ which is equal to unity on G and to zero almost everywhere on the interval $x_2 = 0$, $0 < x_1 < 1$. Namely, we put $\theta = \theta_k$ on the triangle t_k, where

$$\theta_k = \begin{cases} \dfrac{4}{\pi} \arctan \dfrac{x_2}{x_1 - 2^{-k-1}} & \text{for } 2^{-k-1} < x_1 < 3 \cdot 2^{-k-2}, \\ \dfrac{4}{\pi} \arctan \dfrac{x_2}{2^{-k} - x_1} & \text{for } 3 \cdot 2^{-k-2} < x_1 < 2^{-k}. \end{cases}$$

Clearly,

(2) $$|\nabla \theta_k| \leqslant c(d_k^{-1} + d_{k+1}^{-1})$$

on t_k, where $d_k(x)$ is the distance from x to the point $x_2 = 0$, $x_1 = 2^{-k}$.

The required extension of u is θv. To prove this we need to verify the inequality

(3) $$\| \nabla (\theta v) \|_{L_p(T)} \leqslant c \| v \|_{V_p^1(R)} \, .$$

We have

$$\| \nabla (\theta v) \|_{L_p(T)} \leqslant \| \nabla v \|_{L_p(T)} + \| v \nabla \theta \|_{L_p(T)} \, .$$

By (2)

$$\| v \nabla \theta \|_{L_p(T)}^p \leqslant c \sum_{k \geqslant 0} (\| d_k^{-1} v \|_{L_p(t_k^+)}^p + \| d_{k+1}^{-1} v \|_{L_p(t_k^-)}^p) \, ,$$

where t_k^+ and t_k^- are the right and left halves of t_k. Since $1 \leqslant p < 2$, then

$$\| d_k^{-1} v \|_{L_p(t_k^+)} \leqslant c(\| \nabla v \|_{L_p(t_k^+)} + 2^k \| v \|_{L_p(t_k^+)}) \, .$$

The same estimate holds for $\| d_{k+1}^{-1} v \|_{L_p(t_k^-)}$. Consequently,

$$\| v \nabla \theta \|_{L_p(T)}^p \leqslant c \left(\| \nabla v \|_{L_p(T)}^p + \left\| \frac{v}{|x|} \right\|_{L_p(T)}^p \right) .$$

Applying Lemma 1, we obtain

$$\left\| \frac{v}{|x|} \right\|_{L_p(R)} \leqslant c \| v \|_{V_p^1(R)} .$$

Thus, (3) as well as Lemma are proved.

Clearly, the domain $\Omega_+ = \{x \in \Omega : x_2 > 0\}$ (cf. Fig. 7) can be mapped onto the domain G in Lemma 2 by a quasi-isometric mapping. Therefore any function in $V_p^1(\Omega_+)$ has a norm-preserving extension onto the upper halfplane that vanishes on the halfaxis Ox_1. Applying the same reasoning to $\Omega_- = \Omega \backslash \bar{\Omega}_+$, we conclude that ($\gamma$) holds.

Now we verify (δ). Let $S = \{x : 0 < x_1 < 1, 0 < x_2 < x_1/3\}$. Let σ_k, $k = 0, 1, \ldots$, denote the components of the set $S \backslash T$ (cf. Fig. 7) and let γ denote the union $\gamma_k \cup \gamma_{k+1}$ of legs of the triangle σ_k. Further, let $\tilde{V}_p^1(T)$ be the space of functions $u \in V_p^1(T)$ which satisfy the following condition. The limit values of u out of the triangles t_k and t_{k+1} coincide in their common vertex for $k = 0, 1, \ldots$. We equip $\tilde{V}_p^1(T)$ with the norm of $V_p^1(T)$.

Clearly, (δ) follows immediately from the next lemma.

Lemma 3. *There exists a linear continuous extension operator* $\mathscr{E}_2 \colon \tilde{V}_p^1(T) \to V_p^1(S)$ *with* $p \in (2, \infty)$.

Proof. Consider the rectangle $Q = \{(x, y) : 0 < x < a, 0 < y < b\}$ with vertices O, $A = (a, 0)$, $B = (0, b)$, $C = (a, b)$. Let the function $w \in V_p^1$, $p > 2$, be defined on the triangle OAC and let $w(0) = 0$.

We shall show that there exists a linear extension operator $w \to f \in V_p^1(Q)$ such that $f(0, y) = 0$ for $y \in (0, b)$ and

$$\| f \|_{L_\infty(Q)} \leqslant \| w \|_{L_\infty(OAC)} ,$$

$$\| \nabla f \|_{L_p(Q)} \leqslant c \| \nabla w \|_{L_p(OAC)} .$$

Here, c is a constant that depends only on a/b and p. Clearly, we may assume that Q is a square. We construct an even extension of w across the diagonal OC to the triangle OBC. By η we denote a smooth function of the polar angle such that $\eta(\theta) = 1$ for $\theta < \pi/4$ and $\eta(\pi/2) = 0$. Since $w(0) = 0$, then by Lemma 1

$$\| r^{-1} w \|_{L_p(Q)} \leqslant c \| \nabla w \|_{L_p(Q)} ,$$

where r is the distance to the point O. So $f = \eta w$ is the required extension.

Using the described procedure, we can construct an extension v_k of $u \in \tilde{V}_p^1(T)$ to the triangle σ_k such that $v_k(2^{-k}, y) = u(2^{-k}, 0)$ and

$$\| v_k \|_{L_\infty(\sigma_k)} \leqslant \| u \|_{L_\infty(t_k \cup t_{k+1})} ,$$

$$\| \nabla v_k \|_{L_p(\sigma_k)} \leqslant c \| \nabla u \|_{L_p(t_k \cup t_{k+1})} ,$$

where $k=1,2,\ldots$. For $k=0$ we obtain an extension v_0 of u to the triangle σ_0 satisfying similar inequalities, where $t_k\cup t_{k+1}$ is replaced by t_0.

We define an extension of u to S by $v=u$ on T, $v=v_k$ on σ_k. Clearly,

$$\|\nabla v\|_{L_p(S)}+\|v\|_{L_\infty(S)}\leqslant c(\|\nabla u\|_{L_p(T)}+\|u\|_{L_\infty(T)}). \tag{4}$$

From the integral representation (1.1.10/1) it follows that

$$\operatorname*{osc}_{t_k} u\leqslant c\int_{t_k}|\nabla u(y)|\frac{dy}{|x-y|}.$$

Consequently,

$$\operatorname*{osc}_{t_k} u\leqslant c2^{-k(1-2/p)}\|\nabla u\|_{L_p(t_k)}.$$

So the right-hand side in (4) is equivalent to the norm in $\tilde{V}_p^1(T)$. The lemma is proved.

1.5.3. Extension with Zero Boundary Data

Let G and Ω be bounded domains in R^n, $\Omega\in EV_p^l$. Let $\mathring{V}_p^l(G)$ denote the completion of $\mathscr{D}(G)$ with respect to the norm in $V_p^l(G)$. If $\bar{\Omega}\subset G$ then, multiplying the operator $\mathscr{E}$: $V_p^l(G)\to V_p^l(R^n)$ by a truncating function $\eta\in\mathscr{D}(G)$, $\eta=1$ on Ω, we obviously obtain a linear continuous operator $\mathring{\mathscr{E}}$: $V_p^l(\Omega)\to\mathring{V}_p^l(G)$. If $\Omega\subset G$ and the boundaries ∂G, $\partial\Omega$ have a nonempty intersection, then proving the existence of $\mathring{\mathscr{E}}$ becomes a nontrivial problem. Making no attempt at a detailed study we shall illustrate possibilities that arise here by an example borrowed from the paper by Havin and the author [172]. In that paper, the above-formulated problem arose in connection with certain problems of approximation in the mean by analytic functions.

Let Ω and G be plane domains, $\Omega\in EV_p^1$, $\Omega\subset G$ and let the origin be the only common point of $\partial\Omega$ and ∂G. If R is a sufficiently small positive number then the intersection of the disk $B_R=\{\varrho e^{i\theta}: 0\leqslant\varrho<R\}$ with $G\backslash\bar{\Omega}$ is the union of two disjoint domains ω_1 and ω_2. On the other hand, the intersection of any circle $|z|=\varrho$, $\varrho\in(0,R)$, with each domain ω_j $(j=1,2)$ is a single arc. Let this arc be given by the equation $z=\varrho e^{i\theta}$, $\theta\in(\alpha_j(\varrho),\ \beta_j(\varrho))$, where α_j and β_j are functions satisfying a Lipschitz condition on $[0,R]$, and let $\varrho e^{i\alpha_j(\varrho)}\in\partial\Omega$, $\varrho e^{i\beta_j(\varrho)}\in\partial G$. Further, let $\delta_j(\varrho)=\beta_j(\varrho)-\alpha_j(\varrho)$, $l_j(\varrho)=\varrho\delta_j(\varrho)$.

Theorem. *The following properties are equivalent.*

1. *The function $u\in L_p^1(\Omega)$ can be extended to a function in $\mathring{V}_p^1(G)$.*

2.

$$\int_0^R\frac{|u(\varrho e^{i\alpha_j(\varrho)})|^p}{[l_j(\varrho)]^{p-1}}\,d\varrho<\infty. \tag{1}$$

(Here $u(\varrho e^{i\alpha_j(\varrho)})$ is the boundary value of u at the point $\varrho e^{i\alpha_j(\varrho)}\in\partial\Omega$. This boundary value exists almost everywhere on $\partial\Omega$.)

Proof. Since $\Omega \in EV_p^1$, then to prove that 2 implies 1 we may assume that u has already been extended to a function in $V_p^1(B)$, where B is a disk containing $\bar{G}$.

Let η satisfy a Lipschitz condition in the exterior of $|z|=R$, $\eta=0$ on $R^2\backslash G$, $\eta=1$ on Ω and $\eta(\varrho e^{i\theta})=1-(\theta-\alpha_j(\varrho))/\delta_j(\varrho)$ for $\varrho e^{i\theta}\in\omega_j$, $j=1,2$. Clearly, for $\theta\in(\alpha_j(\varrho),\beta_j(\varrho))$,

$$
\begin{aligned}
(2)\qquad |u(\varrho e^{i\theta})-u(\varrho e^{i\alpha_j(\varrho)})| &\leqslant \int_{\alpha_j(\varrho)}^{\beta_j(\varrho)} \left|\frac{\partial u}{\partial\theta}(\varrho e^{i\theta})\right| d\theta \\
&\leqslant \varrho \int_{\alpha_j(\varrho)}^{\beta_j(\varrho)} |(\nabla u)(\varrho e^{i\theta})|\, d\theta \leqslant \varrho[\delta_j(\varrho)]^{(p-1)/p} \\
&\quad \times \left(\int_{\alpha_j(\varrho)}^{\beta_j(\varrho)} |(\nabla u)(\varrho e^{i\theta})|^p d\theta\right)^{1/p}.
\end{aligned}
$$

So

$$
\int_{\omega_j} \frac{|u(\varrho e^{i\theta})|^p}{[l_j(\varrho)]^p}\varrho\, d\varrho\, d\theta \leqslant c\left(\|\nabla u\|^p_{L_p(\omega_j)} + \int_0^R \frac{|u(\varrho e^{i\alpha_j(\varrho)})|^p}{[l_j(\varrho)]^{p-1}}\, d\varrho\right).
$$

We can easily deduce that the preceding inequality implies $u\eta\in \mathring{V}_p^1(G)$.

If $u\in \mathring{V}_p^1(G)$ then by (2)

$$
\int_0^R \frac{|u(\varrho e^{i\alpha_j(\varrho)})|^p}{[l_j(\varrho)]^{p-1}}\, d\varrho \leqslant \|\nabla u\|^p_{L_p(\omega_j)}.
$$

The theorem is proved.

Since $l_j(\varrho)\leqslant 2\pi\varrho$, then for $p\geqslant 2$ the condition (1) can not be valid for all $u\in V_p^1(\Omega)$ and hence the operator $\mathring{\mathscr{E}}$ does not exist. The same holds for $1\leqslant p<2$ provided $l_j(\varrho)=O(\varrho^{1+\varepsilon})$, $\varepsilon>0$. In fact, the function $u\in V_p^1(\Omega)$, defined near 0 by the equality $u(\varrho e^{i\theta})=\varrho^{1+\delta-2/p}$ with $0<\delta<\varepsilon(p-1)/p$, does not satisfy (1).

Now let $1\leqslant p<2$ and $l_j(\varrho)\geqslant c\varrho$, $c>0$. Using an estimate similar to (2), we arrive at

$$
\int_0^R |u(\varrho e^{i\alpha_j(\varrho)})|^p \frac{d\varrho}{\varrho^{p-1}} \leqslant c(\|\nabla u\|^p_{L_p(\omega_j)} + \|\varrho^{-1}u\|^p_{L_p(\omega_j)})
$$

which together with Hardy's inequality (1.5.2/1) shows that (1) is valid for all $u\in V_p^1(\Omega)$. Consequently, for $p\in[1,2)$ and $l_j(\varrho)\geqslant c\varrho$ the operator $\mathring{\mathscr{E}}$ exists.

§ 1.6. Inequalities for Functions that Vanish on the Boundary along with their Derivatives up to Some Order

Consider the following question. Are any restrictions on Ω necessary for Sobolev's inequalities to be valid for functions in $W_p^l(\Omega)$ that "vanish" on $\partial\Omega$ along with their derivatives up to the order $k-1$ for some $k \leqslant l$? To be precise, we mean functions in the space $\mathring{V}_p^l(\Omega) \cap W_p^k(\Omega)$.

Obviously, no requirements on Ω are needed for $k = l$. Below, we show that the same is true if k satisfies the inequality $2k \geqslant l$. This result can not be refined, for in the case $2k < l$ some conditions must be imposed.

The validity of Sobolev's inequalities for $l \leqslant 2k$ follows from the integral representation for differentiable functions in an arbitrary bounded domain, which is derived in 1.6.2. The necessity of requirements on $\partial\Omega$ in the case $l > 2k$ is shown by an example (cf. 1.6.4). The content of the present section is borrowed from the author's paper [167].

1.6.1. Integral Representation for Functions of One Independent Variable

Lemma. *Let k and l be integers, $1 < l \leqslant 2k$ and let $z \in W_1^l(a,b) \cap \mathring{V}_1^k(a,b)$. Then*

(1) $$z^{(l-1)}(t) = \int_a^b \mathscr{K}(t,\tau) z^{(l)}(\tau)\, d\tau ,$$

where

$$\mathscr{K}(t,\tau) = \begin{cases} \Pi_{2[l/2]-1}\left(\dfrac{2\tau - a - b}{b-a}\right) & \text{for } t > \tau , \\[2ex] \Pi_{2[l/2]-1}\left(\dfrac{a+b-2\tau}{b-a}\right) & \text{for } t < \tau , \end{cases}$$

and Π_{2i-1} is a polynomial of degree $2i-1$, defined by $\Pi_{2i-1}(s) + \Pi_{2i-1}(-s) = 1$ and the boundary conditions $\Pi_{2i-1}(-1) = \cdots = \Pi_{2i-1}^{(i-1)}(-1) = 0$.

Proof. Let l be even, $l = 2q$. Consider the boundary value problem

(2) $$y^{(2q)}(x) = f(x) , \quad y^{(j)}(\pm 1) = 0 , \quad j = 0, 1, \dots, q-1$$

on the interval $[-1, 1]$. Let $g(x,s)$ denote the Green function of this problem. Clearly, $g(-x,-s) = g(x,s)$ and $g(x,s)$ is a polynomial of degree $2q-1$ in x and s for $x > s$ and $x < s$. First, let $x > s$. The derivative $\partial^{2q-1} g(x,s)/\partial x^{2q-1}$ does not depend on x; it is a polynomial of degree $2q-1$ in s and satisfies the boundary conditions (2) at the point $s = -1$. We denote this polynomial by $\Pi_{2q-1}(s)$.

In the case $x > s$, i.e. $-x < -s$, we have

$$\frac{\partial^{2q-1}}{\partial x^{2q-1}} g(x,s) = \frac{\partial^{2q-1}}{\partial x^{2q-1}} [g(-x,-s)] = -\Pi_{2q-1}(-s) .$$

So, differentiating the equality

$$y(x) = \int_{-1}^{1} g(x,s) y^{(2q)}(s)\,ds\,,$$

we obtain

$$y^{(2q-1)}(x) = \int_{-1}^{x} \Pi_{2q-1}(s) y^{(2q)}(s)\,ds - \int_{x}^{1} \Pi_{2q-1}(-s) y^{(2q)}(s)\,ds\,.$$

Passing to the variables t, τ via

$$x = \frac{2t-a-b}{b-a}\,, \qquad s = \frac{2\tau-a-b}{b-a}$$

and setting $z(t)=y(x)$, $z(\tau)=y(s)$, we arrive at

(3)
$$z^{(2q-1)}(t) = \int_{a}^{t} \Pi_{2q-1}\left(\frac{2\tau-a-b}{b-a}\right) z^{(2q)}(\tau)\,d\tau - \int_{t}^{b} \Pi_{2q-1}\left(\frac{a+b-2\tau}{b-a}\right) z^{(2q)}(\tau)\,d\tau\,.$$

The lemma is proved for $l=2q$. In the case $l=2q+1$ we express $(z')^{(2q-1)}$ in terms of $(z')^{(2q)}$ by the formula just derived. This concludes the proof of the lemma.

Remark. For $i=1,2,3$ polynomials Π_{2i-1} are

$$\Pi_1(s) = \tfrac{1}{2}(s+1)\,, \qquad \Pi_3(s) = \tfrac{1}{4}(2-s)(s+1)^2\,,$$
$$\Pi_5(s) = \tfrac{1}{16}(3s^2-9s+8)(s+1)^3\,.$$

1.6.2. Integral Representation for Functions of Several Variables with Zero Boundary Data

The basic result of this subsection is contained in the following theorem.

Theorem. *Let l be a positive integer, $l \leqslant 2k$, and let $u \in L_1^l(\Omega) \cap \mathring{V}_1^k(\Omega)$. Then for almost all $x \in \Omega$*

(1)
$$D^\gamma u(x) = \sum_{\{\beta: |\beta|=l\}} \int_\Omega K_{\beta,\gamma}(x,y) D^\beta u(y) \frac{dy}{|x-y|^{n-1}}\,.$$

Here, γ is an arbitrary multi-index of order $l-1$ and $K_{\beta,\gamma}$ is a measurable function on $\Omega \times \Omega$ such that $|K_{\beta,\gamma}(x,y)| \leqslant c$, where c is a constant that depends only on n, l, k.

Proof. First suppose u is infinitely differentiable on an open set ω, $\bar{\omega} \subset \Omega$. Let L be an arbitrary ray, drawn from the point x; let θ be a unit vector with origin at x and directed along L, $y = x + \tau\theta$, $\tau \in R^1$. Further, let $\pi(x,\theta)$ be the first point of intersection of L with $\partial\Omega$. We also introduce the notation $b(x,\theta) = |\pi(x,\theta) - x|$, $a(x,\theta) = -b(x,-\theta)$.

Since $u \in \mathring{V}_1^k(\Omega)$ and $\nabla_l u \in L(\Omega)$, the function

$$[a(x,\theta), b(x,\theta)] \ni \tau \to z(\tau) = u(x+\tau\theta)$$

satisfies the conditions of Lemma 1.6.1 for almost all θ in the $(n-1)$-dimensional unit sphere S^{n-1}. So, from (1.6.1/3) it follows that

$$(2) \qquad z^{(l-1)}(0) = \int_{a(x,\theta)}^{0} \Pi_{2[l/2]-1}\left(\frac{2\tau - a(x,\theta) - b(x,\theta)}{b(x,\theta) - a(x,\theta)}\right) z^{(l)}(\tau)\,d\tau$$

$$- \int_0^{b(x,\theta)} \Pi_{2[l/2]-1}\left(\frac{a(x,\theta) + b(x,\theta) - 2\tau}{b(x,\theta) - a(x,\theta)}\right) z^{(l)}(\tau)\,d\tau .$$

We note that

$$z^{(l-1)}(0) = \sum_{\{\nu:\, |\nu| = l-1\}} \frac{(l-1)!}{\nu!}\, \theta^\nu D^\nu u(x) .$$

Let γ be any multi-index of order $l-1$ and let $\{P_\gamma(\theta)\}$ be the system of all homogeneous polynomials of degree $l-1$ in the variables $\theta_1, \ldots, \theta_n$ such that

$$\int_{S^{n-1}} P_\gamma(\theta)\, \theta^\nu ds_\theta = \delta_{\gamma\nu} .$$

Before proceeding to further transformations we note that the function $(x,\theta) \to |\pi(x,\theta) - x|$ can be considered as the limit of a sequence of measurable functions on $\Omega \times S^{n-1}$ if Ω is approximated by an increasing nested sequence of polyhedrons. Hence, a and b are measurable functions.

Let $r = |y-x|$, i.e. $\tau = r$, if $\tau > 0$ and $\tau = -r$, if $\tau < 0$. We multiply (2) by $P_\gamma(\theta)$ and integrate over S^{n-1}. Then

$$\frac{(l-1)!}{\gamma!} D^\gamma u(x) = -\int_{S^{n-1}} P_\gamma(\theta)\, ds_\theta \int_0^{b(x,\theta)} \Pi_{2[l/2]-1}\left(\frac{a(x,\theta) + b(x,\theta) - 2r}{b(x,\theta) - a(x,\theta)}\right)$$

$$\times \frac{\partial^l u(r,\theta)}{\partial r^l}\, dr + \int_{S^{n-1}} P_\gamma(\theta)\, ds_\theta \int_0^{-a(x,\theta)} (-1)^l$$

$$\times \Pi_{2[l/2]-1}\left(-\frac{2r + a(x,\theta) + b(x,\theta)}{b(x,\theta) - a(x,\theta)}\right) \frac{\partial^l u(r,-\theta)}{\partial r^l}\, dr .$$

Replacing θ by $-\theta$ in the second summand and noting that $a(x,\theta) = -b(x,-\theta)$ and $P_\gamma(\theta) = (-1)^{l-1} P_\gamma(-\theta)$, we find that the first and the second summands are equal, i.e.

$$D^{\gamma}u(x)=\frac{-2\gamma!}{(l-1)!}\int_{S^{n-1}}P_{\gamma}(\theta)\,ds_{\theta}\int_{0}^{b(x,\theta)}\Pi_{2[l/2]-1}\left(\frac{a(x,\theta)+b(x,\theta)-2r}{b(x,\theta)-a(x,\theta)}\right)\frac{\partial^{l}u(r,\theta)}{\partial r^{l}}dr$$

$$=-2l\gamma!\int_{\Omega(x)}P_{\gamma}(\theta)\Pi_{2[l/2]-1}\left(\frac{a(x,\theta)+b(x,\theta)-2r}{b(x,\theta)-a(x,\theta)}\right)$$

$$\times\sum_{\{\beta:|\beta|=l\}}\frac{\theta^{\beta}}{\beta!}D^{\beta}u(y)\frac{dy}{r^{n-1}},$$

where $\Omega(x)=\{y\in\Omega:\ \theta\in S^{n-1},\ r<b(x,\theta)\}$. Let $K_{\beta,\gamma}(x,\cdot)$ denote the function

$$y\to\frac{-2l\gamma!}{\beta!}P_{\gamma}(\theta)\Pi_{2[l/2]-1}\left(\frac{b(x,\theta)-b(x,-\theta)-2r}{b(x,\theta)+b(x,-\theta)}\right)\theta^{\beta},$$

extended to $\Omega\backslash\Omega(x)$ by zero. Then (1) follows for $x\in\omega$.

Now we remove the assumption that u is smooth on ω. Let u satisfy the condition of the theorem. Clearly, u can be approximated in the seminorm $\|\nabla_l u\|_{L(\Omega)}$ by functions that are smooth on $\bar{\omega}$ and which coincide with u near $\partial\Omega$. This and the continuity of the integral operator with the kernel $|x-y|^{1-n}K_{\beta,\gamma}(x,y)$, mapping $L(\Omega)$ into $L(\omega)$, imply (1) for almost all $x\in\omega$. Since ω is arbitrary, the theorem is proved.

1.6.3. Imbedding Theorems for Functions that Satisfy Zero Boundary Conditions

Now we proceed to applications of Theorem 1.6.2.

Theorem 1. *Let m, l, k be integers, $0\leqslant m<l\leqslant 2k$. Let $p\geqslant 1$ and let $u\in W_p^l(\Omega)\cap \mathring{V}_1^k(\Omega)$ for $n<p(l-m)$. Then $u\in C^m(\Omega)$, $\nabla_m u\in L_\infty(\Omega)$ and*

$$\|\nabla_m u\|_{L_\infty(\Omega)}\leqslant c\,d^{\,l-m-n/p}\|\nabla_l u\|_{L_p(\Omega)},\tag{1}$$

where d is the diameter of Ω.

The imbedding operator of $W_p^l(\Omega)\cap\mathring{V}_1^k(\Omega)$ into $V_\infty^m(\Omega)$ is compact.

Proof. It is sufficient to assume $d=1$. Iterating (1.6.2/1), we obtain the following representation for $D^\gamma u$, $|\gamma|=m<l$,

$$D^{\gamma}u(x)=\int_{\Omega}\sum_{\{\beta:|\beta|=l\}}Q_{\beta\gamma}(x,y)D^{\beta}u(y)\,dy,\tag{2}$$

where $Q_{\beta\gamma}=O(r^{l-m-n}+1)$, if $n\neq l-m$ and $Q_{\beta\gamma}=O(\log 2r^{-1})$, if $n=l-m$.

Applying Hölder's inequality to (2), we obtain (1). Since any function in $V_p^l(\Omega)$ can be approximated in the $V_p^l(\Omega)$-norm by functions that coincide with u near $\partial\Omega$ and are smooth in $\bar{\omega}$, then $\nabla_m u$ is continuous in Ω. Here, as in the proof of Theorem 1.6.2, ω is an arbitrary open set, $\bar{\omega}\subset\Omega$. Thus, (1) is derived.

We construct a covering $\{\mathscr{B}^{(i)}\}$ of R^n by balls with diameter δ, with a multiplicity not exceeding some constant that depends only on n. Let $\Omega_i = \Omega \cap \mathscr{B}^{(i)}$ and let $\{\eta_i\}$ be a smooth partition of unity subordinate to $\{\mathscr{B}^{(i)}\}$ such that $\nabla_j \eta_i = O(\delta^{-j})$. By (1)

$$\| \nabla_m u \|_{L_\infty(\Omega)} \leqslant c \max_i \| \nabla_m(\eta_i u) \|_{L_\infty(\Omega_i)}$$
$$\leqslant c\delta^{l-m-n/p} \| \nabla_l u \|_{L_p(\Omega)} + c(\delta) \|u\|_{V_p^{l-1}(\Omega)} .$$

It remains to note that, by virtue of (2), any bounded subspace of $V_p^l(\Omega) \cap \mathring{V}_1^k(\Omega)$ is compact in $V_p^{l-1}(\Omega)$. The theorem is proved.

Further applications of the integral representation (1.6.2/1) are connected with the results of § 1.4.

Let m and l be integers, $0 \leqslant m < l$, $p > 1$ and let μ be a measure in Ω such that

(3) $$\mu(B_\varrho(x) \cap \Omega) \leqslant K\varrho^s , \quad K = \text{const} , \quad 0 < s \leqslant n ,$$

for any ball $B_\varrho(x)$.

Let ω be an open set, $\bar{\omega} \subset \Omega$, $n > p(l-m) > n-s$ and $q = ps(n-p(l-m))^{-1}$. Further, let $L_q(\omega, \mu)$ be the space of functions on ω which are summable with respect to μ and $L_q(\Omega, \mu, \text{loc}) = \bigcap_\omega L_q(\omega, \mu)$. By Theorem 1.4.5 there exists a unique linear mapping $\gamma: V_p^{l-m}(\Omega) \to L_q(\Omega, \mu, \text{loc})$ such that

(i) if $v \in V_p^{l-m}(\Omega)$ and v is smooth on $\bar{\omega}$, then $\gamma v = v$ on $\bar{\omega}$;

(ii) the operator $\gamma: V_p^{l-m}(\Omega) \to L_q(\omega, \mu)$ is continuous for arbitrary set ω.

Theorem 2. *Let m, l, k be integers, $0 \leqslant m < l \leqslant 2k$, $p > 1$, $s > n - p(l-m) > 0$ and let μ be a measure in Ω, satisfying* (3). *Then for any $u \in L_p^l(\Omega) \cap \mathring{V}_1^k(\Omega)$*

(4) $$\| \gamma(\nabla_m u) \|_{L_q(\Omega, \mu)} \leqslant cK^{1/q} \| \nabla_l u \|_{L_p(\Omega)} ,$$

where $q = ps(n-p(l-m))^{-1}$.

The proof follows immediately from the integral representation (2) and Theorem 1.4.5.

Theorem 3. *Let m, l, k, p, q, s be the same as in Theorem 2 and let μ be a measure in Ω that satisfies the condition*

(5) $$\lim_{\varrho \to 0} \sup_{x \in R^n} \varrho^{-s} \mu(B_\varrho(x) \cap \Omega) = 0 .$$

Then the operator $\gamma \nabla_m$: $W_p^l(\Omega) \cap \mathring{V}_1^k(\Omega) \to L_q(\Omega, \mu)$ is compact.

Proof. Given any $\varepsilon > 0$ there exists a number $\delta > 0$ such that

$$\varrho^{-s} \sup_x \mu(B_\varrho(x) \cap \Omega) < \varepsilon$$

for $\varrho \leqslant \delta$.

We shall use the notation η_i, Ω_i, introduced in the proof of Theorem 1. Clearly,

$$\int_\Omega |\gamma \nabla_m u|^q d\mu \leqslant c \sum_i \int_{\Omega_i} |\gamma \nabla_m (\eta_i u)|^q d\mu \,.$$

This inequality and Theorem 2 imply

$$\|\gamma \nabla_m u\|_{L_q(\Omega,\mu)} \leqslant c\varepsilon \|\nabla_l u\|_{L_p(\Omega)} + C(\varepsilon)\|u\|_{V_p^{l-1}(\Omega)} \,.$$

It remains to use the fact that a unit ball in $W_p^l(\Omega) \cap \mathring{V}_1^k(\Omega)$ is compact in $V_p^{l-1}(\Omega)$.

Remark 1. From Corollary 8.6/1 and Theorem 8.8.1/4 it follows that Theorems 2 and 3 remain valid for $n = p(l-m)$ if the conditions (3) and (5) are replaced by

$$\mu(B_\varrho(x) \cap \Omega) \leqslant K |\log \varrho|^{q(1-p)/p} \,, \quad 0 < \varrho < \tfrac{1}{2} \,,$$

$$\lim_{\varrho \to 0} \sup_{x \in R^n} |\log \varrho|^{q(p-1)/p} \mu(B_\varrho(x) \cap \Omega) = 0 \,,$$

where $q > p > 1$.

Remark 2. Sometimes assertions similar to Theorems 1, 2, 3 can be refined via the replacement of $\|\nabla_l u\|_{L_p(\Omega)}$ by $\|(-\Delta)^{l/2} u\|_{L_p(\Omega)}$, where Δ is the Laplace operator. Namely, for any bounded domain Ω and any function $u \in \mathring{V}_2^1(\Omega)$ such that $\Delta u \in L_p(\Omega)$, $2p > n$, we have

$$\|u\|_{L_\infty(\Omega)} \leqslant c(\operatorname{diam} \Omega)^{2-n/p} \|\Delta u\|_{L_p(\Omega)} \,.$$

This inequality results from an obvious estimate for the Green function of the Dirichlet problem for the Laplace operator, which in turn follows from the maximum principle.

Analogous estimates can be derived from pointwise estimates for the Green function $G_m(x,s)$ of the Dirichlet problem for the m-harmonic operator in an n-dimensional domain (see Maz'ja [164], Maz'ja and Dončev [169]). For instance, for $n = 5, 6, 7$, $m = 2$ or $n = 2m+1$, $2m+2$, $m > 2$, we have

$$|G_m(x,s)| \leqslant c|x-s|^{2m-n}, \quad c = c(m,n) \,.$$

This along with Theorem 1.4.1/2 implies

$$\|\gamma u\|_{L_q(\Omega,\mu)} \leqslant c K^{1/q} \|\Delta^m u\|_{L_p(\Omega)} \,,$$

where $u \in \mathring{V}_2^m(\Omega)$; $n > 2mp$, $p > 1$ and μ is a measure in Ω satisfying (3).

1.6.4. The Necessity of the Condition $l \leqslant 2k$

Here we show that the condition $l \leqslant 2k$ can not be weakened in the theorems of the preceding subsection. We present an example of a domain $\Omega \subset R^n$ for which $V_p^l(\Omega) \cap \mathring{V}_p^k(\Omega)$, $l > 2k$, is not imbedded into $L_\infty(\Omega)$ for $pl > n > 2pk$ and is not imbedded into $L_{pn/(n-pl)}(\Omega)$ for $n > pl$.

Consider the function

$$v_\delta(x) = (1 - \delta^{-2}|x|^2)^k$$

in the ball $B_\delta(0)$. Since v_δ vanishes on $\partial B_\delta(0)$ along with its derivatives up to order $k-1$, then $|\nabla_m v_\delta| \leqslant c\delta^{-k}\varepsilon^{k-m}$ for $k \geqslant m$ in an ε-neighborhood of $\partial B_\delta(0)$. It is also clear that $|\nabla_m v_\delta| = O(\delta^{-m})$ in $B_\delta(0)$ and that $|\nabla_m v_\delta| = 0$ for $m \geqslant 2k+1$.

We denote by P and Q the lower and upper points at which the axis $0x_n$ intersects $\partial B_\delta(0)$, and construct the balls $B_\varepsilon(P)$, $B_\varepsilon(Q)$, $\varepsilon < \delta/2$. Let η be a smooth function on R^n that vanishes on $B_{1/2}(0)$ and equal to unity on $R^n \backslash B_1(0)$. On $B_\delta(0)$ we introduce the function

$$w(x) = v_\delta(x)\,\eta(\varepsilon^{-1}(x-P))\,\eta(\varepsilon^{-1}(x-Q))$$

and estimate its derivatives. In the exterior of the balls $B_\varepsilon(P)$, $B_\varepsilon(Q)$ we have

$$|\nabla_j w| = 0\,, \quad \text{for } j > 2k\,, \quad |\nabla_j w| = O(\delta^{-j})\,, \quad \text{for } j \leqslant 2k\,.$$

Besides,

$$|\nabla_j w| \leqslant c \sum_{m=0}^{\min\{j,2k\}} \varepsilon^{m-j} |\nabla_m v_\delta|$$

on $B_\varepsilon(P) \cup B_\varepsilon(Q)$. Hence

$$|\nabla_j w| \leqslant c\delta^{-k}\varepsilon^{k-j}, \quad j = 0, 1, \ldots, l\,,$$

on $B_\varepsilon(P) \cup B_\varepsilon(Q)$. This implies

$$\| \nabla_j w \|^p_{L_p(B_\delta(0))} \leqslant c\delta^{-pk}\varepsilon^{p(k-j)+n} \quad \text{for } j > 2k\,.$$

Similarly, since $n > pk$, then

$$\| \nabla_j w \|^p_{L_p(B_\delta(0))} \leqslant c(\delta^{n-pj} + \delta^{-pk}\varepsilon^{p(k-j)+n}) \leqslant c_1\delta^{n-pj} \quad \text{for } j \leqslant 2k\,.$$

Therefore

$$\| w \|^p_{V_p^l(B_\delta(0))} \leqslant c(\delta^{n-2pk} + \delta^{-pk}\varepsilon^{n-p(l-k)})\,.$$

We set $\varepsilon = \delta^\alpha$, where α is a number satisfying the inequalities

$$\frac{pk}{n-p(l-k)} < \alpha < \frac{n-pk}{n-p(l-k)}\,, \qquad \alpha > 1\,.$$

Then

$$\| w \|^p_{V_p^l(B_\delta(0))} \leqslant c\delta^\beta\,,$$

where $\beta = \alpha(n - p(l-k)) - pk > 0$.

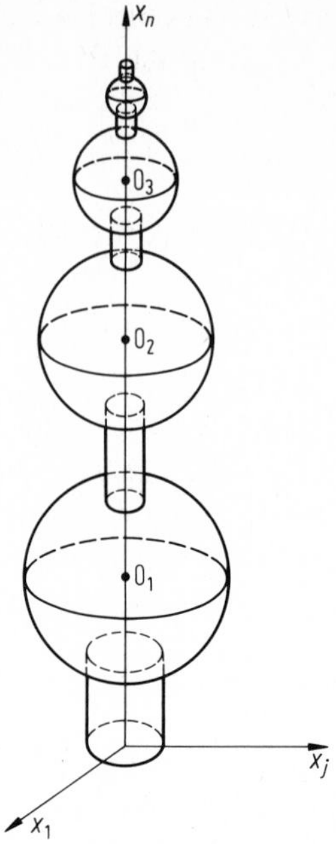

Fig. 8

Consider the domain Ω (Fig. 8) which is the union of balls $\mathscr{B}_i$ with radii δ_i and centers O_i, joined by cylindrical necks $\mathscr{C}_i$ of arbitrary height and with cross section diameter $\varepsilon_i = \delta_i^\alpha$. In each ball $\mathscr{B}_i$ we specify w_i as described above and extend w_i by zero to $\Omega \backslash \mathscr{B}_i$. Then we put

(1) $$u(x) = \sum_{i=1}^{\infty} h_i w_i(x) , \qquad x \in \Omega ,$$

where $\{h_i\}$ is a sequence of numbers such that

(2) $$\sum_{i=1}^{\infty} |h_i|^p \delta_i^\beta < \infty .$$

This condition means that $u \in V_p^l(\Omega)$. The partial sums of the series (1) are functions in $\mathring{V}_p^k(\Omega)$, and so $u \in \mathring{V}_p^k(\Omega)$. Since $w_i = 1$ in the center of $\mathscr{B}_i$, then

$$\|u\|_{L_\infty(\Omega)} \geqslant \sup_i |h_i| .$$

Clearly, the series (2) can converge whereas $h_i \to \infty$. Therefore, $V_p^l(\Omega) \cap \mathring{V}_p^k(\Omega)$ is not imbedded into $L_\infty(\Omega)$.

In the case $n > pl$ we put $|h_i|^p = \delta_i^{lp-n}$. Then

$$\|u\|^q_{L_q(\Omega)} \geqslant c \sum_{i=1}^{\infty} |h_i|^q \delta_i^n = c \sum_{i=1}^{\infty} 1$$

with $q = pn/(n-lp)$. On the other hand,

$$\|u\|^p_{V_p^l(\Omega)} \leqslant c \sum_{i=1}^{\infty} \delta_i^\gamma$$

where $\gamma = (\alpha - 1)(n - p(l-k)) > 0$. So, if $\{\delta_i\}$ is a decreasing geometric progression, then $u \in V_p^l(\Omega) \cap \mathring{V}_p^k(\Omega)$, whereas $u \notin L_q(\Omega)$.

The restrictions on Ω under which the Sobolev theorems hold for the space $V_p^l(\Omega) \cap \mathring{V}_p^k(\Omega)$, $2k < l$, will be considered in subsection 5.6.6.

Chapter 2. Inequalities for Gradients of Functions that Vanish on the Boundary

The present chapter deals with necessary and sufficient conditions for the validity of certain estimates for the norm $\|u\|_{L_q(\Omega,\mu)}$, where $u \in \mathscr{D}(\Omega)$ and μ is a measure in Ω. Here we consider inequalities with the integral

$$\int_{\Omega} [\Phi(x, \nabla u)]^p dx$$

in the right-hand side. The conditions are stated in terms of "isoperimetric" inequalities connecting measures and capacities.

§ 2.1. Conditions for the Validity of Certain Integral Inequalities (The Case $p = 1$)

2.1.1. A Condition in Terms of Arbitrary Admissible Sets

A bounded open set $g \subset R^n$ will be called admissible if $\bar{g} \subset \Omega$ and ∂g is a C^∞-manifold. In Chapters 3–5 this definition will be replaced by a broader one.

Let $\mathscr{N}(x)$ denote the unit normal to the boundary of the admissible set g at a point x that is directed towards the interior of g.

Let $\Phi(x, \xi)$ be a continuous function on $\Omega \times R^n$ which is nonnegative and positive homogeneous of the first degree with respect to ξ. Further, we introduce

$$\sigma(\partial g) = \int_{\partial g} \Phi(x, \mathscr{N}(x))\, ds(x) .$$

Let μ and ν be measures in Ω and $\omega_n = s(\partial B_1)$.

The following theorem contains *a necessary and sufficient condition for the validity of the inequality*

$$\|u\|_{L_q(\Omega,\mu)} \leqslant C \|\Phi(x, \nabla u)\|^{\delta}_{L(\Omega)} \|u\|^{1-\delta}_{L_r(\Omega,\nu)} \tag{1}$$

for all $u \in \mathscr{D}(\Omega)$. This result will be proved using the same arguments as in Theorem 1.4.2/1.

Theorem. 1) *If for all admissible sets*

$$\mu(g)^{1/q} \leqslant \alpha\, \sigma(\partial g)^{\delta} \nu(g)^{(1-\delta)/r} , \tag{2}$$

where $\alpha = \text{const} > 0$, $\delta \in [0, 1]$, $r, q > 0$, $\delta + (1-\delta) r^{-1} \geqslant q^{-1}$, *then (1) holds for all* $u \in \mathscr{D}(\Omega)$ *with* $C \leqslant \alpha r^{\delta} (r\delta + 1 - \delta)^{-\delta - (1-\delta)/r}$.

2) *If* (1) *holds for all* $u \in \mathscr{D}(\Omega)$ *with* $q > 0$, $\delta \in [0, 1]$, *then* (2) *is valid for all admissible sets* g *and* $\alpha \leqslant C$.

Proof. 1) First we note that by Theorem 1.2.4

$$(3) \qquad \int_{\Omega} \Phi(x, \nabla u)\, dx = \int_{\{x: |\nabla u| > 0\}} \Phi\left(x, \frac{\nabla u}{|\nabla u|}\right) |\nabla u|\, dx$$

$$= \int_0^{\infty} dt \int_{\mathscr{E}_t} \Phi\left(x, \frac{\nabla u}{|\nabla u|}\right) ds = \int_0^{\infty} \sigma(\partial \mathscr{L}_t)\, dt\,.$$

Here we used the fact that $|\nabla u| \neq 0$ on $\mathscr{E}_t = \{x: |u(x)| = t\}$ for almost all t and that for such t the sets $\mathscr{L}_t = \{x: |u(x)| > t\}$ are bounded by C^{∞}-manifolds. By Theorem 1.2.3

$$\|u\|_{L_q(\Omega,\mu)} = \left(\int_0^{\infty} \mu(\mathscr{L}_t)\, d(t^q) \right)^{1/q}.$$

Since $\mu(\mathscr{L}_t)$ is a nonincreasing function, then, applying (1.3.3/1), we obtain

$$\|u\|_{L_q(\Omega,\mu)} \leqslant \left(\int_0^{\infty} \mu(\mathscr{L}_t)^{\gamma/q}\, d(t^{\gamma}) \right)^{1/\gamma},$$

where $\gamma = r(r\delta + 1 - \delta)^{-1}$, $\gamma \leqslant q$. Using the fact that the sets $\mathscr{L}_t$ are admissible for almost all t, from (2) we obtain

$$\|u\|_{L_q(\Omega,\mu)} \leqslant \gamma^{1/\gamma} \alpha \left(\int_0^{\infty} \sigma(\partial \mathscr{L}_t)^{\gamma\delta} \nu(\mathscr{L}_t)^{\gamma(1-\delta)/r} t^{\gamma - 1}\, dt \right)^{1/\gamma}.$$

Since $\gamma\delta + \gamma(1-\delta)/r = 1$, then by Hölder's inequality

$$\|u\|_{L_q(\Omega,\mu)} \leqslant \gamma^{1/\gamma} \alpha \left(\int_0^{\infty} \sigma(\partial \mathscr{L}_t)\, dt \right)^{\delta} \left(\int_0^{\infty} \nu(\mathscr{L}_t)\, t^{r-1}\, dt \right)^{(1-\delta)/r}$$

which by virtue of (3) and Theorem 1.2.3 is equivalent to (1).

2) Let g be any admissible subset of Ω and let $d(x) = \operatorname{dist}(x, R^n \backslash g)$, $g_t = \{x \in \Omega, d(x) > t\}$. Let α denote a nondecreasing function, infinitely differentiable on $[0, \infty)$, equal to unity for $d \geqslant 2\varepsilon$ and to zero for $d \leqslant \varepsilon$, where ε is a sufficiently small positive number. Then we substitute $u_{\varepsilon}(x) = \alpha[d(x)]$ into (1).

By Theorem 1.2.4,

$$\int_{\Omega} \Phi(x, \nabla u_{\varepsilon})\, dx = \int_0^{2\varepsilon} \alpha'(t) \int_{\partial g_t} \Phi(x, \mathscr{N}(x))\, ds(x)\ ,$$

where $\mathcal{N}(x)$ is the normal at $x \in \partial g_t$ directed toward the interior of g_t. Since

$$\int_{\partial g_t} \Phi(x, \mathcal{N}(x))\, ds(x) \underset{t\to 0}{\longrightarrow} \sigma(\partial g),$$

then

$$\int_{\Omega} \Phi(x, \nabla u_\varepsilon)\, dx \underset{\varepsilon\to 0}{\longrightarrow} \sigma(\partial g).$$

Let K be a compactum in g such that $\operatorname{dist}(K, \partial g) > 2\varepsilon$. Then $u_\varepsilon(x) = 1$ on K and

$$\|u_\varepsilon\|_{L_q(\Omega,\mu)} \geqslant \mu(K)^{1/q}.$$

Using $0 \leqslant u_\varepsilon(x) \leqslant 1$ and $\operatorname{supp} u_\varepsilon \subset g$, we obtain

$$\|u_\varepsilon\|_{L_r(\Omega,\mu)} \leqslant \nu(g)^{1/r}.$$

Now from (1) we obtain

$$\mu(g)^{1/q} = \sup_{K \subset g} \mu(K)^{1/q} \leqslant C\sigma(\partial g)^{\delta} \nu(g)^{(1-\delta)/r}.$$

The result follows.

2.1.2. A Particular Case (The Condition in Terms of Balls)

In the case $\Phi(x, \xi) = |\xi|$, $\Omega = R^n$, $\nu = m_n$ it follows from (2.1.1/1) that for all balls $B_\varrho(x)$

$$\mu(B_\varrho(x))^{1/q} \leqslant A\varrho^{\delta(n-1)+(1-\delta)n/r}. \tag{1}$$

With minor modification in the proof of Theorem 1.4.2/2 we shall arrive at the converse assertion.

Theorem. *If for all balls $B_\varrho(x)$ the inequality* (1) *holds with $\delta \in [0,1]$; $q, r > 0$, $\delta + (1-\delta)/r \geqslant 1/q$, then* (2.1.1/1) *holds for all $u \in \mathcal{D}(R^n)$ with $C \leqslant cA$.*

Proof. As already shown in the proof of Theorem 1.2.1/2, for any bounded open set g with smooth boundary there exists a sequence $\{B_{\varrho_i}(x_i)\}_{i\geqslant 1}$ of disjoint balls with the properties:

$$(\alpha)\quad g \subset \bigcup_{i\geqslant 1} B_{3\varrho_i}(x_i);$$

$$(\beta)\quad 2m_n(g \cap B_{\varrho_i}(x_i)) = v_n \varrho_i^n,$$

$$(\gamma)\quad s(\partial g) \geqslant c \sum_{i\geqslant 1} \varrho_i^{n-1}.$$

From (1) it follows that

$$\mu(g) \leqslant \sum_{i\geqslant 1} \mu(B_{3\varrho_i}(x_i)) \leqslant A^q \sum_{i\geqslant 1} (3\varrho_i)^{q[\delta(n-1)+(1-\delta)n/r]}. \tag{2}$$

Since $q\delta+(1-\delta)n/r \geqslant 1$, then by (2)

$$\mu(g) \leqslant cA^q \Big(\sum_{i\geqslant 1} \varrho_i^{q\frac{\delta(n-1)+(1-\delta)n/r}{q\delta+(1-\delta)n/r}} \Big)^{q\delta+(1-\delta)n/r}$$

which by Hölder's inequality does not exceed

$$cA^q \Big(\sum_{i\geqslant 1} \varrho_i^{n-1} \Big)^{q\delta} \Big(\sum_{i\geqslant 1} \varrho_i^{n} \Big)^{(1-\delta)q/r}.$$

This and (α), (β), (γ) imply

$$\mu(g)^{1/q} \leqslant cAs(\partial g)^{\delta} m_n(g)^{(1-\delta)q/r}.$$

To conclude the proof it remains to apply Theorem 2.1.1.

2.1.3. One More Inequality Containing the Norms in $L_q(\Omega,\mu)$ and $L_r(\Omega,\nu)$ (The Case $p = 1$)

The following theorem is proved analogously to Theorem 2.1.1.

Theorem. 1) *If for all admissible sets* $g \subset \Omega$

(1) $$\mu(g)^{1/q} \leqslant \alpha\sigma(\partial g)+\beta\nu(g)^{1/r},$$

where $\alpha, \beta =$ const, $q \geqslant 1 \geqslant r$, *then*

(2) $$\| u \|_{L_q(\Omega,\mu)} \leqslant \alpha \| \Phi(x, \nabla u) \|_{L(\Omega)} + \beta \| u \|_{L_r(\Omega,\nu)}$$

holds for all $u \in \mathscr{D}(\Omega)$.

2) *If* (2) *holds for all* $u \in \mathscr{D}(\Omega)$, *then* (1) *holds for all admissible sets* g.

2.1.4. Two Examples of Inequalities Containing Concrete Measures

An important special case of Theorems 2.1.1 and 2.1.3 is inequality (1.4.2/8). We give two more examples that illustrate applications of these theorems.

Example 1. Let $\Omega = R^n$, $R^{n-1} = \{x \in R^n, x_n = 0\}$, $\mu(A) = m_{n-1}(A \cap R^{n-1})$, where A is any Borel subset of R^n. Obviously,

$$\mu(g) \leqslant \tfrac{1}{2} s(\partial g)$$

and hence

$$\| u \|_{L(R^{n-1})} \leqslant \tfrac{1}{2} \| \nabla u \|_{L(R^n)}$$

for all $u \in \mathscr{D}(R^n)$.

Example 2. Let A be any Borel subset of R^n with $m_n(A) < \infty$ and let

$$\mu(A) = \int_A |x|^{-\alpha} dx ,$$

where $\alpha \in [0, 1]$. Further, let B_r be a ball centered at the origin, whose n-dimensional measure equals $m_n(A)$. In other words,

$$r = \left(\frac{n}{\omega_n} m_n(A) \right)^{1/n} .$$

Obviously,

$$\int_A |x|^{-\alpha} dx \leqslant \int_{A \cap B_r} |x|^{-\alpha} dx + r^{-\alpha} m_n(B_r \backslash A) \leqslant \int_{B_r} |x|^{-\alpha} dx .$$

So

$$\mu(A)^{(n-1)/(n-\alpha)} \leqslant (n-\alpha)^{(1-n)/(n-\alpha)} \omega_n^{\alpha(n-1)/n(n-\alpha)} [n m_n(A)]^{(n-1)/n} .$$

Let g be any admissible set in R^n. By virtue of the isoperimetric inequality

$$[n m_n(g)]^{(n-1)/n} \leqslant \omega_n^{-1/n} s(\partial g) ,$$

we have

$$\mu(g)^{(n-1)/(n-\alpha)} \leqslant (n-\alpha)^{(1-n)/(n-\alpha)} \omega_n^{(\alpha-1)/(n-\alpha)} s(\partial g) .$$

This inequality becomes an equality if g is a ball. Therefore

$$\sup_{\{g\}} \frac{\mu(g)^{(n-1)/(n-\alpha)}}{s(\partial g)} = (n-\alpha)^{(1-n)/(n-\alpha)} \omega_n^{(\alpha-1)/(n-\alpha)}$$

and *for all* $u \in \mathscr{D}(R^n)$

(1)
$$\left(\int_{R^n} |u(x)|^{(n-\alpha)/(n-1)} |x|^{-\alpha} dx \right)^{(n-1)/(n-\alpha)} \leqslant (n-\alpha)^{(1-n)/(n-\alpha)} \omega_n^{(\alpha-1)/(n-\alpha)} \| \nabla u \|_{L(R^n)}$$

with the best possible constant.

2.1.5. The Case of a Weighted Norm in the Right-Hand Side

In this subsection we denote by $z = (x, y)$ and $\zeta = (\xi, \eta)$ points in R^{n+m} with $x, \xi \in R^n$, $y, \eta \in R^m$. Further, let $B_r^{(d)}(q)$ be the d-dimensional ball with center $q \in R^d$.

Lemma 1. *Let g be an open subset of R^{n+m} with compact closure and smooth boundary ∂g which satisfies*

(1)
$$\int_{B_r^{(n+m)}(z) \cap g} |\eta|^\alpha d\zeta \Big/ \int_{B_r^{(n+m)}(z)} |\eta|^\alpha d\zeta = \tfrac{1}{2} ,$$

where $\alpha > -m$ *for* $m > 1$ *and* $0 \geqslant \alpha > -1$ *for* $m = 1$. *Then*

$$\int_{B_r^{(n+m)}(z)\cap\partial\mathscr{g}} |\eta|^\alpha ds(\zeta) \geqslant c r^{n+m-1}(r+|y|)^\alpha, \tag{2}$$

where s is the $(n+m-1)$*-dimensional area.*

The proof is based on the next lemma.

Lemma 2. *Let* $\alpha > -m$ *for* $m > 1$ *and* $0 \geqslant \alpha > -1$ *for* $m = 1$. *Then for any* $v \in C^\infty(\overline{B_r^{(n+m)}})$ *there exists a constant V such that*

$$\int_{B_r^{(n+m)}} |v(\zeta)-V||\eta|^\alpha d\zeta \leqslant c r \int_{B_r^{(n+m)}} |\nabla v(\zeta)||\eta|^\alpha d\zeta. \tag{3}$$

Proof. It suffices to derive (3) for $r=1$. We put $B_1^{(n+m)} = B$ and $B_1^{(m)} \times B_1^{(n)} = Q$. Let $R(\zeta)$ denote the distance of a point $\zeta \in \partial Q$ from the origin, i.e. $R(\zeta) = (1+|\zeta|^2)^{1/2}$ for $|\eta|=1$, $|\xi|<1$ and $R(\zeta) = (1+|\eta|^2)^{1/2}$ for $|\zeta|=1$, $|\eta|<1$. Taking into account that B is the quasi-isometric image of Q under the mapping $\zeta \to \zeta/R(\zeta)$, we may deduce (3) from the inequality

$$\int_Q |v(\zeta)-V||\eta|^\alpha d\zeta \leqslant c \int_Q |\nabla v(\zeta)||\eta|^\alpha d\zeta \tag{4}$$

which will be established now. Since $(m+\alpha)\,|\eta|^\alpha = \operatorname{div}(|\eta|^\alpha \eta)$, then, after integration by parts in the left-hand side of (4), we find that it does not exceed

$$(m+\alpha)^{-1}\left(\int_Q |\nabla v||\eta|^{\alpha+1} d\xi + \int_{B_1^{(n)}} d\zeta \int_{\partial B_1^{(m)}} |v(\zeta)-V| ds(\eta)\right). \tag{5}$$

For the sake of brevity we put $T = B_1^{(n)} \times (B_1^{(m)} \backslash B_{1/2}^{(m)})$. Let $m>1$. The second summand in (5) is not greater than

$$c\int_T |\nabla v| d\zeta + c\int_T |v-V| d\zeta.$$

By Lemma 1.11.1, the last assertion and (5) imply (4) where V is the mean value of v in T. (Here it is essential that T is a domain for $m>1$.)

If $m=1$ then T has two components $T_+ = B_1^{(n)} \times (1/2, 1)$ and $T_- = B_1^{(n)} \times (-1, -1/2)$. Using the same argument as in the case $m>1$, we obtain

$$\int_{B_1^{(n)}} |v(\xi, \pm 1) - V_\pm| d\xi \leqslant c \int_{T_\pm} |\nabla v(\zeta)| d\zeta \leqslant c \int_Q |\nabla v(\zeta)||\eta|^\alpha d\zeta,$$

where $V_\pm$ are the mean values of v in $T_\pm$. It remains to note that

$$|V_+ - V_-| \leqslant c \int_{B_1^{(n)}} d\xi \int_{-1}^{1} \left|\frac{\partial v}{\partial \eta}\right| d\eta \leqslant c \int_Q |\nabla v(\zeta)||\eta|^\alpha d\zeta$$

provided $\alpha \leqslant 0$. So for $m=1$ we also have (4) with V replaced by V_+ or V_-. This concludes the proof of the lemma.

Proof of Lemma 1. For the sake of brevity let $B = B_r^{(n+m)}(z)$. In (3) we replace v by a mollification of the characteristic function χ_ϱ of the set g with radius ϱ. Then the left-hand side in (3) is bounded from below by the sum

$$|1-V| \int_{e_1} |\eta|^\alpha d\zeta + |V| \int_{e_0} |\eta|^\alpha d\zeta ,$$

where $e_i = \{\zeta \in B \colon \chi_\varrho(\zeta) = i\}$, $i=0,1$.

Let ε be a sufficiently small positive number. By (1)

$$(\tfrac{1}{2}-\varepsilon)(|1-V|+|V|) \int_B |\eta|^\alpha d\zeta \leqslant cr \int_B |\eta|^\alpha |\nabla \chi_\varrho(\zeta)| d\zeta$$

for sufficiently small values of ϱ. Consequently,

$$\tfrac{1}{2} \int_B |\eta|^\alpha d\zeta \leqslant cr \limsup_{\varrho \to +0} \int_B |\eta|^\alpha |\nabla \chi_\varrho(\zeta)| d\zeta = cr \int_{B \cap \partial g} |\eta|^\alpha ds(\zeta) .$$

It remains to note that

$$\int_B |\eta|^\alpha d\zeta \geqslant c r^{m+n} (r+|y|)^\alpha .$$

The lemma is proved.

Remark 1. Lemma 1 fails for $m=1$, $\alpha>0$. In fact, let $g = \{\zeta \in R^{n+1} \colon \eta > \varepsilon$ or $0 > \eta > -\varepsilon\}$, where $\varepsilon = \text{const} > 0$. Obviously, (1) holds for this g. However

$$\int_{B_r^{(n+1)} \cap \partial g} |\eta|^\alpha ds(\zeta) \leqslant c \varepsilon^\alpha ,$$

which contradicts (2).

Theorem 1. *Let ν be a measure in R^{n+m}, $q \geqslant 1$, $\alpha > -m$. The best constant in*

(6) $$\|u\|_{L_q(R^{n+m}, \nu)} \leqslant C \int_{R^{n+m}} |y|^\alpha |\nabla_z u| dz , \qquad u \in C_0^\infty(R^{n+m}) ,$$

is equivalent to

(7) $$K = \sup_{z;\varrho} (\varrho + |y|)^{-\alpha} \varrho^{1-n-m} [\nu(B_\varrho^{(n+m)}(z))]^{1/q} .$$

Proof. 1) First, let $m>1$ or $0 \geqslant \alpha > -1$, $m=1$. According to Theorem 2.1.3

$$C = \sup_g \frac{[\nu(g)]^{1/q}}{\int_{\partial g} |y|^\alpha ds(z)} ,$$

where g is an arbitrary subset of R^{n+m} with compact closure and smooth boundary. We show that for each g there exists a covering by a sequence of balls $B_{\varrho_i}^{(n+m)}(z_i)$, $i=1,2,\ldots$, such that

$$\sum_i \varrho_i^{n+m-1}(\varrho_i+|y_i|)^\alpha \leqslant c \int_{\partial g} |y|^\alpha ds(z) .$$

Each point $z \in g$ is the center of a ball $B_r^{(n+m)}(z)$ for which (1) is valid. In fact, the ratio in the left-hand side of (1) is a continuous function in r which equals unity for small values of r and converges to zero as $r \to \infty$. By Theorem 1.2.1 there exists a sequence of disjoint balls $B_{r_i}^{(n+m)}(z_i)$ such that

$$g \subset \bigcup_{i=1}^{\infty} B_{3r_i}^{(n+m)}(z_i) .$$

According to Lemma 1

$$\int_{B_{r_i}^{(n+m)}(z_i) \cap \partial g} |y|^\alpha ds(z) \geqslant c r_i^{n+m-1}(r_i+|y_i|)^\alpha .$$

So $\{B_{3r_i}^{(n+m)}(z_i)\}_{i\geqslant 1}$ is the required covering.

Obviously,

$$\begin{aligned} \nu(g) &\leqslant \sum_i \nu(B_{3r_i}^{(n+m)}(z_i)) \leqslant \left(\sum_i [\nu(B_{3r_i}^{(n+m)}(z_i))]^{1/q} \right)^q \\ &\leqslant cK^q \left(\sum_i r_i^{n+m-1}(r_i+|y_i|)^\alpha \right)^q \leqslant \left(cK \int_{\partial g} |y|^\alpha ds(z) \right)^q . \end{aligned}$$

Therefore $C \leqslant cK$ for $m>1$ and for $m=1$, $0 \geqslant \alpha > -1$.

2) Now let $m=1$, $\alpha>0$. We construct a covering of the set $\{\zeta: \eta=0\}$ by balls $\mathscr{B}_j$ with radii ϱ_j, equal to the distance of $\mathscr{B}_j$ from the hyperplane $\{\zeta: \xi=0\}$. We assume that this covering has finite multiplicity. By $\{\varphi_j\}$ we denote a partition of unity subordinate to $\{\mathscr{B}_j\}$ and such that $|\nabla \varphi_j| \leqslant c/\varrho_j$ (see Stein [237], Ch. VI, § 1). Using the present theorem for the case $\alpha=0$, which already has been considered, (or, equivalently, using Theorem 1.4.2/2) we arrive at

$$\|\varphi_j u\|_{L_q(R^{n+1},\nu)} \leqslant c \sup_{\varrho;\, z} \varrho^{-n} [\nu_j(B_\varrho^{(n+1)}(z))]^{1/q} \|\nabla(\varphi_j u)\|_{L(R^{n+1})} ,$$

where ν_j is the restriction of ν to $\mathscr{B}_j$. It is clear that

$$\sup_{\varrho;z} \varrho^{-n}[\nu_j(B_\varrho^{(n+1)}(z))]^{1/q} \leqslant c \sup_{\varrho\leqslant\varrho_j, z\in\mathscr{B}_j} \varrho^{-n}[\nu(B_\varrho^{(n+1)}(z))]^{1/q} .$$

Therefore,

$$\begin{aligned} &\|\varphi_j u\|_{L_q(R^{n+1},\nu)} \\ &\leqslant c \sup_{\varrho\leqslant\varrho_j, z\in\mathscr{B}_j} (\varrho+\varrho_j)^{-\alpha} \varrho^{-n} [\nu(B_\varrho^{(n+1)}(z))]^{1/q} \int_{R^{n+1}} |\nabla(\varphi_j u)| |\eta|^\alpha d\zeta . \end{aligned}$$

Summing over j and using (4), we obtain

$$\|u\|_{L_q(R^{n+1},\nu)} \leqslant cK\left(\int_{R^{n+1}} |\nabla u||\eta|^{\alpha} d\zeta + \int_{R^{n+1}} |u||\eta|^{\alpha-1} d\zeta\right).$$

Since

$$\int_{R^{n+1}} |u||\eta|^{\alpha-1} d\zeta \leqslant \alpha^{-1} \int_{R^{n+1}} |\nabla u||\eta|^{\alpha} d\zeta$$

for $\alpha>0$, then $C\leqslant cK$ for $m=1$, $\alpha>0$.

3) To prove the reverse estimate, in (6) we put $U(\zeta)=\varphi(\varrho^{-1}(\zeta-z))$ where $\varphi\in C_0^\infty(B_2^{(n+m)})$, $\varphi=1$ on $B_1^{(n+m)}$. Since

$$\int_{B_{2\varrho}^{(n+m)}(z)} |\eta|^{\alpha} |\nabla_\zeta u| d\zeta \leqslant c\varrho^{-1} \int_{B_{2\varrho}^{(n+m)}(z)} |\eta|^{\alpha} d\zeta \leqslant c\varrho^{n+m-1}(\varrho+|y|)^{\alpha},$$

the result follows.

Corollary. *Let ν be a measure in R^n, $q\geqslant 1$, $\alpha>-m$. Then the best constant in* (6) *is equivalent to*

$$\sup_{x\in R^n,\varrho>0} \varrho^{1-n-m-\alpha}[\nu(B_\varrho^{(n)}(x))]^{1/q}.$$

For the proof it suffices to note that K, defined in (7), is equivalent to the preceding supremum if $\operatorname{supp}\nu\subset R^n$.

Remark 2. The part of the proof of Theorem 1 for the case $m=1$, $\alpha>0$ is also suitable for $m>1$, $\alpha>1-m$ since for these values of α and for all $u\in C_0^\infty(R^{n+m})$ we have

$$\int_{R^{n+m}} |u||\eta|^{\alpha-1} d\zeta \leqslant (\alpha+m-1)^{-1} \int_{R^{n+m}} |\nabla u||\eta|^{\alpha} d\zeta. \tag{8}$$

This implies that *the best constant C in* (6) *is equivalent to*

$$K_1 = \sup_{z\in R^{n+m};\varrho<|y|/2} |y|^{-\alpha}\varrho^{1-n-m}[\nu(B_\varrho^{(n+m)}(z))]^{1/q}$$

for $m\geqslant 1$, $\alpha>1-m$.

Since (8) is also valid for $\alpha<1-m$ if u vanishes near the subspace $\eta=0$, then following the arguments of the second and third parts of the proof of Theorem 1 with obvious changes, we arrive at the next theorem.

Theorem 2. *Let ν be a measure in $\{\zeta\in R^{n+m}: \eta\neq 0\}$, $q\geqslant 1$, $\alpha<1-m$. Then the best constant in* (6), *where $u\in C_0^\infty(\{\zeta: \eta\neq 0\})$, is equivalent to K_1.*

2.1.6. Inequalities of Hardy-Sobolev Type as Corollaries of Theorem 2.1.5/1

Here we derive certain inequalities for weighted norms which often occur in applications. Particular cases of them are the Hardy inequality

$$\| |x|^{-l} u \|_{L_p(R^n)} \leqslant c \| \nabla_l u \|_{L_p(R^n)}$$

and the Sobolev inequality

$$\| u \|_{L_{pn/(n-lp)}(R^n)} \leqslant c \| \nabla_l u \|_{L_p(R^n)} ,$$

where $lp < n$ and $u \in \mathscr{D}(R^n)$. We retain the notation introduced in 2.1.5.

Corollary 1. *Let*

$$1 \leqslant q \leqslant (m+n)/(m+n-1) , \quad \beta = \alpha - 1 + \frac{q-1}{q}(m+n) - \frac{m}{q} .$$

Then

(1) $$\| |y|^{\beta} u \|_{L_q(R^{n+m})} \leqslant c \| |y|^{\alpha} \nabla u \|_{L(R^{n+m})}$$

for $u \in \mathscr{D}(R^{n+m})$.

Proof. According to Theorem 2.1.5/1 it suffices to establish the uniform boundedness of the value

$$(\varrho + |y|)^{-\alpha} \varrho^{1-n-m} \Bigg(\int_{|z-\zeta|<\varrho} |\eta|^{\beta q} d\zeta \Bigg)^{1/q}$$

with respect to ϱ and z. Obviously, it does not exceed

$$c(\varrho + |y|)^{-\alpha} \varrho^{1-n-m+n/q} \Bigg(\int_{|\eta - y|<\varrho} |\eta|^{\beta q} d\eta \Bigg)^{1/q} .$$

The latter is not greater than $c|y|^{\beta-\alpha} \varrho^{1-(m+n)(q-1)/q}$ for $\varrho \leqslant c|y|$ and $c\varrho^{\beta-\alpha+1-(m+n)(q-1)/q}$ for $\varrho > c|y|$. The result follows.

In (1) let us replace q^{-1}, α, β by $1-p^{-1}+q^{-1}$, $\alpha+(1-p)^{-1} q\beta$, $((1-p^{-1})q+1)\beta$ respectively, and u by $|u|^s$ with $s=(p-1)qp^{-1}+1$. Then applying Hölder's inequality with exponents p and $p/(p-1)$ to its right-hand side, we obtain the following assertion.

Corollary 2. *Let* $m+n>p \geqslant 1$, $p \leqslant q \leqslant p(n+m)(n+m-p)^{-1}$, $\beta = \alpha - 1 + (n+m)(1/p - 1/q) > -m/q$. *Then*

(2) $$\| |y|^{\beta} u \|_{L_q(R^{n+m})} \leqslant c \| |y|^{\alpha} \nabla u \|_{L_p(R^{n+m})}$$

for all $u \in \mathscr{D}(R^{n+m})$.

For $p=2$, $\alpha = 1 - m/2$ the substitution of $u(z) = |y|^{-\alpha} v(z)$ into (2) leads to the next corollary.

Corollary 3. *Let* $m+n>2$, $2<q \leqslant 2(n+m)/(n+m-2)$, $\gamma = -1 + (n+m)(2^{-1} - q^{-1})$. *Then*

$$(3) \qquad \| |y|^{\gamma} v \|_{L_q(R^{n+m})} \leqslant c \left(\int_{R^{n+m}} (\nabla v)^2 dz - \frac{(m-2)^2}{4} \int_{R^{n+m}} \frac{v^2}{|y|^2} dz \right)^{1/2}$$

for all $v \in \mathscr{D}(R^{n+m})$, *subject to the condition* $v(x,0)=0$ *in case* $m=1$.

In particular, the exponent γ vanishes for $q = 2(m+n)/(m+n-2)$ and we obtain

$$c \|v\|^2_{L_{2(m+n)/(m+n-2)}(R^{n+m})} + \frac{(m-2)^2}{4} \int_{R^{n+m}} \frac{v^2}{|y|^2} dz \leqslant \int_{R^{n+m}} (\nabla v)^2 dz ,$$

which is a refinement of both the Sobolev and the Hardy inequalities, the latter having the best constant.

The analogous results for $p \neq 2$ are apparently unknown.

To conclude this subsection we present a generalization of (2) for derivatives of arbitrary integer order l.

Corollary 4. *Let* $m+n > lp$, $1 \leqslant p \leqslant q \leqslant p(m+n-lp)^{-1}(m+n)$, $\beta = \alpha - l + (m+n)(p^{-1} - q^{-1}) > -mq^{-1}$. *Then*

$$(4) \qquad \| |y|^{\beta} u \|_{L_q(R^{n+m})} \leqslant c \| |y|^{\alpha} \nabla_l u \|_{L_p(R^{n+m})}$$

for $u \in \mathscr{D}(R^{n+m})$.

Proof. Let $p_j = p(n+m)(n+m-p(l-j))^{-1}$. Successively applying the inequalities

$$\| |y|^{\beta} u \|_{L_q(R^{n+m})} \leqslant c \| |y|^{\alpha} \nabla u \|_{L_{p_1}(R^{n+m})} ,$$

$$\| |y|^{\alpha} \nabla_j u \|_{L_{p_j}(R^{n+m})} \leqslant c \| |y|^{\alpha} \nabla_{j+1} u \|_{L_{p_{j+1}}(R^{n+m})} , \qquad 1 \leqslant j < l ,$$

which follow from (2), we arrive at (4).

Inequality (4) and its particular cases (1) and (2) obviously fail for $\alpha = l + nq^{-1} - (m+n)p^{-1}$. Nevertheless for this critical α we can obtain similar inequalities which are also invariant under similarity transformations in R^{n+m} by changing the weight function in the left-hand side. For example, we have the following result.

Theorem. *The inequality*

$$(5) \qquad \int_{R^n} \frac{|u(x)|^p dx}{(x_{n-1}^2 + x_n^2)^{1/2}} \leqslant (2p)^p \int_{R^n} |x_n|^{p-1} |\nabla u(x)|^p dx$$

is valid for all $u \in \mathscr{D}(R^n)$.

Proof. We put $\varrho^2 = x_{n-1}^2 + x_n^2$ and denote the integrals in the left and right-hand sides by $\mathscr{I}$ and $\mathscr{J}$ respectively. Integrating by parts, we obtain

$$\mathscr{I} = -p \int_{R^n} x_n \varrho^{-1} |u|^{p-1} \operatorname{sgn} u \frac{\partial u}{\partial x_n} dx + \int_{R^n} x_n^2 \varrho^{-3} |u|^p dx .$$

We denote two summands in the right-hand side by $\mathscr{I}_1$ and $\mathscr{I}_2$. Clearly, by Hölder's inequality we have $|\mathscr{I}_1| \leqslant p \mathscr{I}^{(p-1)/p} \mathscr{J}^{1/p}$. To obtain a bound for $\mathscr{I}_2$ we introduce cylindrical coordinates (z, ϱ, θ) with $z \in R^{n-2}$, $x_{n-1} + ix_n = \varrho \exp(i\theta)$. Then

$$\mathscr{I}_2 = -p \int_{R^{n-2}} dz \int_0^{2\pi} \sin^2\theta d\theta \int_0^\infty |u|^{p-1} \operatorname{sgn} u \frac{\partial u}{\partial \varrho} \varrho d\varrho \leqslant p \mathscr{I}^{(p-1)/p} \mathscr{J}^{1/p} .$$

Thus $\mathscr{I} \leqslant 2p \mathscr{I}^{(p-1)/p} \mathscr{J}^{1/p}$ and (5) follows.

For $p=2$, substituting $u(x) = |x_n|^{-1/2} v(x)$ into (5) we obtain the following assertion which supplements Corollary 3 and improves a variant of the Hardy inequality.

Corollary 5. *The inequality*

$$\int_{R^n} \frac{v^2 dx}{(x_{n-1}^2 + x_n^2)^{1/2} |x_n|} \leqslant 16 \left(\int_{R^n} (\nabla v)^2 dx - \frac{1}{4} \int_{R^n} \frac{v^2 dx}{x_n^2} \right)$$

is valid for all $v \in \mathscr{D}(R^n)$ that vanish for $x_n = 0$.

§ 2.2. On the (p, Φ)-capacity

2.2.1. Definition and Some Properties of the (p, Φ)-capacity

Let e be a compactum in $\Omega \subset R^n$ and let Φ be the function specified in 2.1.1. The number

$$\inf \left\{ \int_\Omega [\Phi(x, \nabla u)]^p dx \colon u \in \mathfrak{N}(e, \Omega) \right\}$$

is called *the (p, Φ)-capacity of e relative to Ω* and is denoted by (p, Φ)-cap(e, Ω). Here

$$\mathfrak{N}(e, \Omega) = \{u \in \mathscr{D}(\Omega) \colon u \geqslant 1 \text{ on } e\} .$$

If $\Omega = R^n$, we omit Ω in the notations (p, Ω)-cap(e, Ω), $\mathfrak{N}(e, \Omega)$, etc.

In case $\Phi(x, \xi) = |\xi|$ we shall speak of *the p-capacity of a compactum e relative to Ω* and we shall use the notation p-cap(e, Φ).

We present several properties of the (p, Φ)-capacity.

(i) *For compact sets $K \subset \Omega$, $F \subset \Omega$, the inclusion $K \subset F$ implies*

$$(p, \Phi)\text{-cap}(K, \Omega) \leqslant (p, \Phi)\text{-cap}(F, \Omega) .$$

This is an obvious consequence of the definition of capacity. From the same definition it follows that the (p, Φ)-capacity of F relative to Ω does not increase under an extension of Ω.

(ii) *The equality*

$$(p, \Phi)\text{-cap}(e, \Omega) = \inf \left\{ \int_\Omega [\Phi(x, \nabla u)]^p dx \colon u \in \mathfrak{P}(e, \Omega) \right\} , \tag{1}$$

where $\mathfrak{P}(e, \Omega) = \{u \colon u \in \mathscr{D}(\Omega),\ u = 1$ *in a neighborhood of* e, $0 \leqslant u \leqslant 1$ *in* $R^n\}$, *is valid.*

Proof. Since $\mathfrak{N}(e, \Omega) \subset \mathfrak{P}(e, \Omega)$ it is sufficient to estimate $(p, \Phi)\text{-cap}(e, \Omega)$ from below. Let $\varepsilon \in (0, 1)$ and let $f \in \mathfrak{N}(e, \Omega)$ be such that

$$\int_\Omega [\Phi(x, \nabla f)]^p dx \leqslant (p, \Phi)\text{-cap}(e, \Omega) + \varepsilon .$$

Let $\{\lambda_m(t)\}_{m \geqslant 1}$ denote a sequence of functions in $C^\infty(R^1)$ satisfying the conditions: $0 \leqslant \lambda'_m(t) \leqslant 1 + m^{-1}$, $\lambda_m(t) = 0$ in a neighborhood of $(-\infty, 0]$ and $\lambda_m(t) = 1$ in a neighborhood of $[1, \infty)$, $0 \leqslant \lambda_m(t) \leqslant 1$ for all t. Since $\lambda_m(f(x)) \in \mathfrak{P}(e, \Omega)$, then

$$\inf \left\{ \int_\Omega [\Phi(x, \nabla u)]^p dx \colon u \in \mathfrak{P}(e, \Omega) \right\} \leqslant \int_\Omega [\lambda'_m(f(x))]^p [\Phi(x, \nabla f(x))]^p dx .$$

Passing to the limit as $m \to \infty$, we obtain

$$\inf \left\{ \int_\Omega [\Phi(x, \nabla u)]^p dx \colon u \in \mathfrak{P}(e, \Omega) \right\}$$
$$\leqslant \int_\Omega [\Phi(x, \nabla f)]^p dx \leqslant (p, \Phi)\text{-cap}(e, \Omega) + \varepsilon .$$

(iii) *For any compactum* $e \subset \Omega$ *and* $\varepsilon > 0$ *there exists a neighborhood* G *such that*

$$(p, \Phi)\text{-cap}(K, \Omega) \leqslant (p, \Phi)\text{-cap}(e, \Omega) + \varepsilon$$

for all compact sets K, $e \subset K \subset G$.

Proof. From (1) it follows that there exists a $u \in \mathfrak{P}(e, \Omega)$ such that

$$\int_\Omega [\Phi(x, \nabla u)]^p dx \leqslant (p, \Phi)\text{-cap}(e, \Omega) + \varepsilon .$$

Let G denote a neighborhood of e in which $u = 1$. It remains to note that

$$(p, \Phi)\text{-cap}(K, \Omega) \leqslant \int_\Omega [\Phi(x, \nabla u)]^p dx$$

for any compactum K, $e \subset K \subset G$.

The next property is proved analogously.

(iv) *For any compactum $e \subset \Omega$ and any $\varepsilon > 0$ there exists an open set ω, $\bar{\omega} \subset \Omega$, such that*

$$(p, \Phi)\text{-cap}(e, \omega) \leqslant (p, \Phi)\text{-cap}(e, \Omega) + \varepsilon .$$

(v) *The Choquet inequality*

$$(p, \Phi)\text{-cap}(K \cup F, \Omega) + (p, \Phi)\text{-cap}(K \cap F, \Omega)$$
$$\leqslant (p, \Phi)\text{-cap}(K, \Omega) + (p, \Phi)\text{-cap}(F, \Omega)$$

holds for any compact sets K, $F \subset \Omega$.

Proof. Let u, v be arbitrary functions in $\mathfrak{P}(K, \Omega)$ and $\mathfrak{P}(F, \Omega)$, respectively. We put $\varphi = \max(u, v)$, $\psi = \min(u, v)$. Obviously, φ and ψ have compact supports and satisfy Lipschitz condition in Ω, $\varphi = 1$ in a neighborhood of $K \cup F$, $\psi = 1$ in a neighborhood of $K \cap F$. Since the set $\{x: u(x) \neq v(x)\}$ is the union of open sets on which either $u > v$, or $u < v$, and since $\nabla u(x) = \nabla v(x)$ almost everywhere on $\{x: u(x) = v(x)\}$, then

$$\int_\Omega [\Phi(x, \nabla \varphi)]^p dx + \int_\Omega [\Phi(x, \nabla \psi)]^p dx = \int_\Omega [\Phi(x, \nabla u)]^p dx + \int_\Omega [\Phi(x, \nabla v)]^p dx .$$

Hence, having noted that mollifications of the functions φ and ψ belong to $\mathfrak{P}(K \cup F, \Omega)$ and $\mathfrak{P}(K \cap F, \Omega)$, respectively, we obtain the required inequality.

A function of compact sets that satisfies conditions (i), (iii), (v) is called a *Choquet capacity.*

Let E be an arbitrary subset of Ω. The number $(p, \Phi)\text{-cap}(E, \Omega) = \sup_{\{K\}} (p, \Phi)\text{-cap}(K, \Omega)$, where $\{K\}$ is a collection of compact sets contained in E, is called the *(p, Φ)-capacity of E relative to Ω.* The number

$$\inf_{\{G\}} (p, \Phi)\text{-cap}(G, \Omega) ,$$

where $\{G\}$ is the collection of all open subsets of Ω containing E, is called the *outer capacity* $(p, \Phi)\text{-}\overline{\text{cap}}(E, \Omega)$ of $E \subset \Omega$. A set E is called *(p, Φ)-capacitable* if

$$(p, \Phi)\text{-cap}(E, \Omega) = (p, \Phi)\text{-}\overline{\text{cap}}(E, \Omega) .$$

From these definitions if follows that any open subset of Ω is (p, Φ)-capacitable. If e is a compactum in Ω, then by property (iii), given $\varepsilon > 0$ there exists an open set G such that

$$(p, \Phi)\text{-cap}(G, \Omega) \leqslant (p, \Phi)\text{-cap}(e, \Omega) + \varepsilon \,.$$

Consequently, all compact subsets of Ω are (p, Φ)-capacitable.

From the general theory of Choquet capacities it follows that analytic sets and, in particular, Borel sets are (p, Φ)-capacitable (see Choquet [45]).

2.2.2. Expression for the (p, Φ)-Capacity Containing an Integral over Level Surfaces

Lemma 1. *For any compactum $F \subset \Omega$ the (p, Φ)-capacity (for $p > 1$) can be defined by*

$$(1) \quad (p, \Phi)\text{-cap}(F, \Omega) = \inf_{u \in \mathfrak{N}(F, \Omega)} \left\{ \int_0^1 \frac{d\tau}{\left(\int_{\mathscr{E}_\tau} [\Phi(x, \nabla u)]^p \frac{ds}{|\nabla u|} \right)^{1/(p-1)}} \right\}^{1-p},$$

where $\mathscr{E}_t = \{x : |u(x)| = t\}$.

We introduce the following notation: Λ is the set of nondecreasing functions $\lambda \in C^\infty(R^1)$ that satisfy the conditions: $\lambda(t) = 0$ for $t \leqslant 0$, $\lambda(t) = 1$ for $t \geqslant 1$, $\operatorname{supp} \lambda' \subset (0, 1)$; Λ_1 is the set of nondecreasing functions that are absolutely continuous on R^1, and satisfy the conditions: $\lambda(t) = 0$ for $t \leqslant 0$, $\lambda(t) = 1$ for $t \geqslant 1$, $\lambda'(t)$ is bounded.

To prove Lemma 1 we shall use the following assertion.

Lemma 2. *Let g be a nonnegative function which is summable on* $[0, 1]$. *Then*

$$(2) \qquad \inf_{\lambda \in \Lambda} \int_0^1 (\lambda')^p g \, dt = \left(\int_0^1 \frac{dt}{g^{1/(p-1)}} \right)^{1-p}.$$

Proof. First we note that by Hölder's inequality

$$1 = \int_0^1 \lambda' \, dt \leqslant \left(\int_0^1 (\lambda')^p g \, dt \right)^{1/p} \left(\int_0^1 \frac{dt}{g^{1/(p-1)}} \right)^{1-1/p}$$

and hence the left-hand side of (2) is not smaller than the right.

Let $\lambda \in \Lambda_1$, $\zeta_\nu(t) = \lambda'(t)$ for $t \in [\nu^{-1}, 1 - \nu^{-1}]$, $\operatorname{supp} \zeta_\nu \subset [\nu^{-1}, 1 - \nu^{-1}]$, $\nu = 1, 2, \ldots$. We set

$$\eta_\nu(t) = \zeta_\nu(t) \left(\int_0^1 \zeta_\nu \, d\tau \right)^{-1}.$$

Since the sequence η_ν converges to λ' on $(0, 1)$ and is bounded, then by Lebesgue's theorem

$$\int_0^1 \eta_\nu^p g\,d\tau \to \int_0^1 (\lambda')^p g\,d\tau .$$

Mollifying η_ν, we obtain the sequence $\{\gamma_\nu\}$, $\gamma_\nu \in C^\infty(R^1)$, $\operatorname{supp} \gamma_\nu \subset (0,1)$,

$$\int_0^1 \gamma_\nu d\tau = 1 , \quad \int_0^1 \gamma_\nu^p g\,d\tau \to \int_0^1 (\lambda')^p g\,d\tau .$$

Setting

$$\lambda_\nu(t) = \int_0^t \gamma_\nu d\tau ,$$

we obtain a sequence of functions in Λ such that

$$\int_0^1 (\lambda_\nu')^p g\,d\tau \to \int_0^1 (\lambda')^p g\,d\tau .$$

Hence,

(3)
$$\inf_{\Lambda} \int_0^1 (\lambda')^p g\,d\tau = \inf_{\Lambda_1} \int_0^1 (\lambda')^p g\,d\tau .$$

Let

$$M_\varepsilon = \{t\colon g(t) \geqslant \varepsilon\} , \quad \lambda_0(t) = \int_0^t \eta\,d\tau ,$$

where $\eta(t) = 0$ on $R^1 \setminus M_\varepsilon$ and

$$\eta(t) = g(t)^{1/(1-p)} \Big(\int_{M_\varepsilon} g^{1/(1-p)} d\tau \Big)^{-1} \quad \text{for } t \in M_\varepsilon .$$

Obviously, $\lambda_0 \in \Lambda_1$, and

$$\int_0^1 (\lambda_0')^p g\,d\tau = \Big(\int_{M_\varepsilon} g^{1/(1-p)} d\tau \Big)^{1-p} .$$

By (3) the left-hand side of (2) does not exceed

$$\Big(\int_{M_\varepsilon} g^{1/(1-p)} d\tau \Big)^{1-p} .$$

We complete the proof by passing to the limit as $\varepsilon \to 0$.

Proof of Lemma 1. Let $u \in \mathfrak{N}(F, \Omega)$, $\lambda \in \Lambda$. From the definition of capacity and Theorem 1.2.4 we obtain

$$(p, \Phi)\text{-cap}(F, \Omega) = \int_\Omega [\lambda'(u)\,\Phi(x, \nabla u)]^p dx = \int_0^1 (\lambda')^p g\,dt ,$$

where

(4)
$$g(t) = \int_{\mathscr{E}_t} [\Phi(x, \nabla u)]^p \frac{ds}{|\nabla u|} .$$

By Lemma 2

$$(p, \Phi)\text{-cap}(F, \Omega) \leqslant \left(\int_0^1 g^{1/(1-p)} d\tau \right)^{1-p}.$$

To prove the opposite inequality it is enough to note that

$$\int_\Omega [\Phi(x, \nabla u)]^p dx \geqslant \int_0^1 g\, d\tau \geqslant \left(\int_0^1 g^{1/(1-p)} d\tau \right)^{1-p}.$$

The lemma is proved.

Recalling the property (2.2.1/1) of (p, Φ)-capacity, note that in passing we have here also proved the following lemma.

Lemma 3. *For any compactum $F \subset \Omega$ the (p, Φ)-capacity $(p>1)$ can be defined as*

$$(p, \Phi)\text{-cap}(F, \Omega) = \inf_{u \in \mathfrak{P}(F, \Omega)} \left\{ \int_0^1 \frac{dt}{\left(\int_{\mathscr{E}_t} [\Phi(x, \nabla u)]^p \frac{ds}{|\nabla u|} \right)^{1/(p-1)}} \right\}^{1-p}.$$

2.2.3. Lower Estimates for the (p, Φ)-Capacity

Lemma. *For any $u \in \mathscr{D}(\Omega)$ and almost all $t \geqslant 0$,*

$$(1) \quad [\sigma(\partial \mathscr{L}_t)]^{p/(p-1)} \leqslant \left[-\frac{d}{dt} m_n(\mathscr{L}_t) \right] \left(\int_{\partial \mathscr{L}_t} [\Phi(x, \nabla u)]^p \frac{ds}{|\nabla u|} \right)^{1/(p-1)},$$

where, as usual, $\mathscr{L}_t = \{x \in \Omega : |u(x)| > t\}$.

Proof. By Hölder's inequality, for almost all t and T, $t<T$,

$$\left(\int_{\mathscr{L}_t \setminus \mathscr{L}_T} |u|^{p-1} \Phi(x, \nabla u)\, dx \right)^{p/(p-1)} \leqslant \int_{\mathscr{L}_t \setminus \mathscr{L}_T} |u|^p dx \left(\int_{\mathscr{L}_t \setminus \mathscr{L}_T} [\Phi(x, \nabla u)]^p dx \right)^{1/(p-1)}.$$

Using Theorem 1.2.4, we obtain

$$\left(\int_t^T \tau^{p-1} \sigma(\partial \mathscr{L}_\tau)\, d\tau \right)^{p/(p-1)} \leqslant \int_{\mathscr{L}_t \setminus \mathscr{L}_T} |u|^p dx \left(\int_t^T d\tau \int_{\mathscr{E}_\tau} [\Phi(x, \nabla u)]^p \frac{ds}{|\nabla u|} \right)^{1/(p-1)}.$$

We divide both sides of the preceding inequality by $(T-t)^{p/(p-1)}$ and estimate the first factor on the right-hand side:

$$\left(\frac{1}{T-t}\int_t^T \tau^{p-1}\sigma(\partial\mathscr{L}_\tau)\,d\tau\right)^{p/(p-1)} \leqslant T^p\frac{m_n(\mathscr{L}_t\setminus\mathscr{L}_T)}{T-t}$$

$$\times\left(\frac{1}{T-t}\int_t^T d\tau\int_{\partial\mathscr{L}_\tau}[\Phi(x,\nabla u)]^p\frac{ds}{|\nabla u|}\right)^{1/(p-1)}.$$

Passing to the limit as $T\to t$, we obtain (1) for almost all $t>0$. The lemma is proved.

From Lemma 2.2.2/3 and from Lemma of the present subsection we immediately obtain the following corollary.

Corollary 1. *The inequality*

$$(2)\qquad (p,\Phi)\text{-cap}(F,\Omega)\geqslant \inf_{u\in\mathfrak{P}(F,\Omega)}\left\{-\int_0^1\frac{d}{d\tau}m_n(\mathscr{L}_\tau)\frac{d\tau}{[\sigma(\partial\mathscr{L}_\tau)]^{p/(p-1)}}\right\}^{1-p}$$

is valid.

Let $\mathscr{C}(\varrho)$ denote the infimum $\sigma(\partial g)$ for all admissible sets such that $m_n(g)\geqslant\varrho$. Then from (2) we obtain the next corollary.

Corollary 2. *The inequality*

$$(3)\qquad (p,\Phi)\text{-cap}(F,\Omega)\geqslant\left(\int_0^{m_n(\Omega)}\frac{d\varrho}{[\mathscr{C}(\varrho)]^{p/(p-1)}}\right)^{1-p}$$

is valid.

By virtue of the classical isoperimetric inequality

$$(4)\qquad s(\partial g)\geqslant n^{(n-1)/n}\omega_n^{1/n}[m_n(g)]^{(n-1)/n},$$

in the case $\Phi(x,\xi)=|\xi|$ we have

$$\mathscr{C}(\varrho)=n^{(n-1)/n}\omega_n^{1/n}\varrho^{(n-1)/n}.$$

Therefore,

$$(5)\qquad p\text{-cap}(F,\Omega)\geqslant\omega_n^{p/n}n^{(n-p)/n}\left|\frac{p-n}{p-1}\right|^{p-1}|m_n(\Omega)^{(p-n)/n(p-1)}$$
$$-m_n(F)^{(p-n)/n(p-1)}|^{1-p}$$

for $p\neq n$ and

$$(6)\qquad p\text{-cap}(F,\Omega)\geqslant n^{n-1}\omega_n\left(\log\frac{m_n(\Omega)}{m_n(F)}\right)^{1-n}$$

for $p=n$.

In particular, for $n>p$,

$$(7)\qquad p\text{-cap}(F)\geqslant\omega_n^{p/n}n^{(n-p)/n}\left(\frac{n-p}{p-1}\right)^{p-1}m_n(F)^{(n-p)/n}.$$

2.2.4. On the p-Capacity of a Ball

We shall show that the estimates (2.2.3/5) and (2.2.3/6) become equalities if Ω and F are concentric balls of radii R and r, $R>r$, i.e.

$$p\text{-cap}(F,\Omega)=\begin{cases}\omega_n\left(\dfrac{|n-p|}{p-1}\right)^{p-1}|R^{(p-n)/(p-1)}-r^{(p-n)/(p-1)}|^{1-p}, & \text{for } n\neq p, \quad (1)\\[2ex] \omega_n\left(\log\dfrac{R}{r}\right)^{1-n}, & \text{for } n=p. \quad (2)\end{cases}$$

Let the centers of the balls Ω and F coincide with the origin O of spherical coordinates (ϱ,ω), $|\omega|=1$. Obviously,

$$\begin{aligned}p\text{-cap}(F,\Omega) &\geqslant \inf_{u\in\mathfrak{N}(F,\Omega)}\int_{\partial B_1} d\omega\int_r^R\left|\frac{\partial u}{\partial\varrho}\right|^p\varrho^{n-1}d\varrho\\ &\geqslant \int_{\partial B_1} d\omega \inf_{u\in\mathfrak{N}(F,\Omega)}\int_r^R\left|\frac{\partial u}{\partial\varrho}\right|^p\varrho^{n-1}d\varrho\,.\end{aligned}$$

The inner integral attains its infimum at the function

$$[r,R]\ni\varrho\to v(\varrho)=\begin{cases}\dfrac{R^{(p-n)/(p-1)}-\varrho^{(p-n)/(p-1)}}{R^{(p-n)/(p-1)}-r^{(p-n)/(p-1)}}, & \text{for } p\neq n,\\[2ex] \dfrac{\log(\varrho R^{-1})}{\log(rR^{-1})}, & \text{for } p=n.\end{cases}$$

This implies the required lower estimates for the p-capacity. The substitution of $v(\varrho)$ into the integral $\int_\Omega|\nabla u|^p dx$ leads to (1), (2).

In particular, the p-capacity of the n-dimensional ball B_r relative to R^n is equal to $\omega_n\left(\dfrac{n-p}{p-1}\right)^{p-1} r^{n-p}$, for $n>p$, and to zero, for $n\leqslant p$. Since the p-capacity is a monotone set function, then for any compactum $p\text{-cap}(F,R^n)=0$, if $n\leqslant p$. In the case $p\leqslant n$ the capacity of a point relative to any open set Ω, containing this point, equals zero. If $p>n$, then the p-capacity of the center of the ball B_R relative to B_R equals $\omega_n\left(\dfrac{p-n}{p-1}\right)^{p-1} R^{n-p}$. Therefore, in the latter case, the p-capacity of any compactum relative to any bounded set that contains this compactum is positive.

2.2.5. On the (p, Φ)-Capacity for $p = 1$

Lemma. *For any compactum* $F \subset \Omega$

$$(1, \Phi)\text{-cap}(F, \Omega) = \inf \sigma(\partial \mathscr{g}),$$

where the infimum is taken over all admissible sets $\mathscr{g}$ *containing F.*

Proof. Let $u \in \mathfrak{N}(F, \Omega)$. Applying Theorem 1.2.4, we obtain

$$\int_{\Omega} \Phi(x, \nabla u)\, dx = \int_0^1 \sigma(\partial \mathscr{L}_t)\, dt \geqslant \inf_{\mathscr{g} \supset F} \sigma(\partial \mathscr{g}).$$

This implies the lower estimate for the capacity.

Let $\mathscr{g}$ be an admissible set containing F. The function $u_\varepsilon(x) = \alpha(d(x))$ defined in the proof of the second part of Theorem 2.1.1 belongs to $\mathfrak{N}(F, \Omega)$ for sufficiently small $\varepsilon > 0$. So

$$(1, \Phi)\text{-cap}(F, \Omega) \leqslant \int_{\Omega} \Phi(x, \nabla u_\varepsilon)\, dx.$$

In the proof of the second part of Theorem 2.1.1 it was shown that the preceding integral converges to $\sigma(\partial \mathscr{g})$, which yields the required upper estimate for the capacity. The lemma is proved.

§ 2.3. Conditions for the Validity of Integral Inequalities (The Case $p \geqslant 1$)

2.3.1. Estimate for the Integral Containing the (p, Φ)-Capacity of the Set $\mathscr{N}_t$

Let $u \in \mathscr{D}(\Omega)$ and let g be the function defined by (2.2.2/4) with $p > 1$. Further, let

(1) $$T \overset{\text{def}}{=} \sup\{t > 0 \colon (p, \Phi)\text{-cap}(\mathscr{N}_t, \Omega) > 0\} > 0,$$

where $\mathscr{N}_t = \{x \in \Omega \colon |u(x)| \geqslant t\}$. From (1) it follows that

(2) $$\psi(t) \overset{\text{def}}{=} \int_0^t \frac{d\tau}{[g(\tau)]^{1/(p-1)}} < \infty$$

for $0 < t < T$.

In fact, let

$$v(x) = t^{-2}[u(x)]^2.$$

Since $v \in \mathfrak{N}(\mathscr{N}_t, \Omega)$, then from Lemma 2.2.2/1 and (1) we obtain

$$\int_0^1 \left(\int_{\{x:\, v(x)=\tau\}} [\Phi(x, \nabla v)]^p \frac{ds}{|\nabla v|} \right)^{1/(1-p)} d\tau \leqslant [(p, \Phi)\text{-cap}(\mathcal{N}_t, \Omega)]^{1/(1-p)} < \infty$$

and it remains to note that

$$\int_0^t \frac{d\tau}{g(\tau)^{1/(p-1)}} = \int_0^1 \left(\int_{\{x:\, v(x)=\tau\}} [\Phi(x, \nabla v)]^p \frac{ds}{|\nabla v|} \right)^{1/(1-p)} d\tau .$$

Since by Theorem 1.2.4

$$\int_0^\infty g(\tau)\, d\tau = \int_\Omega [\Phi(x, \nabla u)]^p dx < \infty ,$$

then $g(t) < \infty$ for almost all $t > 0$ and the function $\psi(t)$ is strictly monotonic. Consequently, on the interval $[0, \psi(T))$ the function $t(\psi)$ which is the inverse of $\psi(t)$ exists.

Lemma. *Let u be a function in $\mathscr{D}(\Omega)$ that satisfies condition* (1). *Then the function $t(\psi)$ is absolutely continuous on any segment $[0, \psi(T-\delta)]$, where $\delta \in (0, T)$, and*

$$\int_\Omega [\Phi(x, \nabla u)]^p dx \geqslant \int_0^{\psi(t)} [t'(\psi)]^p d\psi . \tag{3}$$

If $T = \max|u|$, then we may write the equality sign in (3).

Proof. Let $0 = \psi_0 < \psi_1 < \cdots < \psi_m = \psi(T-\delta)$ be an arbitrary partition of the segment $[0, \psi(T-\delta)]$. By Hölder's inequality,

$$\frac{[t(\psi_{k+1}) - t(\psi_k)]^p}{(\psi_{k+1} - \psi_k)^{p-1}} = \frac{[t(\psi_{k+1}) - t(\psi_k)]^p}{\left[\int_{t(\psi_k)}^{t(\psi_{k+1})} g(\tau)^{1/(1-p)} d\tau \right]^{p-1}} \leqslant \int_{t(\psi_k)}^{t(\psi_{k+1})} g(\tau)\, d\tau$$

and, consequently,

$$\sum_{k=0}^{m-1} \frac{[t(\psi_{k+1}) - t(\psi_k)]^p}{(\psi_{k+1} - \psi_k)^{p-1}} \leqslant \sum_{k=0}^{m-1} \int_{t(\psi_k)}^{t(\psi_{k+1})} g(\tau)\, d\tau \tag{4}$$

$$= \int_0^{T-\delta} g(\tau)\, d\tau \leqslant \int_\Omega [\Phi(x, \nabla u)]^p dx .$$

The last inequality follows from Theorem 1.2.4. By (4) and F. Riesz's theorem (see Natanson [196]), the function $t(\psi)$ is absolutely continuous and its derivative belongs to $L_p(0, \psi(T-\delta))$. By Theorem 1.2.4,

$$\int_\Omega [\Phi(x, \nabla u)]^p dx \geqslant \lim_{\delta \to +0} \int_0^{T-\delta} g(\tau)\, d\tau . \tag{5}$$

Since $t(\psi)$ is a monotonic absolutely continuous function, we can make the change of variable $\tau = t(\psi)$ in the preceding integral. Then

$$\int_0^{T-\delta} g(\tau)\,d\tau = \int_0^{\psi(T-\delta)} t'(\psi)\,g(\psi)\,d\psi = \int_0^{\psi(T-\delta)} [t'(\psi)]^p\,d\psi\,,$$

which, along with (5), yields (3).

If $T = \max|u|$, then we can write the equality sign in (3). The lemma is proved.

Theorem. *Let $u \in \mathscr{D}(\Omega)$. Then for $p \geqslant 1$,*

$$(6)\qquad \int_0^\infty (p,\Phi)\text{-cap}(\mathscr{N}_t,\Omega)\,d(t^p) \leqslant \frac{p^p}{(p-1)^{p-1}} \int_\Omega [\Phi(x,\nabla u)]^p\,dx\,.$$

For $p=1$ the coefficient in front of the integral in the right-hand side of (6) *is equal to unity.*

Proof. To prove (6) it is sufficient to assume that the number T, defined in (1), is positive.

Since by Lemma 2.2.5

$$(1,\Phi)\text{-cap}(\mathscr{N}_t,\Omega) \leqslant \sigma(\partial\mathscr{L}_t)$$

for almost all $t>0$, then (6) follows from (2.1.1/3) for $p=1$.

Consider the case $p>1$. Let $\psi(t)$ be a function defined by (2) and let $t(\psi)$ be the inverse of $\psi(t)$. We make the change of variable:

$$\int_0^\infty (p,\Phi)\text{-cap}(\mathscr{N}_t,\Omega)\,d(t^p) = \int_0^T (p,\Phi)\text{-cap}(\mathscr{N}_t,\Omega)\,d(t^p)$$

$$= \int_0^{\psi(T)} (p,\Phi)\text{-cap}(\mathscr{N}_{t(\psi)},\Omega)\,d(t(\psi)^p)\,.$$

Setting $v = t^{-2}u^2$, $\xi = t^{-2}\tau^2$ in (2), we obtain

$$(7)\qquad \psi(t) = \int_0^1 \left(\int_{\{x:\, v(x)=\xi\}} [\Phi(x,\nabla v)]^p \frac{ds}{|\nabla v|} \right)^{1/(1-p)} d\xi\,.$$

Since $v \in \mathfrak{N}(\mathscr{N}_t,\Omega)$, then by Lemma 2.2.2/1 the right-hand side of (7) does not exceed

$$[(p,\Phi)\text{-cap}(\mathscr{N}_{t(\psi)},\Omega)]^{1/(1-p)}\,.$$

Consequently,

$$\int_0^\infty (p, \Phi)\text{-cap}(\mathcal{N}_t, \Omega)\, d(t^p) \leqslant \int_0^{\psi(T)} \frac{d[t(\psi)]^p}{\psi^{p-1}} = p \int_0^{\psi(T)} \left[\frac{t(\psi)}{\psi}\right]^{p-1} t'(\psi)\, d\psi \,.$$

Applying the Hölder inequality and the Hardy inequality

$$\int_0^{\psi(T)} \frac{[t(\psi)]^p}{\psi^p}\, d\psi \leqslant \left(\frac{p}{p-1}\right)^p \int_0^{\psi(T)} [t'(\psi)]^p d\psi \,, \tag{8}$$

we arrive at

$$\int_0^\infty (p, \Phi)\text{-cap}(\mathcal{N}_t, \Omega)\, d(t^p) \leqslant \frac{p^p}{(p-1)^{p-1}} \int_0^{\psi(T)} [t'(\psi)]^p d\psi \,,$$

which, together with Lemma 2.3.1, yields (6). The theorem is proved.

Remark. The inequality

$$\int_0^\infty (p, \Phi)\text{-cap}(\mathcal{N}_t, \Omega)\, d(t^p) \leqslant C \int_\Omega [\Phi(x, \nabla u)]^p dx \,, \tag{9}$$

with a cruder constant than in (6) can be proved much more simply in the following way. By the monotonicity of capacity, the integral in the left-hand side does not exceed

$$\Xi \overset{\text{def}}{=} (2^p - 1) \sum_{j=-\infty}^{+\infty} 2^{pj} (p, \Phi)\text{-cap}(\mathcal{N}_{2^j}, \Omega) \,.$$

Let $\lambda_\varepsilon \in C^\infty(R^1)$, $\lambda_\varepsilon(t) = 1$ for $t \geqslant 1$, $\lambda_\varepsilon(t) = 0$ for $t \leqslant 0$, $0 \leqslant \lambda'_\varepsilon(t) \leqslant 1 + \varepsilon$, and let

$$u_j(x) = \lambda_\varepsilon(2^{1-j}|u(x)| - 1) \,.$$

Since $u_j \in \mathfrak{N}(\mathcal{N}_{2^j}, \Omega)$, then

$$\Xi \leqslant 2^{p-1} \sum_{j=-\infty}^{\infty} 2^{pj} \int_{\mathcal{N}_{2^{j-1}} \setminus \mathcal{N}_{2^j}} [\Phi(x, \nabla u_j)]^p dx$$

$$\leqslant 2^{2p-1} \sum_{j=-\infty}^{\infty} \int_{\mathcal{N}_{2^{j-1}} \setminus \mathcal{N}_{2^j}} [\lambda'_\varepsilon(2^{1-j}|u| - 1)]^p [\Phi(x, \nabla u)]^p dx$$

$$\leqslant (1+\varepsilon)^p 2^{2p-1} \int_\Omega [\Phi(x, \nabla u)]^p dx \,.$$

Letting ε tend to zero, we obtain (9) with the constant $C = 2^{2p-1}$, which completes the proof.

2.3.2. An Estimate for the Norm in Orlicz Space

We recall the definition of an Orlicz space (cf. M. A. Krasnosel'skiĭ and Ja. B. Rutickiĭ [117]).

On the axis $-\infty < u < \infty$ let the function $M(u)$ admit the representation

$$M(u) = \int_0^{|u|} \varphi(t)\,dt\,,$$

where $\varphi(t)$ is a nondecreasing function, positive for $t>0$ and continuous from the right for $t \geqslant 0$, satisfying the conditions $\varphi(0)=0$, $\varphi(t) \to \infty$ as $t \to \infty$. Further, let

$$\psi(s) = \sup\{t\colon \varphi(t) \leqslant s\}$$

be the right inverse of $\varphi(t)$. The function

$$P(u) = \int_0^{|u|} \psi(s)\,ds$$

is called the complementary function to $M(u)$.

Let $\mathscr{L}_M(\Omega,\mu)$ denote the space of μ-measurable functions for which

$$\|u\|_{\mathscr{L}_M(\Omega,\mu)} = \sup\left\{\left|\int_\Omega uv\,d\mu\right| \colon \int_\Omega P(v)\,d\mu \leqslant 1\right\} < \infty\,.$$

In particular, if $M(u) = q^{-1}|u|^q$, $q>1$, then $P(u) = (q')^{-1}|u|^{q'}$, $q' = q(q-1)^{-1}$ and $\|u\|_{\mathscr{L}_M(\Omega,\mu)} = (q')^{1/q'}\|u\|_{L_q(\Omega,\mu)}$.

The norm in $\mathscr{L}_M(\Omega,\mu)$ of the characteristic function χ_E of the set E is

$$\|\chi_E\|_{\mathscr{L}_M(\Omega,\mu)} = \mu(E)P^{-1}\left(\frac{1}{\mu(E)}\right),$$

where P^{-1} is the inverse of the restriction of P to $[0,\infty)$.

In fact, if $v = P^{-1}(1/\mu(E))\chi_E$, then $\int_\Omega P(v)\,d\mu = 1$, and the definition of the norm in $\mathscr{L}_M(\Omega,\mu)$ implies

$$\|\chi_E\|_{\mathscr{L}_M(\Omega,\mu)} \geqslant \int_\Omega \chi_E v\,d\mu = \mu(E)P^{-1}(1/\mu(E))\,.$$

On the other hand, by Jensen's inequality,

$$\int_\Omega \chi_E v\,d\mu \leqslant \mu(E)P^{-1}\left(\frac{1}{\mu(E)}\int_E P(v)\,d\mu\right),$$

and if we assume $\int_\Omega P(v)\,d\mu \leqslant 1$, then the definition of the norm in $\mathscr{L}_M(\Omega,\mu)$ yields

$$\|\chi_E\|_{\mathscr{L}_M(\Omega,\mu)} \leqslant \mu(E) P^{-1}(1/\mu(E)) \,.$$

Although formally $M(t)=|t|$ does not satisfy the definition of the Orlicz space all the subsequent results concerning $\mathscr{L}_M(\Omega,\mu)$ include this case provided we put $P^{-1}(t)=1$. Then we have $\mathscr{L}_M(\Omega,\mu)=L_1(\Omega,\mu)$.

Theorem. 1) *If there exists a constant β such that for any compactum $F\subset\Omega$*

(1) $$\mu(F)P^{-1}(1/\mu(F)) \leqslant \beta(p,\Phi)\text{-cap}(F,\Omega)$$

with $p\geqslant 1$, then for all $u\in\mathscr{D}(\Omega)$,

(2) $$\||u|^p\|_{\mathscr{L}_M(\Omega,\mu)} \leqslant C\int_\Omega [\Phi(x,\nabla u)]^p\,dx \,,$$

where $C\leqslant p^p(p-1)^{1-p}\beta$.

2) *If* (2) *is valid for any $u\in\mathscr{D}(\Omega)$, then* (1) *holds for all compacta $F\subset\Omega$ with $\beta\leqslant C$.*

Proof. 1) From Theorem 1.2.3 and the definition of the norm in $\mathscr{L}_M(\Omega,\mu)$ we obtain

$$\||u|^p\|_{\mathscr{L}_M(\Omega,\mu)} = \sup\left\{\int_0^\infty\int_{\mathscr{N}_\tau} v\,d\mu\,d(\tau^p) : \int_\Omega P(v)\,d\mu\leqslant 1\right\}$$

$$\leqslant \int_0^\infty \sup\left\{\int_\Omega \chi_{\mathscr{N}_\tau} v\,d\mu : \int_\Omega P(v)\,d\mu\leqslant 1\right\} d(\tau^p) = \int_0^\infty \|\chi_{\mathscr{N}_\tau}\|_{\mathscr{L}_M(\Omega,\mu)}\,d(\tau^p) \,.$$

Consequently,

$$\||u|^p\|_{\mathscr{L}_M(\Omega,\mu)} \leqslant \int_0^\infty \mu(\mathscr{N}_\tau)P^{-1}(1/\mu(\mathscr{N}_\tau))\,d(\tau^p) \,.$$

Using (1) and Theorem 2.3.1, we obtain

$$\||u|^p\|_{\mathscr{L}_M(\Omega,\mu)} \leqslant \beta\int_0^\infty (p,\Phi)\text{-cap}(\mathscr{N}_\tau,\Omega)\,d(\tau^p) \leqslant \frac{p^p\beta}{(p-1)^{p-1}}\int_\Omega [\Phi(x,\nabla u)]^p\,dx \,.$$

2) Let u be any function in $\mathfrak{N}(F,\Omega)$. By (2),

$$\|\chi_F\|_{\mathscr{L}_M(\Omega,\mu)} \leqslant C\int_\Omega [\Phi(x,\nabla u)]^p\,dx \,.$$

By minimizing the right-hand side over the set $\mathfrak{N}(F,\Omega)$, we obtain (1). The theorem is proved.

Remark. Let $\Phi(x,y)$ be a function satisfying the conditions stated in 2.1.1 and let the function $\psi(x,u,y)$: $\Omega\times R^1\times R^n\to R^1$ be such that $\psi(x,u,y) \geqslant [\Phi(x,y)]^p$ and for all $u\in\mathscr{D}(\Omega)$

$$\liminf_{\lambda\to+\infty} \lambda^{-p}\int_\Omega \psi(x,\lambda u,\lambda\nabla u)\,dx \leqslant K\int_\Omega [\Phi(x,\nabla u)]^p dx\,.$$

Then (2) in Theorem can be replaced by the following more general estimate:

$$\| |u|^p \|_{\mathscr{L}_M(\Omega,\mu)} \leqslant C\int_\Omega \psi(x,u,\nabla u)\,dx\,. \tag{3}$$

Here, to prove the necessity of (1) for (3) we must set $u=\lambda v$, where $v\in\mathfrak{N}(F,\Omega)$, in (3) and then pass to the limit as $\lambda\to\infty$. An analogous remark can be made regarding Theorems 2.1.1 and 2.1.2.

2.3.3. The Sobolev Type Inequalities as Corollaries of Theorem 2.3.2

Theorem 2.3.2 contains the following assertion, which is of interest in itself.

Corollary. 1) *If there exists a constant β such that for any compactum $F\subset\Omega$*

$$\mu(F)^{\alpha p} \leqslant \beta(p,\Phi)\text{-cap}(F,\Omega)\,, \tag{1}$$

where $p\geqslant 1$, $\alpha>0$, $\alpha p\leqslant 1$, then for all $u\in\mathscr{D}(\Omega)$

$$\|u\|^p_{L_q(\Omega,\mu)} \leqslant C\int_\Omega [\Phi(x,\nabla u)]^p dx\,, \tag{2}$$

where $q=\alpha^{-1}$ and $C\leqslant p^p(p-1)^{1-p}\beta$.

2) *If* (2) *holds for any $u\in\mathscr{D}(\Omega)$ and if the constant C does not depend on u, then* (1) *is valid for all compacta $F\subset\Omega$ with $\alpha=q^{-1}$ and $\beta\leqslant C$.*

Example 1. From Corollary and the isoperimetric inequality (2.2.3/7) we obtain the Sobolev $(p>1)$-Gagliardo $(p=1)$ inequality

$$\|u\|_{L_{pn/(n-p)}} \leqslant C\|\nabla u\|_{L_p}\,, \tag{3}$$

where $n>p\geqslant 1$, $u\in\mathscr{D}(R^n)$ and

$$C=p(n-p)^{(1-p)/p}\omega_n^{-1/n}n^{(p-n)/pn}\,.$$

Remark. The value of the constant C in (3) is exact only for $p=1$ (cf. Theorem 1.4.2/1). To obtain the best constant we can proceed in the following way.

By Lemma 2.3.1

$$\int_0^{\psi(\max|u|)} [t'(\psi)]^p d\psi = \int_{R^n} |\nabla u|^p dx\,.$$

Putting

$$\psi = \frac{p-1}{\omega_n^{1/(p-1)}(n-p)} r^{(n-p)/(1-p)}, \qquad t(\psi) = \gamma(r)$$

and assuming $t(\psi) = \text{const}$ for $\psi \geqslant \psi(\max|u|)$, we obtain

$$\omega_n \int_0^\infty |\gamma'(r)|^p r^{n-1} dr = \int_{R^n} |\nabla u|^p dx .$$

On the other hand, by Theorem 1.2.3,

$$\int_{R^n} |u|^{pn/(n-p)} dx = \int_0^{\max|u|} m_n(\mathcal{N}_t)\, d(t^{pn/(n-p)}) .$$

The definition of the function $\psi(t)$, Lemma 2.2.3 and the isoperimetric inequality (2.2.3/4) imply

$$\psi(t) \leqslant \omega_n^{1/(1-p)} \frac{p-1}{n-p} \left[\frac{n}{\omega_n} m_n(\mathcal{N}_t) \right]^{(n-p)/n(1-p)} .$$

Consequently,

$$m_n(\mathcal{N}_{t(\psi)}) \leqslant \omega_n n^{-1} r^n$$

and

$$\int_{R^n} |u|^{pn/(n-p)} dx \leqslant \frac{\omega_n}{n} \int_0^\infty r^n d[\gamma(r)^{pn/(n-p)}] .$$

Since

$$\int_0^\infty |\gamma'(r)|^p r^{n-1} dr < \infty ,$$

then $\gamma(r) r^{(n-p)/p} \to 0$ as $r \to \infty$. After integration by parts, we obtain

$$\int_{R^n} |u|^{pn/(n-p)} dx \leqslant \omega_n \int_0^\infty [\gamma(r)]^{pn/(n-p)} r^{n-1} dr .$$

Thus,

$$\sup_{u \in \mathcal{D}} \frac{\|u\|_{L_{pn/(n-p)}}}{\|\nabla u\|_{L_p}} = \omega_n^{-1/n} \sup_{\{\gamma\}} \frac{\left(\int_0^\infty [\gamma(r)]^{pn/(n-p)} r^{n-1} dr \right)^{(n-p)/pn}}{\left(\int_0^\infty |\gamma'(r)|^p r^{n-1} dr \right)^{1/p}} ,$$

where $\{\gamma\}$ is the set of all nonincreasing nonnegative functions on $[0, \infty)$ such that $\gamma(r) r^{(n-p)/p} \to 0$ as $r \to \infty$. Thus, we reduced the question of the best constant in (3) to a one-dimensional variational problem. The latter admits an explicit solution by classical methods of the calculus of variations (G. A. Bliss, J. Lond. Math. Soc., v. 5, 1930). The exact upper bound is attained at any function of the form

$$\gamma(r)=(a+br^{p/(p-1)})^{1-n/p}, \qquad a,b=\text{const}>0,$$

and equals

$$n^{-1/p}\left(\frac{p-1}{n-p}\right)^{(p-1)/p}\left[\frac{p-1}{p}B\left(\frac{n}{p},\frac{n(p-1)}{p}\right)\right]^{-1/n}.$$

Finally, the exact constant in (3) is

$$\pi^{-1/2}n^{-1/p}\left(\frac{p-1}{n-p}\right)^{(p-1)/p}\left\{\frac{\Gamma(1+n/2)\,\Gamma(n)}{\Gamma(n/p)\,\Gamma(1+n-n/p)}\right\}^{1/n},$$

and the equality sign can be written in (3) if

$$u(x)=[a+b\,|x|^{p/(p-1)}]^{1-n/p},$$

where a and b are positive constants (although u does not belong to $\mathscr{D}$ it can be approximated by functions in $\mathscr{D}$ in the $\|\nabla u\|_{L_p}$-norm).

To consider one more application of Corollary we need the following lemma.

Lemma. *If $B_\varrho^{(n-1)}$ is an $(n-1)$-dimensional ball in R^n, $n>2$, then*

$$\text{(4)} \qquad 2\text{-cap}(B_\varrho^{(n-1)},R^n)=\frac{\omega_n}{c_n}\varrho^{n-2},$$

where $c_3=\frac{\pi}{2}$, $c_4=1$, $c_n=(n-4)!!/(n-3)!!$ for odd $n\geqslant 5$ and $c_n=\frac{\pi}{2}(n-4)!!/(n-3)!!$ for even $n\geqslant 6$.

Proof. We introduce ellipsoidal coordinates in R^n: $x_1=\varrho\sinh\psi\cos\theta_1$, $x_j=\varrho\cosh\psi\sin\theta_1\ldots\sin\theta_{j-1}\cos\theta_j$, $j=2,\ldots,n-1$, $x_n=\varrho\cosh\psi\sin\theta_1\ldots\sin\theta_{n-1}$. A standard calculation leads to the formulas

$$dx=\varrho^n(\cosh^2\psi-\sin^2\theta_1)(\cosh\psi)^{n-2}d\psi\,d\omega;$$

$$(\nabla u)^2=\varrho^{-2}\left(\frac{\partial u}{\partial\psi}\right)^2(\cosh^2\psi-\sin^2\theta_1)^{-1}+\ldots,$$

where $d\omega$ is a surface element of the unit ball in R^n and the dots denote a positive quadratic form of all first derivatives of u except $\partial u/\partial\psi$. The equation of the ball $B_\varrho^{(n-1)}$ in the new coordinates is $\psi=0$. Therefore

$$2\text{-cap}(B_\varrho^{(n-1)},R^n)\geqslant\varrho^{n-2}\int_{|\omega|=1}\left(\inf_{\{u\}}\int_0^\infty\left(\frac{\partial u}{\partial\psi}\right)^2(\cosh\psi)^{n-2}d\psi\right)d\omega,$$

where $\{u\}$ is a set of smooth functions on $[0,\infty)$ with compact supports. The infimum in the right-hand side is equal to

$$\left(\int_0^\infty \frac{d\psi}{(\cosh\psi)^{n-2}}\right)^{-1} = c_n^{-1}.$$

This value is attained at the function

$$v = \int_\psi^\infty \frac{d\tau}{(\cosh\tau)^{n-2}} \left(\int_0^\infty \frac{d\tau}{(\cosh\tau)^{n-2}}\right)^{-1},$$

which equals unity on $B_\varrho^{(n-1)}$ and decreases sufficiently rapidly at infinity. Substituting v into the Dirichlet integral, we obtain

$$\text{2-cap}(B_\varrho^{(n-1)}, R^n) \leqslant \omega_n \varrho^{n-2} \int_0^\infty \left(\frac{\partial v}{\partial\psi}\right)^2 (\cosh\psi)^{n-2} d\psi = \frac{\omega_n}{c_n}\varrho^{n-2}.$$

This proves the lemma.

We now recall the definition of the *symmetrization of a compact set K in R^n relative to the $(n-s)$-dimensional subspace R^{n-s}*.

Let any point $x \in R^n$ be denoted by (y, z), where $y \in R^{n-s}$, $z \in R^s$. The image K^* of the compact set K under symmetrization relative to the subspace $z = 0$ is defined by the following conditions:

1) The set K^* is symmetric relative to $z = 0$.

2) Any s-dimensional subspace, parallel to the subspace $y = 0$ and crossing either K or K^*, also intersects the other one and the Lebesgue measures of both cross sections are equal.

3) The intersection of K^* with any s-dimensional subspace, which is parallel to the subspace $y = 0$, is a ball in R^s centered at the hyperplane $z = 0$.

Example 2. Below we follow Pólya and Szegö [213] who established that the 2-capacity does not increase under symmetrization relative to R^{n-1}. Let π be an $(n-1)$-dimensional hyperplane and let $\mathrm{Pr}_\pi \mathscr{F}$ be the projection of $\mathscr{F}$ onto π. We choose π so that $m_{n-1}(\mathrm{Pr}_\pi \mathscr{F})$ attains its maximum value. We symmetrize $\mathscr{F}$ relative to π and obtain a compactum which is also symmetrized relative to a straight line perpendicular to π. So we obtain a body whose capacity does not exceed 2-cap $\mathscr{F}$ and whose intersection with π is an $(n-1)$-dimensional ball with volume $m_{n-1}(\mathrm{Pr}_\pi \mathscr{F})$. Thus the $(n-1)$-dimensional ball has the largest area of orthogonal projections onto an $(n-1)$-dimensional plane among all compacta with fixed 2-capacity.

This and Lemma imply the isoperimetric inequality

$$[m_{n-1}(\mathscr{F} \cap R^{n-1})]^{(n-2)/(n-1)} \leqslant \left(\frac{\omega_{n-1}}{n-1}\right)^{(n-2)/(n-1)} \frac{c_n}{\omega_n}\, \text{2-cap}(\mathscr{F}, R^n),$$

where c_n is the constant defined in Lemma.

Now from Corollary we obtain that the best constant C in the inequality

$$\|u\|_{L_{2(n-1)/(n-2)}(R^{n-1})} \leqslant C\|\nabla u\|_{L_2(R^n)}, \qquad u\in \mathscr{D}(R^n),$$

satisfies

$$\tfrac{1}{2}C \leqslant \left[\left(\frac{\omega_{n-1}}{n-1}\right)^{(n-2)/(n-1)} \frac{c_n}{\omega_n}\right]^{1/2} \leqslant C.$$

2.3.4. A Multiplicative Inequality (The Case $p \geqslant 1$)

Theorem. 1) *For any compactum* $F\subset\Omega$ *let the inequality* (2.3.3/1) *hold with* $p\geqslant 1$, $\alpha>0$. *Further, let* q *be a positive number satisfying one of the conditions: (i)* $q\leqslant q^*=\alpha^{-1}$, *for* $\alpha p\leqslant 1$, *or (ii)* $q<q^*=\alpha^{-1}$, *for* $\alpha p>1$.

Then the inequality

$$(1) \qquad \|u\|_{L_q(\Omega,\mu)} \leqslant C\left(\int_\Omega [\Phi(x,\nabla u)]^p dx\right)^{(1-\varkappa)/p} \|u\|^{\varkappa}_{L_r(\Omega,\mu)},$$

where $r\in(0,q)$, $\varkappa=r(q^*-q)/q(q^*-r)$, $C\leqslant c\beta^{(1-\varkappa)/p}$, *is valid for any* $u\in\mathscr{D}(\Omega)$.

2) *Let* $p\geqslant 1$, $q^*>0$, $r\in(0,q^*]$ *and for some* $q\in(0,q^*]$ *and any* $u\in\mathscr{D}(\Omega)$ *let the inequality* (1) *hold with* $\varkappa=r(q^*-q)/q(q^*-r)$ *and a constant* C *that is independent of* u.

Then (2.3.3/1) *holds for all compacta* $F\subset\Omega$ *with* $\alpha=(q^*)^{-1}$, $\beta\leqslant cC^{p/(1-\varkappa)}$.

Proof. 1). Let $\alpha p\leqslant 1$. Then by Hölder's inequality

$$\int_\Omega |u|^q d\mu = \int_\Omega |u|^{q^*(q-r)/(q^*-r)}|u|^{r(q^*-q)/(q^*-r)}d\mu$$
$$\leqslant \Big(\int_\Omega |u|^{q^*}d\mu\Big)^{(q-r)/(q^*-r)}\Big(\int_\Omega |u|^r d\mu\Big)^{(q^*-q)/(q^*-r)},$$

or, equivalently,

$$\|u\|_{L_q(\Omega,\mu)} \leqslant \|u\|^{1-\varkappa}_{L_{q^*}(\Omega,\mu)}\|u\|^{\varkappa}_{L_r(\Omega,\mu)}.$$

Estimating the first factor by (2.3.3/2), we obtain (1) for $\alpha p\leqslant 1$. Let $\alpha p>1$. By Theorem 1.2.3,

$$\int_\Omega |u|^q d\mu = q\int_0^\infty \mu(\mathscr{N}_t)t^{q-1}dt.$$

To the last integral we apply inequality (1.3.3/2), where $x=t^q$, $f(x)=\mu(\mathscr{N}_t)$, $b=p(q^*)^{-1}>1$, $a>1$ is an arbitrary number, $\lambda=a(q-r)q^{-1}$, $\mu=p(q^*-q)/q^*q$:

$$\int_0^\infty \mu(\mathscr{N}_t)t^{q-1}dt \leqslant c\left(\int_0^\infty [\mu(\mathscr{N}_t)]^a t^{ar-1}dt\right)^{(q^*-q)/a(q^*-r)}$$
$$\times\left(\int_0^\infty [\mu(\mathscr{N}_t)]^{p/q^*}t^{p-1}dt\right)^{q^*(q-r)/p(q^*-r)}.$$

Since $a>1$ and $\mu(\mathcal{N}_t)$ does not increase, we can apply (1.3.3/1) to the first factor in the following way:

$$\int_0^\infty [\mu(\mathcal{N}_t)]^a t^{ar-1} dt \leqslant c \left(\int_0^\infty \mu(\mathcal{N}_t) t^{r-1} dt \right)^a .$$

Thus,

$$\|u\|_{L_q(\Omega,\mu)} \leqslant c \left(\int_0^\infty [\mu(\mathcal{N}_t)]^{p/q^*} t^{p-1} dt \right)^{(1-\varkappa)/p} \|u\|^{\varkappa}_{L_r(\Omega,\mu)} .$$

From condition (2.3.3/1) and Theorem 2.3.1 we obtain

$$\int_0^\infty [\mu(\mathcal{N}_t)]^{p/q^*} t^{p-1} dt \leqslant c\beta \int_\Omega [\Phi(x, \nabla u)]^p dx .$$

The proof of the first part of the theorem is completed.

2) Let G be a bounded open set, $\bar{G} \subset \Omega$. We fix a number $\delta > 0$ and we put

$$\beta_\delta = \sup \frac{\mu(F)^{p\alpha}}{(p, \Phi)\text{-cap}(F, G)}$$

on the set of all compacta F in G satisfying the condition (p, Φ)-$\text{cap}(F, G) \geqslant \delta$. (If (p, Φ)-$\text{cap}(F, G) = 0$ for any compactum $F \subset G$, then the substitution of an arbitrary $u \in \mathfrak{N}(F, G)$ into (1) immediately leads to $\mu = 0$.) Obviously,

$$\beta_\delta \leqslant \delta^{-1} \mu(G)^{p\alpha} < \infty .$$

Let v be an arbitrary function in $\mathfrak{N}(F, G)$ and let $\gamma = \max(pr^{-1}, q^* r^{-1})$. We substitute the function $u = v^\gamma$ into (1). Then

$$\mu(F)^{1/q} \leqslant cC \left(\int_\Omega v^{p(\gamma-1)} [\Phi(x, \nabla v)]^p dx \right)^{(1-\varkappa)/p} \|v^\gamma\|^{\varkappa}_{L_r(\Omega,\mu)} . \tag{2}$$

Let $\psi(t)$ be the function defined in (2.3.1/2), where u is replaced by v. In our case $T = \max v = 1$. Clearly,

$$\int_G v^{\gamma r} d\mu = \int_0^\infty \mu(\mathcal{N}_t) d(t^{\gamma r}) = \int_0^1 \mu(\mathcal{N}_t) [\psi(t)]^{q^*/p'} \frac{d(t^{\gamma r})}{[\psi(t)]^{q^*/p'}} ,$$

where $\mathcal{N}_t = \{x \in G : v(x) \geqslant t\}$. Since $\mathcal{N}_t \supset F$, then by Lemma 2.2.2/3

$$\mu(\mathcal{N}_t) \psi(t)^{q^*/p'} \leqslant \frac{\mu(\mathcal{N}_t)}{[(p, \Phi)\text{-cap}(\mathcal{N}_t, G)]^{q^*/p}} \leqslant \beta_\delta^{q^*/p} .$$

Hence

$$\int_G v^{\gamma r} d\mu \leqslant \beta_\delta^{q^*/p} \int_0^1 [\psi(t)]^{-q^*/p'} d(t^{\gamma r}) .$$

Since $[\psi(t)]^{-q^*/p'}$ is a nonincreasing function, then from (1.3.3/1) we obtain

$$\int_G v^{\gamma r} d\mu \leqslant \beta_\delta^{q^*/p} \left(\int_0^1 [\psi(t)]^{q^*(1-p)/\gamma r} d(t^p) \right)^{\gamma r/p}$$

$$\leqslant \beta_\delta^{q^*/p} \psi(1)^{(\gamma r - q^*)/p'} \left(\int_0^1 \frac{d(t^p)}{[\psi(t)]^{p-1}} \right)^{\gamma r/p}.$$

Setting $t = t(\psi)$ in the last integral and applying the inequality (2.3.1/8) and Lemma 2.3.1, we obtain

$$\int_0^{\psi(1)} \frac{d[t(\psi)]^p}{\psi^{p-1}} \leqslant c \int_0^{\psi(1)} [t'(\psi)]^p d\psi = c \int_G [\Phi(x, \nabla v)]^p dx .$$

Thus,

$$\|v^\gamma\|_{L_r(\Omega,\mu)} \leqslant c\beta_\delta^{q^*/pr} \psi(1)^{(\gamma r - q^*)/rp'} \left(\int_G [\Phi(x, \nabla v)]^p dx \right)^{\gamma/p} \tag{3}$$

$$\leqslant c\beta_\delta^{q^*/pr} [(p, \Phi)\text{-cap}(F, G)]^{(q^* - \gamma r)/rp} \left(\int_G [\Phi(x, \nabla v)]^p dx \right)^{\gamma/p}.$$

The last inequality follows from the estimate

$$[\psi(1)]^{p-1} \leqslant [(p, \Phi)\text{-cap}(F, G)]^{-1}$$

(see Lemma 2.2.2/3). Since $0 \leqslant v \leqslant 1$ and $\gamma \geqslant 1$, then from (2) and (3) it follows that

$$\mu(F)^{1/q} \leqslant cC\beta_\delta^{q^*\varkappa/pr} [(p, \Phi)\text{-cap}(F, G)]^{\varkappa(q^* - \gamma r)/rp} \left(\int_G [\Phi(x, \nabla v)]^p dx \right)^{[1+\varkappa(\gamma-1)]/p}.$$

Minimizing

$$\int_G [\Phi(x, \nabla v)]^p dx$$

on the set $\mathfrak{P}(F, G)$, we obtain

$$\mu(F)^{1/q} \leqslant cC\beta_\delta^{q^*\varkappa/pr} [(p, \Phi)\text{-cap}(F, G)]^{1/p + \varkappa(q^* - r)/pr}$$

$$= cC\beta_\delta^{q^*\varkappa/pr} [(p, \Phi)\text{-cap}(F, G)]^{q^*/qp}.$$

Hence

$$\mu(F)^{p/q^*} \leqslant cC^{qp/q^*} \beta_\delta^{(q^*-q)/(q^*-r)} (p, \Phi)\text{-cap}(F, G) .$$

Consequently,

$$\beta_\delta \leqslant cC^{pq(q^*-r)/q^*(q-r)} = cC^{p/(1-\varkappa)} .$$

Since β_δ is majorized by a constant that depends on neither δ nor G, then using property (iv) of (p, Φ)-capacity we obtain $\beta \leqslant cC^{p/(1-\varkappa)}$. The theorem is proved.

2.3.5. An Estimate for the Norm in $L_q(\Omega,\mu)$ with $q<p$ (The Necessary and Sufficient Condition)

The necessary and sufficient condition for the validity of (2.3.3/2) with $q \geqslant p$ was stated in Corollary 2.3.3. Now we obtain the same result for $p>q\geqslant 1$.

Let $S=\{g_j\}_{j=-\infty}^{\infty}$ be any sequence of admissible subsets of Ω with $\bar{g}_i \subset g_{i+1}$. We put $\mu_i=\mu(g_i)$, $\gamma_i=(p,\Phi)\text{-cap}(\bar{g}_i, g_{i+1})$ and

$$\beta=\sup_{\{S\}}\left[\sum_{i=-\infty}^{\infty}\left(\frac{\mu_i^{p/q}}{\gamma_i}\right)^{q/(p-q)}\right]^{(p-q)/q}. \tag{1}$$

(The summands of the form 0/0 are considered to be zeros.)

Theorem. 1) *If $\beta<\infty$, then*

$$\|u\|^p_{L_q(\Omega,\mu)} \leqslant C\int_\Omega [\Phi(x,\nabla u)]^p dx\,, \tag{2}$$

where $u\in\mathscr{D}(\Omega)$ and $p>q>0$, $C\leqslant c\beta$.

2) *Let $p>q\geqslant 1$. If a constant C exists such that* (2) *holds for all $u\in\mathscr{D}(\Omega)$, then $\beta\leqslant cC$.*

Proof. 1) Let $t_j=2^{-j}+\varepsilon_j$, $j=0,\pm 1,\pm 2,\ldots$, where ε_j is a decreasing sequence of positive numbers satisfying $\varepsilon_j 2^j\to 0$ as $j\to\pm\infty$. We assume further that the sets $\mathscr{L}_{t_j}$ are admissible. Obviously,

$$\|u\|^q_{L_q(\Omega,\mu)}=\sum_{j=-\infty}^{\infty}\int_{t_j}^{t_{j-1}}\mu(\mathscr{L}_t)\,d(t^q)\leqslant c\sum_{j=-\infty}^{\infty}2^{-qj}\mu(\mathscr{L}_{t_j})\,.$$

Let $g_j=\mathscr{L}_{t_j}$. We rewrite the last sum as

$$c\sum_{j=-\infty}^{\infty}\left(\frac{\mu_j^{p/q}}{\gamma_j}\right)^{q/p}(2^{-pj}\gamma_j)^{q/p}$$

and apply Hölder's inequality. Then

$$\|u\|^q_{L_q(\Omega,\mu)}\leqslant c\beta^{q/p}\left(\sum_{j=-\infty}^{\infty}2^{-pj}\gamma_j\right)^{q/p}.$$

Let $\lambda_\varepsilon\in C^\infty(R^1)$, $\lambda_\varepsilon(t)=1$ for $t\geqslant 1$, $\lambda_\varepsilon(t)=0$ for $t\leqslant 0$, $0\leqslant\lambda'_\varepsilon(t)\leqslant 1+\varepsilon$, $(\varepsilon>0)$ and let

$$u_j(x)=\lambda_\varepsilon\left[\frac{|u(x)|-t_{j+1}}{t_j-t_{j+1}}\right].$$

Since $u_j\in\mathfrak{N}(\bar{g}_j, g_{j+1})$, then

$$\sum_{j=-\infty}^{\infty}2^{-pj}\gamma_j\leqslant c\sum_{j=-\infty}^{\infty}(t_j-t_{j+1})^p\int_{g_{j+1}\setminus g_j}[\Phi(x,\nabla u_j)]^p dx$$

$$= c \sum_{j=-\infty}^{\infty} \int_{g_{j+1} \setminus g_j} \left[\lambda_\varepsilon' \left(\frac{u - t_{j+1}}{t_j - t_{j+1}} \right) \right]^p [\Phi(x, \nabla u)]^p dx .$$

Letting ε tend to zero, we obtain

$$\sum_{j=-\infty}^{\infty} 2^{-pj} \gamma_j \leqslant c \int_\Omega [\Phi(x, \nabla u)]^p dx . \tag{3}$$

2) We consider the sequence $S = \{g_j\}_{j=-\infty}^{\infty}$ and set $\tau_{N+1} = 0$,

$$\tau_k = \sum_{j=k}^{N} \left(\frac{\mu_j}{\gamma_j} \right)^{1/(p-q)} ,$$

where $k = -N, -N+1, \ldots, 0, \ldots, N-1, N$. Let u_k denote an arbitrary function in $\mathfrak{P}(\bar{g}_k, g_{k+1})$ and define the function $u = (\tau_k - \tau_{k+1}) u_k + \tau_{k+1}$ on $g_{k+1} \setminus g_k$, $u = \tau_{-N}$ on g_{-N}, $u = 0$ in $\Omega \setminus g_{N+1}$. Since $u \in \mathscr{D}(\Omega)$, the inequality (2) is true for it. Clearly,

$$\int_\Omega u^q d\mu = \int_0^\infty \mu(\mathscr{L}_t) d(t^q) = \sum_{k=-N}^{N} \int_{\tau_{k+1}}^{\tau_k} \mu(\mathscr{L}_t) d(t^q) \geqslant \sum_{k=-N}^{N} \mu_k (\tau_k^q - \tau_{k+1}^q) .$$

From this along with (2) and the inequality $(\tau_k - \tau_{k+1})^q \leqslant \tau_k^q - \tau_{k+1}^q$ we obtain

$$\left[\sum_{k=-N}^{N} \mu_k (\tau_k - \tau_{k+1})^q \right]^{p/q} \leqslant C \sum_{k=-N}^{N} \int_{g_{k+1} \setminus g_k} [\Phi(x, \nabla u)]^p dx$$

$$= C \sum_{k=-N}^{N} (\tau_k - \tau_{k+1})^p \int_{g_{k+1} \setminus g_k} [\Phi(x, \nabla u_k)]^p dx .$$

Since u_k is an arbitrary function in $\mathfrak{P}(\bar{g}_k, g_{k+1})$, then by minimizing the last sum, we obtain

$$\left[\sum_{k=-N}^{N} \mu_k (\tau_k - \tau_{k+1})^q \right]^{p/q} \leqslant C \sum_{k=-N}^{N} (\tau_k - \tau_{k+1})^p \gamma_k .$$

Substituting

$$\tau_k - \tau_{k+1} = \mu_k^{1/(p-q)} \gamma_k^{1/(q-p)} ,$$

we finally arrive at

$$\left[\sum_{k=-N}^{N} \left(\frac{\mu_k^{p/q}}{\gamma_k} \right)^{q/(p-q)} \right]^{(p-q)/q} \leqslant C .$$

The theorem is proved.

2.3.6. An Estimate for the Norm in $L_q(\Omega,\mu)$ with $q<p$ (Sufficient Condition)

Lemma. *Let g_1, g_2, g_3 be admissible subsets of Ω such that $\bar{g}_1 \subset g_2$, $\bar{g}_2 \subset g_3$. We set*

$$\gamma_{ij} = (p, \Phi)\text{-cap}(\bar{g}_i, g_j)\,,$$

where $i<j$. Then

$$\gamma_{12}^{-1/(p-1)} + \gamma_{23}^{-1/(p-1)} \leqslant \gamma_{13}^{-1/(p-1)}\,.$$

Proof. Let ε be any positive number. We choose functions $u_k \in \mathfrak{P}(\bar{g}_k, g_{k+1})$, $k=1,2$, so that

$$\gamma_{k,k+1}^{-1/(p-1)} \leqslant \int_0^1 \left[\int_{\mathscr{E}_\tau^k} [\Phi(x, \nabla u_k)]^p \frac{ds}{|\nabla u_k|}\right]^{-1/(p-1)} d\tau + \varepsilon\,,$$

where $\mathscr{E}_\tau^k = \{x\colon u_k(x) = \tau\}$. We put $u(x) = \frac{1}{2} u_2(x)$ for $x \in g_3 \backslash g_2$ and $u(x) = (u_1(x)+1)/2$ for $x \in g_2$. Then

$$\int_0^1 \left[\int_{\mathscr{E}_\tau^1} [\Phi(x, \nabla u_1)]^p \frac{ds}{|\nabla u_1|}\right]^{1/(1-p)} d\tau = \int_{1/2}^1 \left[\int_{\mathscr{E}_\tau} [\Phi(x, \nabla u)]^p \frac{ds}{|\nabla u|}\right]^{1/(1-p)} d\tau\,,$$

$$\int_0^1 \left[\int_{\mathscr{E}_\tau^2} [\Phi(x, \nabla u_2)]^p \frac{ds}{|\nabla u_2|}\right]^{1/(1-p)} d\tau = \int_0^{1/2} \left[\int_{\mathscr{E}_\tau} [\Phi(x, \nabla u)]^p \frac{ds}{|\nabla u|}\right]^{1/(1-p)} d\tau\,,$$

where $\mathscr{E}_\tau = \{x\colon u(x) = \tau\}$. Therefore,

$$\gamma_{12}^{1/(1-p)} + \gamma_{23}^{1/(1-p)} \leqslant \int_0^1 \left(\int_{\mathscr{E}_\tau} [\Phi(x, \nabla u)]^p \frac{ds}{|\nabla u|}\right)^{1/(1-p)} d\tau + 2\varepsilon\,.$$

Since $u \in \mathfrak{P}(\bar{g}_1, g_3)$, then by Lemma 2.2.2/3 the right-hand side of the last inequality does not exceed $\gamma_{13}^{1/(1-p)} + 2\varepsilon$. The lemma is proved.

Let $\nu(t)$ denote

$$\inf\, (p, \Phi)\text{-cap}(\bar{g}, \Omega)\,,$$

where the infimum is taken over all admissible sets g that satisfy

$$\mu(g) \geqslant t\,.$$

It can be easily checked that condition (2.3.2/1) is equivalent to

$$\beta\nu(t) \geqslant t P^{-1}(1/t)$$

and condition (2.3.3/1) to

$$\beta\nu(t) \geqslant t^{\alpha p}\,.$$

The theorem of the present subsection yields the following sufficient condition for the boundedness of the value β, defined by (2.3.5/1):

$$\int_0^{\mu(\Omega)} \left[\frac{\tau}{\nu(\tau)}\right]^{q/(p-q)} d\tau < \infty .$$

By Theorem 2.3.5 this is a condition for the validity of (2.3.5/2) with $p>q\geqslant 1$.

Theorem. *If* $p>q\geqslant 1$, *then*

$$\sup_{\{S\}} \sum_{j=-\infty}^{\infty} \left(\frac{\mu_j^{p/q}}{\gamma_j}\right)^{q/(p-q)} \leqslant \frac{p}{p-q} \int_0^{\mu(\Omega)} \left[\frac{\tau}{\nu(\tau)}\right]^{q/(p-q)} d\tau, \tag{1}$$

where the notation of subsection 2.3.5 *is retained.*

Proof. Let the integral in the right-hand side converge, let N be a positive integer and let $\Gamma_j = (p, \Phi)\text{-cap}(\bar{g}_j, g_{N+1})$ for $j\leqslant N$, $\Gamma_{N+1}=\infty$. By Lemma,

$$\gamma_j^{1/(1-p)} \leqslant \Gamma_j^{1/(1-p)} - \Gamma_{j+1}^{1/(1-p)}, \quad j\leqslant N .$$

Since $q(p-1)/(p-q)\geqslant 1$, then

$$|a-b|^{q(p-1)/(p-q)} \leqslant |a^{q(p-1)/(p-q)} - b^{q(p-1)/(p-q)}|$$

and hence

$$\gamma_j^{-q/(p-q)} \leqslant \Gamma_j^{-q/(p-q)} - \Gamma_{j+1}^{-q/(p-q)} .$$

This implies

$$\sigma_N \overset{\text{def}}{=} \sum_{j=-N}^{N} \left(\frac{\mu_j^{p/q}}{\gamma_j}\right)^{q/(p-q)} \leqslant \sum_{j=-N}^{N} \mu_j^{p/(p-q)} (\Gamma_j^{-q/(p-q)} - \Gamma_{j+1}^{-q/(p-q)})$$

$$\leqslant \sum_{j=-N+1}^{N} (\mu_j^{p/(p-q)} - \mu_{j-1}^{p/(p-q)}) \Gamma_j^{-q/(p-q)} + \mu_{-N}^{p/(p-q)} \Gamma_{-N}^{-q(p-q)} .$$

It is clear that $\Gamma_j \geqslant (p, \Phi)\text{-cap}(\bar{g}_j, \Omega) \geqslant \nu(\mu_j)$. Since the function ν does not decrease then

$$\mu_{-N}^{p/(p-q)} [\nu(\mu_{-N})]^{q/(p-q)} \leqslant \int_0^{\mu_{-N}} \frac{d(\tau^{p/(p-q)})}{[\nu(\tau)]^{q/(p-q)}} .$$

Similarly,

$$(\mu_j^{p/(p-q)} - \mu_{j-1}^{p/(p-q)}) [\nu(\mu_j)]^{q/(p-q)} \leqslant \int_{\mu_{j-1}}^{\mu_j} \frac{d(\tau^{p/(p-q)})}{[\nu(\tau)]^{q/(p-q)}} .$$

Consequently,

$$\sigma_N \leqslant \int_0^{\mu_N} [\nu(\tau)]^{q/(q-p)} d(\tau^{p/(p-q)}) .$$

The result follows.

2.3.7. An Inequality with the Norms in $L_q(\Omega,\mu)$ and $L_r(\Omega,\nu)$ (The Case $p \geqslant 1$)

The next theorem gives conditions for the validity of the inequality

$$\|u\|^p_{L_q(\Omega,\mu)} \leqslant C\left(\int_\Omega [\Phi(x,\nabla u)]^p dx + \|u\|^p_{L_r(\Omega,\nu)}\right) \tag{1}$$

for all $u \in \mathscr{D}(\Omega)$ with $q \geqslant p \geqslant r$, $p > 1$ (compare with Theorem 2.1.3).

Theorem. *Inequality* (1) *holds if and only if*

$$\mu(g)^{p/q} \leqslant cC[(p,\Phi)\text{-cap}(\bar{g},\mathscr{G}) + [\nu(\mathscr{G})]^{p/r}] \tag{2}$$

for all admissible sets g and $\mathscr{G}$ with $\bar{g} \subset \mathscr{G}$.

Proof. Sufficiency. By virtue of Theorem 1.2.3 and inequality (1.3.3/1),

$$\|u\|^p_{L_q(\Omega,\mu)} = \left[\int_0^\infty \mu(\mathscr{L}_t)\, d(t^q)\right]^{p/q}$$
$$\leqslant \int_0^\infty [\mu(\mathscr{L}_t)]^{p/q} d(t^p) \leqslant c \sum_{j=-\infty}^{+\infty} 2^{-pj} \mu(g_j)^{p/q},$$

where $g_j = \mathscr{L}_{t_j}$ and $\{t_j\}$ is the sequence of levels defined in the proof of the first part of Theorem 2.3.4. We set $\gamma_j = (p,\Phi)\text{-cap}(\bar{g}_j, g_{j+1})$ and make use of condition (2):

$$\|u\|^p_{L_q(\Omega,\mu)} \leqslant cC\left[\sum_{j=-\infty}^{+\infty} 2^{-pj}\gamma_j + \sum_{j=-\infty}^{+\infty} 2^{-pj}\nu(g_j)^{p/r}\right]. \tag{3}$$

We can estimate the first sum in the right-hand side of this inequality by means of (2.3.5/3). The second sum does not exceed

$$c\int_0^\infty [\nu(\mathscr{L}_t)]^{p/r} d(t^p) \leqslant c\left(\int_0^\infty \nu(\mathscr{L}_t)\, d(t^r)\right)^{p/r} = c\|u\|^p_{L_r(\Omega,\nu)}.$$

Necessity. Let g and $\mathscr{G}$ be admissible and let $\bar{g} \subset \mathscr{G}$. We substitute any function $u \in \mathfrak{P}(\bar{g},\mathscr{G})$ into (1). Then

$$\mu(g)^{p/q} \leqslant C\left[\int_\Omega [\Phi(x,\nabla u)]^p dx + \nu(\mathscr{G})^{p/r}\right].$$

Minimizing the first summand on the right over the set $\mathfrak{P}(\bar{g},\mathscr{G})$, we obtain (2).

Remark. Obviously, a sufficient condition for the validity of (1) is the inequality

(4) $$\mu(\mathcal{g})^{p/q} \leqslant C_1[(p, \Phi)\text{-cap}(\mathcal{g}, \Omega) + \nu(\mathcal{g})^{p/r}],$$

which is simpler than (2). In contrast to (1) it contains only one set $\mathcal{g}$. However, as the following example shows, the latter condition is not necessary.

Let $\Omega = R^3$, $q = p = r = 2$, $\Phi(x, y) = |y|$, and let the measures μ and ν be defined as follows:

$$\mu(A) = \sum_{k=0}^{\infty} s(A \cap \partial B_{2^k}),$$

$$\nu(A) = \sum_{k=0}^{\infty} s(A \cap \partial B_{2^k+1}),$$

where A is any Borel subset of R^3 and s is two-dimensional Hausdorff measure. Condition (4) is not fulfilled for these measures and the 2-capacity. Indeed, for the sets $\mathcal{g}_k = B_{2^k+1} \backslash \bar{B}_{2^k-1}$, $k = 2, 3, \ldots$, we have $\mu(\mathcal{g}_k) = \pi 4^{k+1}$, $\nu(\mathcal{g}_k) = 0$, $2\text{-cap}(\mathcal{g}_k, R^3) = 4\pi(2^k + 1)$.

We shall show that (1) is true. Let $u \in \mathcal{D}(R^3)$ and let (ϱ, ω) be spherical coordinates with center 0. Obviously,

$$[u(2^k, \omega)]^2 \leqslant 2 \int_{2^k}^{2^k+1} \left(\frac{\partial u}{\partial \varrho}(\varrho, \omega)\right)^2 d\varrho + 2[u(2^k+1, \omega)]^2.$$

Hence

$$4^k \int_{\partial B_1} [u(2^k, \omega)]^2 d\omega \leqslant 2 \int_{B_{2^k+1} \backslash B_{2^k}} \left(\frac{\partial u}{\partial \varrho}\right)^2 dx + 2 \cdot 4^k \int_{\partial B_1} [u(2^k+1, \omega)]^2 d\omega.$$

Summing over k, we obtain

$$\int_{R^3} u^2 d\mu \leqslant c\left(\int_{R^3} |\nabla u|^2 dx + \int_{R^3} u^2 d\nu\right).$$

The proof is complete.

2.3.8. An Estimate for the Integral $\int_\Omega |u|^2 d\sigma$ with a Charge σ

The following assertion yields a condition that is close in a certain sense to being necessary and sufficient for the validity of the inequality

(1) $$\int_\Omega |u|^p dx \leqslant c \int_\Omega [\Phi(x, \nabla u)]^p dx, \qquad u \in \mathcal{D}(\Omega),$$

where σ is an arbitrary charge in Ω, not a nonnegative measure as in Theorem 2.3.4. (Theorem 2.1.3 contains a stronger result for $p = 1$.)

Theorem. *Let σ^+ and σ^- be the positive and negative parts of the charge σ.*

1) *If for some* $\varepsilon \in (0,1)$ *and for all admissible sets* g *and* $\mathscr{G}$ *with* $\bar{g} \subset \mathscr{G}$ *we have the inequality*

$$\sigma^-(g) \leqslant C_\varepsilon(p, \Phi)\text{-cap}(\bar{g}, \mathscr{G}) + (1-\varepsilon)\sigma^-(\mathscr{G}), \tag{2}$$

where $C_\varepsilon =$ const, *then* (1) *is valid with* $C \leqslant cC_\varepsilon$.

2) *If for all* $u \in \mathscr{D}(\Omega)$ *inequality* (1) *holds, then*

$$\sigma^+(g) \leqslant C(p, \Phi)\text{-cap}(\bar{g}, \mathscr{G}) + \sigma^-(\mathscr{G}) \tag{3}$$

for all admissible sets g *and* $\mathscr{G}$, $\bar{g} \subset \mathscr{G}$.

Proof. Let $\delta = (1-\varepsilon)^{-1/2p}$ and $g_j = \mathscr{L}_{\delta^j}$, $j = 0, \pm 1, \ldots$. By Theorem 1.2.3,

$$\|u\|^p_{L_p(\Omega,\sigma^+)} = \int_0^\infty \sigma^+(\mathscr{L}_t)\, d(t^p) = \sum_{j=-\infty}^{\infty} \int_{\delta^j}^{\delta^{j+1}} \sigma^+(\mathscr{L}_t)\, d(t^p)$$

$$\leqslant \sum_{j=-\infty}^{\infty} \sigma^+(\mathscr{L}_{\delta^j})(\delta^{(j+1)p} - \delta^{jp}).$$

This and (2) imply

$$\|u\|^p_{L_p(\Omega,\sigma^+)} \leqslant C_\varepsilon \sum_{j=-\infty}^{\infty} (p, \Phi)\text{-cap}(\bar{\mathscr{L}}_{\delta^j}, \mathscr{L}_{\delta^{j-1}})(\delta^{(j+1)p} - \delta^{jp}) \tag{4}$$

$$+ (1-\varepsilon) \sum_{j=-\infty}^{\infty} \sigma^-(\mathscr{L}_{\delta^{j-1}})(\delta^{(j+1)p} - \delta^{jp}).$$

Using the same arguments as in the derivation of (2.3.5/3), we obtain that the first sum in (4) does not exceed

$$\frac{(\delta^p - 1)\delta^p}{(\delta - 1)^p} \int_\Omega [\Phi(x, \nabla u)]^p dx .$$

Since $\sigma^-(\mathscr{L}_t)$ is a nondecreasing function, then

$$(\delta^{(j-1)p} - \delta^{(j-2)p})\sigma^-(\mathscr{L}_{\delta^{j-1}}) \leqslant \int_{\delta^{j-2}}^{\delta^{j-1}} \sigma^-(\mathscr{L}_t)\, d(t^p)$$

and hence

$$\sum_{j=-\infty}^{\infty} \sigma^-(\mathscr{L}_{\delta^{j-1}})(\delta^{(j+1)p} - \delta^{jp}) \leqslant \delta^{2p} \int_0^\infty \sigma^-(\mathscr{L}_t)\, d(t^p).$$

Thus,

$$\|u\|^p_{L_p(\Omega,\sigma^+)} \leqslant C_\varepsilon \frac{(\delta^p - 1)\delta^p}{(\delta - 1)^p} \int_\Omega [\Phi(x, \nabla u)]^p dx + \delta^{2p}(1-\varepsilon)\|u\|^p_{L_p(\Omega,\sigma^+)}.$$

It remains to note that $\delta^{2p}(1-\varepsilon) = 1$.

2) The proof of the second part of the theorem is the same as that of necessity in Theorem 2.3.7. The theorem is proved.

2.3.9. A Multiplicative Inequality with the Norms in $L_q(\Omega, \nu)$ and $L_r(\Omega, \nu)$ (The Case $p \geqslant 1$)

The following assertion gives a necessary and sufficient condition for the validity of the multiplicative inequality

$$\|u\|^p_{L_q(\Omega,\mu)} \leqslant C \left\{ \int_\Omega [\Phi(x, \nabla u)]^p dx \right\}^\delta \|u\|^{p(1-\delta)}_{L_r(\Omega,\nu)} \tag{1}$$

for $p \geqslant 1$ (cf. Theorem 2.1.1).

Theorem. 1) *Let g and G be any admissible sets such that $\bar{g} \subset G$. If a constant α exists such that*

$$\mu(g)^{p/q} \leqslant \alpha[(p, \Phi)\text{-cap}(\bar{g}, G)]^\delta \nu(G)^{(1-\delta)p/r}, \tag{2}$$

then (1) *is valid for all functions $u \in \mathscr{D}(\Omega)$ with $C \leqslant c\alpha$, $1/q \leqslant (1-\delta)/r + \delta/p$, $r, q > 0$.*

2) *If* (1) *is true for all $u \in \mathscr{D}(\Omega)$, then* (2) *is true for all admissible sets g and G such that $\bar{g} \subset G$. The constant α in* (2) *satisfies $\alpha \leqslant C$.*

Proof. 1) By Theorem 1.2.3 and inequality (1.3.3/1),

$$\|u\|_{L_q(\Omega,\mu)} = \left[\int_0^\infty \mu(\mathscr{L}_\tau) d(\tau^q) \right]^{1/q} \leqslant \gamma^{1/\gamma} \left[\int_0^\infty \mu(\mathscr{L}_\tau)^{\gamma/q} \tau^{\gamma-1} d\tau \right]^{1/\gamma},$$

where $\gamma = pr[p(1-\delta)+\delta r]^{-1}$, $\gamma \leqslant q$. Consequently,

$$\|u\|^p_{L_q(\Omega,\mu)} \leqslant c \left[\sum_{j=-\infty}^{\infty} 2^{-\gamma j} \mu(g_j)^{\gamma/q} \right]^{p/\gamma}$$

$$\leqslant c\alpha \left\{ \sum_{j=-\infty}^{\infty} 2^{-\gamma j} [(p, \Phi)\text{-cap}(\bar{g}_j, g_{j+1})]^{\delta\gamma/p} \nu(g_{j+1})^{(1-\delta)\gamma/r} \right\}^{p/\gamma},$$

where $g_j = \mathscr{L}_{t_j}$ and $\{t_j\}$ is the sequence of levels defined in the proof of the first part of Theorem 2.3.5. Hence,

$$\|u\|^p_{L_q(\Omega,\mu)} \leqslant c\alpha \left[\sum_{j=-\infty}^{\infty} 2^{-pj} (p, \Phi)\text{-cap}(\bar{g}_j, g_{j+1}) \right]^\delta \times \left[\sum_{j=-\infty}^{\infty} 2^{-rj} \nu(g_{j+1}) \right]^{(1-\delta)p/r}. \tag{3}$$

It was shown in the proof of Theorem 2.3.5 that

$$\sum_{j=-\infty}^{\infty} 2^{-pj} (p, \Phi)\text{-cap}(\bar{g}_j, g_{j+1}) \leqslant c \int_\Omega [\Phi(x, \nabla u)]^p dx .$$

Obviously, the second sum in (3) does not exceed $c\|u\|^r_{L_r(\Omega,\nu)}$. Thus (1) follows.

2) Let g and $\mathscr{G}$ be admissible sets with $\bar{g} \subset \mathscr{G}$. We substitute any function $u \in \mathfrak{P}(\bar{g}, \mathscr{G})$ into (1). Then

$$\mu(g)^{p/q} \leqslant C\left[\int_\Omega [\Phi(x, \nabla u)]^p dx\right]^\delta \nu(\mathscr{G})^{(1-\delta)p/r},$$

which yields (2). The theorem is proved.

§ 2.4. Continuity and Compactness of Imbedding Operators of $\mathring{L}^1_p(\Omega)$ and $\mathring{W}^1_p(\Omega)$ into the Orlicz Space

Let $\mathring{L}^l_p(\Omega)$ and $\mathring{W}^l_p(\Omega)$ be completions of $\mathscr{D}(\Omega)$ with respect to the norms $\|\nabla_l u\|_{L_p(\Omega)}$ and $\|\nabla_l u\|_{L_p(\Omega)} + \|u\|_{L_p(\Omega)}$.

The present section deals with some consequences of Theorem 2.3.2, containing necessary and sufficient conditions for boundedness and compactness of imbedding operators which map $\mathring{L}^1_p(\Omega)$ and $\mathring{W}^1_p(\Omega)$ into the space $\mathscr{L}_{p,M}(\Omega, \mu)$ with the norm $\||u|^p\|^{1/p}_{\mathscr{L}_M(\Omega,\mu)}$, where μ is a measure in Ω. In case $p=2$, $M(t)=|t|$ these results will be used in § 2.5 in the study of the Dirichlet problem for the Schrödinger operator.

2.4.1. Conditions for Boundedness of Imbedding Operators

With each compactum $F \subset \Omega$ we associate the number

$$\pi_{p,M}(F, \Omega) = \begin{cases} \dfrac{\mu(F) P^{-1}(1/\mu(F))}{p\text{-cap}(F, \Omega)} & \text{for } p\text{-cap}(F, \Omega) > 0\,, \\ 0 & \text{for } p\text{-cap}(F, \Omega) = 0\,. \end{cases}$$

In case $p=2$, $M(t)=|t|$ we shall use the notation $\pi(F, \Omega)$ instead of $\pi_{p,M}(F, \Omega)$.

The following assertion is a particular case of Theorem 2.3.2.

Theorem 1. 1) *If for any compactum* $F \subset \Omega$

$$\pi_{p,M}(F, \Omega) \leqslant \beta\,,$$

then for all $u \in \mathscr{D}(\Omega)$

$$\||u|^p\|_{\mathscr{L}_M(\Omega,\mu)} \leqslant C \int_\Omega |\nabla u|^p dx\,, \tag{1}$$

where $C \leqslant p^p (p-1)^{1-p} \beta$.

2) *If* (1) *is valid for all* $u \in \mathscr{D}(\Omega)$, *then* $\pi_{p,M}(F, \Omega) \leqslant C$ *for all compacta* $F \subset \Omega$.

Using this assertion we shall prove the following theorem.

Theorem 2. *The inequality*

$$\||u|\|^p_{\mathscr{L}_M(\Omega,\mu)} \leqslant C \int_\Omega (|\nabla u|^p + |u|^p)\,dx\,, \tag{2}$$

where $p<n$, is valid for all $u \in \mathscr{D}(\Omega)$ if and only if, for some $\delta>0$,

$$\sup\{\pi_{p,M}(F,\Omega) : F \subset \Omega,\ \operatorname{diam}(F) \leqslant \delta\} < \infty\,, \tag{3}$$

where, as usual, F is a compact subset of Ω.

Proof. Sufficiency. We construct a cubic grid in R^n with edge length $c\delta$, where c is a sufficiently small number depending only on n. With each cube $\mathscr{Q}_i$ of the grid we associate a concentric cube $2\mathscr{Q}_i$ with double the edge length and with faces parallel to those of $\mathscr{Q}_i$. We denote an arbitrary function in $\mathscr{D}(\Omega)$ by u. Let η_i be an infinitely differentiable function in R^n which is equal to unity in $\mathscr{Q}_i$, to zero outside $2\mathscr{Q}_i$ and such that $|\nabla \eta_i| \leqslant c_0/\delta$.

By Theorem 1

$$\begin{aligned}\||u\eta_i|^p\|_{\mathscr{L}_M(\Omega,\mu)} &\leqslant c \sup\left\{\frac{\mu(F)P^{-1}(1/\mu(F))}{p\text{-cap}(F, 2\mathscr{Q}_i\cap\Omega)} : F\subset 2\mathscr{Q}_i\cap\Omega\right\} \int_{2\mathscr{Q}_i\cap\Omega} |\nabla(u\eta_i)|^p dx\\ &\leqslant c\sup\{\pi_{p,M}(F,\Omega): F\subset\Omega,\ \operatorname{diam}(F)\leqslant\delta\} \int_{2\mathscr{Q}_i\cap\Omega} |\nabla(u\eta_i)|^p dx\,.\end{aligned}$$

Summing over i and noting that

$$\||u|^p\|_{\mathscr{L}_M(\Omega,\mu)} \leqslant \left\|\sum_i |u\eta_i|^p\right\|_{\mathscr{L}_M(\Omega,\mu)} \leqslant \sum_i \||u\eta_i|^p\|_{\mathscr{L}_M(\Omega,\mu)}\,,$$

we obtain the required inequality

$$\begin{aligned}\||u|^p\|_{\mathscr{L}_M(\Omega,\mu)} \leqslant c\sup\{\pi_{p,M}(F,\Omega): F\subset\Omega,\ \operatorname{diam}(F)\leqslant\delta\}\\ \times\int_\Omega (|\nabla u|^p + \delta^{-p}|u|^p)\,dx\,.\end{aligned} \tag{4}$$

Necessity. Let F be any compactum in Ω and let $\operatorname{diam}(F)\leqslant\delta<1$. We include F inside two open concentric balls B and $2B$ with diameters δ and 2δ, respectively. Then we substitute an arbitrary $u \in \mathfrak{P}(F, 2B\cap\Omega)$ into (2).

Since $u=1$ on F, then by (2)

$$\|\chi_F\|_{\mathscr{L}_M(\Omega,\mu)} \leqslant C\left(\int_{2B} |\nabla u|^p dx + \int_{2B} |u|^p dx\right).$$

Consequently,

$$\mu(F)P^{-1}(1/\mu(F)) \leqslant C(1+c\delta^p)\int_{2B} |\nabla u|^p dx\,.$$

Minimizing the last integral over the set $\mathfrak{P}(F, 2B \cap \Omega)$ we obtain

$$\mu(F) P^{-1}(1/\mu(F)) \leqslant C(1 + c\delta^p) p\text{-cap}(F, 2B \cap \Omega) .$$

It remains to note that since $p < n$, then

$$p\text{-cap}(F, 2B \cap \Omega) \leqslant c p\text{-cap}(F, \Omega) , \tag{5}$$

where c depends only on n and p.

In fact, if $u \in \mathfrak{N}(F, \Omega)$ and $\eta \in \mathscr{D}(2B)$, $\eta = 1$ on B, $|\nabla \eta| \leqslant c\delta$, then $u\eta \in \mathfrak{N}(F, \Omega \cap 2B)$ and hence

$$\begin{aligned} p\text{-cap}(F, 2B \cap \Omega) &\leqslant \int_{\Omega \cap 2B} |\nabla(u\eta)|^p dx \\ &\leqslant c\left(\int_{2B} |\nabla u|^p dx + \delta^{-p} \int_{2B} |u|^p dx\right) \\ &\leqslant c\left(\int_{\Omega} |\nabla u|^p dx + \|u\|^p_{L_{pn/(n-p)}(\Omega)}\right) . \end{aligned}$$

This and the Sobolev theorem imply (5). The theorem is proved.

2.4.2. Criteria for Compactness

The following two theorems give necessary and sufficient conditions for the compactness of imbedding operators that map $\mathring{L}^1_p(\Omega)$ and $\mathring{W}^1_p(\Omega)$ into $\mathscr{L}_{p,M}(\Omega, \mu)$.

Theorem 1. *The conditions*

$$\lim_{\delta \to 0} \sup\{\pi_{p,M}(F, \Omega) : F \subset \Omega, \operatorname{diam}(F) \leqslant \delta\} = 0 , \tag{1}$$

$$\lim_{\varrho \to \infty} \sup\{\pi_{p,M}(F, \Omega) : F \subset \Omega \backslash B_\varrho\} = 0 \tag{2}$$

are necessary and sufficient for any set of functions in $\mathscr{D}(\Omega)$, *bounded in* $\mathring{L}^1_p(\Omega)$ $(p < n)$, *to be relatively compact in* $\mathscr{L}_{p,M}(\Omega, \mu)$.

Theorem 2. *The condition* (1) *and*

$$\lim_{\varrho \to \infty} \sup\{\pi_{p,M}(F, \Omega) : F \subset \Omega \backslash B_\varrho, \operatorname{diam}(F) \leqslant 1\} = 0 \tag{3}$$

are necessary and sufficient for any set of functions in $\mathscr{D}(\Omega)$, *bounded in* $\mathring{W}^1_p(\Omega)$ $(p < n)$, *to be relatively compact in* $\mathscr{L}_{p,M}(\Omega, \mu)$.

To prove Theorems 1 and 2 we start with the following lemma.

Lemma. *Let $\mu^{(\varrho)}$ be the restriction of μ to the ball B_ϱ. In order for an arbitrary set, bounded in $\mathring{L}_p^1(\Omega)$ or in $\mathring{W}_p^1(\Omega)$, $p<n$, to be relatively compact in $\mathscr{L}_{p,M}(\Omega,\mu^{(\varrho)})$ for all $\varrho>0$ it is necessary and sufficient that*

$$\lim_{\delta\to 0}\sup\{\pi_{p,M}(F,\Omega)\colon F\subset B_\varrho\cap\Omega,\ \operatorname{diam}(F)\leqslant\delta\}=0 \tag{4}$$

for any $\varrho>0$.

Proof. Sufficiency. Since capacity does not increase under extension of Ω, then for any compactum $F\subset B_\varrho\cap\Omega$,

$$\pi_{p,M}(F,B_\varrho\cap\Omega)\leqslant\pi_{p,M}(F,\Omega)\,.$$

This along with (4) implies

$$\lim_{\delta\to 0}\sup\{\pi_{p,M}(F,B_\varrho\cap\Omega)\colon F\subset B_\varrho\cap\Omega,\ \operatorname{diam}(F)\leqslant\delta\}=0$$

for all $\varrho>0$. The latter, together with (2.4.1/4), where the role of Ω is played by $B_{2\varrho}\cap\Omega$, yields

$$\||u|^p\|_{\mathscr{L}_M(\Omega,\mu^{(2\varrho)})}\leqslant\varepsilon\int_{B_{2\varrho}\cap\Omega}|\nabla u|^p dx+C_1(\varepsilon)\int_{B_{2\varrho}\cap\Omega}|u|^p dx$$

for any $\varepsilon>0$ and for all $u\in\mathscr{D}(B_{2\varrho}\cap\Omega)$. Replacing u by $u\eta$, where η is a truncating function, which is equal to unity on B_ϱ and to zero outside $B_{2\varrho}$, we obtain

$$\||u|^p\|_{\mathscr{L}_M(\Omega,\mu^{(\varrho)})}\leqslant\varepsilon\int_\Omega|\nabla u|^p dx+C_2(\varepsilon)\int_{B_{2\varrho}\cap\Omega}|u|^p dx\,. \tag{5}$$

It remains to note that in case $p<n$ any set, bounded in $\mathring{L}_p^1(\Omega)$ (and, *a fortiori*, in $\mathring{W}_p^1(\Omega)$), is compact in $L_p(B_\varrho\cap\Omega)$ for any $\varrho>0$. The sufficiency of (3) is proved.

Necessity. Let $F\subset B_\varrho\cap\Omega$ be a compactum and let $\operatorname{diam}(F)\leqslant\delta<1$. We include F inside concentric balls B and $2B$ with radii δ and 2δ respectively. By u we denote an arbitrary function in $\mathfrak{P}(F,2B\cap\Omega)$. Since any set of functions in $\mathscr{D}(\Omega)$, bounded in $\mathring{W}_p^1(\Omega)$, is relatively compact in $\mathscr{L}_{p,M}(\Omega,\mu^{(\varrho)})$, then for all $v\in\mathscr{D}(\Omega)$

$$\|\chi_B|v|^p\|_{\mathscr{L}_M(\Omega,\mu^{(\varrho)})}\leqslant\varepsilon(\delta)\int_\Omega(|\nabla v|^p+|v|^p)dx\,,$$

where χ_B is the characteristic function of B and $\varepsilon(\delta)\to 0$ as $\delta\to 0$. To prove this inequality we must note that Theorem 2.4.2/2, applied to the measure $\mu^{(\varrho)}$, implies $\mu^{(\varrho)}(2B)\to 0$ as $\delta\to 0$. Since u equals zero outside $2B\cap\Omega$ then

$$\int_\Omega|u|^p dx\leqslant c\delta^p\int_\Omega|\nabla u|^p dx\,.$$

Therefore,

$$\mu(F)P^{-1}(1/\mu(F)) \leqslant (1+c\delta^p)\varepsilon(\delta)\int_{2B} |\nabla u|^p dx .$$

Minimizing the last integral over $\mathfrak{P}(F, 2B \cap \Omega)$ and using (2.4.1/5) we arrive at

$$\pi_{p,M}(F, \Omega) \leqslant (1+c\delta^p)\varepsilon(\delta) .$$

The necessity of (4) follows. The lemma is proved.

Proof of Theorem 1. Sufficiency. Let $\zeta \in C^\infty(R^n)$, $0 \leqslant \zeta \leqslant 1$, $|\nabla \zeta| \leqslant c\varrho^{-1}$, $\zeta = 0$ in a neighborhood of $B_{\varrho/2}$, $\zeta = 1$ outside B_ϱ. It is clear that

$$\| |u|^p \|^{1/p}_{\mathscr{L}_M(\Omega,\mu)} \leqslant \|(1-\zeta)^p |u|^p\|^{1/p}_{\mathscr{L}_M(\Omega,\mu)} + \|\zeta^p |u|^p\|^{1/p}_{\mathscr{L}_M(\Omega,\mu)} \tag{6}$$
$$\leqslant \| |u|^p \|^{1/p}_{\mathscr{L}_M(\Omega,\mu^{(\varrho)})} + \| |\zeta u|^p \|^{1/p}_{\mathscr{L}_M(\Omega,\mu)} .$$

By virtue of the first part of Theorem 2.4.1/1, applied to the set $\Omega \backslash \bar{B}_{\varrho/2}$, by (2) and the inequality

$$\pi_{p,M}(F, \Omega \backslash \bar{B}_{\varrho/2}) \leqslant \pi_{p,M}(F, \Omega) ,$$

given any ε, there exists a number $\varrho > 0$ such that

$$\| |\zeta u|^p \|^{1/p}_{\mathscr{L}_M(\Omega,\mu)} \leqslant \varepsilon \| \nabla(\zeta u) \|_{L_p(\Omega)} .$$

Since $|\nabla \zeta| \leqslant c\varrho^{-1} \leqslant c|x|^{-1}$ and

$$\| |x|^{-1} u \|_{L_p(\Omega)} \leqslant c \| \nabla u \|_{L_p(\Omega)} ,$$

then

$$\| |\zeta u|^p \|^{1/p}_{\mathscr{L}_M(\Omega,\mu)} \leqslant c\varepsilon \| \nabla u \|_{L_p(\Omega)} .$$

The last inequality along with (6) implies

$$\| |u|^p \|^{1/p}_{\mathscr{L}_M(\Omega,\mu)} \leqslant \| |u|^p \|^{1/p}_{\mathscr{L}_M(\Omega,\mu^{(\varrho)})} + c\varepsilon \| \nabla u \|_{L_p(\Omega)} . \tag{7}$$

Obviously, (1) implies (4). Therefore, Lemma guarantees that any set of functions in $\mathscr{D}(\Omega)$, bounded in $\mathring{L}^1_p(\Omega)$, is compact in $\mathscr{L}_{p,M}(\Omega, \mu^{(\varrho)})$. This together with (7) completes the proof of the first part of the theorem.

Necessity. Let F be a compactum in Ω with $\operatorname{diam}(F) \leqslant \delta < 1$. Duplicating the proof of necessity in Lemma and replacing $\mu^{(\varrho)}$ there by μ, we arrive at the inequality $\pi_{p,M}(F, \Omega) \leqslant (1+c\delta^p)\varepsilon(\delta)$ and hence at (1).

Now let $F \subset \Omega \backslash \bar{B}_\varrho$. Using the compactness in $\mathscr{L}_{p,M}(\Omega, \mu)$ of any set of functions in $\mathscr{D}(\Omega)$, which are bounded in $\mathring{L}^1_p(\Omega)$, we obtain

$$\| \chi_{\Omega \backslash B_\varrho} |u|^p \|^{1/p}_{\mathscr{L}_M(\Omega,\mu)} \leqslant \varepsilon_\varrho \| \nabla u \|_{L_p(\Omega)} ,$$

where $\varepsilon_\varrho \to 0$ as $\varrho \to 0$ and u is an arbitrary function in $\mathscr{D}(\Omega)$. In particular, the last inequality holds for any $u \in \mathfrak{P}(F, \Omega)$ and therefore

$$\mu(F) P^{-1}(1/\mu(F)) \leqslant \varepsilon_\varrho^p \| \nabla u \|_{L_p(\Omega)}^p .$$

Minimizing the right-hand side over the set $\mathfrak{P}(F, \Omega)$, we arrive at (2). The theorem is proved.

Proof of Theorem 2. We shall use the same notation as in the proof of Theorem 1.

Sufficiency. From (2.4.1/4), where $\delta = 1$ and Ω is replaced by $\Omega \backslash \bar{B}_{\varrho/2}$, together with (3), it follows that given any $\varepsilon > 0$, there exists a $\varrho > 0$ such that

$$\| |\zeta u|^p \|_{\mathscr{L}_M(\Omega, \mu)}^{1/p} \leqslant \varepsilon (\| \nabla (u\zeta) \|_{L_p(\Omega)} + \| \zeta u \|_{L_p(\Omega)}) .$$

This together with (6) yields

$$\| |u|^p \|_{\mathscr{L}_M(\Omega, \mu)}^{1/p} \leqslant \| |u|^p \|_{\mathscr{L}_M(\Omega, \mu^{(\varrho)})}^{1/p} + c\varepsilon \| u \|_{W_p^1(\Omega)} .$$

The remainder of the proof is the same as the proof of sufficiency in the preceding theorem.

Necessity. The condition (1) can be derived in the same way as in the proof of necessity in Theorem 2.4.2/1.

Let $F \subset \Omega \backslash \bar{B}_\varrho$, $\varrho > 8$, $\operatorname{diam}(F) \leqslant 1$. From the compactness in $\mathscr{L}_{p,M}(\Omega, \mu)$ of any set of functions in $\mathscr{D}(\Omega)$, bounded in $\mathring{W}_p^1(\Omega)$, it follows that

$$\| \chi_{\Omega \backslash B_{\varrho/2}} |u|^p \|_{\mathscr{L}_M(\Omega, \mu)} \leqslant \varepsilon_\varrho \| u \|_{W_p^1(\Omega)}^p ,$$

where $\varepsilon_\varrho \to 0$ as $\varrho \to \infty$ and u is an arbitrary function in $\mathscr{D}(\Omega)$. We include F inside concentric balls B and $2B$ with radii 1 and 2 and let u denote any function in $\mathfrak{P}(F, 2B \cap \Omega)$. Using the same argument as in the proof of necessity in Lemma 2.4.2 we arrive at

$$\pi_{p,M}(F, \Omega) \leqslant (1+c)\varepsilon_\varrho ,$$

which is equivalent to (3). The theorem is proved.

Remark. Let us compare (1) and (4). Clearly, (4) results from (1). The following example shows that the converse assertion is not valid.

Consider a sequence of unit balls $\mathscr{B}^{(\nu)}$ $(\nu = 1, 2, \ldots)$, with $\operatorname{dist}(\mathscr{B}^{(\nu)}, \mathscr{B}^{(\mu)}) \geqslant 1$ for $\mu \neq \nu$. Let $\Omega = R^n$ and $\mu(F) = \int_F p(x)\,dx$, where

$$p(x) = \begin{cases} \varrho^{-2+\nu^{-1}} & \text{for } x \in \mathscr{B}^{(\nu)}, \\ 0 & \text{for } x \bar{\in} \bigcup_{\nu=1}^{\infty} \mathscr{B}^{(\nu)}. \end{cases}$$

Here ϱ is the distance of x from the center of $\mathscr{B}^{(\nu)}$.

We shall show that the measure μ satisfies the condition (4) with $p=2$, $M(t)=t$. First of all we note that for any compactum $F\subset\mathscr{B}^{(\nu)}$

$$\mu(F)=\int_F \varrho^{-2+1/\nu}dx\leqslant\int_{\partial B_1}\int_0^{r(F)}\varrho^{n-3+1/\nu}d\varrho\, d\omega\,,$$

where

$$r(F)=\left[\frac{n}{\omega_n}m_n(F)\right]^{1/n}.$$

To estimate cap(F), i.e. 2-cap(F,R^n), we apply the isoperimetric inequality (2.2.3/12):

$$\omega_n^{-1}(n-2)^{-1}\operatorname{cap}(F)\geqslant\left[\frac{n}{\omega_n}m_n(F)\right]^{(n-2)/n}=[r(F)]^{n-2}.$$

Now

$$\pi(F,R^n)\leqslant\frac{r(F)^{1/\nu}}{(n-2)(n-2+1/\nu)}$$

and (4) follows.

If F is the ball $\{x\colon \varrho\leqslant\delta\}$, then

$$\pi(F,R^n)=\frac{\delta^{1/\nu}}{(n-2)(n-2+1/\nu)}.$$

Consequently

$$\sup\{\pi(F,R^n)\colon F\subset R^n,\ \operatorname{diam}(F)\leqslant 2\delta\}\geqslant\lim_{\nu\to\infty}\frac{\delta^{1/\nu}}{(n-2)(n-2+1/\nu)}=(n-2)^{-2}$$

and (1) is not valid.

§ 2.5. Application to the Spectral Theory of the Multidimensional Schrödinger Operator

In this section we shall show how the method and results of § 2.4 can be applied to the spectral theory of the Schrödinger operator.

2.5.1. Preliminaries and Notation

We start with some definitions from the theory of quadratic forms in a Hilbert space H. Let $\mathscr{L}$ be a dense linear subset of H and let $S[u,u]$ be a quadratic form defined on $\mathscr{L}$. If there exists a constant γ such that for all $u\in\mathscr{L}$

(1) $$S[u,u]\geqslant\gamma\|u\|_H^2,$$

then the form S is called semibounded from below. The largest constant γ in (1) is called the greatest lower bound of the form S and is denoted by $\gamma(S)$.

If $\gamma(S)>0$, then S is called positive definite. For such a form the set $\mathscr{L}$ is pre-Hilbert space with inner product $S[u,u]$. If $\mathscr{L}$ is a Hilbert space the form S is called closed. If any Cauchy sequence in the metric $S[u,u]^{1/2}$ that converges to zero in H also converges to zero in the metric $S[u,u]^{1/2}$, then S is said to be closable. Completing $\mathscr{L}$ and extending S by continuity onto the completion $\bar{\mathscr{L}}$, we obtain the closure $\bar{S}$ of the form S.

Now, suppose that the form S is only semibounded from below. We do not assume $\gamma(S)>0$. Then for any $c>-\gamma(S)$ the form

$$S[u,u]+c[u,u] \tag{2}$$

is positive definite. By definition, S is closable if the form (2) is closable for some, and therefore for any, $c>-\gamma(S)$. The form $\overline{S+cE}-cE$ is called the closure $\bar{S}$ of S.

It is well known and it can be easily checked that a semibounded closable form generates a unique selfadjoint operator $\tilde{S}$, for which

$$(\tilde{S}u,u)=S[u,u] \qquad \text{for all } u\in\mathscr{L}.$$

Let Ω be an open subset of R^n, $n>2$, and let h be a positive number. We shall consider the quadratic form

$$S_h[u,u]=h\int_\Omega|\nabla u|^2dx-\int_\Omega|u|^2d\mu(x)$$

defined on $\mathscr{D}(\Omega)$.

We shall study the operator $\tilde{S}_h$ generated by the form $S_h[u,u]$ under the condition that the latter is closable. If the measure μ is absolutely continuous with respect to the Lebesgue measure m_n and the derivative $p=d\mu/dm_n$ is locally square summable, then the operator $\tilde{S}_h$ is the Friedrichs extension of the Schrödinger operator $-h\Delta-p(x)$.

In this section, when speaking of capacity, we mean 2-capacity and use the notation cap.

Before we proceed to the study of the operator $\tilde{S}_h$ we formulate two lemmas on estimates for capacity which will be used later. For the proofs of these lemmas see the end of the section.

Lemma 1. *Let F be a compactum in $\Omega\cap B_r$. Then for $R>r$*

$$\operatorname{cap}(F,B_R\cap\Omega)\leqslant\begin{cases}\left(1+\dfrac{2r}{R-r}\log\dfrac{Re^{1/2}}{r}\right)\operatorname{cap}(F,\Omega) & \text{for } n=3\,,\\[2ex] \left(1+\dfrac{2}{n-3}\,\dfrac{r}{R-r}\right)\operatorname{cap}(F,\Omega) & \text{for } n>3\,.\end{cases}$$

Lemma 2. *Let F be a compactum in $\Omega\backslash\bar{B}_R$. Then for $r<R$*

$$\operatorname{cap}(F, \Omega\backslash\bar{B}_r) \leqslant \left(1+(n-2)^{-1}\frac{r}{R-r}\right)\operatorname{cap}(F,\Omega)\,.$$

All the facts concerning the operator $\tilde{S}_h$ will be formulated in terms of the function

$$\pi(F,\Omega)=\begin{cases}\dfrac{\mu(F)}{\operatorname{cap}(F,\Omega)} & \text{for } \operatorname{cap}(F,\Omega)>0\,,\\[2mm] 0 & \text{for } \operatorname{cap}(F,\Omega)=0\,,\end{cases}$$

which is a particular case of the function $\pi_{p,M}(F,\Omega)$, introduced in § 2.4, for $M(t)=|t|$, $p=2$.

2.5.2. Positiveness of the Form $S_1[u,u]$

The following assertion is a particular case of Theorem 2.4.1/1.

Theorem. 1) *If for any compactum* $F\subset\Omega$

(1) $$\pi(F,\Omega)\leqslant\beta\,,$$

then for all $u\in\mathscr{D}(\Omega)$

(2) $$\int_\Omega |u|^2\mu(dx)\leqslant C\int_\Omega|\nabla u|^2dx\,,$$

where $C\leqslant 4\beta$.

2) *If* (2) *holds for all* $u\in\mathscr{D}(\Omega)$, *then for any compactum* $F\subset\Omega$

(3) $$\pi(F,\Omega)\leqslant C\,.$$

Corollary. *If*

$$\sup_{F\subset\Omega}\pi(F,\Omega)<\tfrac{1}{4}\,,$$

then the form $S_1[u,u]$ *is positive, closable in* $L_2(\Omega)$ *and, hence, it generates a selfadjoint positive operator* $\tilde{S}_1$ *in* $L_2(\Omega)$.

Proof. The positiveness of $S_1[u,u]$ follows from Theorem. Moreover, inequality (2) implies

(4) $$S_1[u,u]\geqslant\left[1-4\sup_{F\subset\Omega}\pi(F,\Omega)\right]\int_\Omega|\nabla u|^2dx\,.$$

Let $\{u_\nu\}_{\nu\geqslant1}$, $u_\nu\in\mathscr{D}(\Omega)$ be a Cauchy sequence in the metric $S_1[u,u]^{1/2}$ and let u_ν converge to zero in $L_2(\Omega)$. Then by (4), u_ν converges to zero in $\mathring{L}_2^1(\Omega)$ and it is a Cauchy sequence in $L_2(\Omega,\mu)$. Since

$$\int_\Omega|u_\nu|^2d\mu\leqslant 4\sup_{F\subset\Omega}\pi(F,\Omega)\int_\Omega|\nabla u_\nu|^2dx\,,$$

then $u_\nu \to 0$ in $L_2(\Omega, \mu)$. Thus, $S_1[u_\nu, u_\nu] \to 0$ and therefore the form $S_1[u, u]$ is closable in $L_2(\Omega)$. The corollary is proved.

We note that close necessary and sufficient conditions for the validity of the inequality

$$\int_\Omega |u|^2 d\sigma \leqslant C \int_\Omega |\nabla u|^2 dx, \quad u \in \mathscr{D}(\Omega),$$

where σ is an arbitrary charge in Ω, are contained in Theorem 2.3.8 for $\Phi(x, y) = |y|$, $p = 2$. The conditions in question coincide for $\sigma \geqslant 0$. They become the condition $\sup\{\pi(F, \Omega) : F \subset \Omega\} < \infty$, which follows from Theorem.

2.5.3. Semiboundedness of the Schrödinger Operator

Theorem. 1) *If*

(1) $$\lim_{\delta \to 0} \sup \{\pi(F, \Omega) : F \subset \Omega, \operatorname{diam}(F) \leqslant \delta\} < \tfrac{1}{4},$$

then the form $S_1[u, u]$ is semibounded from below and closable in $L_2(\Omega)$.

2) *If the form $S_1[u, u]$ is semibounded from below in $L_2(\Omega)$, then*

(2) $$\lim_{\delta \to 0} \sup \{\pi(F, \Omega) : F \subset \Omega, \operatorname{diam}(F) \leqslant \delta\} \leqslant 1.$$

Proof. 1) If Π is a sufficiently large integer, then there exists $\delta > 0$ such that

(3) $$\sup \{\pi(F, \Omega) : F \subset \Omega, \operatorname{diam}(F) \leqslant \delta\} \leqslant \frac{1}{4}\left(\frac{\Pi - 1}{\Pi + 2}\right)^n.$$

We construct a cubic grid in R^n with edge length $H = \delta/(\Pi + 2)\sqrt{n}$. We include each cube $\mathscr{Q}_i$ of the grid inside concentric cubes $\mathscr{Q}_i^{(1)}$ and $\mathscr{Q}_i^{(2)}$ with faces parallel to those of $\mathscr{Q}_i$. Let the edge lengths of $\mathscr{Q}_i^{(1)}$ and $\mathscr{Q}_i^{(2)}$ be $(\Pi + 1)H$ and $(\Pi + 2)H$, respectively. Since $\operatorname{diam}(\mathscr{Q}_i^{(2)}) = \delta$, then for any compactum $F \subset \mathscr{Q}_i^{(2)} \cap \Omega$

(4) $$\pi(F, \Omega \cap \mathscr{Q}_i^{(2)}) \leqslant \pi(F, \Omega) \leqslant \frac{1}{4}\left(\frac{\Pi - 1}{\Pi + 2}\right)^n.$$

Let u denote an arbitrary function in $\mathscr{D}(\Omega)$ and let η denote an infinitely differentiable function on R^n which is equal to unity in $\mathscr{Q}_i^{(1)}$ and to zero outside $\mathscr{Q}_i^{(2)}$. By (4) and Theorem 2.5.2 we have

$$\int_{\mathscr{Q}_i^{(2)}} |u\eta|^2 d\mu \leqslant \left(\frac{\Pi - 1}{\Pi + 2}\right)^n \int_{\mathscr{Q}_i^{(2)}} |\nabla (u\eta)|^2 dx.$$

This implies

$$\int_{\mathcal{Q}_i^{(1)}} |u|^2 d\mu \leqslant \left(\frac{\Pi-1}{\Pi+2}\right)^n \int_{\mathcal{Q}_i^{(2)}} (|\nabla u|^2 + \frac{c_1}{H^2}|u|^2)\,dx\,.$$

Summing over i and noting that the multiplicity of the covering $\{\mathcal{Q}_i^{(2)}\}$ does not exceed $(\Pi+2)^n$ and that of $\{\mathcal{Q}_i^{(1)}\}$ is not less than Π^n, we obtain

$$\int_\Omega |u|^2 d\mu \leqslant (1-\Pi^{-n}) \int_\Omega \left(|\nabla u|^2 + c\frac{\Pi^2}{\delta^2}|u|^2\right) dx\,. \tag{5}$$

Thus, the form $S_1[u,u]$ is semibounded. Moreover, if K is a sufficiently large constant, then

$$S_1[u,u] + K\int_\Omega |u|^2 dx \geqslant \varepsilon \int_\Omega |\nabla u|^2 dx\,, \qquad \varepsilon > 0\,.$$

Further, using the same argument as in the proof of Corollary 2.5.2, we can easily deduce that the form $S_1[u,u]$ is closable in $L_2(\Omega)$.

2) Let F be an arbitrary compactum in Ω with $\operatorname{diam}(F) \leqslant \delta < 1$. We enclose F in a ball B with radius δ and construct the concentric ball B' with radius $\delta^{1/2}$.

We denote an arbitrary function in $\mathfrak{P}(F, B' \cap \Omega)$ by u. In virtue of the semiboundedness of the form $S_1[u,u]$ there exists a constant K such that

$$\int_{B'} u^2 d\mu \leqslant \int_{B'} (\nabla u)^2 dx + K\int_{B'} u^2 dx\,.$$

Obviously, the right-hand side of the preceding inequality does not exceed

$$(1+K\lambda^{-1}\delta) \int_{B'\cap\Omega} (\nabla u)^2 dx\,,$$

where λ is the first eigenvalue of the Dirichlet problem for the Laplace operator in the unit ball.

Minimizing the Dirichlet integral and taking into account that $u=1$ on F, we obtain

$$\mu(F) \leqslant (1+K\lambda^{-1}\delta)\operatorname{cap}(F, B'\cap\Omega)\,.$$

By Lemma 2.5.1

$$\operatorname{cap}(F, B'\cap\Omega) \leqslant (1+o(1))\operatorname{cap}(F,\Omega)\,,$$

where $o(1)\to 0$ as $\delta \to 0$. Hence

$$\sup\{\pi(F,\Omega)\colon F\subset\Omega,\ \operatorname{diam}(F)\leqslant\delta\} \leqslant 1+o(1)\,.$$

It remains to pass to the limit as $\delta\to 0$. The theorem is proved.

The two assertions stated below are obvious corollaries of Theorem. The second is a special case of Theorem 2.4.1/2.

Corollary 1. *The condition*

$$\lim_{\delta\to 0} \sup\{\pi(F,\Omega): F\subset\Omega,\ \operatorname{diam}(F)\leqslant\delta\}=0 \tag{6}$$

is necessary and sufficient for the semiboundedness of the form $S_h[u,u]$ in $L_2(\Omega)$ for all $h>0$.

Corollary 2. *The inequality*

$$\int_\Omega |u|^2 d\mu \leqslant C\int_\Omega (|\nabla u|^2+|u|^2)\,dx\,,$$

where u is an arbitrary function in $\mathscr{D}(\Omega)$ and C is a constant independent of u, is valid if and only if

$$\sup\{\pi(F,\Omega): F\subset\Omega,\ \operatorname{diam}(F)\leqslant\delta\}<\infty \tag{7}$$

for some $\delta>0$.

We shall give an example that illustrates an application of Theorem 2.5.2 and Theorem of the present subsection to the Schrödinger operator generated by a singular measure.

Example: Let M be a plane Borel subset of R^3. We define the measure $\mu(F)=m_2(F\cap M)$ for any compactum $F\subset R^3$. (In the sense of distribution theory the potential $p(x)$ is equal to the Dirac δ-function concentrated on the plane set M.) Then

$$\pi(F,R^3)=\frac{m_2(F\cap M)}{\operatorname{cap}(F)}\leqslant\frac{m_2(F\cap M)}{\operatorname{cap}(F\cap M)}\,.$$

Since

$$\operatorname{cap}(F\cap M)\geqslant 8\pi^{-1/2}[m_2(F\cap M)]^{1/2}$$

(cf. Example 2.3.3), then

$$\pi(F,R^3)\leqslant\frac{\pi^{1/2}}{8}[m_2(F\cap M)]^{1/2}\,. \tag{8}$$

By Theorem 2.5.2 the form

$$S_1[u,u]=\int_{R^3}|\nabla u|^2dx-\int_M|u|^2m_2(dx)$$

is positive if $m_2(M)\leqslant 4\pi^{-1}$. Using Corollary, from (8) we obtain that the form $S_h[u,u]$ is semibounded and closable in $L_2(R^3)$ for all $h>0$ for any plane set M.

2.5.4. Discreteness of the Negative Spectrum

Let ϱ be a fixed positive number and let $\mu^{(\varrho)}$ be the restriction of a measure μ to the ball $B_\varrho=\{x: |x|<\varrho\}$. Further, let $\mu_{(\varrho)}=\mu-\mu^{(\varrho)}$.

In order to exclude the influence of singularities of the measure μ, which are located at a finite distance, we shall assume that any subset of $\mathscr{D}(\Omega)$, bounded in $\mathring{W}_2^1(\Omega)$ (or in $\mathring{L}_2^1(\Omega)$), is compact in $L_2(\mu^{(\varrho)})$. In Lemma 2.4.2 it is shown that this condition is equivalent to

$$\lim_{\delta\to 0}\sup\{\pi(F,\Omega): F\subset B_\varrho\cap\Omega,\ \operatorname{diam}(F)\leqslant\delta\}=0 \tag{1}$$

for any $\varrho>0$.

Now we formulate two well-known assertions which will be used below.

Lemma 1 (*Friedrichs* [68]). *Let $A[u,u]$ be a closed quadratic form in a Hilbert space H with domain $\mathbf{D}[A]$, $\gamma(A)$ being its positive greatest lower bound. Further, let $B[u,u]$ be a real form, compact in $\mathbf{D}[A]$. Then the form $A-B$ is semibounded from below in H, closed in $\mathbf{D}[A]$ and its spectrum is discrete to the left of $\gamma(A)$.*

Lemma 2. (*Glazman* [74]). *For the negative spectrum of a selfadjoint operator A to be infinite it is necessary and sufficient that there exists a linear manifold of infinite dimension on which $(Au,u)<0$.*

Now we proceed to the study of conditions for the spectrum of the Schrödinger operator to be discrete.

Theorem. *Let the condition* (1) *hold.*

1) *If*

$$\lim_{\delta\to\infty}\ \lim_{\varrho\to\infty}\sup\{\pi(F,\Omega): F\subset\Omega\backslash B_\varrho,\ \operatorname{diam}(F)\leqslant\delta\}<\tfrac{1}{4}, \tag{2}$$

then the form $S_1[u,u]$ is semibounded from below, closable in $L_2(\Omega)$ and the negative spectrum of the operator $\tilde{S}_1$ is discrete.

2) *If the form $S_1[u,u]$ is semibounded from below, closable in $L_2(\Omega)$ and the negative spectrum of the operator $\tilde{S}_1$ is discrete, then*

$$\lim_{\delta\to\infty}\ \lim_{\varrho\to\infty}\sup\{\pi(F,\Omega): F\subset\Omega\backslash B_\varrho,\ \operatorname{diam}(F)\leqslant\delta\}\leqslant 1\,. \tag{3}$$

Proof. 1) We shall show that the form $S_1[u,u]$ is semibounded from below, closable in $L_2(\Omega)$ and for any positive γ the spectrum of the operator $\tilde{S}_1+2\gamma I$ is discrete to the left of γ. This will yield the first part of the theorem.

By virtue of (2) there exists a sufficiently large integer Π such that

$$\mathit{lim}_{\varrho\to\infty}\sup\{\pi(F,\Omega): F\subset\Omega\backslash B_\varrho,\ \operatorname{diam}(F)\leqslant\delta\}\leqslant\frac{1}{4}\left(\frac{\Pi-2}{\Pi+2}\right)^n$$

for all $\delta>0$.

Given any δ, we can find a sufficiently large number $\varrho = \varrho(\delta)$ so that

$$\sup\{\pi(F, \Omega): F \subset \Omega \setminus B_\varrho,\ \operatorname{diam}(F) \leqslant \delta\} \leqslant \frac{1}{4}\left(\frac{\Pi-1}{\Pi+2}\right)^n.$$

Hence

$$\sup\left\{\frac{\mu_{(\varrho)}(F)}{\operatorname{cap}(F,\Omega)}: F \subset \Omega,\ \operatorname{diam}(F) \leqslant \delta\right\} \leqslant \frac{1}{4}\left(\frac{\Pi-1}{\Pi+2}\right)^n.$$

If we replace $\mu_{(\varrho)}$ here by μ, then we obtain the condition (2.5.3/3) which was used in the first part of Theorem 2.5.3 for the proof of inequality (2.5.3/5). We rewrite that inequality, replacing μ by $\mu_{(\varrho)}$:

$$(4) \qquad \int_\Omega |u|^2 d\mu_{(\varrho)} \leqslant (1-\Pi^{-n}) \int_\Omega \left(|\nabla u|^2 + c\frac{\Pi^2}{\delta^2}|u|^2\right) dx.$$

Let γ denote an arbitrary positive number. We specify $\delta > 0$ by the equality $c\Pi^2(1-\Pi^{-n})\delta^{-2} = \gamma$ and find ϱ corresponding to δ. Then

$$\int_\Omega |u|^2 d\mu_{(\varrho)} \leqslant (1-\Pi^{-n}) \int_\Omega |\nabla u|^2 dx + \gamma \int_\Omega |u|^2 dx.$$

Hence the form

$$A[u,u] = \int_\Omega |\nabla u|^2 - \int_\Omega |u|^2 d\mu_{(\varrho)} + 2\gamma \int_\Omega |u|^2 dx$$

majorizes

$$\Pi^{-n} \int_\Omega |\nabla u|^2 dx + \gamma \int_\Omega |u|^2 dx.$$

This means that the form $A[u,u]$ has a positive lower bound γ and is closable in $L_2(\Omega)$. Let $\bar{A}[u,u]$ denote the closure of the form $A[u,u]$. Clearly, the domain of the form $\bar{A}[u,u]$ coincides with $\mathring{W}_2^1(\Omega)$.

By virtue of (1) and Corollary 2.5.3/2 the form

$$B[u,u] = \int_\Omega |u|^2 d\mu^{(\varrho)}$$

is continuous in $W_2^1(\Omega)$ and is closable in $\mathring{W}_2^1(\Omega)$. Lemma 2.4.2 ensures the compactness of the form $\bar{B}[u,u]$ in $\mathring{W}_2^1(\Omega)$. It remains to apply Lemma 1 to $\bar{A}[u,u]$ and $\bar{B}[u,u]$.

2) Suppose

$$\limsup_{\varrho\to\infty} \{\pi(F,\Omega): F \subset \Omega \setminus B_\varrho,\ \operatorname{diam}(F) \leqslant \delta\} > 1+\alpha, \qquad \alpha > 0$$

for some δ. Then there exists a sequence of compacta F_ν with $\operatorname{diam}(F_\nu) \leqslant \delta$, which tends to infinity and satisfies

(5) $$\mu(F_\nu) > (1+\alpha)\,\mathrm{cap}(F_\nu, \Omega)\,.$$

We include F_ν in a ball $B_\delta^{(\nu)}$ with radius δ. Let $B_\varrho^{(\nu)}$ denote a concentric ball with a sufficiently large radius ϱ which will be specified later. Without loss of generality, we may obviously assume that the balls $B_\delta^{(\nu)}$ are disjoint.

By Lemma 2.5.2

$$\mathrm{cap}(F_\nu, B_\varrho^{(\nu)} \cap \Omega) \leqslant (1+\varepsilon(\varrho))\,\mathrm{cap}(F_\nu, \Omega)\,,$$

where $\varepsilon(\varrho) \to 0$ as $\varrho \to \infty$. This and (5) imply

(6) $$\mu(F_\nu) > K\,\mathrm{cap}(F_\nu, B_\varrho^{(\nu)} \cap \Omega)\,,$$

where

$$K = \frac{1+\alpha}{1+\varepsilon(\varrho)}\,.$$

Let ϱ be chosen so that the constant K exceeds 1. By virtue of (6) there exists a function u_ν in $\mathfrak{P}(F_\nu, B_\varrho^{(\nu)} \cap \Omega)$ such that

$$\int_{B_\varrho^{(\nu)}} u_\nu^2 d\mu > K \int_{B_\varrho^{(\nu)}} (\nabla u_\nu)^2 dx\,.$$

Hence

$$S_1[u_\nu, u_\nu] < -(K-1)\frac{\lambda}{\varrho^2}\int_\Omega u_\nu^2 dx\,,$$

where λ is the first eigenvalue of the Dirichlet problem for the Laplace operator in the unit ball.

Now, Lemma 2 implies that the spectrum of the operator $\tilde{S}_1$ has a limit point to the left of $-(K-1)\lambda\varrho^{-2}$. So we arrived at a contradiction.

2.5.5. Discreteness of the Negative Spectrum of the Operator $\tilde{S}_h$ for all h

The following assertion contains a necessary and sufficient condition for the discreteness of the negative spectrum of the operator $\tilde{S}_h$ for all $h>0$. We note that although the measure μ in Theorem 2.5.4 is supposed to have no strong singularities at a finite distance (condition (2.5.1/3)), the corresponding criterion for the family of all operators $\{\tilde{S}_h\}_{h>0}$ is obtained for an arbitrary nonnegative measure.

Corollary. *The conditions*

(1) $$\lim_{\delta\to 0} \sup\{\pi(F, \Omega) \colon F \subset \Omega,\ \mathrm{diam}(F) \leqslant \delta\} = 0$$

and

(2) $$\lim_{\varrho\to\infty} \sup\{\pi(F, \Omega) \colon F \subset \Omega \backslash B_\varrho,\ \mathrm{diam}(F) \leqslant 1\} = 0$$

are necessary and sufficient for the semiboundedness of the form $S_h[u,u]$ in $L_2(\Omega)$ and for the discreteness of the negative spectrum of the operator $\tilde{S}_h$ for all $h>0$.

We also note that the semiboundedness of the form $S_h[u,u]$ for all $h>0$ implies that $S_h[u,u]$ is closable in $L_2(\Omega)$ for all $h>0$.

Proof. Sufficiency. We introduce the notation

$$l(\delta) = \lim_{\varrho\to\infty} \sup\{\pi(F,\Omega)\colon F\subset\Omega\backslash B_\varrho,\ \mathrm{diam}(F)\leqslant\delta\}.$$

First we note that (1) implies (2.5.4/1). Therefore, according to Theorem 2.5.4, the condition $l(\delta)\equiv 0$, combined with (1), is sufficient for the semiboundedness of the form $S_h[u,u]$ and for the discreteness of the negative spectrum of the operator $\tilde{S}_h$ for all $h>0$.

To prove the sufficiency of the conditions $l(1)=0$ and (1) we represent an arbitrary compactum F with $\mathrm{diam}(F)\leqslant\delta'$, $\delta'>\delta$, as the union $\bigcup_{\nu=1}^{N} F_\nu$, where $\mathrm{diam}(F_\nu)\leqslant\delta$ and N depends only on δ'/δ and n. Since $\mathrm{cap}(F,\Omega)$ is a nondecreasing function of F, then

$$\frac{\mu(F)}{\mathrm{cap}(F,\Omega)}\leqslant\sum_{\nu=1}^{N}\frac{\mu(F_\nu)}{\mathrm{cap}(F_\nu,\Omega)}.$$

This and the monotonicity of $l(\delta)$ immediately imply $l(\delta)\leqslant l(\delta')\leqslant Nl(\delta)$ which proves the equivalence of the conditions $l(\delta)\equiv 0$ and $l(1)=0$.

Necessity. If the form $S_h[u,u]$ is semibounded for all $h>0$, then by Corollary 2.5.3/1 the condition (1) holds together with (2.5.4/1). But under (2.5.4/1) Theorem 2.5.4 implies the necessity of $l(\delta)\equiv 0$ which is equivalent to $l(1)=0$. The corollary is proved.

2.5.6. Finiteness of the Negative Spectrum

Theorem. *Suppose that the condition* (2.5.4/1) *holds.*

1) *If*

$$\lim_{\varrho\to\infty}\sup\{\pi(F,\Omega)\colon F\subset\Omega\backslash B_\varrho\}<\tfrac{1}{4}, \tag{1}$$

then the form $S_1[u,u]$ is semibounded from below, closable in $L_2(\Omega)$ and the negative spectrum of the operator $\tilde{S}_1$ is finite.

2) *If the form $S_1[u,u]$ is semibounded from below, closable in $L_2(\Omega)$ and the negative spectrum of the operator $\tilde{S}_1$ is finite, then*

$$\lim_{\varrho\to\infty}\sup\{\pi(F,\Omega)\colon F\subset\Omega\backslash B_\varrho\}\leqslant 1. \tag{2}$$

Proof. 1) Since for any compactum $F\subset\Omega$

$$\frac{\mu(F)}{\mathrm{cap}(F,\Omega)}\leqslant\frac{\mu(F\backslash B_\varrho)}{\mathrm{cap}(F\backslash B_\varrho,\Omega)}+\frac{\mu(F\cap\bar{B}_\varrho)}{\mathrm{cap}(F\cap\bar{B}_\varrho,\Omega)}, \tag{3}$$

then conditions (2.5.4/1) and (1) imply

$$\lim_{\delta\to 0}\{\pi(F,\Omega)\colon F\subset\Omega,\ \operatorname{diam}(F)\leqslant\delta\}<\tfrac{1}{4}\,.$$

According to the preceding inequality and Theorem 2.5.3, the form $S_1[u,u]$ is semibounded and closable in $L_2(\Omega)$. From (2.5.3/5) it follows that the metric

$$C\int_\Omega |u|^2dx+S_1[u,u]$$

is equivalent to the metric of the space $\mathring{W}_2^1(\Omega)$ for C large enough.

Turning to condition (1) we note that there exists a positive constant α such that

$$\sup\{\pi(F,\Omega)\colon F\subset\Omega\backslash B_{\varrho_0}\}<\tfrac{1}{4}-\alpha$$

for sufficiently large ϱ_0. Hence

$$\sup\left\{\frac{\mu_{(\varrho_0)}(F)}{\operatorname{cap}(F,\Omega)}\colon F\subset\Omega\right\}<\frac{1}{4}-\alpha$$

and by Theorem 2.5.2 the form

$$(1-4\alpha)\int_\Omega|\nabla u|^2dx-\int_\Omega|u|^2\mu_{(\varrho_0)}(dx)$$

is positive. Therefore for any $u\in\mathscr{D}(\Omega)$

$$S_1[u,u]\geqslant 4\alpha\int_\Omega|\nabla u|^2dx-\int_\Omega|u|^2\mu^{(\varrho_0)}(dx)\,.$$

We estimate the right-hand side from inequality (2.4.2/5) with $\varepsilon=2\alpha$, $p=2$, $M(t)=|t|$:

$$S_1[u,u]\geqslant 2\alpha\int_\Omega|\nabla u|^2dx-K\int_{B_{2\varrho_0}\cap\Omega}|u|^2dx\,. \tag{4}$$

Passing to the closure of the form $S_1[u,u]$ we obtain (4) for all $u\in\mathring{W}_2^1(\Omega)$.

Since any set, bounded in $\mathring{L}_2^1(\Omega)$, is compact in the metric

$$\left(\int_{B_\varrho\cap\Omega}|u|^2dx\right)^{1/2}$$

for any $\varrho>0$, the form

$$2\alpha\int_\Omega|u|^2dx-K\int_{B_{2\varrho_0}\cap\Omega}|u|^2dx$$

is nonnegative up to a finite-dimensional manifold. Taking (4) into account, we may say that the same is true for the form $S_1[u, u]$. Now the result follows from Lemma 2.5.4/2.

2) Suppose

$$\limsup_{\varrho\to\infty} \{\pi(F, \Omega) \colon F \subset \Omega \backslash B_\varrho\} > 1+\alpha\,,$$

where $\alpha > 0$.

Let $\{\varrho_k\}_{k\geqslant 1}$ denote an increasing sequence of positive numbers such that

$$\varrho_k \varrho_{k+1}^{-1} \xrightarrow[k\to\infty]{} 0\,. \tag{5}$$

We construct the subsequence $\{\varrho_{k_\nu}\}_{\nu\geqslant 1}$, defined as follows: Let $k_1 = 1$. We find a compactum F_1, contained in $\Omega\backslash \bar{B}_{\varrho_{k_1}}$, such that $\pi(F_1, \Omega) > 1+\alpha$. Further we select k_2 to be so large that F_1 is contained in $B_{\varrho_{k_2}}$. Let F_2 denote a compactum in $\Omega\backslash B_{\varrho_{k_2+1}}$ such that $\pi(F_2, \Omega) > 1+\alpha$. If numbers $k_1, \dots, k_\nu$ and compacta $F_1, \dots, F_\nu$ have already been chosen, then $k_{\nu+1}$ is defined by the condition $F_\nu \subset B_{\varrho_{k_{\nu+1}}}$. The set $F_{\nu+1} \subset \Omega\backslash B_{\varrho_{k_{\nu+1}+1}}$ must be chosen to satisfy the inequality

$$\pi(F_{\nu+1}, \Omega) > 1+\alpha\,.$$

Thus we obtained a sequence of compacta $F_\nu \subset \Omega$ with F_ν in the spherical shell $R_\nu = B_{\varrho_{k_{\nu+1}}} \backslash \bar{B}_{\varrho_{k_\nu+1}}$ and subject to the condition

$$\mu(F_\nu) > (1+\alpha)\,\mathrm{cap}(F_\nu, \Omega)\,. \tag{6}$$

We introduce the notation $R'_\nu = B_{\varrho_{k_{\nu+1}+1}} \backslash \bar{B}_{\varrho_{k_\nu}}$. By Lemma 2.5.1/2

$$\mathrm{cap}(F_\nu, \Omega\cap R'_\nu) \leqslant \left(1 + (n-2)^{-1} \frac{\varrho_{k_\nu}}{\varrho_{k_\nu+1} - \varrho_{k_\nu}}\right) \mathrm{cap}(F_\nu, \Omega\cap B_{\varrho_{k_{\nu+1}+1}})\,.$$

The latter along with condition (5) implies

$$\mathrm{cap}(F_\nu, \Omega\cap R'_\nu) \leqslant [1+o(1)]\,\mathrm{cap}(F_\nu, \Omega\cap B_{\varrho_{k_{\nu+1}+1}})\,. \tag{7}$$

From Lemma 2.5.1 it follows that

$$\mathrm{cap}(F_\nu, \Omega\cap B_{\varrho_{k_{\nu+1}+1}}) \leqslant [1+o(1)]\,\mathrm{cap}(F_\nu, \Omega)\,.$$

According to (7),

$$\mathrm{cap}(F_\nu, \Omega\cap R'_\nu) \leqslant [1+o(1)]\,\mathrm{cap}(F_\nu, \Omega)\,.$$

Hence by (6), for sufficiently large ν,

$$\mu(F_\nu) > (1+\alpha')\,\mathrm{cap}(F_\nu, \Omega\cap R'_\nu)\,,$$

where α' is a positive constant.

Now we can find a sequence of functions $u_\nu \in \mathfrak{P}(F, \Omega \cap R'_\nu)$ such that

$$\int_{R'_\nu \cap \Omega} u_\nu^2 \mu(dx) > (1+\alpha') \int_{R'_\nu \cap \Omega} (\nabla u_\nu)^2 dx \,,$$

which yields the inequality $S_1[u_\nu, u_\nu] < 0$. It remains to note that the supports of the functions $u_{2\nu}$ are disjoint and therefore the last inequality holds for all linear combinations of $u_{2\nu}$. This and Lemma 2.5.4/2 imply that the negative spectrum of the operator $\tilde{S}_1$ is infinite. The theorem is proved.

2.5.7. Infiniteness and Finiteness of the Negative Spectrum of the Operator $\tilde{S}_h$ for all h

We shall find criteria for the infiniteness and for the finiteness of the negative spectrum of the operator $\tilde{S}_h$ for all h. We underline that here, as in the proof of the discreteness criterion in Corollary 2.5.5, we obtain necessary and sufficient conditions without additional assumptions on the measure μ.

Corollary 1. *Conditions* (2.5.5/1) *and*

(1) $$\sup\{\pi(F, \Omega): F \subset \Omega\} = \infty$$

are necessary and sufficient for the semiboundedness of the form $S_h[u, u]$ *in* $L_2(\Omega)$ *and for the infiniteness of the spectrum of the operator* $\tilde{S}_h$ *for all* $h > 0$.

Proof. By Corollary 2.5.3/1 condition (2.5.5/1) is equivalent to the semiboundedness of the form $S_h[u, u]$ for all $h > 0$.

We must prove that the criterion

(2) $$\lim_{\varrho \to \infty} \sup\{\pi(F, \Omega): F \subset \Omega \backslash B_\varrho\} = \infty \,,$$

which follows from Theorem 2.5.6, is equivalent to (1). Obviously, (1) is a consequence of (2). Assume the condition (1) is valid. Taking into account (2.5.5/1), we obtain

$$\sup\{\pi(F, \Omega): F \subset B_\varrho \cap \Omega\} < \infty$$

for any ϱ. On the other hand, (1) implies

$$\lim_{\varrho \to \infty} \sup\{\pi(F, \Omega): F \subset B_\varrho \cap \Omega\} = \infty \,.$$

We choose a sequence $\varrho_\nu \to \infty$ such that

$$\sup\{\pi(F, \Omega): F \subset B_{\varrho_{\nu+1}} \cap \Omega\} > 2 \sup\{\pi(F, \Omega): F \subset B_{\varrho_\nu} \cap \Omega\} \,.$$

From this and inequality (2.5.6/3) we obtain

$$\sup\{\pi(F, \Omega): F \subset R_{\varrho_\nu, \varrho_{\nu+1}} \cap \Omega\} \geqslant \sup\{\pi(F, \Omega): F \subset B_{\varrho_\nu} \cap \Omega\} \,,$$

where $R_{\varrho,\varrho'} = B_{\varrho'} \setminus \bar{B}_\varrho$. Hence

$$\sup\{\pi(F, \Omega) : F \subset R_{\varrho_\nu, \varrho_{\nu+1}} \cap \Omega\} \xrightarrow[\nu \to \infty]{} \infty$$

and the result follows.

Corollary 2. *Conditions* (2.5.5/1) *and*

(3) $$\lim_{\varrho \to \infty} \sup\{\pi(F, \Omega) : F \subset \Omega \setminus B_\varrho\} = 0$$

are necessary and sufficient for the semiboundedness of $\tilde{S}_h$ and for the finiteness of the negative spectrum of $\tilde{S}_h$ for all $h > 0$.

The necessity and sufficiency of conditions (2.5.5/1) and (3) immediately follow from Theorem 2.5.6.

2.5.8. Proofs of Lemmas 2.5.1 and 2.5.2

The following facts are well known (cf. Landkof [125]). For $n \geqslant 3$ and for any open set $\Omega \subset R^n$ there exists a unique Green function $G(x, y)$ of the Dirichlet problem for the Laplace operator.

Let μ be a nonnegative measure in Ω. Let V^μ denote the Green potential of the measure μ, i.e.

$$V^\mu(x) = \int_\Omega G(x, y)\mu(dy) .$$

Obviously, V^μ is a harmonic function outside the support of the measure μ. There exists a unique capacitary distribution of a compactum F with respect to Ω, i.e. a measure μ_F, supported on F, such that $V^{\mu_F}(x) \leqslant 1$ in Ω and

$$\mu_F(F) = (n-2)^{-1} \omega_n^{-1} \operatorname{cap}(F, \Omega) .$$

The potential V^{μ_F} is called the capacitary potential of F relative to Ω. If F is the closure of an open set with C^∞-smooth boundary, then V^{μ_F} is a smooth function in $\Omega \setminus F$ up to F, equal to unity on F and continuous in Ω.

Proof of Lemma 2.5.1. Using the continuity of the capacity from the right, we can easily reduce the proof for an arbitrary compactum to the consideration of a compactum $F \subset B_r \cap \Omega$, which is the closure of an open set with a C^∞-smooth boundary.

Let V^{μ_F} denote the capacitary potential of F relative to Ω and let η denote a continuous piecewise linear function, equal to unity on $[0, r]$ and to zero outside $[0, R]$.

The function $u(x) = \eta(|x|)\, V^{\mu_F}(x)$ can be approximated in $\mathring{L}_2^1(\Omega \cap B_R)$ by functions in $\mathfrak{N}(F, B_R \cap \Omega)$. Hence

(1) $$\operatorname{cap}(F, B_R \cap \Omega) \leqslant \int_{B_R \cap \Omega} |\nabla u|^2 dx .$$

We extend V^{μ_F} to be zero outside Ω. It is readily checked that

(2) $$\int_{B_R \cap \Omega} |\nabla u|^2 dx = \int_{B_R} |\nabla V^{\mu_F}|^2 \eta^2 dx + A + B\,,$$

where

$$A = \frac{1}{R-r} \int_{\partial B_r} (V^{\mu_F})^2 s(dx)\,,$$

$$B = \frac{n-1}{(R-r)^2} \int_{B_R \backslash B_r} (V^{\mu_F})^2 \frac{R-|x|}{|x|} dx\,.$$

Obviously,

(3) $$\int_{\Omega} |\nabla V^{\mu_F}|^2 \eta^2 dx \leqslant \operatorname{cap}(F, \Omega)\,.$$

Now we note that

$$\int_{\partial B_\varrho} V^{\mu_F} s(dx) = \int_F \mu_F(dy) \int_{\partial B_\varrho} G(x,y) s(dx) \leqslant \int_F \mu_F(dy) \int_{\partial B_\varrho} \frac{s(dx)}{|x-y|^{n-2}}\,.$$

The integral over ∂B_ϱ is a single layer potential and it is equal to a constant on ∂B_ϱ. Hence, for $y \in B_\varrho$,

$$\int_{\partial B_\varrho} \frac{s(dx)}{|x-y|^{n-2}} = \omega_n \varrho\,.$$

Thus

(4) $$\int_{\partial B_\varrho} V^{\mu_F} s(dx) \leqslant (n-2)^{-1} \varrho \operatorname{cap}(F, \Omega)\,.$$

The following inequality is a direct consequence of the maximum principle:

$$V^{\mu_F}(x) \leqslant \frac{r^{n-2}}{|x|^{n-2}} \quad \text{for } |x| \geqslant r\,.$$

Now, the bound for A is:

(5) $$A \leqslant (R-r)^{-1} \int_{\partial B_r} V^{\mu_F} s(dx) \leqslant \frac{r}{(n-2)(R-r)} \operatorname{cap}(F, \Omega)\,.$$

We introduce spherical coordinates (ϱ, ω) in the integral B. Then

$$B = \frac{n-1}{(R-r)^2} \int_r^R \varrho^{n-2}(R-\varrho) d\varrho \int_{\partial B_\varrho} (V^{\mu_F})^2 \omega(dx)\,.$$

Hence

$$B \leqslant \frac{(n-1) r^{n-2}}{R-r} \int_r^R d\varrho \int_{\partial B_\varrho} V^{\mu_F} \omega(dx)\,.$$

Using (4), we obtain

$$B \leqslant \frac{n-1}{n-2} \frac{r^{n-2}}{R-r} \int_r^R \varrho^{2-n} d\varrho \operatorname{cap}(F, \Omega),$$

which along with (1) – (3) and (5) gives the final result.

Proof of Lemma 2.5.2. The general case can be easily reduced to the consideration of a compactum $F \subset \Omega \backslash \bar{B}_R$, which is the closure of an open set with a smooth boundary. Let V^{μ_F} denote the capacitary potential of F relative to Ω, extended by zero outside Ω.

The function

$$u(x) = \begin{cases} V^{\mu_F}(x) & \text{for } x \in \Omega \backslash B_R, \\ \dfrac{R(|x|-r)}{|x|(R-r)} V^{\mu_F}(x) & \text{for } x \in \Omega \cap (B_R \backslash B_r), \\ 0 & \text{for } x \in \Omega \cap B_r \end{cases}$$

can be approximated in $\mathring{L}_2^1(\Omega \backslash \bar{B}_r)$ by functions in $\mathfrak{N}(F, \Omega \backslash \bar{B}_r)$. Therefore

$$\operatorname{cap}(F, \Omega \backslash \bar{B}_r) \leqslant \int_{\Omega \backslash \bar{B}_r} (\nabla u)^2 dx .$$

This implies

$$\operatorname{cap}(F, \Omega \backslash \bar{B}_r) \leqslant \int_\Omega (\nabla V^{\mu_F})^2 dx + \frac{r}{R(R-r)} \int_{\partial B_R} (V^{\mu_F})^2 s(dx) . \tag{6}$$

Since $V^{\mu_F} \leqslant 1$ and

$$\int_{\partial B_R} V^{\mu_F} s(dx) \leqslant (n-2)^{-1} R \operatorname{cap}(F, \Omega)$$

(cf. (4)), then

$$\frac{r}{R(R-r)} \int_{\partial B_r} (V^{\mu_F})^2 s(dx) \leqslant \frac{r}{R-r} (n-2)^{-1} \operatorname{cap}(F, \Omega),$$

which together with (6) completes the proof.

§ 2.6. On a Degenerate Quadratic Form

In the preceding sections of the present chapter we showed that rather general inequalities, containing the integral $\int_\Omega [\Phi(x, \nabla u)]^p dx$, are equivalent to isoperimetric inequalities which relate (p, Φ)-capacity and measures. Although such criteria are of primary interest, we should note that their verification in concrete cases is often difficult. Even for rather simple quadratic forms $[\Phi(x, \xi)]^2 = \sum_{i,j=1}^n a_{ij}(x) \xi_i \xi_j$ the estimates for the corresponding capacities by measures are unknown.

Thus, the general necessary and sufficient conditions obtained in the present chapter can not diminish the value of straightforward methods of investigation of integral inequalities without using capacity. In the present section this will be illustrated using as an example the quadratic form $[\Phi(x,\xi)]^2 = (|x_n|+|x'|^2)\xi_n^2+|\xi'|^2$, where $x'=(x_1,\dots,x_{n-1})$, $\xi'=(\xi_1,\dots,\xi_{n-1})$.

According to Corollary 2.3.3 the inequality

$$\int_{R^{n-1}} [u(x',0)]^2 dx' \leqslant c \int_{R^n} [\Phi(x,\nabla u)]^2 dx \tag{1}$$

is valid for all $u\in\mathscr{D}(R^n)$ if and only if

$$m_{n-1}(\{x\in g, x_n=0\}) \leqslant c(2,\Phi)\text{-cap}(g)$$

for any admissible set g. A straightforward proof of the preceding isoperimetric inequality is unknown to the author. Nevertheless, the estimate (1) is true and will be proved in the sequel.

Theorem 1. *Let*

$$[\Phi(x,\nabla u)]^2 = (|x_n|+|x'|^2)(\partial u/\partial x_n)^2 + \sum_{i=1}^{n-1} (\partial u/\partial x_i)^2 .$$

Then (1) *is valid for all* $u\in\mathscr{D}(R^n)$.

Proof. Let the integral in the right-hand side of (1) be designated by $Q(u)$. For any $\delta\in(0,1/2)$ we have

$$\int_{R^{n-1}} |u(x',0)|^2 dx' \leqslant 2\int_{R^n} \frac{(|x_n|+|x'|^2)^{1/2}}{|x_n|^{(1-\delta)/2}|x'|^{\delta}} \left| u\frac{\partial u}{\partial x_n}\right| dx \tag{2}$$

$$\leqslant 2[Q(u)]^{1/2}\left(\int_{R^n} |x_n|^{\delta-1}|x'|^{-2\delta}|u|^2 dx\right)^{1/2} .$$

To give a bound for the last integral we use the following well-known generalization of the Hardy-Littlewood inequality:

$$\int_{R^{n-1}} \left(\int_{R^{n-1}} \frac{f(y)\,dy}{|x'-y|^{n-1-\delta}}\right)^2 \frac{dx'}{|x'|^{2\delta}} \leqslant c\int_{R^{n-1}} [f(y)]^2 dy . \tag{3}$$

(For the proof of this estimate see Lizorkin [138]. It can also be derived as a corollary to Theorem 8.3.) Since the convolution with the kernel $|x'|^{\delta+1-n}$ corresponds to the multiplication by $|\xi'|^{-\delta}$ of the Fourier transform, then (3) can be rewritten as

$$\int_{R^{n-1}} |u|^2|x'|^{-2\delta} dx' \leqslant c\int_{R^{n-1}} [(-\Delta_{x'})^{\delta/2}u]^2 dx' ,$$

where $(-\Delta_{x'})^{\delta/2}$ is the fractional power of the Laplace operator. Now we find that the right-hand side in (2) does not exceed

$$c\left(Q(u)+\int_{R^n}|x_n|^{\delta-1}[(-\Delta_{x'})^{\delta/2}u]^2dx\right). \tag{4}$$

From the almost obvious estimate

$$\int_0^\infty g^2t^{\delta-1}dt\leqslant c\left(\int_0^\infty (g')^2t\,dt+\int_0^\infty g^2dt\right)$$

it follows that

$$|\xi'|^{2\delta}\int_{R^n}|(F_{x'\to\xi'}u)(\xi',x_n)|^2|x_n|^{\delta-1}dx_n$$

$$\leqslant c\left(\int_{R^1}\left|\left(F_{x'\to\xi'}\frac{\partial u}{\partial x_n}\right)(\xi',x_n)\right|^2|x_n|dx_n+|\xi'|^2\int_{R^1}|(F_{x'\to\xi'}u)(\xi',x_n)|^2dx_n\right)$$

where $F_{x'\to\xi'}$ is the Fourier transform in R^{n-1}. So the second integral in (4) does not exceed

$$c\int_{R^n}(|x_n|(\partial u/\partial x_n)^2+(\nabla_{x'}u)^2)dx\,.$$

The result follows.

The next assertion shows that Theorem 1 is exact in a certain sense.

Theorem 2. *The space of restrictions to $R^{n-1}=\{x\in R^n\colon x_n=0\}$ of functions in the set $\{u\in\mathscr{D}(R^n)\colon Q(u)+\|u\|^2_{L_2(R^n)}\leqslant 1\}$ is not relatively compact in $L_2(B_1^{(n-1)})$, where $B_\varrho^{(n-1)}=\{x'\in R^{n-1}\colon|x'|<\varrho\}$.*

Proof. Let φ denote a function in $C_0^\infty(B_1^{(n-1)})$ such that $\varphi(y)=\varphi(-y)$, $\|\varphi\|_{L_2(R^{n-1})}=1$ and introduce the sequence $\{\varphi_m\}_{m=1}^\infty$ defined by $\varphi_m(y)=m^{(n-1)/2}\varphi(my)$. Since this sequence is normalized and weakly convergent to zero in $L_2(B_1^{(n-1)})$, it contains no subsequences that converge in $L_2(B_1^{(n-1)})$. Further, let $\{v_m\}_{m=1}^\infty$ be the sequence of functions in R^n defined by

$$v_m(x)=F^{-1}_{\eta'\to x'}\exp\{-\langle\eta\rangle^2|x_n|\}F_{x'\to\eta'}\varphi_m\,,$$

where $\eta\in R^{n-1}$, $\langle\eta\rangle=(|\eta|^2+1)^{1/2}$.

Consider the quadratic form

$$T(u)=\int_{R^n}\left[(|x_n|+|x'|^2)\left|\frac{\partial u}{\partial x_n}\right|^2+|\nabla_{x'}u|^2+|u|^2\right]dx\,.$$

It is clear that

$$T(u)=(2\pi)^{1-n}\int_{R^n}\left(|x_n|\left|\frac{\partial Fu}{\partial t}\right|^2+\left|\frac{\partial}{\partial t}\nabla_\eta Fu\right|^2+\langle\eta\rangle^2|Fu|^2\right)d\eta\,dx_n\,.$$

By differentiating the function $T(v_m)$ we obtain from the preceding equality that $T(v_m)$ does not exceed

$$c\int_{R^n}[(1+\langle\eta\rangle^2|x_n|+\langle\eta\rangle^4|x_n|^3)\langle\eta\rangle^2|F\varphi_m|^2+\langle\eta\rangle^4|\nabla F\varphi_m|^2]$$
$$\times\exp(-2\langle\eta\rangle^2|x_n|)\,d\eta\,dx_n\,.$$

So we obtain

$$T(v_m)\leqslant c\int_{R^{n-1}}(\langle\eta\rangle^2|\nabla F\varphi_m|^2+|F\varphi_m|^2)\,d\eta$$

$$=c_1\left(\sum_{i=1}^{n-1}\|x_i\varphi_m\|^2_{W_2^1(R^{n-1})}+\|\varphi_m\|^2_{L_2(R^{n-1})}\right)\leqslant \text{const}\,.$$

Let $\psi\in C_0^\infty(B_2^{(n-1)})$, $\psi=1$ on $B_1^{(n-1)}$. It is clear that $(v_m\psi)|_{R^{n-1}}=\varphi_m$ and $T(v_m\psi)\leqslant$ const. The sequence $\{v_m\psi/(T(v_m\psi))^{1/2}\}_{m=1}^\infty$ is the required counterexample. The theorem is proved.

§ 2.7. On the Completion in the Metric of a Generalized Dirichlet Integral

Consider the quadratic form

$$S[u,u]=\int_{R^n}\left(a_{ij}(x)\frac{\partial u}{\partial x_i}\,\frac{\partial u}{\partial x_j}+u^2\right)dx\,,$$

where $\|a_{ij}(x)\|_{i,j=1}^n$ is a uniformly positive definite matrix, whose elements $a_{ij}(x)$ are smooth real functions.

Let the completion of $\overset{\circ}{C}{}^{0,1}$ with respect to the norm $(S[u,u])^{1/2}$ be denoted by $\overset{\circ}{H}(S)$. Further, we introduce the space $H(S)$ obtained as the completion of the set of functions in $C^{0,1}$ with the finite integral $S[u,u]$ with respect to the norm $(S[u,u])^{1/2}$.

If the elements of the matrix $\|a_{ij}\|_{i,j=1}^n$ are bounded functions, then $\overset{\circ}{H}(S)=\overset{\circ}{W}{}_2^1$, $H(S)=W_2^1$ and both spaces, obviously, coincide. It is also known that $\overset{\circ}{H}(S)=H(S)$ if the functions a_{ij} do not grow too rapidly at infinity. Here we consider the problem of the coincidence of $\overset{\circ}{H}(S)$ and $H(S)$ in the general case.

Let $E\subset R^n$. In the present section the set E is said to have finite $H(S)$-capacity if there exists a function $u\in C^{0,1}\cap H(S)$ which is equal to unity on E.

Theorem 1. *The spaces $\overset{\circ}{H}(S)$ and $H(S)$ coincide if and only if, for arbitrary domain G with finite $H(S)$-capacity, there exists a sequence of functions $\{\varphi_m\}_{m\geqslant 1}$ in $\overset{\circ}{C}{}^{0,1}$ that converges in measure to unity on G and is such that*

$$\lim_{m\to\infty}\int_G a_{ij}(x)\frac{\partial\varphi_m}{\partial x_i}\,\frac{\partial\varphi_m}{\partial x_j}\,dx=0\,. \tag{1}$$

Before we proceed to the proof we note that if G is a bounded domain then the sequence $\{\varphi_m\}_{m\geqslant 1}$ always exists. We can put $\varphi_m=\varphi$, where $\varphi\in C_0^{0,1}$, $\varphi=1$ on G.

Proof. Sufficiency. We show that any function $u\in C^{0,1}\cap H(S)$ can be approximated in $H(S)$ by functions in $\mathring{H}(S)$. Without loss of generality we may assume that $u\geqslant 0$.

First we note that if $t>0$ then $\mathscr{L}_t=\{x: u(x)>t\}$ is a set of finite $H(S)$-capacity. In fact, the function $v(x)=t^{-1}\min\{u(x),t\}$ equals unity on $\mathscr{L}_t$, satisfies a Lipschitz condition and $S[v,v]\leqslant t^{-2}S[u,u]<\infty$.

From the Lebesgue theorem it follows that the sequences $\min\{u,m\}$, $(u-m^{-1})_+$, $m=1,2,\dots$, converge to u in $H(S)$ (see 3.1.2). So we may assume from the very beginning that u is bounded and vanishes in the exterior of a bounded set G of finite $H(S)$-capacity.

We denote the components of the set G by G_j and then define the sequence

$$u^{(m)}(x)=\begin{cases} u(x) & \text{for } x\in \bigcup_{j\leqslant m} G_j,\\ 0 & \text{for } x\in R^n\setminus \bigcup_{j\leqslant m} G_j,\end{cases}$$

$j=1,2,\dots$. It is clear that $u^{(m)}\to u$ in $H(S)$ as $m\to\infty$. Since each $u^{(m)}$ vanishes in the exterior of a finite number of domains, we may assume without loss of generality that G is a domain.

Let $\{\varphi_m\}$ be the sequence of functions specified for the domain G in the statement of the theorem. Replacing $\{\varphi_m\}$ by the sequence $\{\psi_m\}$, defined by $|\psi_m|=\min\{2,|\varphi_m|\}$, $\operatorname{sgn}\psi_m=\operatorname{sgn}\varphi_m$, we obtain a bounded sequence with the same properties. Obviously, $\psi_m u\in\mathring{H}(S)$ and $\psi_m u\to u$ in L_2. Moreover,

$$\text{(2)}\qquad \int_{R^n} a_{ij}\frac{\partial}{\partial x_i}(u-u\psi_m)\frac{\partial}{\partial x_j}(u-u\psi_m)\,dx$$

$$\leqslant 2\int_G (1-\psi_m)^2 a_{ij}\frac{\partial u}{\partial x_i}\frac{\partial u}{\partial x_j}dx+2\int_G u^2 a_{ij}\frac{\partial\psi_m}{\partial x_i}\frac{\partial\psi_m}{\partial x_j}dx\,.$$

Since the sequence $(1-\psi_m)^2\sum_{i,j} a_{ij}\frac{\partial u}{\partial x_i}\frac{\partial u}{\partial x_j}$ converges to zero in G with respect to the measure m_n and is majorized by the summable function $9\sum_{i,j} a_{ij}\frac{\partial u}{\partial x_i}\frac{\partial u}{\partial x_j}$, the first integral on the right in (2) converges to zero. The convergence to zero of the second integral follows from the boundedness of u and equality (1). Thus $u\psi_m\to u$ in $H(S)$. The required approximation is constructed.

Necessity. Let G be an arbitrary domain in R^n with finite $H(S)$-capacity. Let u denote a function in $C^{0,1}\cap H(S)$ which is equal to unity on G. Since

$H(S)$ and $\overset{\circ}{H}(S)$ coincide, u can be approximated in $H(S)$ by the sequence $\{\varphi_m\}_{m\geqslant 1}$ contained in $C_0^{0,1}$. Noting that $u=1$ on G and $\varphi_m \to u$ in $L_2(G)$, we obtain that $\varphi_m \to 1$ in G in measure. Furthermore,

$$\int_G a_{ij} \frac{\partial \varphi_m}{\partial x_i} \frac{\partial \varphi_m}{\partial x_j} dx = \int_G a_{ij} \frac{\partial}{\partial x_i}(u-\varphi_m) \frac{\partial}{\partial x_j}(u-\varphi_m)\, dx \underset{m\to\infty}{\longrightarrow} 0 .$$

So the theorem is proved.

Although the above result is not very descriptive it facilitates verification of concrete conditions for coincidence or non-coincidence of $H(S)$ and $\overset{\circ}{H}(S)$. We now present some of them.

Theorem 2 (cf. the author's paper [148]). *The spaces $H(S)$ and $\overset{\circ}{H}(S)$ coincide provided $n=1$ or $n=2$.*

Proof. Taking into account Theorem 1 and the discussion which follows its statement we arrive at the equality $H(S)=\overset{\circ}{H}(S)$ if we show that any domain G with finite $H(S)$-capacity is bounded. In case $n=1$ this is obvious. Let $n=2$ and $u\in C^{0,1}\cap H(S)$, $u=1$ on G.

Let O and P denote arbitrary points in G and let the axis Ox_2 be directed from O to P. Then

$$S[u,u] \geqslant c\int_0^{|P|} dx_2 \int_{R^1} \left(\left(\frac{\partial u}{\partial x_1}\right)^2 + u^2\right) dx_1 \geqslant c_1 \int_0^{|P|} \max_{x_1} [u(x_1,x_2)]^2 dx_2 .$$

Taking into account that G is a domain and $u=1$ on G we arrive at

$$\max_{x_1} [u(x_1,x_2)]^2 \geqslant 1 .$$

Therefore $\operatorname{diam}(G) \leqslant c S[u,u]$, which completes the proof.

The following assertion shows that for $n\geqslant 3$ the form $S[u,u]$ must be subjected to certain conditions by necessity. The result is due to Ural'ceva [246]. Our proof, though formally different, is based on the same idea.

Theorem 3. *Let $n>2$. Then there exists a form $S[u,u]$ for which $H(S)\neq \overset{\circ}{H}(S)$.*

Proof. (1) Consider the domain $G=\{x: 0<x_n<\infty, |x'|<f(x_n)\}$ where $x'=(x_1,\dots,x_{n-1})$ and f is a positive decreasing function in $C^\infty[0,\infty)$, $f(0)<1$. For $x\notin G$ we put $a_{ij}(x)=\delta_i^j$.

For arbitrary functions a_{ij} on G, for any $u\in C^{0,1}$, $u=1$ on G, we have $S[u,u]=\|u\|^2_{W_2^1}$. This implies that G is a domain with finite $H(S)$-capacity if and only if $\operatorname{cap}(G)<\infty$ (here, as before, cap is the Wiener capacity, i.e. 2-cap). Clearly,

$$\operatorname{cap}(G) \leqslant \sum_{j=0}^{\infty} \operatorname{cap}(\{x \in G : j \leqslant x_n \leqslant j+1\})$$

$$\leqslant \sum_{j=0}^{\infty} \operatorname{cap}(\{x : |x'| \leqslant f(j), j \leqslant x_n \leqslant j+1\}) .$$

This and the well-known estimates for the capacity of the cylinder (cf. Landkof [125] or Proposition 9.1.3/1 of the present book) yield

$$\operatorname{cap}(G) \leqslant c \sum_{j=0}^{\infty} [f(j)]^{n-3} \qquad \text{for } n > 3 ,$$

$$\operatorname{cap}(G) \leqslant c \sum_{j=0}^{\infty} |\log f(j)|^{-1} \qquad \text{for } n = 3 .$$

Therefore G is a domain with finite $H(S)$-capacity provided

$$\int_0^{\infty} [f(t)]^{n-3} dt < \infty \qquad \text{for } n > 3 ,$$

$$\int_0^{\infty} |\log f(t)|^{-1} dt < \infty \qquad \text{for } n = 3 .$$

(2) In the interior of G we define the quadratic form $a_{ij}(x)\xi_i\xi_j$ by

$$a_{ij}(x)\xi_i\xi_j = \xi^2 + \left(\frac{g(x_n)}{f(x_n)}\right)^{n-1} \eta(x) \left(f'(x_n) \sum_{i=1}^{n-1} x_i\xi_i + \xi_n\right)^2 ,$$

where $\eta \in C_0^{\infty}(G)$, $0 \leqslant \eta \leqslant 1$, $\eta(x) = 1$ on the set $\{x : 1 < x_n < \infty, |x'| < \frac{1}{2} f(x_n)\}$ and g is an arbitrary positive function on $[0, \infty)$ that satisfies the condition

$$\int_0^{\infty} [g(t)]^{1-n} dt < \infty .$$

Using the change of variable $x_n = y_n$, $x_i = f(y_n) y_i$, $1 \leqslant i \leqslant n-1$, we map G onto the cylinder $\{y : 0 < y_n < \infty, |y'| < 1\}$. Obviously,

$$\int_G \left(\frac{g(x_n)}{f(x_n)}\right)^{n-1} \eta(x) \left(f'(x_n) \sum_{i=1}^{n-1} x_i \frac{\partial \varphi}{\partial x_i} + \frac{\partial \varphi}{\partial x_n}\right)^2 dx$$

$$\geqslant \int_C [g(y_n)]^{n-1} \left(\frac{\partial \varphi}{\partial y_n}\right)^2 dy ,$$

where $C = \{y : 1 < y_n < \infty, |y'| < \frac{1}{2}\}$. Applying the Cauchy inequality to the last integral we obtain

$$\int_1^\infty [g(t)]^{1-n} dt \int_G a_{ij} \frac{\partial\varphi}{\partial x_i} \frac{\partial\varphi}{\partial x_j} dx \geqslant \int_{|y'|\leqslant 1/2} \left(\int_1^\infty \left| \frac{\partial\varphi}{\partial y_n} \right| dy_n \right)^2 dy' .$$

If $\varphi \in \overset{\circ}{C}{}^{0,1}$ then the right-hand side exceeds

$$\int_{|y'|<1/2} \max_{1<y_n<\infty} [\varphi(y', y_n)]^2 dy' \geqslant \int_{C_1} \varphi^2 dy ,$$

where $C_1 = \{y \in C: y_n < 2\}$. Passing to the variables $x_1, \ldots, x_n$ on the right we arrive at

$$\int_1^\infty [g(t)]^{1-n} dt \int_G a_{ij} \frac{\partial\varphi}{\partial x_i} \frac{\partial\varphi}{\partial x_j} dx \geqslant \int_{G_1} \varphi^2 \frac{dx}{[f(x_n)]^{n-1}} ,$$

where $G_1 = \{x: |x'| < \frac{1}{2} f(x_n), 1 < x_n < 2\}$. So for any sequence $\{\varphi_m\}_{m \geqslant 1}$ of functions in $\overset{\circ}{C}{}^{0,1}$ that converges in measure to unity in G we have

$$\liminf_{m\to\infty} \int_G a_{ij} \partial\varphi_m/\partial x_i \cdot \partial\varphi_m/\partial x_j dx > 0 .$$

To conclude the proof, it remains to make use of Theorem 1.

Theorem 3 has an interesting application to the problem of the selfadjointness of an elliptic operator in $L_2(R^n)$, $n \geqslant 3$, cf. [246]. Let the operator

$$u \to S_0 u = -\frac{\partial}{\partial x_i} \left(a_{ij}(x) \frac{\partial u}{\partial x_j} \right) + u$$

be defined on C_0^∞. If $\|a_{ij}\|_{i,j=1}^n$ is the matrix constructed in Theorem 3, then $H(S) = \overset{\circ}{H}(S)$ and hence there exists a function $w \in H(S)$ which does not vanish identically and is orthogonal to any $v \in C_0^\infty$ in $H(S)$, i.e.

$$0 = \int_{R^n} \left(a_{ij} \frac{\partial w}{\partial x_i} \frac{\partial v}{\partial x_j} + wv \right) dx = \int_{R^n} w S_0 v \, dx .$$

Therefore the range of the closure $\bar{S}_0$ does not coincide with L_2. If $\bar{S}_0$ is selfadjoint then $w \in \operatorname{Dom}(\bar{S}_0)$ and $\bar{S}_0 w = 0$. This obviously implies $w = 0$. We arrived at a contradiction, which means that $\bar{S}_0$ is not selfadjoint. Thus, the condition of the uniform positive definiteness of the matrix $\|a_{ij}(x)\|_{i,j=1}^n$ alone is insufficient for the selfadjointness of $\bar{S}_0$.

In conclusion we note that the topic of the present section was considered also in the paper by Laptev [126] who studied the form

$$S[u, u] = \int_{R^n} (\alpha(x)(\nabla u)^2 + u^2) dx ,$$

where $\alpha(x) \geqslant \text{const} > 0$. He presented an example of a function α for which $H(S) \neq \overset{\circ}{H}(S)$ and showed that $H(S)$ and $\overset{\circ}{H}(S)$ coincide in each of the following three cases: (*i*) α is a nondecreasing function in $|x|$, (*ii*) $\alpha(x) = O(|x|^2+1)$, (*iii*) $n=3$ and α depends only on $|x|$.

§ 2.8. Comments to Chapter 2

§ 2.1. Most of the results of this section are borrowed from the author's paper [152] (see also Maz'ja [165]). The content of subsection 2.1.5 follows the author's paper [163] and that of subsection 2.1.6 is published here for the first time. The existence of inequality (2.1.6/3) was conjectured and communicated to the author by Taščijan who derived a similar estimate in [242] using a device different from the presentation in subsection 2.1.6. Estimates similar to (2.1.6/4) are generally well known (except, probably, certain values of the parameters p, q, l, α) but are established by other methods (cf., for instance, Il'in [104]). Theorem 2.1.6 was proved for $p=2$ in the author's paper [155] where it turned out to be useful in the study of the degenerate oblique derivative problem.

§ 2.2. The capacity generated by the integral

$$\int_\Omega f(x, u, \nabla u)\, dx$$

was introduced by Choquet [45] where it served as an illustration of general capacity theory. Here the presentation follows the author's paper [152].

Lemma 2.2.2/1 for $p=2$, $\Phi(x,\xi) = |\xi|$ is the so-called "Dirichlet principle with prescribed level surfaces" verified in the book by Pólya and Szegö [213] under rigid assumptions on level surfaces of the function u. As for the general case their proof can be viewed as a convincing heuristic argument. The same book also contains the isoperimetric property of the capacity (cf. (2.2.3/5) and (2.2.3/6)).

Lemma 2.2.5 is a straightforward generalization of a similar assertion due to Fleming [64] on 1-capacity.

§ 2.3, 2.4. The basic results of these sections were obtained by the author in [144, 146] for $p=2$, $\Phi(x,\xi) = |\xi|$, $M(u) = |u|$ and in [152] for the general case. We shall return to inequalities similar to (2.3.1/6) in Chapter 7.

The properties of symmetrization are studied in the books by Pólya and Szegö [213] and by Hadwiger [85]. See also the book by Hayman [92] where only circular symmetrization and the symmetrization with respect to a straight line in R^2 are considered. Nevertheless, Hayman's proofs can be generalized to the n-dimensional case.

Inequality (2.3.3/3) is (up to a constant) the Sobolev ($p>1$)-Gagliardo ($p=1$) inequality. The best constant for the case $p=1$ (see (1.4.2/8) was found independently by Federer and Fleming [63] and by the author [141] using the same method.

The best constant for $p>1$, presented in Remark 2.3.1, was obtained by Aubin [19] and Talenti [241] (the case $n=3$, $p=2$ was considered earlier by Rosen [220]).

§ 2.5. The presentation follows the author's paper [146]. The study of the spectrum of the Schrödinger operator by direct methods of spectral analysis is due to Friedrichs, Glazman, Molčanov, Birman, and others. The first result in this direction is the Friedrichs theorem on the discreteness of the spectrum of the operator $-\Delta+q(x)$ to the left of the point $\liminf_{x\to\infty} q(x)$ [68]. Molčanov [189] established a necessary and sufficient condition for compactness of the imbedding into $L_2(\Omega)$ of the space obtained as the completion of $\mathscr{D}(\Omega)$ with respect to the norm

$$\left\{\int_\Omega (|\nabla u|^2+q(x)|u|^2)\,dx\right\}^{1/2}, \qquad q(x)\geqslant 0\,.$$

Thus he obtained a criterion for the discreteness of the spectrum of the Dirichlet problem for the Schrödinger operator with a potential, semibounded from below. Molčanov was the first to discover the importance of the Wiener capacity in the study of the spectrum of singular elliptic operators. A number of results on the spectrum of the Schrödinger operator are presented in the monograph by Glazman [74] who used the so-called splitting method. Birman [29, 30] established some new results in the perturbation theory of quadratic forms in Hilbert spaces. In particular, he proved that the discreteness (the finiteness) of the negative spectrum of the operator $S_h=-h\Delta-p(x)$ in R^n for $p(x)\geqslant 0$ and for all $h>0$ is equivalent to the compactness of the imbedding of $W_2^1(R^n)(\mathring{L}_2^1(R^n))$ into the space with the norm $\left(\int_{R^n}|u|^2 p(x)\,dx\right)^{1/2}$. Using such criteria, Birman derived necessary or sufficient conditions for the discreteness, finiteness or infiniteness of the negative spectrum of S_h for all $h>0$. The statement of these conditions make no use of capacity. The results of Birman's paper [30] were developed in the author's paper [146] the content of which is followed here. Later, related problems were considered in the thesis by Hansson [87].

The theorems of § 2.5 turned out to be useful in the study of the asymptotic behavior of eigenvalues of the Dirichlet problem for the Schrödinger operator. Rosenbljum [221] considered the operator $H=-\Delta+q(x)$ in R^n with $q=q_+-q_-$, where $q_-\in L_{n/2,\mathrm{loc}}$, $n\geqslant 3$. We state one of his results. Let a cubic grid be constructed in R^n with d as the edge length of each cube and let $F(d)$ be the union of those cubes $\mathscr{Q}$ of the grid which satisfy the condition

$$\sup\left\{\frac{\int_E q_-(x)\,dx}{\operatorname{cap}(E)} : E\subset 2\mathscr{Q}\right\}>\gamma\,,$$

where $2\mathcal{Q}$ is the concentric homothetic cube having edge length $2d$, $\gamma=\gamma(n)$ is a large enough number.

Then for $\lambda>0$, the number $\mathcal{N}(-\lambda, H)$ of eigenvalues of H which are less than $-\lambda$ satisfies the inequality

$$\mathcal{N}(-\lambda, H) \leqslant c_1 \int\limits_{F(c_2\lambda^{-1/2})} (c_3\lambda - q(x))_+^{n/2} dx\,,$$

where c_1, c_2, c_3 are certain constants depending only on n.

§ 2.6. The results are due to the author. We note that the proof of Theorem 2.6/2 implies non-discreteness of the spectrum of the Steklov problem

$$-\sum_{i,j=1}^{n} \frac{\partial}{\partial x_i}\left(a_{ij}(x)\frac{\partial u}{\partial x_j}\right) + a(x)u = 0 \qquad \text{in } \Omega\,,$$

$$\sum_{i,j=1}^{n} a_{ij}\cos(\nu, x_j)\frac{\partial u}{\partial x_i} = \lambda u \qquad \text{on } \partial\Omega$$

under the condition that $\partial\Omega$ is characteristic at least at one point. Here ν is a normal to $\partial\Omega$ and the matrix $\|a_{ij}\|_{i,j=1}^{n}$ is nonnegative, $a(x)>0$. The coefficients a_{ij}, a and the surface $\partial\Omega$ are assumed to be smooth.

Chapter 3. On Summability of Functions in the Space $L_1^1(\Omega)$

The present chapter contains conditions on Ω which are necessary and sufficient for the imbedding operator $L_1^1(\Omega) \to L_q(\Omega)$ to be continuous or compact.

§ 3.1. Preliminaries

3.1.1. Notation

In this chapter, as well as in Chapters 4 and 5, we shall use the symbols introduced in 1.1.1 and the following notation.

A bounded open subset $\mathscr{G}$ of the set Ω is called admissible if $\Omega \cap \partial \mathscr{G}$ is a manifold of the class C^∞ (this term was understood in a more restrictive sense in Chapter 2).

Let $\bar{E}$ be the closure of the set $E \subset R^n$ and let ∂E be the boundary of E. Further, let $\operatorname{clos}_\Omega E$ be the closure of E in Ω and let $\partial_i E$ be the inner part of ∂E with respect to Ω, i.e. $\partial_i E = \Omega \cap \partial E$.

We put $\Omega_\varrho = \Omega \cap B_\varrho$, $u^+ = \max\{u, 0\}$, $u_- = u_+ - u$, $\mathscr{E}_t = \{x : |u(x)| = t\}$, $\mathscr{L}_t = \{x : |u(x)| > t\}$, $\mathscr{N}_t = \{x : |u(x)| \geqslant t\}$.

As before, we shall write

$$\| u \|_{L_q(\Omega)} = \left(\int_\Omega | u |^q dx \right)^{1/q}.$$

This notation also will be used for $q \in (0,1)$ when the right-hand side is a pseudonorm. (We recall that a linear space is called pseudonormed if a functional $\|x\| > 0$, defined on its elements, satisfies the conditions: 1) if $\|x\| = 0$, then $x = 0$; 2) $\|\alpha x\| = |\alpha| \, \|x\|$, where $\alpha \in R^1$; 3) if $\|x_m\| \to 0$, $\|y_m\| \to 0$, then $\|x_m + y_m\| \to 0$.) Clearly, in the case $0 < q < 1$ the functional

$$\varrho(u, v) = \int_\Omega |u - v|^q dx$$

satisfies the axioms of a metric.

Let $C^{0,1}(\Omega)$ denote the space of functions which satisfy a Lipschitz condition on any compact subset of Ω.

If Ω is a domain, we equip the space $L_p^l(\Omega)$, $p \geqslant 1$, $l = 1, 2, \ldots$ (cf. 1.1.2) with the norm

$$\|\nabla_l u\|_{L_p(\Omega)} + \|u\|_{L_p(\omega)},$$

where ω is an open nonempty set with compact closure $\bar{\omega} \subset \Omega$. From (1.1.11/2) it follows that varying ω leads to an equivalent norm.

Further, let $W^l_{p,r}(\Omega) = L^l_p(\Omega) \cap L_r(\Omega)$ be the space equipped with the norm for $r \geqslant 1$ and with the pseudonorm for $r \in (0,1)$ as follows:

$$\|u\|_{W^l_{p,r}(\Omega)} = \|\nabla_l u\|_{L_p(\Omega)} + \|u\|_{L_r(\Omega)}.$$

In accordance with 1.1.4, $W^l_{p,p}(\Omega) = W^l_p(\Omega)$. By Theorems 1.1.5/1 and 1.1.5/2 the sets $L^l_p(\Omega) \cap C^\infty(\Omega)$ and $W^l_p(\Omega) \cap C^\infty(\Omega)$ are dense in $L^l_p(\Omega)$ and $W^l_p(\Omega)$ respectively.

3.1.2. Lemmas on Approximation of Functions in $W^1_{p,r}(\Omega)$ and $L^1_p(\Omega)$

Lemma 1. *If $v \in L^1_p(\Omega)$ then the sequence of functions*

$$v^{(m)}(x) = \begin{cases} \min\{v(x), m\} & \text{if } v(x) \geqslant 0, \\ \max\{v(x), -m\} & \text{if } v(x) \leqslant 0, \end{cases}$$

($m = 1, 2, \ldots$) converges to v in $L^1_p(\Omega)$.

The same is true for the sequence

$$v_{(m)}(x) = \begin{cases} v(x) - m^{-1} & \text{if } v(x) \geqslant m^{-1}, \\ 0 & \text{if } |v(x)| < m^{-1}, \\ v(x) + m^{-1} & \text{if } v(x) \leqslant -m^{-1}. \end{cases}$$

Proof. Since functions in $L^1_p(\Omega)$ are absolutely continuous on almost all lines parallel to coordinate axes (Theorem 1.1.3/1), then, almost everywhere in Ω,

$$\nabla v^{(m)} = \chi^{(m)} \nabla v,$$

where $\chi^{(m)}$ is the characteristic function of the set $\{x : |v(x)| < m^{-1}\}$. Therefore

$$\int_\Omega |\nabla(v - v^{(m)})|^p dx = \int_\Omega |\nabla v|^p (1 - \chi^{(m)})^p dx.$$

The convergence to zero of the last integral follows from the monotone convergence theorem.

The proof for the sequence $v_{(m)}$ is similar.

Lemma 2. *The set of functions in $L^1_p(\Omega) \cap C^\infty(\Omega) \cap L_\infty(\Omega)$ $(p \geqslant 1)$ with bounded supports is dense in $W^1_{p,r}(\Omega)$ $(\infty > r > 0)$.*

Proof. Let $v \in W^1_{p,r}(\Omega)$. Since $v^{(m)} \to v$ and $v_{(m)} \to v$ in $W^1_{p,r}(\Omega)$, the set of bounded functions $v \in L^1_p(\Omega)$ with $m_n(\operatorname{supp} u) < \infty$ is dense in $W^1_{p,r}(\Omega)$.

Suppose v satisfies these conditions. We define the sequence

$$v_m(x)=\eta(m^{-1}x)v(x)\,,\qquad m=1,2,\dots\,,$$

where $\eta\in C_0^\infty(B_2)$, $\eta=1$ on B_1. Obviously,

$$\|v_m-v\|_{W^1_{p,r}(\Omega)}\leqslant c\|\nabla v\|_{L_p(\Omega\setminus B_m)}+cm^{-1}\|v\|_{L_\infty(\Omega)}[m_n(\operatorname{supp} v)]^{1/p}$$
$$+\|v\|_{L_r(\Omega\setminus B_m)}\to 0$$

as $m\to\infty$. In order to approximate each v_m by smooth functions it is sufficient to use a partition of unity and mollifying operators (cf. the proof of Theorem 1.1.11/2).

From Lemma 2 we obtain the following corollary.

Corollary. *If Ω is a domain with finite volume, then the set of functions in $L_p^1(\Omega)\cap C^\infty(\Omega)\cap L_\infty(\Omega)$ with bounded supports is dense in $L_p^1(\Omega)$.*

Lemma 3. *Let G be an open subset of Ω and let $u\in C^{0,1}(\Omega)\cap L_p^1(\Omega)$, $u=0$ outside G. Then there exists a sequence of functions in $L_p^1(\Omega)\cap C^\infty(\Omega)$ that also vanish outside G which converges to u in $L_p^1(\Omega)$.*

Proof. Since u can be approximated in $L_p^1(\Omega)$ by the sequence $u_{(m)}$ defined in Lemma 1, we may assume that $u=0$ outside some open set $g\subset G$ with $\operatorname{clos}_\Omega g\subset G$.

We let $\{\mathscr{B}^{(k)}\}$ denote a locally finite covering of g by open balls $\mathscr{B}^{(k)}$, $\overline{\mathscr{B}^{(k)}}\subset G$, and then we repeat the proof of Theorem 1.1.5/1. The lemma is proved.

Remark. If we assume that the function u referred to in the statement of Lemma 3 is continuous on $\bar\Omega$, then we may also assume the functions of an approximating sequence to have the same property (cf. Remark 1.1.5).

If, in addition to the condition of Lemma 3, $u\in L_r(\Omega)$, then the approximating sequence can be taken to be convergent in $W^1_{p,r}(\Omega)$.

Both of these assertions are immediate corollaries of Lemma 3 and are proved similarly.

§ 3.2. Classes of Sets $\mathscr{J}_\alpha$ and the Imbedding $L_1^1(\Omega)\subset L_q(\Omega)$

3.2.1. Classes $\mathscr{J}_\alpha$

Definition. A bounded domain Ω belongs to *the class* $\mathscr{J}_\alpha\left(\alpha\geqslant\dfrac{n-1}{n}\right)$ if there exists a constant $M\in(0,m_n(\Omega))$ such that

$$\mathfrak{A}_\alpha(M)\overset{\text{def}}{=}\sup_{\{\mathscr{G}\}}\frac{m_n(\mathscr{G})^\alpha}{s(\partial_i\mathscr{G})}<\infty\,, \tag{1}$$

where $\{\mathscr{G}\}$ is a collection of admissible subsets of Ω with $m_n(\mathscr{G}) \leqslant M$ and s is the $(n-1)$-dimensional area.

Condition (1) gives a characterization of the boundary of Ω "locally". We shall briefly comment on this property. If Ω is a domain with sufficiently smooth boundary then it can be easily seen that the $(n-1)$-dimensional area of the surface $\partial \mathscr{G} \cap \partial\Omega$ is bounded from below (up to a constant factor) by the area of $\partial_i \mathscr{G} = \Omega \cap \partial \mathscr{G}$ for any $\mathscr{G}$ of sufficiently small volume. So by the classical isoperimetric inequality

$$m_n(\mathscr{G})^{(n-1)/n} \leqslant \text{const} \cdot s(\partial_i \mathscr{G}) ,$$

and hence Ω belongs to the class $\mathscr{J}_{(n-1)/n}$. If $\partial\Omega$ has cusps directed into Ω, then it is intuitively clear that the last inequality still holds. If a cusp is directed outward from the domain then there exists a sequence of sets $\mathscr{G}_\nu \subset \Omega$ for which

$$\lim_{\nu\to\infty} \frac{m_n(\mathscr{G}_\nu)^{(n-1)/n}}{s(\partial_i \mathscr{G}_\nu)} = \infty .$$

Along with this property the domain may satisfy (1) for some $\alpha > (n-1)/n$. The exponent α characterizes the degree of sharpness of a cusp.

In what follows we shall see that it is "isoperimetric" inequalities of the type (1) (and more complicated ones) which determine the order of summability of functions in Sobolev spaces.

Lemma 1. *Let Ω be an open unit ball and let g be an open subset of Ω such that $\partial_i g$ is a manifold of the class $C^{0,1}$. Then*

$$\min\{m_n(g), m_n(\Omega\backslash g)\} \leqslant \frac{v_n}{2}\, v_{n-1}^{n/(1-n)} s(\partial_i g)^{n/(n-1)} . \tag{2}$$

The constant in (2) *is the best possible.*

Proof. It is sufficient to assume that $2m_n(g) < v_n$. Applying the spherical symmetrization of g with respect to a ray l that emanates from the center of the ball Ω, we obtain a set $f \subset \Omega$ symmetric with respect to l and such that

$$m_n(f) = m_n(g) , \quad s(\partial_i f) \leqslant s(\partial_i g) .$$

The spherical symmetrization with respect to a ray is defined similarly to the symmetrization with respect to an $(n-s)$-dimensional subspace (subsection 2.3.3); we just need to replace the s-dimensional subspaces orthogonal to R^{n-s} by $(n-s)$-dimensional spheres centered at the origin of the ray.

Let b be a ball such that $b \cap \partial\Omega = \partial f \cap \partial\Omega$ and $m_n(b \cap \Omega) = m_n(f)$. Since

$$m_n[f \cup (b\backslash\Omega)] = m_n(b) ,$$

then by the isoperimetric property of the ball we have

$$s(\Omega \cap \partial b) \leqslant s(\partial_i f) .$$

An elementary calculation shows that the minimum value of $s(\Omega \cap \partial b)$ over all balls with $m_n(\Omega \cap b) = \text{const} < \frac{1}{2} m_n(\Omega)$ is attained at the ball which is orthogonal to $\partial\Omega$.

It can be easily checked that the function

$$\frac{s(\Omega \cap \partial b_\varrho)}{[m_n(\Omega \cap b_\varrho)]^{(n-1)/n}},$$

where b_ϱ is a ball with radius ϱ, orthogonal to Ω and such that $m_n(b_\varrho \cap \Omega) < \frac{1}{2} m_n(\Omega)$, decreases. The result follows.

The next corollary follows immediately from Lemma 1.

Corollary 1. *If Ω is an n-dimensional ball, then $\Omega \in \mathscr{J}_{(n-1)/n}$ and*

$$\mathfrak{A}_{(n-1)/n}(\tfrac{1}{2} m_n(\Omega)) = v_{n-1}^{-1}(v_n/2)^{(n-1)/n},$$

where v_s is the volume of the s-dimensional unit ball.

Corollary 2. *A bounded domain starshaped with respect to a ball belongs to the class $\mathscr{J}_{(n-1)/n}$.*

Proof. According to Lemma 1.1.8 the set $\bar{\Omega}$ is the quasi-isometric image of a ball. This along with Lemma 1 implies

$$m_n(g)^{(n-1)/n} \leqslant C(M) s(\partial_i g) \tag{3}$$

for any constant $M \in (0, m_n(\Omega))$ and for all open sets $g \subset \Omega$ such that $\partial_i g$ is a manifold of the class $C^{0,1}$ and $m_n(g) \leqslant M$. Here $C(M)$ is a constant that is independent of g. The corollary is proved.

Remark. Condition (1) does not hold for $\alpha < (n-1)/n$ since in this case

$$\lim_{\varrho \to 0} \frac{m_n(B_\varrho)^\alpha}{s(\partial B_\varrho)} = c \lim_{\varrho \to 0} \varrho^{1-n+n\alpha} = \infty .$$

We give an example of a domain which does not belong to the class $\mathscr{J}_\alpha$ for any α.

Example. Consider the domain Ω represented in Fig. 9. For the sequence of subsets $Q_m (m = 3, 4, \ldots)$ we have

$$m_2(Q_m) = m^{-4}, \quad s(\partial_i Q_m) = m^{-2m},$$

$$\frac{m_2(Q_m)^\alpha}{s(\partial_i Q_m)} = m^{2m-4\alpha} \xrightarrow[m\to\infty]{} \infty$$

and hence $\Omega \notin \mathcal{J}_\alpha$.

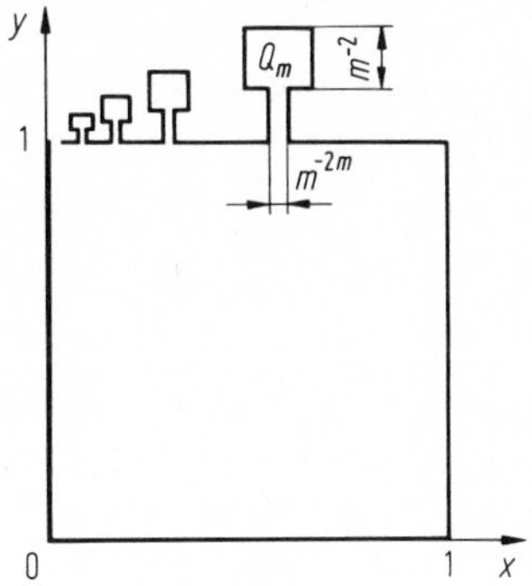

Fig. 9

Lemma 2. *If a bounded open set is the union of a finite number of open sets of the class $\mathcal{J}_\alpha$ then it also belongs to $\mathcal{J}_\alpha$.*

Proof. Let $\Omega = \Omega_1 \cup \Omega_2$, $\Omega_k \in \mathcal{J}_\alpha (k=1,2)$ and let $M = \min\{M_1, M_2\}$ where M_1 and M_2 are constants for Ω_1 and Ω_2 in the definition of the class $\mathcal{J}_\alpha$. Let $\mathcal{G}$ denote an admissible subset of Ω with $m_n(\mathcal{G}) \leqslant M$.

Since

$$m_n(\mathcal{G}) \leqslant m_n(\mathcal{G} \cap \Omega_1) + m_n(\mathcal{G} \cap \Omega_2)$$

and $s(\Omega \cap \partial \mathcal{G}) \geqslant s(\Omega_k \cap \partial \mathcal{G})$, then

$$\frac{m_n(\mathcal{G})^\alpha}{s(\Omega \cap \partial \mathcal{G})} \leqslant c \sum_{k=1}^{2} \frac{m_n(\Omega_k \cap \mathcal{G})^\alpha}{s(\Omega_k \cap \partial \mathcal{G})}.$$

This along with Lemma 1.1.9/1 and Corollary 3.2.1/2 implies the next corollary.

Corollary 3. *A bounded domain having the cone property belongs to the class $\mathcal{J}_{(n-1)/n}$.*

3.2.2. A Technical Lemma

The following assertion will be used in 3.2.3.

Lemma. *Let $\mathcal{G}$ be an admissible subset of Ω such that $s(\partial_i \mathcal{G}) < \infty$. Then there exists a sequence of functions $\{w_m\}_{m \geqslant 1}$ with the properties:*

1) $w_m \in C^{0,1}(\Omega)$,
2) $w_m = 0$ *in* $\Omega \setminus \mathscr{G}$,
3) $w_m \in [0,1]$ *in* Ω,
4) *for any compactum* $e \subset \mathscr{G}$ *there exists a number* $m(e)$, *such that* $w_m(x) = 1$ *for* $x \in e$ *and* $m \geqslant m(e)$,
5) $\limsup\limits_{m \to \infty} \int\limits_{\Omega} |\nabla w_m| dx = s(\partial_i \mathscr{G})$

Proof. Let ω be a bounded open set, $\bar{\omega} \subset \Omega$, $s[(\Omega \setminus \omega) \cap \partial \mathscr{G}] < m^{-1}$. There exists a small positive number $\varepsilon = \varepsilon(m)$ such that for some locally finite (in Ω) covering of $(\Omega \setminus \omega) \cap \partial \mathscr{G}$ by open balls $\mathscr{B}_i$ with radii $r_i < \varepsilon$ the inequality

$$\sum_i r_i^{n-1} < 2m^{-1} \tag{1}$$

holds. Obviously, we may assume that each ball $\mathscr{B}_i$ intersects $(\Omega \setminus \omega) \cap \partial \mathscr{G}$.

We introduce the notation: $2\mathscr{B}_i$ is the ball with radius $2r_i$ concentric with $\mathscr{B}_i$; $C_1 = \bigcup\limits_i \mathscr{B}_i$, $C_2 = \bigcup\limits_i 2\mathscr{B}_i$; $\varrho(x) = \operatorname{dist}(x, \partial_i \mathscr{G})$.

Let $g = \{x : x \in \mathscr{G},\ \varrho(x) < \delta\}$, where $\delta = \delta(m)$ is a small number, $\delta \in (0, \varepsilon)$, such that $g \cap \partial \omega$ is contained in C_1 (this can be achieved since the covering $\{\mathscr{B}_i\}$ is locally finite in Ω).

We construct a function $v(x)$, which is equal to zero in $\Omega \setminus \mathscr{G}$, to $\delta^{-1}\varrho(x)$ for $x \in g \cap \omega$ and to unity on the remaining portion of Ω. This function is discontinuous on the sets $(\Omega \setminus \omega) \cap \partial \mathscr{G}$ and $g \cap \partial \omega$. We eliminate this defect by using a truncating function $\eta(x)$ which is defined as follows.

Let $\eta_i \in C^{0,1}(R^n)$, $\eta_i = 1$ outside $2\mathscr{B}_i$, $\eta = 0$ in $\mathscr{B}_i$, $0 \leqslant \eta_i \leqslant 1$, $|\nabla \eta_i| \leqslant r_i^{-1}$ in $2\mathscr{B}_i$ and $\eta(x) = \inf\limits_i \{\eta_i(x)\}$.

Obviously, $\eta \in C^{0,1}(\Omega)$, $\eta = 0$ in C_1, $\eta = 1$ outside C_2. Consider the function $w_m = \eta v$, which equals zero in $C_1 \cap \Omega$ and hence vanishes in a neighborhood of the set of discontinuities of v. Clearly,

$$\int\limits_{\Omega} |\nabla w_m| dx = \int\limits_{\Omega \setminus C_1} |\nabla (\eta v)| dx \leqslant \int\limits_{\Omega \setminus C_1} |\nabla \eta| dx + \int\limits_{\Omega \setminus C_1} |\nabla v| dx .$$

We note that

$$\int\limits_{\Omega \setminus C_1} |\nabla \eta| dx \leqslant \sum_i \int\limits_{\Omega \setminus C_1} |\nabla \eta_i| dx \leqslant \sum_i \int\limits_{2\mathscr{B}_i} |\nabla \eta_i| dx \leqslant c \sum_i r_i^{n-1} .$$

Here and henceforth in this lemma c is a constant that depends only on n. The preceding inequalities along with (1) imply

$$\int\limits_{\Omega \setminus C_1} |\nabla \eta| dx \leqslant c m^{-1} .$$

Further, since by Theorem 1.2.4

$$\int\limits_{\Omega \setminus C_1} |\nabla v| dx \leqslant \delta^{-1} \int\limits_{g \cap \omega} |\nabla \varrho| dx = \delta^{-1} \int\limits_0^{\delta} s(\Gamma_\tau) d\tau ,$$

where $\Gamma_\tau = \{x \in \omega \cap g \colon \varrho(x) = \tau\}$, then for sufficiently small $\delta = \delta(m)$

$$\int_{\Omega \setminus C_1} |\nabla v| \, dx \leqslant s(\partial_i \mathcal{G}) + cm^{-1}.$$

Finally we have

$$\int_\Omega |\nabla w_m| \, dx \leqslant s(\partial_i \mathcal{G}) + cm^{-1}.$$

The function w_m is equal to zero outside $\mathcal{G}$ and to unity outside an ε-neighborhood of $\Omega \cap \partial \mathcal{G}$. The lemma is proved.

3.2.3. The Imbedding $L_1^1(\Omega) \subset L_q(\Omega)$

Let G be an open subset of Ω and let

$$\mathfrak{A}_G^{(\alpha)} \overset{\text{def}}{=} \sup \frac{[m_n(\mathcal{G})]^\alpha}{s(\partial_i \mathcal{G})}, \tag{1}$$

where the supremum is taken over all admissible sets $\mathcal{G}$ with $\operatorname{clos}_\Omega \mathcal{G} \subset G$.

Lemma 1. 1) *If $\mathfrak{A}_G^{(\alpha)} < \infty$, $\alpha \leqslant 1$, then for all functions $u \in C^{0,1}(\Omega) \cap L_1^1(\Omega)$ that equal zero outside G*

$$\|u\|_{L_q(\Omega)} \leqslant C \|\nabla u\|_{L_1(\Omega)}, \tag{2}$$

where $q = \alpha^{-1}$ and $C \leqslant \mathfrak{A}_G^{(\alpha)}$.

2) *If for all functions $u \in C^{0,1}(\Omega) \cap L_1^1(\Omega)$ that are equal to zero outside G inequality* (2) *holds, then $C \geqslant \mathfrak{A}_G^{(\alpha)}$.*

Proof. 1) By Lemma 3.1.2/3 it is sufficient to prove (2) for functions $u \in C^\infty(\Omega) \cap L_1^1(\Omega)$ that equal zero outside G.

Since

$$\|u\|_{L_q(\Omega)}^q = \int_0^\infty m_n(\mathcal{N}_t) \, d(t^q),$$

then (1.3.1/1) implies

$$\|u\|_{L_q(\Omega)} \leqslant \int_0^\infty m_n(\mathcal{N}_t)^{1/q} dt.$$

Now we note that, for almost all $t > 0$,

$$m_n(\mathcal{N}_t)^{1/q} \leqslant \mathfrak{A}_G^{(\alpha)} s(\mathcal{E}_t).$$

From this inequality and Theorem 1.2.4 we obtain

$$\|u\|_{L_q(\Omega)} \leqslant \mathfrak{A}_G^{(\alpha)} \int_0^\infty s(\mathcal{E}_t) \, dt = \mathfrak{A}_G^{(\alpha)} \|\nabla u\|_{L_1(\Omega)}.$$

2) Let $\mathcal{G}$ be an admissible subset of G, $\operatorname{clos}_\Omega \mathcal{G} \subset G$. We insert the sequence $\{w_m\}_{m \geqslant 1}$ specified in Lemma 3.2.2 into (2). For any compactum $e \subset \mathcal{G}$ we have

$$\left(\int_e |w_m|^q dx\right)^{1/q} \leqslant Cs(\partial_i \mathcal{G})$$

and hence $m_n(\mathcal{G})^{1/q} \leqslant Cs(\partial_i \mathcal{G})$. The lemma is proved.

For any domain Ω with finite volume we put

$$\mathfrak{A}_\alpha = \mathfrak{A}_\alpha(\tfrac{1}{2} m_n(\Omega)) .$$

Theorem. *Let Ω be a domain with $m_n(\Omega) < \infty$.*

1) *If $\Omega \in \mathcal{J}_\alpha$, where $\alpha \in [(n-1)/n, 1]$, then, for all $u \in L_1^1(\Omega)$,*

$$\inf_{c \in R^1} \| u - c \|_{L_q(\Omega)} \leqslant C \| \nabla u \|_{L_1(\Omega)} , \tag{3}$$

where $q = \alpha^{-1}$ and $C \leqslant \mathfrak{A}_\alpha$.

2) *If for all $u \in L_1^1(\Omega)$ inequality* (3) *is true, then $\Omega \in \mathcal{J}_\alpha$ with $\alpha = q^{-1}$ and $2^{(q-1)/q} C \geqslant \mathfrak{A}_\alpha$ for $q > 1$, $C \geqslant \mathfrak{A}_\alpha$ for $0 < q \leqslant 1$.*

Proof. 1) By Corollary 3.1.2 it is sufficient to obtain (3) for functions $u \in L_1^1(\Omega) \cap L_\infty(\Omega) \cap C^\infty(\Omega)$ with bounded supports. Let τ denote a number such that

$$2 m_n(\{x: u(x) \geqslant \tau\}) \geqslant m_n(\Omega) ,$$

$$2 m_n(\{x: u(x) > \tau\}) \leqslant m_n(\Omega) .$$

According to Lemma 1,

$$\left(\int_\Omega (u-\tau)_+^q dx\right)^{1/q} \leqslant \mathfrak{A}_\alpha \int_{\{x:\, u(x) > \tau\}} |\nabla u| dx$$

and

$$\left(\int_\Omega (\tau - u)_+^q dx\right)^{1/q} \leqslant \mathfrak{A}_\alpha \int_{\{x:\, u(x) < \tau\}} |\nabla u| dx ,$$

which completes the proof of the first part of the theorem.

2) For all $u \in L_1^1(\Omega)$, let inequality (3) hold and let $\mathcal{G}$ be any admissible subset of Ω with $2 m_n(\mathcal{G}) \leqslant m_n(\Omega)$. We insert the sequence $\{w_m\}$ specified in Lemma 3.2.2 into (3). For any compactum $e \subset \mathcal{G}$ we have

$$\inf_{c \in R^1} \left(\int_e |1 - c|^q dx + \int_{\Omega \setminus \mathcal{G}} |c|^q dx \right)^{1/q} \leqslant Cs(\partial_i \mathcal{G})$$

and consequently,

$$\min_c (|1-c|^q m_n(\mathcal{G}) + |c|^q m_n(\Omega \setminus \mathcal{G}))^{1/q} \leqslant Cs(\partial_i \mathcal{G}).$$

The minimum value of the left-hand side with $q > 1$ is attained at

$$c = \frac{m_n(\mathcal{G})^{1/(q-1)}}{m_n(\mathcal{G})^{1/(q-1)} + m_n(\Omega \setminus \mathcal{G})^{1/(q-1)}} .$$

Hence

$$\frac{[m_n(\mathscr{G})\, m_n(\Omega \setminus \mathscr{G})]^{1/q}}{[m_n(\mathscr{G})^{1/(q-1)} + m_n(\Omega \setminus \mathscr{G})^{1/(q-1)}]^{(q-1)/q}} \leqslant Cs(\partial_i \mathscr{G}) .$$

Taking into account the condition $2m_n(\mathscr{G}) \leqslant m_n(\Omega)$, we obtain

$$m_n(\mathscr{G})^{1/q} \leqslant 2^{(q-1)/q} Cs(\partial_i \mathscr{G}) .$$

The case $0 < q \leqslant 1$ is treated similarly. The theorem is proved.

Lemma 2. *Let Ω be a domain with $m_n(\Omega) < \infty$. The space $L_p^1(\Omega)$ is imbedded into $L_q(\Omega)$ ($p \geqslant 1$, $q > 0$) if and only if*

$$\inf_{c \in R^1} \| u - c \|_{L_q(\Omega)} \leqslant C \| \nabla u \|_{L_p(\Omega)} \tag{4}$$

for all $u \in L_p^1(\Omega)$.

Proof. Necessity. Let $\mathscr{Z}$ be the subspace of functions equal to a constant on Ω and let $\dot{W}_{p,q}^1(\Omega)$ be the factor space $W_{p,q}^1(\Omega)/\mathscr{Z}$, equipped with the norm

$$\inf_{c \in \mathscr{Z}} \| u - c \|_{L_q(\Omega)} + \| \nabla u \|_{L_p(\Omega)} .$$

Let $\mathscr{E}$ denote the identity mapping of $\dot{W}_{p,q}^1(\Omega)$ into $\dot{L}_p^1(\Omega)$. This mapping is linear, continuous and one to one. Since $L_p^1(\Omega) \subset L_q(\Omega)$ then $\mathscr{E}$ is surjective. By the Banach theorem (cf. Bourbaki [34], I, 3, 3), $\mathscr{E}$ is an isomorphism and hence (4) holds.

Sufficiency. Let (4) be true. We must show that $\mathscr{E}$ is surjective. By (4) the image of $\dot{W}_{p,q}^1(\Omega)$ is closed in $L_p^1(\Omega)$. So it is sufficient to take into account that, by Corollary 3.1.2, the space $\dot{W}_{p,q}^1(\Omega)$ considered as a subspace of $\dot{L}_p^1(\Omega)$ is dense in $\dot{L}_p^1(\Omega)$. The lemma is proved.

Theorem and Lemma 2 immediately imply the next corollary.

Corollary. *If Ω is a domain with $m_n(\Omega) < \infty$ then $L_1^1(\Omega)$ is imbedded into $L_q(\Omega)$, $q \geqslant 1$, if and only if*

$$\sup m_n(\mathscr{G})^{1/q} / s(\partial_i \mathscr{G}) < \infty ,$$

where the supremum is taken over all admissible subsets $\mathscr{G}$ of Ω with $m_n(\mathscr{G}) \leqslant \frac{1}{2} m_n(\Omega)$.

Remark. Since a plane domain Ω bounded by a quasicircle belongs to the class EV_1^1 (cf. 1.4.8), the imbedding $L_1^1(\Omega) \subset L_2(\Omega)$ holds. The last assertion along with Lemma 3.2.1 and the Corollary just formulated implies that the union of a finite number of quasidisks belongs to the class $\mathscr{J}_{1/2}$.

3.2.4. The Function λ_M

Definition. Let $M \in (0, m_n(\Omega))$. Let $\lambda_M(\mu)$ denote the greatest lower bound of the numbers $s(\partial_i \mathscr{G})$ considered over all admissible sets $\mathscr{G} \subset \Omega$ that satisfy the condition $\mu \leqslant m_n(\mathscr{G}) \leqslant M$.

Obviously, $\lambda_M(\mu)$ is nondecreasing in μ and nonincreasing in M.

We can give an equivalent definition of the class $\mathscr{J}_\alpha$ in terms of the function λ_M. Namely, $\Omega \in \mathscr{J}_\alpha$ if and only if

$$\liminf_{\mu \to +0} \mu^{-\alpha} \lambda_M(\mu) > 0 . \tag{1}$$

Lemma. *If $M \in (0, m_n(\Omega))$ and Ω is a domain with finite volume, then*

$$\lambda_M(\mu) > 0 \quad \textit{for all } \mu \in (0, M] .$$

Proof. Let $0 < \mu \leqslant \min\{M, m_n(\Omega) - M\}$ and let ω be a domain with smooth boundary such that $\bar{\omega} \subset \Omega$ and $2 m_n(\Omega \backslash \omega) < \mu$. If $\mathscr{G}$ is an admissible subset of Ω, $M \geqslant m_n(\mathscr{G}) \geqslant \mu$, then, obviously,

$$2 m_n(\mathscr{G} \cap \omega) \geqslant \mu \quad \text{and} \quad 2 m_n(\omega \backslash \mathscr{G}) \geqslant m_n(\Omega) - M \geqslant \mu .$$

Since $\partial\omega$ is a smooth surface then

$$\inf_{c \in R^1} \| u - c \|_{L(\omega)} \leqslant C(\omega) \| \nabla u \|_{L(\omega)}$$

for all $u \in L_1^1(\omega)$. So, according to the second part of Theorem 3.2.3,

$$\min\{m_n(\mathscr{G} \cap \omega),\, m_n(\omega \backslash \mathscr{G})\} \leqslant C(\omega) s(\omega \cap \partial \mathscr{G})$$

for any admissible subset $\mathscr{G}$ of Ω. Thus,

$$\mu \leqslant C(\omega) s(\Omega \cap \partial \mathscr{G})$$

and hence $\lambda_M(\mu) > 0$ for small values of μ. Since $\lambda_M(\mu)$ is nondecreasing in μ, then $\lambda_M(\mu) > 0$ for all $\mu \in (0, M]$. The lemma is proved.

It can easily be seen that the condition of the connectedness of Ω as well as the condition $m_n(\Omega) < \infty$ are essential for the validity of Lemma.

From Lemma we immediately obtain the next corollary.

Corollary. *If Ω is a domain of the class $\mathscr{J}_\alpha$ and $m_n(\Omega) < \infty$, then the value*

$$\sup\{m_n(\mathscr{G})^\alpha / s(\partial_i \mathscr{G}) \colon \mathscr{G} \textit{ is an admissible subset of } \Omega,\ m_n(\mathscr{G}) \leqslant M\}$$

is finite for arbitrary constant $M \in (0, m_n(\Omega))$.

In what follows we shall write $\lambda(\mu)$ instead of $\lambda_{m_n(\Omega)/2}(\mu)$.

3.2.5. An Example of a Domain in $\mathscr{J}_1$

We shall show that the union Ω of the squares $Q_m = \{(x, y): 2^{-m-1} \leqslant x \leqslant 3 \cdot 2^{-m-2},\ 0 < y < 2^{-m-2}\}$ and the rectangles $R_m = \{(x, y): 3 \cdot 2^{-m-2} < x < 2^{-m},\ 0 < y < 1\}$ $(m = 0, 1, \ldots)$ (Fig. 10) belongs to the class $\mathscr{J}_1$ and does not belong to $\mathscr{J}_\alpha$ for $\alpha < 1$.

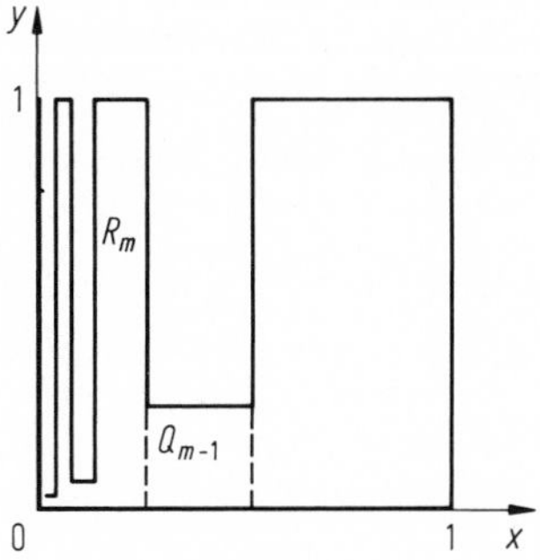

Fig. 10

Let T be the triangle $\{(x, y): 0 < y < x/3,\ 0 < x < 1\}$ contained in Ω. Further let $v = u$ on $\Omega \backslash T$ and $v = 3yx^{-1}u$ on T. Clearly,

$$\|v\|_{L(\Omega)} \leqslant \left\| \frac{\partial v}{\partial y} \right\|_{L(\Omega)} \leqslant \left\| \frac{\partial u}{\partial y} \right\|_{L(\Omega)} + c \left\| \frac{u}{r} \right\|_{L(T)},$$

where $r = (x^2 + y^2)^{1/2}$. Consequently,

$$\|u\|_{L(\Omega)} \leqslant \|\nabla u\|_{L(\Omega)} + c \left\| \frac{u}{r} \right\|_{L(T)}.$$

Since by the obvious inequality

$$\int_0^1 |w(r)|\, dr \leqslant \int_0^1 |w_r'|\, r\, dr, \qquad w(1) = 0,$$

$L_1^1(\Omega)$ is imbedded into the space with the norm $\|r^{-1}u\|_{L(T)}$, then $L_1^1(\Omega) \subset L(\Omega)$. Applying Lemma 3.2.3/2 we obtain $\Omega \in \mathscr{J}_1$. On the other hand, the rectangles $G_m = R_m \cap \{(x, y): y > 2^{-m-1}\}$ satisfy $\lim m_2(G_m)/s(\partial_i G_m) = 1$. Therefore $c_1\mu \leqslant \lambda(\mu) \leqslant c_2\mu$ for small values of μ.

§ 3.3. Subareal Mappings and the Classes $\mathscr{J}_\alpha$

In this section we introduce and study the properties of "subareal" mappings of a domain, i.e. the mappings which do not essentially enlarge the $(n-1)$-dimensional area of surfaces. We shall use these mappings to verify the conditions for concrete domains to be in $\mathscr{J}_\alpha$.

3.3.1. Subareal Mappings

Consider a locally quasi-isometric mapping

$$\Omega \ni x \to \xi \in R^n .$$

Let ξA denote the image of an arbitrary set $A \subset \Omega$ under the mapping ξ. Let ξ'_x be the matrix $(\partial \xi_i / \partial x_k)_{i,k=1}^n$ and let $\det \xi'_x$ be the Jacobian of ξ. The notations x'_ξ and $\det x'_\xi$ have a similar meaning.

Definition. The mapping ξ is called *subareal* if there exists a constant k such that

(1) $$s(\xi \partial_i \mathscr{G}) \leqslant k s(\partial_i \mathscr{G})$$

for any admissible subset $\mathscr{G}$ of Ω.

Lemma 1. *The mapping ξ is subareal if and only if*

(2) $$|\det x'_\xi| \geqslant k \, \|x'_\xi\|$$

for almost all $x \in \Omega$, where $\|\cdot\|$ is the norm of a matrix.

To prove this lemma we shall need the following assertion.

Lemma 2. *Let $u \in C^\infty(\Omega) \cap L_1^1(\Omega)$ and let E be any measurable subset of Ω. In order that*

(3) $$\int_E |\nabla_x u| \, dx \geqslant k \int_{\xi E} |\nabla_\xi u| \, d\xi$$

with a constant k that is independent of u and E, it is necessary and sufficient for the mapping ξ to satisfy (2). *Moreover,* (2) *follows from the validity of* (3) *for any ball in Ω.*

Proof. The sufficiency follows immediately from (2) along with

$$\int_{\xi E} |\nabla_\xi u| \, d\xi = \int_E \left| \sum_{i=1}^n \frac{\partial u}{\partial x_i} \nabla_\xi x_i \right| |\det \xi'_x| \, dx$$

$$= \int_E |\nabla_x u| \, |(x'_\xi)^* \alpha| \, |\det x'_\xi|^{-1} dx ,$$

where $\alpha = |\nabla_x u|^{-1} \nabla_x u$.

Necessity. We fix a unit vector α and consider the ball $B_\varrho(x_0) \subset \Omega$. We put $u(x) = \alpha x$. By virtue of (3)

$$\int_{B_\varrho(x_0)} dx \geqslant k \int_{\xi B_\varrho(x_0)} |\nabla_\xi u|\, d\xi = k \int_{B_\varrho(x_0)} |(x'_\xi)^* \alpha|\, |\det x'_\xi|^{-1} dx\,.$$

Passing to the limit as $\varrho \to 0$ and using the fact that α is arbitrary, we obtain (3) for almost all $x_0 \in \Omega$. The lemma is proved.

Proof of Lemma 1. Sufficiency. Let $\mathscr{G}$ be an arbitrary admissible subset of Ω. We choose an arbitrary point $y \in \partial_i \mathscr{G}$. Let $\mathscr{U}_y$ be a neighborhood of y so small that the set $\overline{\mathscr{U}_y \cap \mathscr{G}}$ is represented by the inequality $x_n \leqslant f(x_1, \ldots, x_{n-1})$ in some Cartesian coordinate system with an infinitely differentiable f.

Let δ be a fixed small positive number. Let $\mathscr{V}_\varepsilon$ denote the set of points $x \in \mathscr{U}_y$ defined by the equation $x_n = \varepsilon + f(x_1, \ldots, x_{n-1})$ where $\varepsilon \in [0, \delta]$. We put

$$u_\delta(x) = \begin{cases} 1 & \text{for } x_n < f(x_1, \ldots, x_{n-1})\,, \\ 1 - \varepsilon\delta^{-1} & \text{for } x \in \mathscr{V}_\varepsilon\,, \\ 0 & \text{for } x_n \geqslant f(x_1, \ldots, x_{n-1}) + \delta\,. \end{cases}$$

Obviously, $u_\delta(x)$ is a Lipschitz function. By (2) and Lemma 2

$$\int_{\mathscr{U}_y} |\nabla_x u_\delta|\, dx \geqslant k \int_{\xi \mathscr{U}_y} |\nabla_\xi u_\delta|\, d\xi\,.$$

Using Theorem 1.2.4, we can rewrite the last inequality as

$$\delta^{-1} \int_0^\delta s(\mathscr{V}_\varepsilon)\, d\varepsilon \geqslant k\delta^{-1} \int_0^\delta s(\xi \mathscr{V}_\varepsilon)\, d\varepsilon\,.$$

Since $s(\mathscr{V}_\varepsilon)$ is continuous, then

$$s(\mathscr{V}_0) \geqslant k \liminf_{\delta \to 0} \delta^{-1} \int_0^\delta s(\xi \mathscr{V}_\varepsilon)\, d\varepsilon\,.$$

So, taking into account the lower semicontinuity of the area, we obtain

$$s(\mathscr{V}_0) \geqslant k s(\xi \mathscr{V}_0)\,.$$

The latter implies (1), since y is an arbitrary point.

Necessity. Let ξ be a subareal mapping of Ω. Consider an arbitrary $u \in C^\infty(\Omega) \cap L_1^1(\Omega)$. According to Theorem 1.2.2, the level sets of $|u|$ are smooth manifolds for almost all $t > 0$. Let B be an arbitrary ball in Ω. By Theorem 1.2.4

$$\int_B |\nabla_x u|\, dx = \int_0^\infty s(B \cap \mathscr{E}_t)\, dt\,,$$

$$\int_{\xi B} |\nabla_\xi u|\, d\xi = \int_0^\infty s(\xi B \cap \xi \mathscr{E}_t)\, dt\,.$$

By the definition of subareal mappings, $s(\mathscr{E}_t) \geqslant k s(\xi \mathscr{E}_t)$. Consequently, (3) holds. Now it remains to refer to Lemma 2. Lemma 1 is proved.

3.3.2. An Estimate for the Function λ in Terms of Subareal Mappings

The following theorem yields lower bounds for the function λ, introduced at the end of subsection 3.2.4.

Theorem. *Let Ω be a domain with finite volume for which there exists a subareal mapping onto a bounded domain $\xi\Omega$ that is starshaped with respect to a ball.*

We put

$$\pi(\mu) = \inf_{\{\mathscr{G}\}} \int_{\mathscr{G}} |\det \xi_x'|\, dx\,,$$

where the infimum is taken over all admissible subsets $\mathscr{G}$ of Ω that satisfy

$$\mu \leqslant m_n(\mathscr{G}) \leqslant \tfrac{1}{2} m_n(\Omega)\,.$$

Then there exists a constant Q such that

(1) $$Q\lambda(\mu) \geqslant \pi(\mu)^{(n-1)/n}\,.$$

Proof. Let $\mathscr{G}$ be an admissible subset of Ω with $m_n(\mathscr{G}) < \frac{1}{2} m_n(\Omega)$. We put

$$M = \sup_{\{\mathscr{G}\}} m_n(\xi \mathscr{G})\,.$$

Since $|\det \xi_x'| \geqslant \text{const} > 0$ on any compact subset of Ω, then $M < m_n(\xi\Omega)$. Taking into account the fact that $\xi\Omega$ is starshaped with respect to a ball and the fact that $\xi\mathscr{G}$ is a manifold of the class $C^{0,1}$, by (3.2.1/2) we obtain

$$[m_n(\xi \mathscr{G})]^{(n-1)/n} \leqslant C s(\xi(\partial_i \mathscr{G}))\,.$$

The latter along with (3.3.1/1) implies

$$[m_n(\xi \mathscr{G})]^{(n-1)/n} \leqslant C k s(\partial_i \mathscr{G})\,.$$

So if $m_n(\mathscr{G}) \geqslant \mu$ then

$$\pi(\mu)^{(n-1)/n} \leqslant [m_n(\xi \mathscr{G})]^{(n-1)/n} \leqslant C k \lambda(\mu)\,.$$

The theorem is proved.

3.3.3. Estimates for the Function λ for Concrete Domains

We give some applications of Theorem 3.3.2.

Example 1. Consider the domain

$$\Omega=\left\{x\in R^n\colon \left(\sum_{i=1}^{n-1} x_i^2\right)^{1/2}<f(x_n),\ 0<x_n<a\right\},$$

where f is a nonnegative convex function with $f'(a-0)<\infty$ and $f(0)=0$ (cf. Fig. 11).

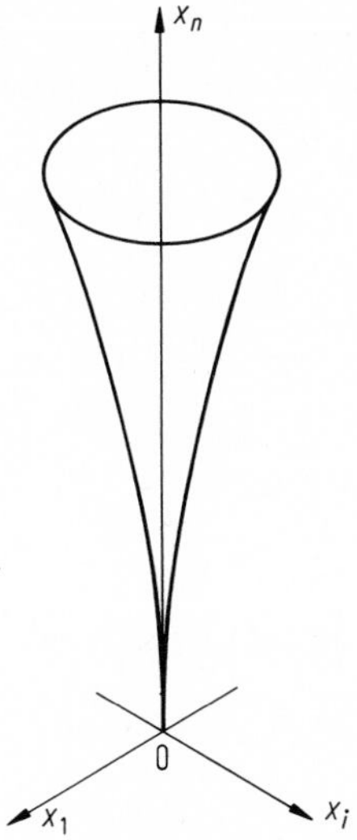

Fig. 11

We shall show that the function $\lambda(\mu)$ specified for Ω satisfies

(1) $$k[f(\alpha(\mu))]^{n-1}\leqslant\lambda(\mu)\leqslant[f(\alpha(\mu))]^{n-1},$$

where $k\in(0,1)$ and $\alpha(\mu)$ is defined by

$$\mu=v_{n-1}\int_0^{\alpha(\mu)}[f(\tau)]^{n-1}d\tau\,.$$

Proof. Consider the domain $G_t=\Omega\cap\{x\colon 0<x_n<t\}$, where t is subjected to the condition

$$m_n(G_t)=v_{n-1}\int_0^t[f(\tau)]^{n-1}d\tau\leqslant\tfrac{1}{2}m_n(\Omega)\,.$$

Obviously,

$$s(\Omega\cap\partial G_t)=v_{n-1}[f(t)]^{n-1}.$$

Since by the definition of $\lambda(\mu)$, $\lambda[m_n(G_t)]\leqslant s(\Omega\cap\partial G_t)$, the right-hand side of (1) is proved.

The mapping $x\to\xi=(x_1,\dots,x_{n-1},f(x_n))$ maps Ω onto the cone

$$\xi\Omega=\left\{\xi\colon \sum_{i=1}^{n-1}\xi_i^2<\xi_n^2,\ 0<\xi_n<f(a)\right\}.$$

The condition (3.3.1/2) is equivalent to the boundedness of f'. Hence the mapping $x\to\xi$ is subareal.

It remains to give the lower bound for the function $\pi(\mu)$ defined in Theorem 3.3.2. Since the Jacobian of the mapping $x\to\xi$ is equal to $f'(x_n)$, we must estimate the integral

$$\int_{\mathscr{G}} f'(x_n)\,dx \tag{2}$$

from below, provided $\frac{1}{2}m_n(\Omega)>m_n(\mathscr{G})\geqslant\mu$. Since f' is nondecreasing, the integral (2) attains its minimum value at the set $G_{\alpha(\mu)}$. Therefore,

$$\int_{\mathscr{G}} f'(x_n)\,dx\geqslant\int_0^{\alpha(\mu)} f'(c)\,dc\int_{|x'|\leqslant f(c)}dx'=\frac{v_{n-1}}{n}[f(\alpha(\mu))]^n.$$

Thus

$$\pi(\mu)\geqslant n^{-1}v_{n-1}[f(\alpha(\mu))]^n.$$

Applying Theorem 3.3.2 to the latter inequality we obtain the left-hand side of (1). The proof is complete.

For the domain

$$\Omega=\left\{x\colon \sum_{i=1}^{n-1}x_i^2<x_n^{2\beta},\ 0<x_n<a\right\}\qquad(\beta\geqslant 1)$$

from (1) it immediately follows that

$$c_1\mu^\alpha\leqslant\lambda(\mu)\leqslant c_2\mu^\alpha,\qquad \alpha=\frac{\beta(n-1)}{\beta(n-1)+1} \tag{3}$$

for small values of μ. Consequently, $\Omega\in\mathscr{J}_{\frac{\beta(n-1)}{\beta(n-1)+1}}$ and $\Omega\notin\mathscr{J}_\alpha$ for $\alpha<\dfrac{\beta(n-1)}{\beta(n-1)+1}$.

Example 2. Consider the domain

$$\Omega=\left\{x\colon 0<x_n<\infty,\ \left(\sum_{i=1}^{n-1}x_i^2\right)^{1/2}<f(x_n)\right\},$$

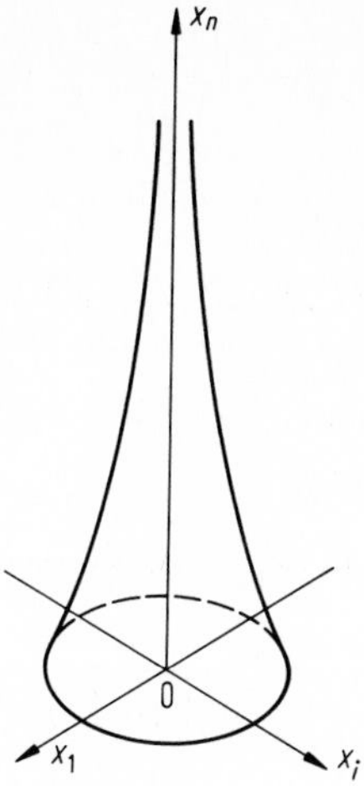

Fig. 12

where f is a nonnegative convex function with $f'(+0) > -\infty$ and $f(+\infty) = 0$ (cf. Fig. 12). Suppose $m_n(\Omega) < \infty$, i.e.

$$\int_0^\infty [f(t)]^{n-1} dt < \infty .$$

We can show that

$$k[f(\alpha(\mu))]^{n-1} \leqslant \lambda(\mu) \leqslant [f(\alpha(\mu))]^{n-1} , \tag{4}$$

where $k \in (0, 1)$ and $\alpha(\mu)$ is defined by

$$\mu = v_{n-1} \int_{\alpha(\mu)}^\infty [f(t)]^{n-1} dt .$$

The proof is the same as in the previous example. The role of the auxiliary subareal mapping is played by the mapping

$$x \to \xi = (x_1, \ldots, x_{n-1}, -f(x_n))$$

onto the cone

$$\left\{\xi : \sum_{i=1}^{n-1} \xi_i^2 < \xi_n^2, \; 0 > \xi_n > -f(0)\right\} .$$

In particular, for the domain

$$\Omega = \{x: x_1^2 + \cdots + x_{n-1}^2 < (1 + x_n)^{-2\beta}, \; 0 < x_n < \infty\} , \qquad \beta(n-1) > 1 ,$$

we have

(5) $$c_1\mu^\alpha \leqslant \lambda(\mu) \leqslant c_2\mu^\alpha\,, \qquad \alpha = \frac{\beta(n-1)}{\beta(n-1)-1}\,,$$

for small μ, i.e. $\Omega \in \mathscr{J}_{\frac{\beta(n-1)}{\beta(n-1)-1}}$ and $\Omega \notin \mathscr{J}_\alpha$ for $\alpha < \dfrac{\beta(n-1)}{\beta(n-1)-1}$.

Example 3. Consider the plane spiral domain Ω (cf. Fig. 13) defined in polar coordinates by

$$1-\varepsilon_1(\theta) > \varrho > 1-\varepsilon_2(\theta)\,, \qquad 0<\theta<\infty\,.$$

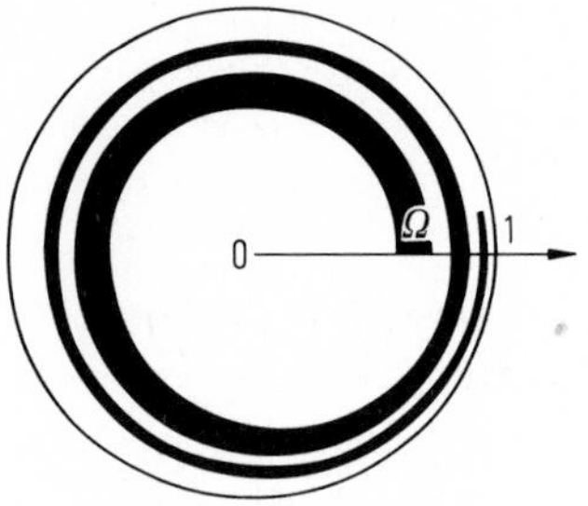

Fig. 13

Here $0<\varepsilon_2(\theta+2\pi)<\varepsilon_1(\theta)<\varepsilon_2(\theta)<1$, ε_1, ε_2 are functions satisfying a uniform Lipschitz condition on $[0,\infty)$ and such that $\varepsilon_2-\varepsilon_1$ is convex on $[0,\infty)$. Further, we suppose that the area of Ω is finite, i.e.

$$\int_0^\infty (\varepsilon_2-\varepsilon_1)\,d\theta < \infty\,.$$

Applying Theorem 3.3.2 to the subareal mapping ξ:

$$\xi_1 = 1-\varrho-\tfrac{1}{2}[\varepsilon_1(\theta)+\varepsilon_2(\theta)]\,, \qquad \xi_2 = \tfrac{1}{2}[\varepsilon_2(\theta)-\varepsilon_1(\theta)]$$

of Ω onto the triangle

$$|\xi_1|<\xi_2\,, \qquad 0<\xi_2<\tfrac{1}{2}[\varepsilon_2(\theta)-\varepsilon_1(\theta)]$$

and using the same arguments as in Example 1, we obtain

(6) $$c_1[\varepsilon_2(\theta(\mu))-\varepsilon_1(\theta(\mu))] \leqslant \lambda(\mu) \leqslant c_2[\varepsilon_2(\theta(\mu))-\varepsilon_1(\theta(\mu))]\,,$$

where $\theta(\mu)$ is the function defined by

(7) $$\mu = \iint\limits_{\{\varrho e^{i\theta}\in\Omega:\,\theta>\theta(\mu)\}} \varrho\, d\varrho\, d\theta\,.$$

In particular, for the domain

(8) $\{\varrho e^{i\theta}\colon 1-(8+\theta)^{1-\beta}>\varrho>1-(8+\theta)^{1-\beta}-c(8+\theta)^{-\beta},\ 0<\theta<\infty\}$,

where $0<c<2\pi(\beta-1)$, $\beta>1$, we have $c_1\mu^{\alpha}\leqslant\lambda(\mu)\leqslant c_2\mu^{\alpha}$ with $\alpha=\beta/(\beta-1)$ for small μ. Thus, the domain (8) belongs to $\mathscr{J}_{\beta/(\beta-1)}$.

A more complicated example of a domain in $\mathscr{J}_{\alpha}$, $\alpha>1$, is considered in the following section.

Remark. Incidentally, if $x\to\xi$ is a subareal mapping of Ω onto a bounded starshaped domain, then, obviously, $L_1^1(\Omega)$ is imbedded into the space with the norm

$$\left(\int_{\Omega}|u|^{n/(n-1)}|\det\xi'_x|\,dx\right)^{(n-1)/n}.$$

In particular, for domains in Examples 1 and 2 we have

$$L_1^1(\Omega)\subset L_{n/(n-1)}(\Omega,|f'(x_n)|\,dx).$$

This is an illustration of the natural idea that the limit exponent $n/(n-1)$ is also preserved for "bad" domains if we consider a weighted Lebesgue measure, degenerating at "bad" boundary points, instead of m_n.

In connection with this remark we note that although the present chapter deals with the problem of the summability of functions in $L_1^1(\Omega)$ with respect to Lebesgue measure, the proofs from the subsection 3.2.3 do not change essentially after replacing $L_q(\Omega)$ by the space $L_q(\Omega,\mu)$, where μ is an arbitrary measure in Ω (cf. Chapter 2).

§ 3.4. Two-sided Estimates for the Function λ for the Domain in Nikodým's Example

In this section we consider the domain Ω specified in Example 1.1.4/1 provided $\varepsilon_m=\delta(2^{-m-1})$, where δ is a Lipschitz function on $[0,1]$ such that $\delta(2t)\sim\delta(t)$. We shall show that $\lambda(\mu)\sim\delta(\mu)$.

Lemma. *If $\mathscr{G}$ is an admissible subset of Ω, $\mathscr{G}\cap C=\varnothing$, then*

(1) $$s(\partial_i\mathscr{G})\geqslant k\delta(m_2(\mathscr{G}))\,,\qquad k=\text{const}>0\,.$$

Proof. Let $\mathscr{G}_m=(A_m\cup B_m)\cap\mathscr{G}$. Let N denote the smallest number for which

$$s(\partial_i\mathscr{G}_N)\geqslant\delta(2^{-N-1})\,.$$

This and the obvious inequality $m_2(\mathscr{G}_m) \leqslant 2^{-m-1}$ imply

(2) $$\delta\left[m_2\left(\bigcup_{m \geqslant N} \mathscr{G}_m\right)\right] \leqslant \delta(2^{-N}) \leqslant ks(\partial_i \mathscr{G}) .$$

Since

$$s(\partial_i \mathscr{G}_m) < \delta(2^{-m-1})$$

for all $m < N$, then $A_m \cup B_m$ does not contain components of $\partial_i \mathscr{G}$, connecting the polygonal line *abcd* with the segment *ef* (cf. Fig. 14). So for $m < N$

$$2s(\partial_i \mathscr{G}_m) \geqslant s(\partial_e \mathscr{G}_m) ,$$

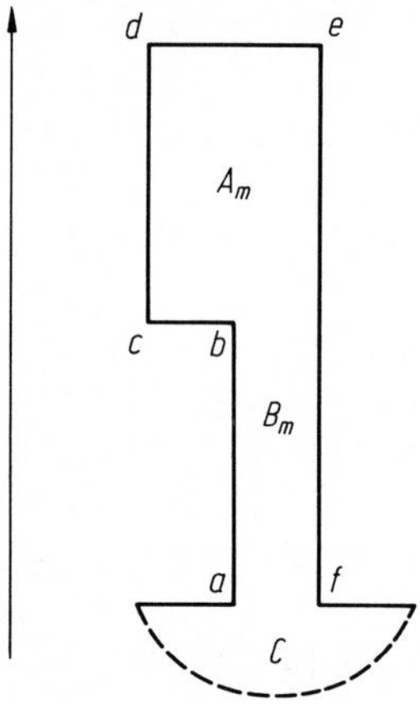

Fig. 14

where $\partial_e A = \partial A \setminus \partial_i A$. From this along with the isoperimetric inequality

$$s(\partial \mathscr{G}_m)^2 \geqslant 4\pi m_2(\mathscr{G}_m)$$

we obtain

(3) $$m_2(\mathscr{G}_m)^{1/2} \leqslant cs(\partial_i \mathscr{G}_m) .$$

Summing (3) over m and using the inequality

$$\left(\sum_m a_m\right)^{1/2} \leqslant \sum_m a_m^{1/2} \quad (a_m > 0) ,$$

we obtain

(4) $$\left[m_2\left(\bigcup_{m<N} \mathscr{G}_m\right)\right]^{1/2} \leqslant cs(\partial_i \mathscr{G}) .$$

Combining (2) with (4), we arrive at the required estimate.

Proposition. *The function* λ *satisfies*

$$k_1\delta(\mu) \leqslant \lambda(\mu) \leqslant k_2\delta(\mu)\,,$$

where k_1 *and* k_2 *are positive constants.*

Proof. From (1) and Theorem 1.2.4 it follows that

$$k\int_0^\infty \delta(m_2(\mathcal{N}_t))\,dt \leqslant \int_\Omega |\nabla u|\,dx \tag{5}$$

for all $u \in C^\infty(\Omega)$ that vanish on C. From Lemma 3.1.2/3 we obtain that this inequality is valid for all $u \in C^{0,1}(\Omega)$, $u = 0$ on C.

Now let u be an arbitrary function in $C^{0,1}(\Omega)$ and let η be a continuous piecewise linear function on $[0,1]$ that is equal to zero on $[0, 1/3]$ and to unity on $(2/3, 1)$. We put

$$u^{(1)}(x,y) = u(x,y)\,\eta(y)\,,$$

$$u^{(2)}(x,y) = u(x,y)(1-\eta(y))\,.$$

Since $|u| \leqslant |u^{(1)}| + |u^{(2)}|$, then

$$\mathcal{N}_t \subset \mathcal{N}^{(1)}_{t/2} \cup \mathcal{N}^{(2)}_{t/2}$$

and hence

$$m_2(\mathcal{N}_t) \leqslant m_2(\mathcal{N}^{(1)}_{t/2}) + m_2(\mathcal{N}^{(2)}_{t/2})\,.$$

Taking into account the condition $\delta \in C^{0,1}[0,1]$, we obtain

$$\delta(m_2(\mathcal{N}_t)) \leqslant \delta(m_2(\mathcal{N}^{(1)}_{t/2})) + k\,m_2(\mathcal{N}^{(2)}_{t/2})\,.$$

This and estimate (5) applied to $u^{(1)}$ yield

$$\int_0^\infty \delta(m_2(\mathcal{N}_t))\,dt \leqslant K\left(\iint_\Omega |\nabla u^{(1)}|\,dx\,dy + \iint_\Omega |u^{(2)}|\,dx\,dy\right).$$

Here the right-hand side does not exceed

$$K\left(\iint_\Omega |\nabla u|\,dx\,dy + \iint_\omega |u|\,dx\,dy\right), \tag{6}$$

where $\omega = \Omega \cap \{(x,y) \colon |y| < 2/3\}$.

We give a bound for the integral over ω in (6). Let $(x,y) \in \omega$ and let $(x,z) \in C$. Obviously,

$$|u(x,y)| \leqslant |u(x,z)| + \int |\nabla u(x,\bar{y})|\,d\bar{y}\,,$$

where the integration is taken over a vertical segment, contained in Ω and passing through $(x,0)$. After integration over x, y, z we obtain

$$\iint_\omega |u|\,dx\,dy \leqslant c\left(\iint_C |u|\,dx\,dy + \iint_\Omega |\nabla u|\,dx\,dy\right).$$

Thus,

$$\int_0^\infty \delta(m_2(\mathcal{N}_t))\,dt \leqslant K\left(\iint_\Omega |\nabla u|\,dx\,dy + \iint_C |u|\,dx\,dy\right).$$

The rectangle C belongs to the class $\mathcal{J}_{1/2}$. Therefore, if $u=0$ on a subset of Ω with area not less than $\frac{1}{2}m_2(\Omega)$, then

$$\iint_C |u|\,dx\,dy \leqslant K\iint_C |\nabla u|\,dx\,dy\,.$$

Consequently,

(7) $$\int_0^\infty \delta(m_2(\mathcal{N}_t))\,dt \leqslant K\iint_C |\nabla u|\,dx\,dy\,.$$

Inserting the sequence $\{w_m\}$, constructed in Lemma 3.2.2, into (7), we obtain (1) for any admissible set with area which does not exceed $\frac{1}{2}m_n(\Omega)$. Thus, the lower bound for $\lambda(\mu)$ is obtained.

In order to derive the estimate $\lambda(\mu)\leqslant c\,\delta(\mu)$ it is sufficient to note that the sequence $\{\mathcal{G}_m\}_{m\geqslant 1}$, where $\mathcal{G}_m$ is the interior of $A_m \cup B_m$, satisfies

$$s(\partial_i\mathcal{G}_m) = \delta(2^{-m-1}),$$

$$\tfrac{1}{3}\delta(2^{-m-1}) \leqslant m_2(\mathcal{G}_m) \leqslant \tfrac{2}{3}\delta(2^{-m-1}).$$

The proposition is proved.

Obviously, a domain Ω belongs to $\mathcal{J}_\alpha(\alpha\geqslant 1)$ if and only if

(8) $$\liminf_{t\to+0} t^{-\alpha}\delta(t) > 0\,.$$

We shall return to the domain considered here in § 4.5.

§ 3.5. Compactness of the Imbedding $L_1^1(\Omega)\subset L_q(\Omega)$ $(q\geqslant 1)$

3.5.1. The Class $\mathring{\mathcal{J}}_\alpha$

Definition. The set Ω belongs to *the class* $\mathring{\mathcal{J}}_\alpha$, $\alpha>(n-1)/n$, if

(1) $$\limsup_{\mu\to 0}\frac{m_n(\mathcal{G})^\alpha}{s(\partial_i\mathcal{G})} = 0\,,$$

where the supremum is taken over all admissible subsets $\mathscr{G}$ of Ω that satisfy $m_n(\mathscr{G}) \leqslant \mu$.

Remark 1. It is clear that (1) is equivalent to

$$\lim_{\mu\to 0} \mu^{-\alpha}\lambda_M(\mu) = \infty\,, \tag{2}$$

where M is a fixed number in $(0, m_n(\Omega))$.

Remark 2. The exponent α in the definition of the class $\mathring{\mathscr{J}}_\alpha$ exceeds $(n-1)/n$ since in case $\alpha = (n-1)/n$ we have

$$[m_n(B_\varrho)]^{(n-1)/n} = \text{const} \cdot s(\partial B_\varrho)\,.$$

3.5.2. A Criterion for Compactness

Theorem. *Let $m_n(\Omega) < \infty$ and let Ω be a domain. For the compactness of the imbedding $\mathring{L}_1^1(\Omega) \subset L_q(\Omega)$, where $n/(n-1) > q \geqslant 1$, it is necessary and sufficient that Ω belong to $\mathring{\mathscr{J}}_\alpha$ with $\alpha = q^{-1}$.*

Proof. Sufficiency. Let u be an arbitrary function in $L_1^1(\Omega) \cap L_\infty(\Omega) \cap C^\infty(\Omega)$ with bounded support. By Corollary 3.1.2 the set of such functions is dense in $L_1^1(\Omega)$. Obviously,

$$\int_\Omega |u|^q dx \leqslant c\left(\int_{\mathscr{N}_\tau} |u|^q dx + \tau^q m_n(\Omega)\right)$$
$$\leqslant c_1\left(\int_\Omega (|u| - \tau)_+^q dx + \tau^q m_n(\Omega)\right)$$

for $\tau \geqslant 0$. Let τ be such that

$$m_n(\mathscr{N}_\tau) \geqslant \mu\,, \qquad m_n(\mathscr{L}_\tau) \leqslant \mu\,,$$

where μ is an arbitrary number in $(0, M]$ and M is the constant in the definition of $\mathscr{J}_\alpha$.

Using Lemma 3.2.3/1, we obtain

$$\int_\Omega (|u| - \tau)_+^q dx \leqslant \frac{\mu}{[\lambda_M(\mu)]^q}\left(\int_\Omega |\nabla u|\,dx\right)^q.$$

Let ω be a bounded set with smooth boundary such that

$$\bar{\omega} \subset \Omega\,, \qquad 2m_n(\Omega \backslash \omega) < \mu\,.$$

Since $m_n(\mathscr{N}_\tau) \geqslant \mu$, then $2m_n(\omega \cap \mathscr{N}_\tau) \geqslant \mu$. Consequently,

$$\int_\omega |u|^q dx \geqslant 2^{-1}\mu\tau^q .$$

Thus,

(1) $$c\|u\|_{L_q(\Omega)} \leqslant \frac{\mu^{1/q}}{\lambda_M(\mu)} \int_\Omega |\nabla u| dx + \left[\frac{m_n(\Omega)}{\mu}\right]^{1/q} \|u\|_{L_q(\omega)} .$$

Let $\{u_k\}_{k\geqslant 1}$ be a sequence satisfying

$$\|\nabla u_k\|_{L(\Omega)} + \|u_k\|_{L(\omega)} \leqslant 1 .$$

Since the boundary of ω is smooth, the imbedding operator $L_1^1(\omega)\to L_q(\omega)$ is compact and we may suppose that $\{u_k\}_{k\geqslant 1}$ is a Cauchy sequence in $L_q(\omega)$. By (1)

$$c\|u_m - u_l\|_{L_q(\Omega)} \leqslant 2\frac{\mu^{1/q}}{\lambda_M(\mu)} + \left[\frac{m_n(\Omega)}{\mu}\right]^{1/q} \|u_m - u_l\|_{L_q(\omega)}$$

and hence

$$c \limsup_{m,l\to\infty} \|u_m - u_l\|_{L_q(\Omega)} \leqslant 2\frac{\mu^{1/q}}{\lambda_M(\mu)} .$$

It remains to pass to the limit in the right-hand side as $\mu\to +0$ and take (3.5.1/2) into account.

Necessity. Let the imbedding $L_1^1(\Omega) \subset L_q(\Omega)$ be compact. Then $L_1^1(\Omega) \subset L_1(\Omega)$ and elements of a unit ball in $W_1^1(\Omega)$ have absolutely equicontinuous norms in $L_q(\Omega)$. Hence, for all $u\in L_1^1(\Omega)$

(2) $$\left(\int_{\mathscr{G}} |u|^q dx\right)^{1/q} \leqslant \varepsilon(\mu)\int_\Omega (|\nabla u| + |u|) dx ,$$

where $\mathscr{G}$ is an arbitrary admissible subset of Ω whose measure does not exceed μ and $\varepsilon(\mu)$ converges to zero as $\mu\to +0$.

We insert the sequence $\{w_m\}$ constructed in Lemma 3.2.2 into (2). Then, for any compactum $K\subset \mathscr{G}$,

$$m_n(K)^{1/q} \leqslant c\varepsilon(\mu)(s(\partial_i\mathscr{G}) + m_n(\mathscr{G}))$$

and hence

$$m_n(\mathscr{G})^{1/q} \leqslant c_1\varepsilon(\mu) s(\partial_i\mathscr{G}) .$$

The theorem is proved.

Example. The condition (3.5.1/1) for the domain

$$\Omega = \{x = (x', x_n),\ x' = (x_1, \ldots, x_{n-1}) \colon |x'| < f(x_n),\ 0 < x_n < a\}$$

(cf. Example 3.3.3/1) is equivalent to

(3) $$\lim_{x\to 0}\left(\int_0^x [f(\tau)]^{n-1} d\tau\right)^\alpha [f(x)]^{1-n} = 0 .$$

Since

$$\int_0^x [f(\tau)]^{n-1} d\tau \leqslant [f(x)]^{n-1} x\,,$$

then (3) holds if

$$\lim_{x\to 0} x^{\alpha}[f(x)]^{(n-1)(\alpha-1)} = 0$$

(in particular, (3) always holds for $\alpha = 1$).

§ 3.6. The Imbedding $W^1_{1,r}(\Omega, \partial\Omega) \subset L_q(\Omega)$

3.6.1. The Class $\mathscr{K}_{\alpha,\beta}$

Let $r>0$, $u \in C(\bar{\Omega})$ and

$$\| u \|_{L_r(\partial\Omega)} = \left(\int_{\partial\Omega} | u |^r ds \right)^{1/r},$$

where s is $(n-1)$-dimensional Hausdorff measure. If $r \geqslant 1$, then $\| u \|_{L_r(\partial\Omega)}$ is a norm and it is a pseudonorm for $r \in (0,1)$ (cf. 3.1.1).

Definition 1. We denote by $W^1_{p,r}(\Omega, \partial\Omega)$ the completion of the set of functions in $L^1_p(\Omega) \cap C^\infty(\Omega) \cap C(\bar{\Omega})$ with respect to the norm (pseudonorm)

$$\| \nabla u \|_{L_p(\Omega)} + \| u \|_{L_r(\partial\Omega)}\,.$$

In this section we study the conditions for the imbedding $W^1_{1,r}(\Omega, \partial\Omega) \subset L_q(\Omega)$. Contrary to Sobolev's theorem for domains of the class $C^{0,1}$, the norm in $L_r(\partial\Omega)$ does not always play the role of a "weak perturbation" for the $L_1(\Omega)$-norm of the gradient in the inequality

$$\| u \|_{L_q(\Omega)} \leqslant c(\| \nabla u \|_{L_1(\Omega)} + \| u \|_{L_r(\partial\Omega)})\,. \tag{1}$$

In the case of a "bad" boundary the exponent q may depend on the order of summability of the function on the boundary.

In particular, we shall see that functions in $W^1_{1,r}(\Omega, \partial\Omega)$ are summable of order $q = n/(n-1)$ in Ω, if $r = n/(n-1)$ and Ω is an arbitrary open set.

Definition 2. An open set Ω belongs to *the class* $\mathscr{K}_{\alpha,\beta}$, if there exists a constant $\mathscr{E}$ such that

$$[m_n(g)]^{\alpha} \leqslant \mathscr{E}[s(\partial_i g) + s(\partial_e g)^{\beta}]\,, \tag{2}$$

for any admissible set $g \subset \Omega$ (here $\partial_e g = \partial g \cap \partial\Omega$).

3.6.2. Examples of Sets in $\mathscr{K}_{\alpha,\beta}$

Example 1. An arbitrary open set Ω belongs to the class $\mathscr{K}_{(n-1)/n,1}$, since the condition (3.6.1/2) for $\alpha = (n-1)/n$, $\beta = 1$ is the classical isoperimetric inequality

(1) $$[m_n(g)]^{(n-1)/n} \leqslant \frac{[\Gamma(1+n/2)]^{1/n}}{n\sqrt{\pi}} s(\partial g)$$

(cf. subsection 6.1.5 and Remark 6.2.2).

Proposition. *If $\Omega \in \mathscr{K}_{\alpha,1}$, where $\alpha \geqslant (n-1)/n$, then $\Omega \in \mathscr{K}_{\alpha\beta,\beta}$, where β is an arbitrary number in $[(n-1)/n\alpha, 1]$.*

Proof. From (1) and

(2) $$[m_n(g)]^{\alpha} \leqslant \mathscr{E} s(\partial g)$$

it follows that

$$[m_n(g)]^{\alpha\beta} \leqslant c\,\mathscr{E}^{\theta} s(\partial g) \quad \text{with} \quad \beta = \theta + (1-\theta)(n-1)/n\alpha$$

for any $\theta \in [0,1]$. If $s(\partial_e g) \leqslant s(\partial_i g)$, then

(3) $$[m_n(g)]^{\alpha\beta} \leqslant 2c\,\mathscr{E}^{\theta} s(\partial_i g)\,.$$

Otherwise if $s(\partial_e g) > s(\partial_i g)$, then (2) yields

(4) $$[m_n(g)]^{\alpha\beta} \leqslant \mathscr{E}^{\beta} [s(\partial g)]^{\beta}\,.$$

Combining (3) with (4) we complete the proof.

Example 2. We shall show that the plane domain

$$\Omega = \{(x,y)\colon 0 < x < \infty,\ 0 < y < (1+x)^{\gamma-1}\}\,,$$

where $0 < \gamma \leqslant 1$, belongs to $\mathscr{K}_{1/\gamma,1}$ and by Proposition, $\Omega \in \mathscr{K}_{\beta/\gamma,\beta}$, where β is an arbitrary number in $[\gamma/2, 1]$.

Let g be an arbitrary admissible subset of Ω. Obviously,

(5) $$s(\partial g) \geqslant s(\mathrm{Pr}_{Ox}\, g)\,,$$

where s is the length and Pr_{Ox} is the orthogonal projection onto the axis Ox. Since $\gamma \leqslant 1$, then

$$\int_{\mathrm{Pr}_{Ox} g} (1+x)^{\gamma-1} dx \leqslant \int_0^{s(\mathrm{Pr}_{Ox} g)} (1+x)^{\gamma-1} dx = \gamma^{-1}[s(\mathrm{Pr}_{Ox} g)+1)^{\gamma} - 1]$$
$$\leqslant \gamma^{-1}[s(\mathrm{Pr}_{Ox} g)]^{\gamma}\,.$$

Consequently,

(6) $$\left(\int_{\mathrm{Pr}_{Ox} g} (1+x)^{\gamma-1} dx \right)^{1/\gamma} \leqslant \gamma^{-1/\gamma} s(\partial g)\,.$$

Taking into account that

$$m_2(g) \leqslant \int_{\mathrm{Pr}_{Ox} g} (1+x)^{\gamma-1} dx\,,$$

from (6) we obtain

(7) $$m_2(g)^{1/\gamma} \leqslant \gamma^{-1/\gamma} s(\partial g),$$

which means that $\Omega \in \mathscr{K}_{1/\gamma,1}$.

Example 3. We shall show that any set Ω in $\mathscr{J}_\alpha$ with finite volume belongs to the class $\mathscr{K}_{\alpha,\beta}$, where β is an arbitrary positive number.

For any admissible subset g of Ω satisfying the condition $m_n(g) \leqslant M$ we have

(8) $$m_n(g)^\alpha \leqslant \mathfrak{A}(M) s(\partial_i g).$$

Let $m_n(g) > M$ and

(9) $$2\alpha_n s(\partial_e g) < M^{(n-1)/n}, \quad \text{where } \alpha_n = \frac{[\Gamma(1+n/2)]^{1/n}}{n\sqrt{\pi}}.$$

By virtue of the isoperimetric inequality (1),

$$M^{(n-1)/n} \leqslant m_n(g)^{(n-1)/n} \leqslant \alpha_n(s(\partial_i g) + s(\partial_e g))$$

and hence

$$M^{(n-1)/n} \leqslant 2\alpha_n s(\partial_i g).$$

This implies

(10) $$m_n(g)^\alpha \leqslant m_n(\Omega)^\alpha 2\alpha_n M^{(1-n)/n} s(\partial_i g).$$

If (9) is not valid, then

(11) $$m_n(g)^\alpha \leqslant m_n(\Omega)^\alpha (2\alpha_n)^\beta s(\partial_e g)^\beta.$$

From (8), (10) and (11) it follows that Ω belongs to $\mathscr{K}_{\alpha,\beta}$.

3.6.3. On the Continuity of the Imbedding Operator $W^1_{1,r}(\Omega, \partial\Omega) \to L_q(\Omega)$

Theorem. *If $\Omega \in \mathscr{K}_{\alpha,\beta}$, where $\alpha \leqslant 1$, $\beta \geqslant \alpha$, then* (3.6.1/1) *is valid for all $u \in W^1_{1,1/\beta}(\Omega, \partial\Omega)$ with $q = 1/\alpha$, $r = 1/\beta$.*

Proof. Consider the case $1 > \beta \geqslant \alpha$. Let u be an arbitrary function in $C^\infty(\Omega) \cap C(\bar{\Omega})$ with bounded support. From Theorem 1.2.3 and Lemma 1.3.3/1 we obtain

(1) $$\|u\|_{L_{1/\alpha}(\Omega)} \leqslant \left(\int_0^\infty m_n(\mathscr{N}_t)^{\alpha/\beta} d(t^{1/\beta})\right)^\beta.$$

We introduce the set

$$A_t = \{t : s(\mathscr{E}_t) \leqslant s(\bar{\mathscr{N}}_t \cap \partial\Omega)^\beta\}$$

and represent the integral above in the form

$$\int_{A_t} + \int_{CA_t},$$

where CA_t is the complement of A_t with respect to the positive halfaxis. We give a bound for the integral

$$I_1 = \int_{A_t} m_n(\mathcal{N}_t)^{\alpha/\beta} d(t^{1/\beta}) .$$

Since $\Omega \in \mathcal{K}_{\alpha,\beta}$, then

$$m_n(\mathcal{N}_t)^\alpha \leqslant 2\,\mathcal{E}\, s(\bar{\mathcal{N}}_t \cap \partial\Omega)^\beta$$

for almost all $t \in A_t$ and hence

(2) $$I_1 \leqslant (2\,\mathcal{E})^{1/\beta} \int_{A_t} s(\bar{\mathcal{N}}_t \cap \partial\Omega)\, d(t^{1/\beta}) \leqslant (2\,\mathcal{E})^{1/\beta} \int_{\partial\Omega} |u|^{1/\beta} ds .$$

Now we consider the integral

$$I_2 = \int_{CA_t} [m_n(\mathcal{N}_t)]^{\alpha/\beta} d(t^{1/\beta}) .$$

Obviously,

$$I_2 \leqslant \beta^{-1} \int_0^\infty [m_n(\mathcal{N}_t)]^\alpha dt \sup_{\tau \in CA_t} (\tau [m_n(\mathcal{N}_\tau)]^\alpha)^{(1-\beta)/\beta} .$$

By (3.6.1/2) we have

$$[m_n(\mathcal{N}_\tau)]^\alpha \leqslant 2\,\mathcal{E}\, s(\mathcal{E}_\tau)$$

for $\tau \in CA_t$, and hence

$$I_2 \leqslant 2\,\mathcal{E}\,\beta^{-1} \int_0^\infty s(\mathcal{E}_t)\, dt \sup_{\tau > 0} (\tau [m_n(\mathcal{N}_\tau)]^\alpha)^{(1-\beta)/\beta} .$$

The preceding inequality and Theorem 1.2.4 yield

(3) $$I_2 \leqslant 2\,\mathcal{E}\,\beta^{-1} \| \nabla u \|_{L_1(\Omega)} \| u \|_{L_{1/\alpha}(\Omega)}^{(1-\beta)/\beta} .$$

From (1) – (3) it follows that

$$\| u \|_{L_{1/\alpha}(\Omega)} \leqslant c\,\mathcal{E} \left(\| \nabla u \|_{L_1(\Omega)}^\beta \| u \|_{L_{1/\alpha}(\Omega)}^{1-\beta} + \| u \|_{L_{1/\beta}(\partial\Omega)} \right) .$$

Now consider the case $\beta \geqslant 1$. The condition $\Omega \in \mathcal{K}_{\alpha,\beta}$ implies

(4) $$\int_0^\infty [m_n(\mathcal{N}_t)]^\alpha dt \leqslant \mathcal{E} \left(\int_0^\infty s(\mathcal{E}_t)\, dt + \int_0^\infty [s(\bar{\mathcal{N}}_t \cap \partial\Omega)]^\beta dt \right) .$$

Applying Theorem 1.2.3 and Lemma 1.3.3/1, we obtain

$$\int_\Omega |u|^{1/\alpha} dx \leqslant \left(\int_0^\infty [m_n(\mathcal{N}_t)]^\alpha dt \right)^{1/\alpha} ,$$

$$\left(\int_0^\infty [s(\bar{\mathcal{N}}_t \cap \partial\Omega)]^\beta dt \right)^{1/\beta} \leqslant \int_0^\infty s(\bar{\mathcal{N}}_t \cap \partial\Omega)\, d(t^{1/\beta}) = \int_{\partial\Omega} |u|^{1/\beta} ds .$$

These estimates along with (4) lead to

$$\|u\|_{L_{1/\alpha}(\Omega)} \leqslant \mathscr{E}\,(\|\nabla u\|_{L_1(\Omega)} + \|u\|_{L_{1/\beta}(\partial\Omega)})\,. \tag{5}$$

This concludes the proof.

We give an example which shows that Theorem is not true if $\Omega \in \mathscr{K}_{\alpha,\beta}$, $\alpha > \beta$ and $r = 1/\beta$.

Example. In Example 3.6.2/2 we showed that the domain

$$\Omega = \{(x,y)\colon 0 < x < \infty,\ 0 < y < (1+x)^{2\beta-1}\}$$

belongs to the class $\mathscr{K}_{1/2,\beta}$ with $\beta \in (0, 1/2)$. Consider the sequence of functions

$$\Omega \ni (x,y) \to u_m(x,y) = (1+x)^{-\varkappa_m}\,, \qquad \varkappa_m > \beta\,.$$

Each of these functions obviously belongs to $W^1_{1,1/\beta}(\Omega, \partial\Omega)$, since it can be approximated in the norm of the space mentioned after multiplication by an "expanding" sequence of truncating functions. We have

$$\|u_m\|_{L_2(\Omega)} = 2^{-1/2}(\varkappa_m - \beta)^{-1/2}\,, \qquad \|\nabla u_m\|_{L(\Omega)} = \varkappa_m/(\varkappa_m - 2\beta + 1)\,,$$

$$\|u_m\|_{L_{1/\beta}(\partial\Omega)} > \beta^{\beta}(\varkappa_m - \beta)^{-\beta}\,.$$

For $u = u_m$ and $\varkappa_m \to \beta + 0$ the left-hand side of the inequality

$$\|u\|_{L_2(\Omega)} \leqslant C(\|\nabla u\|_{L(\Omega)} + \|u\|_{L_{1/\beta}(\partial\Omega)})$$

grows more rapidly than its right-hand side and hence (3.6.1/1) is not true for $q = \alpha^{-1}$, $r = \beta^{-1}$.

Remark. A review of the proof of Theorem 3.6.3 shows that the theorem also remains valid for $\beta < \alpha$, provided (3.6.1/1) in its statement is replaced by

$$\|u\|_{L_q(\Omega)} \leqslant C\left(\|\nabla u\|_{L(\Omega)} + \int_0^\infty [s(\bar{\mathscr{N}}_t \cap \partial\Omega)]^{1/r} dt\right). \tag{6}$$

Corollary. *The inequality*

$$\|u\|_{L_{n/(n-1)}(\Omega)} \leqslant \frac{[\Gamma(1+n/2)]^{1/n}}{n\sqrt{\pi}}(\|\nabla u\|_{L(\Omega)} + \|u\|_{L(\partial\Omega)}) \tag{7}$$

holds for arbitrary bounded set Ω *and* $u \in W^1_{1,1}(\Omega, \partial\Omega)$. *The constant in* (7) *is the best possible.*

The proof follows immediately from the isoperimetric inequality (3.6.2/1) and (5). That the constant is exact was already remarked in 1.4.2, where the inequality (1.4.2/8) was derived.

§ 3.7. Comments to Chapter 3

A substantial part of the results presented in this chapter were stated in the author's paper [159].

§ 3.1. Lemma 3.1.2/1 was established by Deny and Lions [51].

§ 3.2. Lemma 3.2.1/1 was proved by Burago and the author [35]. The other results of this section (except Lemma 3.2.3/2) are due to the author. An assertion similar to Theorem 3.2.3 concerning functions in $BV(\Omega)$, i.e. functions whose gradients are vector charges, was simultaneously (and by the same device) proved by Fleming and Rishel [65].

For the further development of the idea concerning the relation between integral and geometrical inequalities see Burago and Maz'ja [35] (the summability of traces on $\partial\Omega$ of functions in $BV(\Omega)$, the best constants in certain inequalities for functions in $BV(\Omega)$, etc.; these results are presented in Chapter 6), Miranda [188], Michael and Simon [186], Hoffman and Spruck [98], Otsuki [209], Aubin [19] (the Sobolev-Gagliardo inequalities for functions on manifolds), Federer [61, 62] (imbedding theorems for currents), Klimov [109–111] (imbedding theorems involving Orlicz spaces). Lemma 3.2.3/2 was proved by Deny and Lions [51].

§ 3.3. The contents of this section are borrowed from the author's paper [150].

§ 3.4. The estimates for the function λ are presented in Maz'ja [165].

§ 3.5. The results of this section are due to the author (see [141], [159]).

§ 3.6. The contents of this section are taken from the author's thesis [143].

Chapter 4. On Summability of Functions in the Space $L_p^1(\Omega)$

§ 4.1. Conductivity

4.1.1. The Equivalence of Certain Definitions of Conductivity

Let Ω be an open set in R^n. Let F and G denote bounded closed (in Ω) and open subsets of Ω, respectively, $F \subset G$.

The set $K = G \backslash F$ is called a *conductor*. In what follows $U_\Omega(K)$ is the class of functions $f \in C^{0,1}(\Omega)$ with $f(x) \geqslant 1$ for $x \in F$ and $f(x) \leqslant 0$ for $x \in \Omega \backslash G$.

The number

$$c_p(K) = \inf \left\{ \int_\Omega |\nabla f|^p dx \colon f \in U_\Omega(K) \right\}$$

is called *the p-conductivity of the conductor K*.

Lemma 1. *Let $V_\Omega(K)$ denote the class of functions $\{f \in C^\infty(\Omega)\colon f(x) = 1$ for $x \in F$, $f(x) = 0$ for $x \in \Omega \backslash G\}$. Then*

$$c_p(K) = \inf \left\{ \int_\Omega |\nabla f|^p dx \colon f \in V_\Omega(K) \right\}.$$

Proof. Since $U_\Omega(K) \supset V_\Omega(K)$, it suffices to obtain only the lower bound for $c_p(K)$. Let $\varepsilon \in (0,1)$ and let $f \in U_\Omega(K)$ be such that

$$\int_\Omega |\nabla f|^p dx \leqslant c_p(K) + \varepsilon .$$

We put $\psi = (1+\varepsilon)^2 f - \varepsilon$ and $\varphi = \min(\psi_+, 1)$. Then

$$\| \nabla \psi \|_{L_p(\Omega)} \leqslant (c_p(K) + \varepsilon)^{1/p} (1+\varepsilon)^2 . \tag{1}$$

We introduce some notation: $\Phi_1 = \{x\colon \varphi = 1\}$, $\Phi_2 = \{x\colon \varphi = 0\}$, $Q = \{x\colon 1 > \varphi(x) > 0\}$. Since $Q = \{x\colon (1+\varepsilon)^{-1} > f > \varepsilon(1+\varepsilon)^{-2}\}$, then $\operatorname{clos}_\Omega Q \subset K$.

We construct a locally finite (in Ω) covering of the set $\operatorname{clos}_\Omega Q$ by open balls $\mathscr{B}_{0,i}$, $i = 1, 2, \ldots$. Let $\mathfrak{A}_0$ denote the union of these balls. Because of the inclusion $\operatorname{clos}_\Omega Q \subset K$ we can choose the covering to satisfy $\operatorname{clos}_\Omega \mathfrak{A}_0 \subset K$.

Next we construct locally finite (in Ω) coverings of the sets $\Phi_k\backslash\mathfrak{A}_0$ ($k=1,2$) by open balls $\mathscr{B}_{k,i}$ such that the closures in Ω of the sets $\mathfrak{A}_k=\bigcup_i \mathscr{B}_{k,i}$ ($k=1,2$) are disjoint with $\operatorname{clos}_\Omega Q$. The latter is possible since $(\Phi_k\backslash\mathfrak{A}_0)\cap\operatorname{clos}_\Omega Q=\varnothing$. Clearly, $F\subset\mathfrak{A}_1$ and $(\Omega\backslash G)\subset\mathfrak{A}_2$.

Let $\alpha_{k,i}\in\mathscr{D}(\mathscr{B}_{k,i})$, $k=0,1,2$; $i=1,2,\dots$, and let

$$\sum_{k=0}^{2}\sum_{i=1}^{\infty}\alpha_{k,i}=1 \quad \text{in } \Omega .$$

For any $i=1,2,\dots$ we introduce a function $\beta_i\in\mathscr{D}(\mathscr{B}_{0,i})$ such that

$$\|\nabla(\alpha_{0,i}\varphi-\beta_i)\|_{L_p(\Omega)}\leqslant\varepsilon^i .$$

Next we put $v_{0,i}=\beta_i$, $v_{1,i}=\alpha_{1,i}$, $v_{2,i}=0$,

$$u=\sum_{k=0}^{2}\sum_{i=1}^{\infty}v_{k,i} . \tag{2}$$

The function u is infinitely differentiable in Ω since each point of Ω is contained only in a finite number of balls $\mathscr{B}_{k,i}$ and therefore (2) has a finite number of summands. Obviously,

$$\|\nabla(\varphi-\psi)\|_{L_p(\Omega)}\leqslant\sum_{k=0}^{2}\sum_{i=1}^{\infty}\|\nabla(\alpha_{k,i}\varphi-v_{k,i})\|_{L_p(\Omega)} .$$

Since $\varphi=1$ on $\mathscr{B}_{1,i}$, $v_{1,i}=\alpha_{1,i}$ and $\varphi=0$ on $\mathscr{B}_{2,i}$, $v_{2,i}=0$, then

$$\|\nabla(\varphi-u)\|_{L_p(\Omega)}\leqslant\sum_{i=1}^{\infty}\|\nabla(\alpha_{0,i}\varphi-\beta_i)\|_{L_p(\Omega)}\leqslant\varepsilon/(1-\varepsilon) . \tag{3}$$

Because $F\subset\mathfrak{A}_1$ and $F\cap\mathfrak{A}_0=\varnothing$ we have $v_{0,i}=\beta_i=0$, $v_{2,i}=0$, $v_{1,i}=\alpha_{1,i}$, $\alpha_{0,i}=0$, $\alpha_{2,i}=0$ on F. Therefore

$$u=\sum_{i=1}^{\infty}v_{1,i}=\sum_{k=0}^{2}\sum_{i=1}^{\infty}\alpha_{k,i}=1 \quad \text{on } F .$$

Besides, $v_{k,i}=0$ on $\Omega\backslash G$ and hence $u=0$ on the same set. Thus, $u\in V_\Omega(K)$.

Finally, by (1) and (3)

$$\|\nabla u\|_{L_p(\Omega)}\leqslant(1+\varepsilon)^2(c_p(K)+\varepsilon)^{1/p}+\varepsilon(1-\varepsilon)^{-1} ,$$

which completes the proof.

Let $T_\Omega(K)=\{f\in V_\Omega(K)\colon 0\leqslant f(x)\leqslant 1 \text{ on } K\}$.
Henceforth, the following modification of Lemma 1 will be useful.

Lemma 2. *The equality*

$$c_p(K) = \inf\left\{\int_\Omega |\nabla f|^p dx : f \in T_\Omega(K)\right\}$$

is valid.

Proof. Since $T_\Omega(K) \subset V_\Omega(K)$, it suffices to obtain only the lower bound for $c_p(K)$. Let $\varepsilon > 0$, $\lambda_\varepsilon \in C^\infty(-\infty, +\infty)$, $\lambda_\varepsilon(t) = 1$ for $t \geqslant 1$, $\lambda_\varepsilon(t) = 0$ for $t \leqslant 0$, $0 \leqslant \lambda'_\varepsilon(t) \leqslant 1 + \varepsilon$. Further, let $\varphi \in V_\Omega(K)$. We introduce the function $f = \lambda_\varepsilon(\varphi) \in T_\Omega(K)$. Obviously,

$$\int_\Omega |\nabla f|^p dx = \int_\Omega [\lambda'_\varepsilon(\varphi)]^p |\nabla \varphi|^p dx \leqslant (1+\varepsilon)^p \int_\Omega |\nabla \varphi|^p dx$$

and consequently,

$$\inf\left\{\int_\Omega |\nabla f|^p dx : f \in T_\Omega(K)\right\} \leqslant c_p(K) .$$

The result follows.

4.1.2. Some Properties of Conductivity

We shall comment on some simple properties of p-conductivity.

Consider two conductors $K = G \backslash F$ and $K' = G' \backslash F'$ contained in Ω. We say that K' is a part of K ($K' \subset K$) if $F \subset F' \subset G' \subset G$.

The definition of p-conductivity immediately implies the following proposition.

Proposition 1. *If $K' \subset K$, then*

$$c_p(K) \leqslant c_p(K') .$$

Proposition 2. *Given any $\varepsilon > 0$ and any conductor K with finite p-conductivity, we can construct a conductor $K' \subset K$ such that*

$$\varepsilon \geqslant c_p(K') - c_p(K) \geqslant 0 . \tag{1}$$

The conductor K' can be chosen so that $\partial_i F'$ and $\partial_i G'$ are C^∞-manifolds.

Proof. The right inequality follows from Proposition 1.

Let a function $f \in U_\Omega(K)$ satisfy

$$c_p(K) + \varepsilon/2 > \int_\Omega |\nabla f|^p dx , \tag{2}$$

and let

$$2\delta = 1 - \left[\frac{\varepsilon + 2c_p(K)}{2\varepsilon + 2c_p(K)}\right]^{1/p} .$$

We may assume that the sets $\{x \in \Omega : f(x) = 1 - \delta\}$ and $\{x \in \Omega : f(x) = \delta\}$ are C^∞-manifolds since otherwise δ can be replaced by an arbitrarily close number having the aforementioned property. We construct the conductor K' as follows: $K' = G' \backslash F'$, where $F' = \{x \in \Omega: f(x) \geqslant 1-\delta\}$, $G' = \{x \in \Omega: f(x) > \delta\}$. Then (2) implies

$$\frac{c_p(K)+\varepsilon/2}{(1-2\delta)^p} > \int_\Omega \left| \nabla \left(\frac{f(x)-\delta}{1-2\delta} \right) \right|^p dx \,.$$

The function $(1-2\delta)^{-1}(f-\delta)$ is contained in $U_\Omega(K')$. Hence

$$\frac{c_p(K)+\varepsilon/2}{(1-2\delta)^p} > c_p(K') \,,$$

which is equivalent to the left inequality in (1).

The proposition is proved.

Proposition 3. *Let* $K_1 = G_1 \backslash F_1$ and $K_2 = G_2 \backslash F_2$ *be any conductors in* Ω. *Then*

(3) $$c_p(K_\cup) + c_p(K_\cap) \leqslant c_p(K_1) + c_p(K_2) \,,$$

where $K_\cup = (G_1 \cup G_2) \backslash (F_1 \cup F_2)$, $K_\cap = (G_1 \cap G_2) \backslash (F_1 \cap F_2)$.

Proof. Let ε be an arbitrary positive number and let f_1, f_2 be functions in $U_\Omega(K_1)$, $U_\Omega(K_2)$, respectively, satisfying

(4) $$\int_{K_i} |\nabla f_i|^p dx < c_p(K_i) + \varepsilon \,.$$

We introduce the functions

$$M = \sup\{f_1, f_2\} \,, \qquad m = \inf\{f_1, f_2\} \,.$$

It is clear that M and m satisfy the Lipschitz condition in Ω and that $M \geqslant 1$ on $F_1 \cup F_2$, $M \leqslant 0$ on $\Omega \backslash (G_1 \cup G_2)$, as well as $m \geqslant 1$ on $F_1 \cap F_2$, $m \leqslant 0$ on $\Omega \backslash (G_1 \cap G_2)$. Besides,

$$\int_{K_\cup} |\nabla M|^p dx + \int_{K_\cap} |\nabla m|^p dx = \sum_{i=1}^{2} \int_{K_i} |\nabla f_i|^p dx \,.$$

This along with (4) and Lemma 4.1.1/1 implies (3).

4.1.3. The Dirichlet Principle with Prescribed Level Surfaces and its Corollaries

The proofs of the following Lemmas 1, 2 and Corollaries 1, 2 do not in principle differ from the proofs of similar assertions on the (p, Φ)-capacity in 2.2.1 – 2.2.3.

Lemma 1. *For any conductor* K *in* Ω *with finite p-conductivity we have*

$$c_p(K) = \inf_{u\in V_\Omega(K)} \left(\int_0^1 \| \nabla f \|^{-1}_{L_{p-1}(\mathscr{E}_\tau)} d\tau \right)^{1-p}, \tag{1}$$

where $\mathscr{E}_\tau = \{x \in \Omega: f(x) = \tau\}$.

Lemma 2. *Let f be in* $C^\infty(\Omega) \cap L^1_p(\Omega)$. *Then for almost all t*

$$[s(\mathscr{E}_t)]^{p/(p-1)} \| \nabla f \|^{-1}_{L_{p-1}(\mathscr{E}_t)} \leqslant -\frac{d}{dt}[m_n(\mathscr{L}_t)], \tag{2}$$

where $\mathscr{L}_t = \{x: f(x) > t\}$.

Corollary 1. *For any conductor K in Ω the inequality*

$$c_p(K) \geqslant \inf \left\{ \left(-\int_0^1 \frac{d}{dt} m_n(\mathscr{L}_t) \frac{dt}{[s(\mathscr{E}_t)]^{p/(p-1)}} \right)^{1-p} : f \in V_\Omega(K) \right\} \tag{3}$$

is valid.

Corollary 2. *Let F be an open set closed in Ω and let G, H be bounded open subsets of Ω such that*

$$F \subset G, \qquad \operatorname{clos}_\Omega G \subset H.$$

The conductors

$$K^{(1)} = G \backslash F, \quad K^{(2)} = H \backslash \operatorname{clos}_\Omega G, \quad K^{(3)} = H \backslash F$$

satisfy the inequality

$$[c_p(K^{(1)})]^{-1/(p-1)} + [c_p(K^{(2)})]^{-1/(p-1)} \leqslant [c_p(K^{(3)})]^{-1/(p-1)}. \tag{4}$$

We present one more property of p-conductivity which is proved similarly to Theorem 2.3.1 (cf. also Remark 2.3.1).

Lemma 3. *Let* $u \in C^{0,1}(\Omega)$, $u = 0$ *in the exterior of an open bounded set* $G \subset \Omega$ *and let* $\mathscr{K}_t$ *be the conductor* $G \backslash \mathscr{N}_t$. *Then for* $p \geqslant 1$

$$\int_0^\infty c_p(\mathscr{K}_t)\, d(t^p) \leqslant \frac{p^p}{(p-1)^{p-1}} \int_\Omega |\nabla u|^p dx. \tag{5}$$

(For $p = 1$ the coefficient in front of the second integral in (5) *is equal to unity.)*

§ 4.2. A Multiplicative Inequality for Functions that Vanish on a Subset of Ω

In this section we find a necessary and sufficient condition for the validity of the inequality

(1) $$\|u\|_{L_q(\Omega)} \leqslant C \|\nabla u\|_{L_p(\Omega)}^{1-\varkappa} \|u\|_{L_r(\Omega)}^{\varkappa}$$

for all functions that vanish on some subset of Ω.

Let G be an open bounded subset of Ω. For $p>1$ we put

$$\mathfrak{A}_G^{(p,\alpha)} = \sup_{\{F\}} \frac{[m_n(F)]^\alpha}{[c_p(G\backslash F)]^{1/p}},$$

where $\{F\}$ is the collection of closed (in Ω) subsets of G with $c_p(G\backslash F)>0$.

Let $\mathfrak{A}_G^{(1,\alpha)}$ denote the value $\mathfrak{A}_G^{(\alpha)}$ introduced in 3.2.3, i.e.

$$\mathfrak{A}_G^{(1,\alpha)} = \sup_{\{\mathscr{G}\}} \frac{[m_n(\mathscr{G})]^\alpha}{s(\partial_i \mathscr{G})},$$

where $\{\mathscr{G}\}$ is the collection of admissible subsets of G.

The following assertion is a generalization of Lemma 3.2.3/1 (the case $q^* \geqslant p = 1$).

Lemma. *Let $p \geqslant 1$ and let G be an open bounded subset of Ω.*

1) *If $\mathfrak{A}_G^{(p,\alpha)} < \infty$ and the numbers q, α, p satisfy either one of the following conditions*

$$\text{(i)} \quad q \leqslant q^* = \alpha^{-1} \quad \textit{for } \alpha p \leqslant 1,$$

$$\text{(ii)} \quad q < q^* = \alpha^{-1} \quad \textit{for } \alpha p > 1,$$

then for all functions $u \in C^{0,1}(\Omega)$ that vanish in the exterior of G, the inequality (1) *is valid with $r \in (0,q)$, $\varkappa = r(q^*-q)/q(q^*-r)$, $C \leqslant c(\mathfrak{A}_G^{(p,\alpha)})^{1-\varkappa}$.*

2) *Let $q^*>0$, $r \in (0,q^*)$ and for some $q \in (0,q^*]$ and for any function $u \in C^{0,1}(\Omega)$ that vanishes in the exterior of G, let the inequality* (1) *be valid with $\varkappa = r(q^*-q)/q(q^*-r)$ and with a constant C that is independent of u. Then $C \geqslant c(\mathfrak{A}_G^{(p,\alpha)})^{1-\varkappa}$.*

Proof. 1) Duplicating the proof of the first part of Theorem 2.3.4 (for $\mu = m_n$) we arrive at

(2) $$\|u\|_{L_q(\Omega)} \leqslant c \left(\int_0^\infty [m_n(\mathscr{N}_t)]^{p\alpha} t^{p-1} dt \right)^{(1-\varkappa)/p} \|u\|_{L_r(\Omega)}^{\varkappa}.$$

For $p>1$ this implies

$$\|u\|_{L_q(\Omega)} \leqslant c(\mathfrak{A}_G^{(p,\alpha)})^{1-\varkappa} \left(\int_0^\infty c_p(\mathscr{K}_t) t^{p-1} dt \right)^{(1-\varkappa)/p} \|u\|_{L_r(\Omega)}^{\varkappa},$$

where $\mathscr{K}_t$ is the conductor $G\backslash \mathscr{N}_t$. Now the result follows from Lemma 4.1.3/3.

In the case $p=1$ inequality (1) results from (2) along with Lemma 3.1.2/3 and the formula

(3) $$\int_\Omega |\nabla u|\,dx = \int_0^\infty s(\mathscr{E}_t)\,dt$$

(cf. Theorem 1.2.4).

2) Let $p>1$. We fix a small positive number $\delta>0$ and put

$$\beta_\delta = \sup \frac{[m_n(F)]^{p\alpha}}{c_p(G\backslash F)}$$

on the set of all $F \subset G$ with $c_p(G\backslash F) \geqslant \delta$. (The substitution of an arbitrary function in $T_\Omega(G\backslash F)$ into (1) implies

$$[c_p(G\backslash F)]^{1-\varkappa} \geqslant C^{-p}[m_n(F)]^{p/q}[m_n(G)]^{-\varkappa p/r},$$

this means that the collection of sets F, contained in G and satisfying the inequality $c_p(G\backslash F) \geqslant \delta$, is not empty.) Obviously, $\beta_\delta \leqslant \delta^{-1} m_n(G)^{p\alpha}$. Further, we must duplicate the proof of the second part of Theorem 2.3.4 with Lemma 2.2.2/1 replaced by Lemma 4.1.3/1 and with (p, Φ)-cap(F, Ω) replaced by $c_p(G\backslash F)$. Then we arrive at $\beta_\delta \leqslant c C^{p(1-\varkappa)}$ which, since δ is arbitrary, implies $C \geqslant c(\mathfrak{A}_G^{(p,\alpha)})^{1-\varkappa}$ for $p>1$.

Consider the case $p=1$. Let $\mathscr{G}$ be any admissible subset of G. We insert the sequence of functions $\{w_m\}_{m\geqslant 1}$ specified in Lemma 3.2.2 into (1). Then

$$[s(\partial_i \mathscr{G})]^{1-\varkappa} \geqslant C^{-1}[m_n(e)]^{1/q}[m_n(\mathscr{G})]^{-\varkappa/r},$$

which, since e is arbitrary, yields

$$s(\partial_i \mathscr{G}) \geqslant C^{-1}[m_n(\mathscr{G})]^\alpha .$$

The lemma is proved.

Corollary. *If* $p_1 > p \geqslant 1$ *and* $\alpha_1 - p_1^{-1} = \alpha - p^{-1}$, *then* $\mathfrak{A}_G^{(p_1,\alpha_1)} \leqslant c\,\mathfrak{A}_G^{(p,\alpha)}$.

Proof. We put $|u|^{q_1/q}$ with $q_1 > q$, $q_1^{-1} - p_1^{-1} = q^{-1} - p^{-1}$ in place of u in (1). Then

(4) $$\|u\|_{L_{q_1}(\Omega)}^{q_1/q} \leqslant c\left(\frac{q_1}{q}\right)^{1-\varkappa}(\mathfrak{A}_G^{(p,\alpha)})^{1-\varkappa}\||u|^{(q_1-q)/q}\nabla u\|_{L_p(\Omega)}^{1-\varkappa}\|u\|_{L_{r_1}(\Omega)}^{\varkappa q_1/q}$$

where $r_1 = r q_1/q$. Applying the Hölder inequality, we obtain

$$\int_\Omega |u|^{p(q_1-q)/q}|\nabla u|^p dx \leqslant \left(\int_\Omega |u|^{(q_1-q)pp_1/(p_1-p)q}dx\right)^{(p_1-p)/p_1}$$

$$\times\left(\int_\Omega |\nabla u|^{p_1}dx\right)^{p/p_1} = \|u\|_{L_{q_1}(\Omega)}^{(p_1-p)q_1/p_1}\|\nabla u\|_{L_{p_1}(\Omega)}^p .$$

The preceding inequality and (4) imply

$$\|u\|_{L_{q_1}(\Omega)} \leqslant c(\mathfrak{A}_G^{(p,\alpha)})^{1-\varkappa_1} \|\nabla u\|_{L_{p_1}(\Omega)}^{1-\varkappa_1} \|u\|_{L_{r_1}(\Omega)}^{\varkappa_1},$$

where $\varkappa_1 = r_1(q_1^* - q_1)/q_1(q_1^* - r_1)$, $q_1^* = \alpha_1^{-1}$. Using the second part of Lemma 1 we obtain that $\mathfrak{A}_G^{(p_1,\alpha_1)} \leqslant c\mathfrak{A}_G^{(p,\alpha)}$. The corollary is proved.

§ 4.3. The Classes of Sets $\mathscr{J}_{p,\alpha}$

4.3.1. The Definition and Simple Properties of $\mathscr{J}_{p,\alpha}$

Definition 1. A domain Ω belongs to *the class* $\mathscr{J}_{p,\alpha}$ $(p \geqslant 1, \alpha > 0)$ if there exists a constant $M \in (0, m_n(\Omega))$ such that

$$\text{(1)} \qquad \mathfrak{A}_{p,\alpha}(M) \stackrel{\text{def}}{=} \sup_{\{K\}} \frac{[m_n(F)]^\alpha}{[c_p(K)]^{1/p}} < \infty,$$

where $\{K\}$ is the collection of conductors $K = G \backslash F$ in Ω with positive p-conductivity and such that $m_n(G) \leqslant M$.

Proposition 4.1.2/2 implies that $m_n(F) = 0$ for any conductor $K = G\backslash F$ with zero p-conductivity provided $\Omega \in \mathscr{J}_{p,\alpha}$.

Remark. The class $\mathscr{J}_{p,\alpha}$ is empty for $\alpha < (n-p)/np$, $n > p$, since in this case $c_p(B_{2r} \backslash \bar{B}_r) = \text{const}\, r^{n-p}$ and therefore

$$\frac{[m_n(B_r)]^\alpha}{[c_p(B_{2r}\backslash \bar{B}_r)]^{1/p}} = \text{const}\, r^{n(\alpha - (n-p)/np)} \to \infty \qquad \text{as } r \to 0.$$

Proposition 1. *If a domain Ω is the union of a finite number of domains in $\mathscr{J}_{p,\alpha}$, then Ω is in the same class.*

Proof. Let $\Omega = \Omega_1 \cup \Omega_2$, $\Omega_i \in \mathscr{J}_{p,\alpha}$, $i = 1, 2$. Then there exist constants M_1, M_2 such that

$$[m_n(F_i)]^\alpha \leqslant \mathfrak{A}_{p,\alpha}^{(i)}(M_i)\, [c_p(K_i)]^{1/p}$$

for any conductor $K_i = G_i \backslash F_i$ in Ω_i with $m_n(G_i) \leqslant M_i$.

Put $M = \min\{M_1, M_2\}$ and let K denote a conductor $G\backslash F$ with $m_n(G) \leqslant M$. Further let $G_i = G \cap \Omega_i$, $K_i = G_i \backslash F_i$. If $c_p(K_1) = 0$ then $m_n(F_1) = 0$ and hence $m_n(F) = m_n(F_2)$. Therefore

$$[m_n(F)]^\alpha \leqslant \mathfrak{A}_{p,\alpha}^{(2)}(M_2)\, [c_p(K_2)]^{1/p} \leqslant \mathfrak{A}_{p,\alpha}^{(2)}(M_2)\, [c_p(K)]^{1/p}.$$

In the case $c_p(K_i) > 0$, $i = 1, 2$, we have

$$\frac{[m_n(F)]^\alpha}{[c_p(K)]^{1/p}} \leqslant c \left(\frac{[m_n(F_1)]^\alpha}{[c_p(K_1)]^{1/p}} + \frac{[m_n(F_2)]^\alpha}{[c_p(K_2)]^{1/p}} \right) \leqslant c \sum_{i=1}^{2} \mathfrak{A}_{p,\alpha}^{(i)}(M_i).$$

The proposition is proved.

Definition 2. We say that $\mathscr{K}$ is an *admissible conductor* if $\mathscr{K} = \mathscr{G} \setminus \text{clos}_\Omega\, g$, where $\mathscr{G}$ and g are admissible subsets of Ω (cf. the definition at the beginning of 3.1.1).

Proposition 2. *We have*

$$\mathfrak{A}_{p,\alpha}(M) = \sup_{\{\mathscr{K}\}} \frac{[m_n(g)]^\alpha}{[c_p\mathscr{K})]^{1/p}}, \tag{2}$$

where $\{\mathscr{K}\}$ *is the collection of admissible conductors* $\mathscr{K} = \mathscr{G} \setminus \text{clos}_\Omega\, g$ *with positive p-conductivity and with* $m_n(\mathscr{G}) \leqslant M$. (Hence we may restrict ourselves to admissible conductors in the definition of the class $\mathscr{I}_{p,\alpha}$.)

Proof. We prove the inequality

$$\mathfrak{A}_{p,\alpha}(M) \leqslant \sup_{\{\mathscr{K}\}} \frac{[m_n(g)]^\alpha}{[c_p(\mathscr{K})]^{1/p}}. \tag{3}$$

The reverse inequality is obvious. Let K be any conductor in Definition 1. Given any $\varepsilon > 0$ we can find an admissible conductor $\mathscr{K} = \mathscr{G} \setminus \text{clos}_\Omega\, g$, $\mathscr{K} \subset K$, such that $c_p(K) \geqslant (1-\varepsilon)\, c_p(\mathscr{K})$ (cf. Proposition 4.1.2/2). It is clear that $m_n(\mathscr{G}) \leqslant M$ and

$$\frac{[m_n(F)]^\alpha}{[c_p(K)]^{1/p}} \leqslant \frac{[m_n(g)]^\alpha}{(1-\varepsilon)^{1/p}[c_p(\mathscr{K})]^{1/p}},$$

which immediately implies (3).

4.3.2. Identity of the Classes $\mathscr{I}_{1,\alpha}$ and $\mathscr{J}_\alpha$

Lemma. *The classes* $\mathscr{I}_{1,\alpha}$ *and* $\mathscr{J}_\alpha$ *coincide and*

$$\mathfrak{A}_{1,\alpha}(M) = \sup_{\{\mathscr{G}\}} \frac{[m_n(\mathscr{G})]^\alpha}{s(\partial_i \mathscr{G})}, \tag{1}$$

where $\{\mathscr{G}\}$ *is the collection of admissible subsets of* Ω *with* $m_n(\mathscr{G}) \leqslant M$.

Proof. Let $\mathscr{G}$ be an admissible subset of Ω with $m_n(\mathscr{G}) \leqslant M$ and let $\{w_m\}_{m\geqslant 1}$ be the sequence of functions specified in Lemma 3.2.2. The properties of $\{w_m\}$ imply $s(\partial_i \mathscr{G}) \geqslant c_1(\mathscr{G} \setminus e)$ for any compactum e contained in $\mathscr{G}$. If $\Omega \in \mathscr{I}_{1,\alpha}$, then $[m_n(e)]^\alpha \leqslant \mathfrak{A}_{1,\alpha}(M)\, s(\partial_i \mathscr{G})$ and hence

$$[m_n(\mathscr{G})]^\alpha = \sup_{e \subset \mathscr{G}} [m_n(e)]^\alpha \leqslant \mathfrak{A}_{1,\alpha}(M)\, s(\partial_i \mathscr{G}).$$

Suppose $\Omega \in \mathscr{J}_\alpha$. Let K be an arbitrary conductor $G \setminus F$ with $m_n(G) \leqslant M$. By (4.2/3) for any $f \in T_\Omega(K)$ we obtain

(2) $$\int_\Omega |\nabla f| dx \geqslant \inf_{\{\mathscr{G}\}} \{s(\partial_i \mathscr{G}) : G \supset \mathscr{G} \supset F\} \geqslant \inf_{\{\mathscr{G}\}} \frac{s(\partial_i \mathscr{G})}{[m_n(\mathscr{G})]^\alpha} [m_n(F)]^\alpha .$$

By Lemma 4.1.1/2 we have

$$\inf\{\int |\nabla f| dx : f \in T_\Omega(K)\} = c_1(K) ,$$

so (2) implies

$$\mathfrak{A}_{1,\alpha}(M) \leqslant \sup_{\{\mathscr{G}\}} \frac{[m_n(\mathscr{G})]^\alpha}{s(\partial_i \mathscr{G})} .$$

The result follows.

4.3.3. A Necessary and Sufficient Condition for the Validity of a Multiplicative Inequality for Functions in $W_{p,s}^1(\Omega)$

Lemmas 4.2, 4.3.2 imply the following obvious assertion.

Corollary. 1) *Let $\mathfrak{A}_{p,\alpha}(M) < \infty$ for some $M \in (0, m_n(\Omega))$.*

Then for all $u \in C^{0,1}(\Omega)$ with $m_n(\operatorname{supp} u) \leqslant M$ inequality (4.2/1) *is valid with $r \in (0, q)$, $\varkappa = r(q^* - q)/q(q^* - r)$, q being the number specified in Lemma* 4.2/1 *and $C \leqslant c[\mathfrak{A}_{p,\alpha}(M)]^{1-\varkappa}$.*

2) *If* (4.2/1) *is valid for all $u \in C^{0,1}(\Omega)$ with $m_n(\operatorname{supp} u) \leqslant M < m_n(\Omega)$, then $C \geqslant c[\mathfrak{A}_{p,\alpha}(M)]^{1-\varkappa}$.*

The introduction of the classes $\mathscr{I}_{p,\alpha}$ is justified by the following theorem.

Theorem. 1) *Let $\Omega \in \mathscr{I}_{p,\alpha}$ and let q be a positive number satisfying any one of the conditions:* (i) *$q \leqslant q^* = \alpha^{-1}$ for $p \leqslant q^*$ or* (ii) *$q < q^*$ for $p > q^*$.*

Then for any $u \in W_{p,s}^1(\Omega)$ we have

(1) $$\|u\|_{L_q(\Omega)} \leqslant (C_1 \|\nabla u\|_{L_p(\Omega)} + C_2 \|u\|_{L_s(\Omega)})^{1-\varkappa} \|u\|_{L_r(\Omega)}^\varkappa ,$$

where $s < q^*$, $r < q$, $\varkappa = r(q^* - q)/q(q^* - r)$, $C_2 = cM^{(s-q^*)/sq^*}$ and $C_1 \leqslant c\mathfrak{A}_{p,\alpha}(M)$.

2) *Let $q^* > 0$ and for some $q \in (0, q^*]$ and all $u \in W_{p,s}^1(\Omega)$, let inequality* (1) *be valid with $0 < s < q^*$, $0 < r < q^*$, $\varkappa = r(q^* - q)/q(q^* - r)$.*

Then $\Omega \in \mathscr{I}_{p,\alpha}$ with $\alpha = 1/q^*$. Moreover, if the constant M in the definition of the class $\mathscr{I}_{p,\alpha}$ is specified by $M = cC_2^{sq^*/(s-q^*)}$, where c is a small enough positive constant depending only on p, q^*, s, then $C_1 \geqslant c\mathfrak{A}_{p,\alpha}(M)$.

Proof. 1) By Lemma 4.1.1/1 it suffices to obtain (1) for functions $u \in L_p^1(\Omega) \cap L_\infty(\Omega) \cap C^\infty(\Omega)$ with bounded supports. Let $T = \inf\{t : m_n(\mathscr{N}_t) < M\}$. Clearly, $m_n(\mathscr{L}_t) \leqslant M \leqslant m_n(\mathscr{N}_t)$. Further we note that

(2) $$\int_\Omega |u|^q dx \leqslant \int_{\Omega \backslash \mathscr{N}_T} |u|^q dx + cT^q m_n(\mathscr{N}_T) + c\int_{\mathscr{N}_T} (|u| - T)^q dx .$$

To get a bound for the first summand on the right we rewrite it as follows:

$$\int_{\Omega\setminus\mathscr{N}_T} |u|^q dx = \int_{\Omega\setminus\mathscr{N}_T} |u|^{q^*(q-r)/(q^*-r)} |u|^{r(q^*-q)/(q^*-r)} dx$$

and use the Hölder inequality

$$\int_{\Omega\setminus\mathscr{N}_T} |u|^q dx \leqslant \left(\int_{\Omega\setminus\mathscr{N}_T} |u|^{q^*} dx\right)^{(q-r)/(q^*-r)} \left(\int_{\Omega\setminus\mathscr{N}_T} |u|^r dx\right)^{(q^*-q)/(q^*-r)} .$$

Since $u < T$ on $\Omega\setminus\mathscr{N}_T$ then the right-hand side of the latter estimate does not exceed

$$T^{(q^*-s)(q-r)/(q^*-r)} \left(\int_{\Omega\setminus\mathscr{N}_T} |u|^s dx\right)^{(q-r)/(q^*-r)} \left(\int_{\Omega\setminus\mathscr{N}_T} |u|^r dx\right)^{(q^*-q)/(q^*-r)} .$$

This implies

$$\text{(3)} \qquad \int_{\Omega\setminus\mathscr{N}_T} |u|^q dx \leqslant M^{(s-q^*)(q-r)/s(q^*-r)} \left(\int_{\Omega\setminus\mathscr{N}_T} |u|^r dx\right)^{(q^*-q)/(q^*-r)}$$

$$\times \left(\int_{\mathscr{N}_T} |u|^s dx\right)^{(q^*-s)(q-r)/s(q^*-r)} \left(\int_{\Omega\setminus\mathscr{N}_T} |u|^s dx\right)^{(q-r)/(q^*-r)}$$

$$\leqslant M^{(s-q^*)(q-r)/s(q^*-r)} \left(\int_{\Omega} |u|^s dx\right)^{q^*(q-r)/s(q^*-r)}$$

$$\times \left(\int_{\Omega} |u|^r dx\right)^{(q^*-q)/(q^*-r)} .$$

Next we estimate the second summand on the right in (2). Since $|u(x)| \geqslant T$ on $\mathscr{N}_T$ and $m_n(\mathscr{N}_T) \geqslant M$ then

$$T^q m_n(\mathscr{N}_T) \leqslant M^{(s-q^*)(q-r)/s(q^*-r)} \left(\int_{\mathscr{N}_T} |u|^s dx\right)^{q^*(q-r)/s(q^*-r)}$$

$$\times \left(\int_{\mathscr{N}_T} |u|^r dx\right)^{(q^*-q)/(q^*-r)} .$$

Combining this inequality with (3) and (2) we arrive at

$$\|u\|_{L_q(\Omega)} \leqslant c\|(|u|-T)^+\|_{L_q(\Omega)} + cM^{(1-\varkappa)(s-q^*)/sq^*} \|u\|^{1-\varkappa}_{L_s(\Omega)} \|u\|^{\varkappa}_{L_r(\Omega)} .$$

It remains to apply the first part of Corollary to $(|u|-T)^+$.

2) Let M be an arbitrary constant satisfying

$$2c_0 M^{1/s-1/q^*} C_2 < 1 ,$$

where c_0 is a constant that depends only on s, p, q, q^*, r which will be specified at the end of the proof.

Let δ denote a small enough positive number; by K we mean the conductor $G\backslash F$ in Ω with $m_n(G)\leqslant M$, $c_p(K)\geqslant\delta$. Further we introduce the function $\beta_\delta=\sup[m_n(G)]^{p/q}/c_p(K)$ where the supremum is taken over the above set of conductors. It is clear that $\beta_\delta<\infty$ and

$$\mathfrak{A}_{p,\alpha}(M)=\lim_{\delta\to+0}\beta_\delta^{1/p}\,. \tag{4}$$

Since $s<q^*$ then for any $u\in T_\Omega(K)$ we have

$$\|u\|_{L_s(\Omega)}\leqslant c\left(\sup_{0<t<1}\frac{[m_n(\mathcal{N}_t)]^{1/q^*}}{[c_p(G\backslash\mathcal{N}_t)]^{1/p}}\|\nabla u\|_{L_p(\Omega)}\right)^{q^*(s-t)/s(q^*-t)}\|u\|_{L_t(\Omega)}^{t(q^*-s)/s(q^*-t)}\,,$$

where $t<s$ (cf. the proof of the first part of Lemma 4.2/1).

Now we note that $[m_n(\mathcal{N}_t)]^{p/q^*}\leqslant\beta_\delta c_p(G\backslash\mathcal{N}_t)$ since $c_p(G\backslash\mathcal{N}_t)\geqslant c_p(K)\geqslant\delta$. Besides,

$$\|u\|_{L_t(\Omega)}\leqslant M^{1/t-1/s}\|u\|_{L_s(\Omega)}\,.$$

Consequently,

$$\|u\|_{L_s(\Omega)}\leqslant cM^{1/s-1/q}\beta_\delta^{1/p}\|\nabla u\|_{L_p(\Omega)}\,.$$

Using the preceding estimate, from (1) we obtain

$$[m_n(F)]^{1/q}\leqslant(C_1+c\beta_\delta^{1/p}M^{1/s-1/q^*}C_2)^{1-\varkappa}\|\nabla u\|_{L_p(\Omega)}^{1-\varkappa}\|u\|_{L_r(\Omega)}^{\varkappa}\,.$$

Further, we must duplicate the proof of the second part of Theorem 2.3.4 with Lemma 2.2.2/3 replaced by Lemma 4.1.3/1 and with (p,Φ)-cap(F,G) replaced by $c_p(K)$. As a result we obtain

$$\beta_\delta^{1/p}\leqslant c(C_1+\beta_\delta^{1/p}M^{1/s-1/q^*}C_2)\,.$$

The latter and the definition of the constant M imply

$$\beta_\delta(M)\leqslant(2c_0C_1)^p\,.$$

It remains to make use of (4). This completes the proof.

4.3.4. The Function $\nu_{M,p}$ and the Relationship of the Classes $\mathcal{J}_{p,\alpha}$ and $\mathcal{J}_\alpha$

Definition. Let $\nu_{M,p}(t)$ be the infimum of $c_p(K)$ taken over the collection of all conductors $K=G\backslash F$ with $m_n(F)\geqslant t$, $m_n(G)\leqslant M$.

By an argument similar to that in the proof of Proposition 4.3.1/2 we can prove that we may restrict ourselves to admissible conductors in this definition.

Inequality (4.2.3/3) immediately implies the following assertion on the connection of $\nu_{M,p}$ with the function λ_M introduced in 3.2.4.

Proposition 1. *The inequality*

(1) $$v_{M,p}(t) \geqslant \left(\int_t^M [\lambda_M(\sigma)]^{p/(1-p)}\, d\sigma\right)^{1-p}$$

is valid.

Obviously, for $p \geqslant 1$

(2) $$\mathfrak{A}_{p,\alpha}(M) = \sup_{0<t\leqslant M} t^{\alpha}[v_{M,p}(t)]^{-1/p}.$$

Hence $\Omega \in \mathscr{I}_{p,\alpha}$ if and only if

(3) $$\liminf_{t\to+0} t^{-\alpha p} v_{M,p}(t) > 0.$$

We have noted already in 3.2.4 that $\Omega \in \mathscr{J}_{\alpha} = \mathscr{I}_{1,\alpha}$ if and only if

$$\liminf_{t\to+0} t^{-\alpha}\lambda_M(t) > 0.$$

Proposition 2. *If* $\Omega \in \mathscr{J}_{\alpha+(p-1)/p}$ *then* $\Omega \in \mathscr{I}_{p,\alpha}$ *and*

(4) $$\mathfrak{A}_{p,\alpha}(M) \leqslant \left(\frac{p-1}{p\alpha}\right)^{(p-1)/p} \mathfrak{A}_{1,\alpha+(p-1)/p}(M).$$

Proof. From (1) we obtain

$$v_{M,p}(t) \geqslant [\mathfrak{A}_{1,\alpha+(p-1)/p}(M)]^{-p}\left(\int_t^M \sigma^{-(p\alpha+p-1)/(p-1)}\, d\sigma\right)^{1-p}$$

$$> \left(\frac{p\alpha}{p-1}\right)^{p-1} [\mathfrak{A}_{1,\alpha+(p-1)/p}(M)]^{-p} t^{\alpha p}.$$

The result follows.

By Corollary 4.2 the class $\mathscr{I}_{p,\alpha}$ is a part of the class $\mathscr{I}_{p_1,\alpha_1}$ and $\mathfrak{A}_{p_1,\alpha_1}(M) \leqslant c\,\mathfrak{A}_{p,\alpha}(M)$ provided $p_1 > p \geqslant 1$ and $\alpha_1 - p_1^{-1} = \alpha - p^{-1}$.

4.3.5. Estimates for $v_{M,p}$ for Certain Concrete Domains

We consider some domains for which explicit two-sided estimates for $v_{M,p}$ are valid.

Example 1. Let Ω be the domain $\{x: |x'| < f(x_n),\ 0 < x_n < a\}$ considered at the beginning of subsection 3.3.3.

We show that

(1) $$k^p\left(\int_{\alpha(\mu)}^{\alpha(M)} [f(\tau)]^{(1-n)/(p-1)}\, d\tau\right)^{1-p} \leqslant v_{M,p}(\mu) \leqslant \left(\int_{\alpha(\mu)}^{\alpha(M)} [f(\tau)]^{(1-n)/(p-1)}\, d\tau\right)^{1-p},$$

where k is the constant in the inequality (4.3.2/2) that depends on M and the function α is specified by

$$\mu = v_{n-1} \int_0^{\alpha(\mu)} [f(\tau)]^{n-1} d\tau .$$

Consider the conductor $K_{\mu,M} = G_{\alpha(M)} \setminus \operatorname{clos}_\Omega G_{\alpha(\mu)}$, where $G_\alpha = \{x \in \Omega: 0 < x_n < \alpha\}$. Let the function u be defined by $u(x) = 0$ outside $G_{\alpha(M)}$, $u(x) = 1$ on $G_{\alpha(\mu)}$, and

$$u(x) = \int_{x_n}^{\alpha(M)} \frac{d\tau}{[f(\tau)]^{(n-1)/(p-1)}} \left(\int_{\alpha(\mu)}^{\alpha(M)} \frac{d\tau}{[f(\tau)]^{(n-1)/(p-1)}} \right)^{-1} \quad \text{on } G_{\alpha(M)} \setminus G_{\alpha(\mu)} .$$

Clearly, u is contained in $U_\Omega(K_{\mu,M})$. So by inserting u into the integral

$$\int_\Omega |\nabla u|^p dx$$

we obtain

$$c_p(K_{\mu,M}) \leqslant \left(\int_{\alpha(\mu)}^{\alpha(M)} [f(\tau)]^{(1-n)/(p-1)} d\tau \right)^{1-p} .$$

Taking into account the definition of $v_{M,p}(\mu)$, we arrive at the right inequality (1).

Substituting the left inequality (3.3.3/1) into (4.3.4/1) we obtain the required lower bound for $v_{M,p}$.

From (1) we obtain that $\Omega \in \mathscr{I}_{p,\alpha}$ if and only if

$$\limsup_{x \to +0} \left(\int_0^x [f(\tau)]^{n-1} d\tau \right)^{\alpha p/(p-1)} \int_x^a [f(\tau)]^{(1-n)/(p-1)} d\tau < \infty .$$

In particular, for the domain

$$\Omega^{(\lambda)} = \{x: (x_1^2 + \cdots + x_{n-1}^2)^{1/2} < a x_n^\lambda, \ 0 < x_n < 1\} , \tag{2}$$

with $\lambda > (p-1)/(n-1)$, for small t we have $c t^{\alpha p} \leqslant v_{M,p}(t) \leqslant c' t^{\alpha p}$ where $\alpha = [\lambda(n-1) + 1 - p]/p[\lambda(n-1)+1]$. Thus the domain (2) is contained in $\mathscr{I}_{p,\alpha}$ for $p\alpha < 1$.

Example 2. Let Ω be the domain in Example 3.3.3/2. Using the estimates (3.3.3/4) for λ_M and following the same discussion as in Example 1 we obtain

$$k^p \left(\int_{\alpha(M)}^{\alpha(\mu)} [f(\tau)]^{(1-n)/(p-1)} d\tau \right)^{1-p} \leqslant v_{M,p}(\mu) \leqslant \left(\int_{\alpha(M)}^{\alpha(\mu)} [f(\tau)]^{(1-n)/(p-1)} d\tau \right)^{1-p} . \tag{3}$$

Consequently, $\Omega \in \mathscr{I}_{p,\alpha}$ if and only if

$$\limsup_{x\to+\infty}\left(\int_x^\infty [f(\tau)]^{n-1}d\tau\right)^{\alpha p/(p-1)}\int_0^x [f(\tau)]^{(1-n)/(p-1)}d\tau<\infty\,.$$

In particular, for the domain

$$\{x\colon x_1^2+\cdots+x_{n-1}^2<(1+x_n)^{-2\beta},\ 0<x_n<\infty\}$$

with $\beta(n-1)>1$ we have

$$ct^{\alpha p}\leqslant \nu_{M,p}(t)\leqslant c' t^{\alpha p}\quad \text{for small } t\,,$$

provided $\alpha p=[\beta(n-1)-1+p][\beta(n-1)-1]^{-1}$. Here $\alpha p>1$.

For the domain

$$\{x\colon x_1^2+\cdots+x_{n-1}^2<e^{-cx_n},\ 0<x_n<\infty\}\,,\qquad c=\text{const}>0\,,$$

from (3) we obtain

$$c\mu\leqslant \nu_{M,p}(\mu)\leqslant c'\mu$$

and hence this domain is in $\mathcal{I}_{p,1/p}$.

Example 3. Let Ω be the plane domain considered in Example 3.3.3/3. Proposition 3 along with the lower bound (3.3.3/6) for λ yields the following lower bound for $\nu_{M,p}(t)$:

$$\nu_{M,p}(t)\geqslant C_M^{(1)}\left(\int_{\theta(M)}^{\theta(t)}[\delta(\theta)]^{-1/(p-1)}d\theta\right)^{1-p}, \tag{4}$$

where $\theta(t)$ is specified by (3.3.3/7) and $\delta=\varepsilon_2-\varepsilon_1$.

To derive a similar upper bound consider the conductor $G_{\theta(t)}\backslash \operatorname{clos}_\Omega G_{\theta(M)}$, where $G_\theta=\{\varrho e^{i\varphi}\in\Omega\colon 0<\varphi<\theta\}$ and the function u is defined by

$$u=0\quad\text{outside } G_{\theta(t)}\,,\qquad u=1\quad\text{on } G_{\theta(M)}\,,$$

$$u(\theta)=\int_{\theta(M)}^{\theta}[\delta(\varphi)]^{1/(1-p)}d\varphi\left(\int_{\theta(M)}^{\theta(t)}[\delta(\varphi)]^{1/(1-p)}d\varphi\right)^{-1}\quad\text{on } G_{\theta(t)}\backslash \bar G_{\theta(M)}\,.$$

It is clear that

$$\begin{aligned}c_p[G_{\theta(t)}\backslash \operatorname{clos}_\Omega G_{\theta(M)}]&\leqslant \iint_{G_{\theta(t)}\backslash G_{\theta(M)}}|\varrho^{-1}u'(\varphi)|^p\varrho\, d\varrho\, d\varphi\\ &\leqslant C_M^{(2)}\left(\int_{\theta(M)}^{\theta(t)}[\delta(\varphi)]^{1/(1-p)}d\varphi\right)^{1-p}.\end{aligned}$$

This and (4) imply

$$C_M^{(1)}\left(\int_{\theta(M)}^{\theta(t)}[\delta(\varphi)]^{1/(1-p)}d\varphi\right)^{1-p}\leqslant \nu_{M,p}(t)\leqslant C_M^{(2)}\left(\int_{\theta(M)}^{\theta(t)}[\delta(\varphi)]^{1/(1-p)}d\varphi\right)^{1-p}. \tag{5}$$

In particular, for the domain

$$(6)\quad \{\varrho e^{i\theta}: 1-(8+\theta)^{1-\beta} > \varrho > 1-(8+\theta)^{1-\beta} - c(8+\theta)^{-\beta}, 0<\theta<\infty\},$$

with $0<c<2\pi(\beta-1)$, $\beta>1$, we have $ct^{\alpha p} \leqslant \nu_{M,p}(t) \leqslant c' t^{\alpha p}$ for small t, where $\alpha = (\beta-1+p)/p(\beta-1)$. Thus (6) is a bounded domain in the class $\mathscr{I}_{p,\alpha}$ for $p\alpha > 1$.

Example 4. We show that the adjoining nonintersecting cylinders

$$G_j = \{x: |x_n - \alpha_j| < a_j,\ x_1^2 + \cdots + x_{n-1}^2 < b_j^2\}$$

with $\sum_j a_j b_j^{n-1} < \infty$ (cf. Fig. 15) form a domain which is not in $\mathscr{I}_{p,1/p}$ if $\limsup_{j\to\infty} a_j = \infty$. Let

$$F_j = \{x \in G_j: |x_n - \alpha_j| \leqslant a_j/2\}$$

and let $\eta \in C_0^\infty([0,1))$, $\eta(t) = 1$ for $0 \leqslant t < \frac{1}{2}$. We insert the function $\eta(|x_n - \alpha_j|/a_j)$ into the norm $\|\nabla u\|_{L_p(G_j)}$. Then

$$c_p(G_j \backslash F_j) \leqslant c a_j^{-p} m_n(F_j)\ .$$

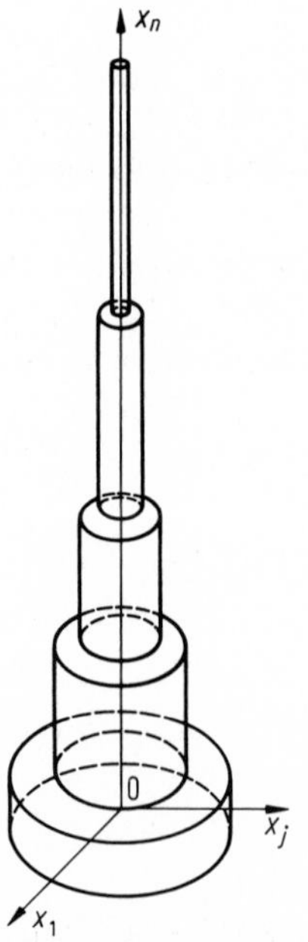

Fig. 15

So

$$\liminf_{\mu\to 0} \mu^{-1} \nu_{M,p}(\mu) = 0 .$$

§ 4.4. The Imbedding $W^1_{p,s}(\Omega) \subset L_{q^*}(\Omega)$ for $q^* < p$

4.4.1. An Estimate for the Norm in $L_{q^*}(\Omega)$ with $q^* < p$ for Functions that Vanish on a Subset of Ω

If $\Omega \in \mathcal{I}_{p,\alpha}$ with $\alpha p \leqslant 1$ then by Theorem 4.3.3 the imbedding operator of $W^1_{p,s}(\Omega)$ into $L_{q^*}(\Omega)$ with $q^* = \alpha^{-1}$ is bounded. The following example shows that inequality (4.3.3/1) with the limit exponent $q = q^* = \alpha^{-1}$ may fail provided $\alpha p > 1$ (or, equivalently, provided $p > q^*$).

Example. Consider the plane domain

$$\Omega = \{(x_1, x_2) \colon |x_1| < (1 + x_2)^{-\beta},\ 0 < x_2 < \infty\}$$

with $\beta > 1$. In Example 4.3.5/2 it was established that this domain is in the class $\mathcal{I}_{p,1/p+1/(\beta-1)}$. We show that inequality (4.3.3/1) is not valid for $q = q^* = p(\beta-1)/(p+\beta-1)$.

The sequence of functions $u_m(x_1, x_2) = (1+x_2)^{\gamma_m}$ with $\gamma_m < 1 + (\beta-1)/p$, $m = 1, 2, \ldots$, satisfies

$$\| u \|^{q^*}_{L_{q^*}(\Omega)} = 2[1 + (\beta-1)/p]/[\beta - 1 - p(\gamma_m - 1)] ,$$

$$\| \nabla u_m \|^p_{L_p(\Omega)} = 2\gamma_m/[\beta - 1 - p(\gamma_m - 1)], \ \| u_m \|^s_{L_s(\Omega)} = 2/(\beta - 1 - \gamma_m s) .$$

Since $s < q^* < p$, then the left-hand side in (4.3.3/1), written for u_m, tends to infinity as $m \to \infty$ more rapidly than the right-hand side. Thus the inclusion $\Omega \in \mathcal{I}_{p,\alpha}$ with $p > q^* = \alpha^{-1}$ is necessary but not sufficient for the validity of (4.3.3/1) with the limit exponent $q = q^*$. The necessary, for $q \geqslant 1$, and sufficient, for $q > 0$, condition will be derived in Theorem 4.4.2.

Let G be a bounded open subset of Ω. Let $S(G)$ denote any nondecreasing sequence $\{G_j\}$ $(-\infty < j < \infty)$ of open subsets of G. We introduce the conductor $K_j = G_{j+1} \backslash \mathrm{clos}_\Omega G_j$ and put

$$\mathfrak{B}^{(p,\alpha)}_G = \sup_{\{S(G)\}} \left[\sum_{j=-\infty}^{+\infty} \frac{[m_n(G_j)]^{\alpha p/(\alpha p - 1)}}{[c_p(K_j)]^{1/(\alpha p - 1)}} \right]^{\alpha - 1/p} ,$$

where $\alpha p > 1$, $p \geqslant 1$.

Lemma. 1) *Let* $\mathfrak{B}^{(p,\alpha)}_G < \infty$. *Then the inequality*

$$\| u \|_{L_{q^*}(\Omega)} \leqslant C \| \nabla u \|_{L_p(\Omega)} \tag{1}$$

is valid for all $u \in C^{0,1}(\Omega)$ *that vanish outside* G, *with* $q^* = \alpha^{-1}$, $\alpha p > 1$ *and* $C \leqslant c \mathfrak{B}^{(p,\alpha)}_G$.

2) *If* (1) *is valid for all* $u \in C^{0,1}(\Omega)$ *that vanish outside* G, *with some* $q^* \in [1,p)$, *then* $C \geqslant c\mathfrak{B}_G^{(p,\alpha)}$.

Proof. 1) By virtue of Theorem 1.2.3

$$\|u\|^{q^*}_{L_{q^*}(\Omega)} = \sum_{j=-\infty}^{+\infty} \int_{2^j}^{2^{j+1}} m_n(\mathcal{N}_t)\, d(t^{q^*}) \leqslant (2^{q^*}-1) \sum_{j=-\infty}^{+\infty} 2^{jq^*} m_n(\mathcal{N}_{2^j}),$$

where, as usual, $\mathcal{N}_t = \{x : |u(x)| \geqslant t\}$. Applying the Hölder inequality, we obtain

$$\|u\|_{L_{q^*}(\Omega)} \leqslant (2^{q^*}-1)^{1/q^*} \left\{ \sum_{j=-\infty}^{+\infty} \left[\frac{[m_n(\mathcal{N}_{2^j})]^{p/q^*}}{c_p(\mathcal{L}_{2^{j-1}} \backslash \mathcal{N}_{2^j})} \right]^{q^*/(p-q^*)} \right\}^{1/q^*-1/p}$$

$$\times \left[\sum_{j=-\infty}^{+\infty} 2^{jp} c_p(\mathcal{L}_{2^{j-1}} \backslash \mathcal{N}_{2^j}) \right]^{1/p}.$$

Let v_j be defined as follows: $v_j = 1$ on $\mathcal{N}_{2^j}$, $v_j = 2^{1-j}|u| - 1$ on $\mathcal{L}_{2^{j-1}} \backslash \mathcal{N}_{2^j}$, $v_j = 0$ on $\Omega \backslash \mathcal{L}_{2^{j-1}}$. Since $v_j \in U_\Omega(\mathcal{L}_{2^{j-1}} \backslash \mathcal{N}_{2^j})$, then

$$c_p(\mathcal{L}_{2^{j-1}} \backslash \mathcal{N}_{2^j}) \leqslant \int_\Omega |\nabla v_j|^p dx = 2^{(1-j)p} \int_{\mathcal{L}_{2^{j-1}} \backslash \mathcal{N}_{2^j}} |\nabla u|^p dx.$$

Therefore,

$$\|u\|_{L_{q^*}(\Omega)} \leqslant 2(2^{q^*}-1)\mathfrak{B}_G^{(p,\alpha)} \left(\sum_{j=-\infty}^{+\infty} \int_{\mathcal{L}_{2^{j-1}} \backslash \mathcal{N}_{2^j}} |\nabla u|^p dx \right)^{1/p} = c\mathfrak{B}_G^{(p,\alpha)} \|\nabla u\|_{L_p(\Omega)}.$$

2) Consider some sequence in $S(G)$ and put

$$t_\nu = \sum_{j=\nu}^{N} \left(\frac{[m_n(G_j)]^{p/q^*}}{c_p(K_j)} \right)^{q^*/(p-q^*)}$$

for $\nu \leqslant N$, $t_\nu = 0$ for $\nu > N$, $t_\nu = t_{-N}$ for $\nu < -N$. Let u_ν denote an arbitrary function in $U_\Omega(K_\nu)$. Further, we define u in Ω by the equality

$$u(x) = (t_\nu - t_{\nu+1}) u_\nu(x) + t_{\nu+1}, \qquad x \in K_\nu.$$

Since $u \in C^{0,1}(\Omega)$ and $u = 0$ outside G, it satisfies (1).

Using Theorem 1.2.3, we obtain

$$\sum_{j=-N}^{N} (t_j^{q^*} - t_{j+1}^{q^*}) m_n(G_j) \leqslant \int_\Omega u^{q^*} dx.$$

This inequality, (1) and the inequality $(t_j - t_{j+1})^{q^*} \leqslant t_j^{q^*} - t_{j+1}^{q^*}$ imply

$$\left[\sum_{j=-N}^{N} (t_j - t_{j+1})^{q^*} m_n(G_j) \right]^{p/q^*} \leqslant C^p \sum_{j=-N}^{N} \int_{K_j} |\nabla u|^p dx$$

$$= C \sum_{j=-N}^{N} (t_j - t_{j+1})^p \int_\Omega |\nabla u_j|^p dx .$$

Since u_j is an arbitrary function in $U_\Omega(K_j)$, then by minimizing the last sum we obtain

$$\left[\sum_{j=-N}^{N} (t_j - t_{j+1})^{q^*} m_n(G_j) \right]^{p/q^*} \leqslant C \sum_{j=-\infty}^{N} c_p(K_j)(t_j - t_{j+1})^p .$$

Finally, noting that

$$t_j - t_{j+1} = \left(\frac{m_n(G_j)}{c_p(K_j)} \right)^{1/(p-q^*)}, \quad |j| \leqslant N ,$$

we arrive at

$$\sum_{j=-N}^{N} \left(\frac{[m_n(G_j)]^{p/q^*}}{c_p(K_j)} \right)^{q^*/(p-q^*)} \leqslant C^{pq^*/(p-q^*)} .$$

4.4.2. The Class $\mathscr{H}_{p,\alpha}$ and the Imbedding $W^1_{p,s}(\Omega) \subset L_{q^*}(\Omega)$ for $q^* < p$

In this subsection we introduce the classes of sets which are adequate for stating a necessary and sufficient condition for the imbedding $W^1_{p,s}(\Omega) \subset L_{q^*}(\Omega)$ with $q^* < p$.

Let $\alpha p > 1$. We put

$$\mathfrak{B}_{p,\alpha}(M) = \sup_{\{S\}} \left[\sum_{j=-\infty}^{+\infty} \frac{[m_n(G_j)]^{\alpha p/(p-1)}}{[c_p(K_j)]^{1/(\alpha p-1)}} \right]^{\alpha - 1/p},$$

where M is a constant in $(0, m_n(\Omega))$ and $\{S\}$ is the collection of all nondecreasing sequences S of bounded open sets G_j, $-\infty < j < \infty$, contained in Ω with $m_n(\bigcup_j G_j) \leqslant M$. The conductor $G_{j+1} \setminus \operatorname{clos}_\Omega G_j$ is denoted by K_j.

Definition. The set Ω belongs to *the class* $\mathscr{H}_{p,\alpha}$ provided $\mathfrak{B}_{p,\alpha}(M) < \infty$ for some $M \in (0, m_n(\Omega))$.

The next corollary immediately follows from Lemma 4.4.1.

Corollary 1. 1) *Let* $\alpha p > 1$ *and* $\mathfrak{B}_{p,\alpha}(M) < \infty$. *Then for all* $u \in C^{0,1}(\Omega)$ *such that* $m_n(\operatorname{supp} u) \leqslant M$ *we have* (4.4.1/1) *with* $q^* = \alpha^{-1}$ *and* $C \leqslant c\mathfrak{B}_{p,\alpha}(M)$.

2) *If* (4.4.1/1) *is valid for all* $u \in C^{0,1}(\Omega)$ *with* $m_n(\operatorname{supp} u) \leqslant M$, *then* $C \geqslant c\mathfrak{B}_{p,\alpha}(M)$.

Duplicating with obvious simplifications the proof of Theorem 4.3.3 we obtain the following theorem from Corollary 1.

Theorem. 1) *Let* $\alpha p > 1$, $\Omega \in \mathscr{H}_{p,\alpha}$. *Then*

$$\|u\|_{L_{q^*}(\Omega)} \leqslant C_1 \|\nabla u\|_{L_p(\Omega)} + C_2 \|u\|_{L_s(\Omega)} \tag{1}$$

for all $u \in W_{p,s}^1(\Omega)$ *with* $q^* = \alpha^{-1}$, $s < q^*$, $C_2 = cM^{(s-q^*)/sq^*}$, $C_1 \leqslant c\mathfrak{B}_{p,\alpha}(M)$.

2) *Let* (1) *be valid for all* $u \in W_{p,s}^1(\Omega)$ *with* $1 \leqslant q^* < p$, $s < q^*$. *Then* $\Omega \in \mathscr{H}_{p,\alpha}$. *Moreover, if* M *in the definition of* $\mathscr{H}_{p,\alpha}$ *is specified by* $M = cC_2^{sq^*/(s-q^*)}$, *where c is a small enough positive constant that depends only on p*, q^*, *s, then* $C_1 \geqslant c\mathfrak{B}_{p,\alpha}(M)$.

Corollary 2. *If* $p_1 > p \geqslant 1$ *and* $\alpha_1 - p_1^{-1} = \alpha - p^{-1}$, *then* $\mathfrak{B}_G^{(p_1,\alpha_1)} \leqslant c\mathfrak{B}_G^{(p,\alpha)}$ *for any G. (Consequently,* $\mathfrak{B}_{p_1,\alpha_1}(M) \leqslant c\mathfrak{B}_{p,\alpha}(M)$ *and* $\mathscr{H}_{p,\alpha} \subset \mathscr{H}_{p_1,\alpha_1}$.)

This assertion can be proved in the same way as Corollary 4.2.

4.4.3. The Imbedding $L_p^1(\Omega) \subset L_{q^*}(\Omega)$ for a Domain with Finite Volume

We present a necessary and sufficient condition for the validity of "the Poincaré inequality"

$$\inf_{c \in R^1} \| u - c \|_{L_{q^*}(\Omega)} \leqslant C \| \nabla u \|_{L_p(\Omega)}, \tag{1}$$

provided Ω is a domain with $m_n(\Omega) < \infty$.

By Lemma 3.2.3/2 the imbedding $L_p^1(\Omega) \subset L_{q^*}(\Omega) (p \geqslant 1, q^* \geqslant 1)$ and inequality (1) are equivalent. The case $m_n(\Omega) = \infty$ is considered in 4.7.5.

Theorem 1. *Let* Ω *be a domain with finite volume.*

1) *If* $\mathfrak{A}_{p,\alpha}(\frac{1}{2}m_n(\Omega)) < \infty$ *for* $\alpha p \leqslant 1$ *or* $\mathfrak{B}_{p,\alpha}(\frac{1}{2}m_n(\Omega)) < \infty$ *for* $\alpha p > 1$, *then* (1) *is valid for all* $u \in L_p^1(\Omega)$ *with* $q^* = \alpha^{-1}$, $C \leqslant c\mathfrak{A}_{p,\alpha}(\frac{1}{2}m_n(\Omega))$ *for* $\alpha p \leqslant 1$ *and* $C \leqslant c\mathfrak{B}_{p,\alpha}(\frac{1}{2}m_n(\Omega))$ *for* $\alpha p > 1$.

2) *If there exists a constant C such that (1) is valid for all* $u \in L_p^1(\Omega)$ *with* $q^* \geqslant 1$, *then* $C \geqslant c\mathfrak{A}_{p,\alpha}(\frac{1}{2}m_n(\Omega))$ *for* $\alpha^{-1} = q^* \geqslant p$ *and* $C \geqslant c\mathfrak{B}_{p,\alpha}(\frac{1}{2}m_n(\Omega))$ *for* $\alpha^{-1} = q^* < p$.

Proof. The proof of *sufficiency* follows the same argument as in the proof of Theorem 3.2.3 except that we must apply Corollary 4.3.3 instead of Lemma 3.2.3/1 for $\alpha p \geqslant 1$ and Corollary 4.4.2/1 for $\alpha p < 1$.

Necessity. Let u be an arbitrary function in $C^{0,1}(\Omega) \cap L_p^1(\Omega)$ with

$$m_n(\operatorname{supp} u) \leqslant \tfrac{1}{2} m_n(\Omega). \tag{2}$$

There exists a number c_0 that satisfies

$$\| u - c_0 \|_{L_{q^*}(\Omega)} = \inf_{c \in R^1} \| u - c \|_{L_{q^*}(\Omega)}. \tag{3}$$

The latter and (1) imply

$$\int_{\operatorname{supp} u} |u - c_0|^{q^*} dx + |c_0|^{q^*} m_n(\Omega \backslash \operatorname{supp} u) \leqslant C^{q^*} \| \nabla u \|_{L_p(\Omega)}^{q^*}.$$

Therefore

$$\tfrac{1}{2} m_n(\Omega) |c_0|^{q^*} \leqslant C^{q^*} \| \nabla u \|_{L_p(\Omega)}^{q^*}.$$

Since

$$\| u \|_{L_{q^*}(\Omega)} \leqslant |c_0| [m_n(\Omega)]^{1/q^*} + \| u - c_0 \|_{L_{q^*}(\Omega)},$$

then, making use of (1) and (3), we obtain

$$\|u\|_{L_{q^*}(\Omega)} \leqslant cC \|\nabla u\|_{L_p(\Omega)}$$

for all $u \in C^{0,1}(\Omega)$ that satisfy (2). A reference to Corollaries 4.3.3 and 4.4.2/1 completes the proof.

Theorem 2. *Let Ω be a domain with finite volume. The space $L^1_p(\Omega)$ is imbedded into $L_{q^*}(\Omega)$ if, and for $q^* \geqslant 1$, only if $\Omega \in \mathscr{I}_{p,1/q^*}$ for $p \leqslant q^*$ and $\Omega \in \mathscr{H}_{p,1/q^*}$ for $p > q^*$.*

Proof. The necessity follows from Lemma 3.2.3/2 and Theorem 1. To prove the sufficiency we must show that (1) is valid provided $\mathfrak{A}_{p,\alpha}(M)$ and $\mathfrak{B}_{p,\alpha}(M)$ are finite for some $M \in (0, \frac{1}{2} m_n(\Omega))$. Let $u \in L^1_p(\Omega) \cap C^{0,1}(\Omega)$ and $T = \inf\{t: m_n(\mathscr{N}_t) \leqslant M\}$. We note that

$$\int_\Omega |u|^{q^*} dx \leqslant c \left[\int_\Omega (|u| - T)_+^{q^*} dx + T^{q^*} M \right].$$

Using Corollaries 4.3.3 and 4.4.2/1 we obtain

$$\|u\|_{L_{q^*}(\Omega)} \leqslant C \|\nabla u\|_{L_p(\Omega)} + c T M^{1/q},$$

where C is a constant that is independent of u. Let ω denote a bounded subdomain of Ω with smooth boundary such that $m_n(\Omega \backslash \omega) < M/2$. Obviously,

$$\int_\omega |u|^p dx \geqslant \int_{\omega \cap \mathscr{N}_T} |u|^p dx \geqslant \tfrac{1}{2} T^p M .$$

Therefore

$$\|u\|_{L_{q^*}(\Omega)} \leqslant C \|\nabla u\|_{L_p(\Omega)} + c M^{1/q^* - 1/p} \|u\|_{L_p(\omega)} . \tag{4}$$

Since ω satisfies

$$\inf_{c \in R^1} \|u - c\|_{L_p(\omega)} \leqslant K \|\nabla u\|_{L_p(\omega)},$$

then (4) implies (1) for Ω.

4.4.4. Sufficient Conditions for Belonging to $\mathscr{H}_{p,\alpha}$

Propositions 1 and 2 which are proved below give the following sufficient conditions for a set to belong to $\mathscr{H}_{p,\alpha}$:

$$\int_0^M \left[\frac{\tau}{\nu_{M,p}(\tau)} \right]^{1/(\alpha p - 1)} d\tau < \infty , \tag{1}$$

$$\int_0^M \left[\frac{\tau}{\lambda_M(\tau)} \right]^{p/(\alpha p - 1)} d\tau < \infty . \tag{2}$$

Proposition 1. *If* $\alpha p > 1$, $\alpha \leqslant 1$, *then*

$$\mathfrak{B}_{p,\alpha}(M) \leqslant \left\{\frac{\alpha p}{\alpha p - 1}\int_0^M \left[\frac{\tau}{\nu_{M,p}(\tau)}\right]^{1/(\alpha p-1)} d\tau\right\}^{\alpha - 1/p}. \tag{3}$$

Proof. Let $G = \bigcup_{j=-\infty}^{+\infty} G_j$, where $\{G_j\}_{j=-\infty}^{+\infty}$ is a nondecreasing sequence of open subsets of Ω with $m_n(G) \leqslant M$. Let K_j denote the conductor $G_{j+1} \backslash \operatorname{clos}_\Omega G_j$.

Since the function $\nu_{M,p}$ does not decrease, then

$$\frac{[m_n(G_j)]^{p/(p-q^*)} - [m_n(G_{j-1})]^{p/(p-q^*)}}{[\nu_{M,p}(m_n(G_j))]^{q^*/(p-q^*)}} \leqslant \int_{m_n(G_{j-1})}^{m_n(G_j)} \frac{d(t^{p/(p-q^*)})}{[\nu_{m,p}(t)]^{q^*/(p-q^*)}}$$

and similarly

$$\frac{[m_n(G_j)]^{p/(p-q^*)}}{[\nu_{M,p}(m_n(G_j))]^{q^*/(p-q^*)}} \leqslant \int_0^{m_n(G_j)} \frac{d(t^{p/(p-q^*)})}{[\nu_{M,p}(t)]^{q^*/(p-q^*)}}.$$

This implies

$$\sum_{|j|\leqslant N} \frac{[m_n(G_j)]^{p/(p-q^*)} - [m_n(G_{j-1})]^{p/(p-q^*)}}{[\nu_{M,p}(m_n(G_j))]^{q^*/(p-q^*)}} + \frac{[m_n(G_{-N-1})]^{p/(p-q^*)}}{[\nu_{M,p}(m_n(G_{-N-1}))]^{q^*/(p-q^*)}}$$
$$\leqslant \int_0^M \frac{d(t^{p/(p-q^*)})}{[\nu_{M,p}(t)]^{q^*/(p-q^*)}}$$

for any $N = 1, 2, \ldots$. Let $K^{(j)}$ denote the conductor $G \backslash \operatorname{clos}_\Omega G_j$. According to the definition of $\nu_{M,p}$ we have $c_p(K^{(j)}) \geqslant \nu_{M,p}(m_n(G_j))$. So,

$$\sum_{|j|\leqslant N} \frac{[m_n(G_j)]^{p/(p-q^*)} - [m_n(G_{j-1})]^{p/(p-q^*)}}{[c_p(K^{(j)})]^{q^*/(p-q^*)}} + \frac{[m_n(G_{-N-1})]^{p/(p-q^*)}}{[c_p(K^{(-N-1)})]^{q^*/(p-q^*)}}$$
$$\leqslant \int_0^M \frac{d(t^{p/(p-q^*)})}{[\nu_{M,p}(t)]^{q^*/(p-q^*)}}.$$

The left-hand side majorizes the expression

$$\sum_{|j|\leqslant N} [m_n(G_j)]^{p/(p-q^*)}\left([c_p(K^{(j)})]^{q^*/(q^*-p)} - [c_p(K^{(j+1)})]^{q^*/(q^*-p)}\right).$$

Since $s = (p-1)q^*/(p-q^*) \geqslant 1$, then

$$|a^s - b^s| \geqslant |a-b|^s$$

for all $a, b > 0$. Therefore the preceding sum exceeds

$$\sum_{|j| \leqslant N} [m_n(G_j)]^{p/(p-q^*)} ([c_p(K^{(j)})]^{1/(1-p)} - [c_p(K^{(j+1)})]^{1/(1-p)})^{q^*(p-1)/(p-q^*)}$$

which by Corollary 4.1.3/2 majorizes the sum

$$\sum_{j=-N}^{N} \frac{[m_n(G_j)]^{p/(p-q^*)}}{[c_p(K_j)]^{q^*/(p-q^*)}}.$$

To complete the proof it remains to make use of the definition of $\mathfrak{B}_{p,\alpha}(M)$.

Proposition 2. *If $\alpha p > 1$, $\alpha \leqslant 1$, then*

$$\mathfrak{B}_{p,\alpha}(M) \leqslant \frac{(\alpha p)^{\alpha-1}(p-1)^{(p-1)/p}}{(\alpha p-1)^{\alpha-1/p}} \left\{ \int_0^M \left[\frac{\tau}{\lambda_M(\tau)} \right]^{p/(\alpha p-1)} d\tau \right\}^{\alpha-1/p}. \tag{4}$$

Proof. By inequalities (4.3.4/1) and (3) we have

$$[\mathfrak{B}_{p,\alpha}(M)]^{p/(\alpha p-1)} \leqslant \frac{\alpha p}{\alpha p-1} \int_0^M \tau^{1/(\alpha p-1)} \left[\int_\tau^M [\lambda_M(\sigma)]^{p/(1-p)} d\sigma \right]^{(p-1)/(\alpha p-1)} d\tau.$$

To find a bound for the right-hand side we apply (1.3/1) in the form

$$\int_0^M \tau^{-r} \left(\int_\tau^M f(\sigma)\, d\sigma \right)^q d\tau \leqslant \left(\frac{q}{1-r} \right)^q \int_0^M \tau^{q-r} [f(\tau)]^q d\tau, \tag{5}$$

where $f(\tau) \geqslant 0$, $r < 1$, $q > 1$. Putting $r = (1-\alpha p)^{-1}$, $q = (p-1)/(\alpha p-1)$ in (5), we arrive at (4).

The following remark will be used in § 4.5.

Remark. Let G be a fixed open subset Ω. Let $\nu_G^{(p)}(t)$ denote the infimum of $c_p(K)$ taken over the collection of all conductors $K = G \backslash F$ with $m_n(F) \geqslant t$.

Replacing $\mathfrak{B}_{p,\alpha}(M)$ by $\mathfrak{B}_G^{(p,\alpha)}$ and $\nu_{M,p}$ by $\nu_G^{(p)}$ in the proof of Proposition 1, we obtain

$$\mathfrak{B}_G^{(p,\alpha)} \leqslant \left\{ \frac{\alpha p}{\alpha p-1} \int_0^M \left[\frac{\tau}{\nu_G^{(p)}(\tau)} \right]^{1/(\alpha p-1)} d\tau \right\}^{\alpha-1/p},$$

which together with Lemma 4.4.1 shows that the condition

$$\int_0^M \left[\frac{\tau}{\nu_G^{(p)}(\tau)} \right]^{1/(\alpha-1)} d\tau < \infty$$

is sufficient for the validity of (4.4.1/1) for all $u \in C^{0,1}(\Omega)$ that vanish outside G.

4.4.5. Necessary Conditions for Belonging to the Classes $\mathcal{I}_{p,\alpha}$, $\mathcal{H}_{p,\alpha}$

By a special choice of conductors K and sequences $\{G_j\}$ in the definitions of $\mathcal{I}_{p,\alpha}$ and $\mathcal{H}_{p,\alpha}$ we obtain some necessary conditions for Ω to be contained in these classes.

Proposition 1. *Let O be an arbitrary point in $\bar{\Omega}$ and let $s(t)$ be the area of the intersection of Ω with the sphere ∂B_t centered at O.*

If $\Omega \in \mathcal{I}_{p,\alpha}$ then

$$\left(\int_0^r s(t)\,dt\right)^{\alpha p/(p-1)} \int_r^\varrho \frac{dt}{[s(t)]^{1/(p-1)}} \leqslant \text{const}$$

for sufficiently small ϱ and for $r<\varrho$.

Proof. If $\Omega \in \mathcal{I}_{p,\alpha}$, then obviously

$$[m_n(\Omega_r)]^\alpha \leqslant \text{const}\,[c_p(\Omega_\varrho \backslash \operatorname{clos}_\Omega \Omega_r)]^{1/p} \tag{1}$$

for small enough ϱ and $r<\varrho$. Let $u=1$ in Ω_r, $u=0$ outside Ω_ϱ and

$$u(x) = \int_{|x|}^\varrho \frac{dt}{[s(t)]^{1/(p-1)}} \left(\int_r^\varrho \frac{dt}{[s(t)]^{1/(p-1)}}\right)^{-1}, \qquad x \in \Omega_\varrho \backslash \Omega_r.$$

Inserting u into the definition of p-conductivity, we obtain

$$c_p(\Omega_\varrho \backslash \operatorname{clos}_\Omega \Omega_r) \leqslant \left(\int_r^\varrho \frac{dt}{[s(t)]^{1/(p-1)}}\right)^{1-p}, \tag{2}$$

which together with (1) completes the proof.

The proof of the following assertion is similar.

Proposition 2. *If $m_n(\Omega)<\infty$ and $\Omega \in \mathcal{I}_{p,\alpha}$, then*

$$\left(\int_r^\infty s(t)\,dt\right)^{\alpha p/(p-1)} \int_\varrho^r \frac{dt}{[s(t)]^{1/(p-1)}} \leqslant \text{const} \tag{3}$$

for large enough ϱ and for $r>\varrho$.

The latter implies the next corollary.

Corollary. *If Ω is an unbounded domain with $m_n(\Omega)<\infty$ and $\Omega \in \mathcal{I}_{p,\alpha}$, then $\alpha p \geqslant 1$.*

Proof. By the Hölder inequality for $r>\varrho$ we have

$$r-\varrho = \int_\varrho^r [s(t)]^{1/p} \frac{dt}{[s(t)]^{1/p}} \leqslant \left(\int_\varrho^r s(t)\,dt\right)^{1/p} \left(\int_\varrho^r \frac{dt}{[s(t)]^{1/(p-1)}}\right)^{(p-1)/p}.$$

Therefore (3) implies

$$r-\varrho \leqslant \text{const} \frac{\left(\int_\varrho^r s(t)\,dt\right)^{1/p}}{\left(\int_r^\infty s(t)\,dt\right)^\alpha}.$$

Let the sequence $\{\varrho_j\}$ be specified by

$$\int_{\varrho_j}^\infty s(t)\,dt = 2^{-j}.$$

Then

$$\varrho_j-\varrho_{j-1} \leqslant \text{const} \frac{\left(\int_{\varrho_{j-1}}^{\varrho_j} s(t)\,dt\right)^{1/p}}{\left(\int_{\varrho_j}^\infty s(t)\,dt\right)^\alpha} = \text{const}\,(2^{\alpha-1/p})^j.$$

If $\alpha p<1$, then the series $\sum_j(\varrho_j-\varrho_{j-1})$ converges, which contradicts the assumption that Ω is unbounded. The result follows.

Since the condition $\Omega\in\mathscr{I}_{p,1/q}$ is necessary for the continuity of the imbedding operator $L_p^1(\Omega)\to L_q(\Omega)$, then, by Corollary, the imbedding $L_p^1(\Omega)\subset L_q(\Omega)$ for unbounded domain Ω with finite volume implies $p\geqslant q$.

Next we present a necessary condition for Ω to belong to $\mathscr{H}_{p,\alpha}$.

Proposition 3. *If $m_n(\Omega)<\infty$ and $\Omega\in\mathscr{H}_{p,\alpha}$, $\alpha p>1$, then*

$$\sum_{j=-\infty}^{+\infty}\left(\int_{\varrho_j}^{+\infty} s(t)\,dt\right)^{\alpha p/(p-1)}\left(\int_{\varrho_{j+1}}^{\varrho_j}\frac{dt}{[s(t)]^{1/(p-1)}}\right)^{(p-1)/(\alpha p-1)} \leqslant \text{const}$$

for any decreasing sequence $\{\varrho_j\}_{j=-\infty}^{+\infty}$ which converges to zero as $j\to+\infty$ and to infinity as $j\to-\infty$.

The proof results from (2) and the lower estimate for $\mathfrak{B}_{p,\alpha}(M)$ using the sequence $S=\{G_j\}_{j=-\infty}^{+\infty}$ with $G_j=\{x\in\Omega: |x|>\varrho_j\}$.

4.4.6. Examples of Domains in $\mathscr{H}_{p,\alpha}$

Example 1. The domain Ω considered in Example 4.3.5/2 is contained in $\mathscr{H}_{p,\alpha}$ provided

(1) $$\int_0^\infty\left(\int_x^\infty [f(t)]^{n-1}dt\right)^{p/(\alpha p-1)}[f(x)]^{(n-1)\beta}dx<\infty,\quad \beta=\frac{(\alpha-1)p-1}{\alpha p-1}.$$

The preceding condition is also necessary under the additional requirements:

(2) $$f(2t)\geqslant cf(t),\quad \int_t^\infty [f(x)]^{n-1}dx\leqslant ct[f(t)]^{n-1}\quad \text{for large } t.$$

From (2) it follows that the integral (1) converges if and only if

$$\int_0^\infty x^{p/(\alpha p-1)}[f(x)]^{n-1}dx<\infty\,. \tag{3}$$

Proof. The sufficiency of (1) immediately follows from the left estimate (4.3.5/3) and Proposition 4.4.4/1.

We proceed to the proof of the necessity of (3). Let $G_j=\{x\in\Omega: x_n<2^{-j}\}$, $-\infty<j<+\infty$ and let

$$u_j(x)=\int_{x_n}^{2^{-j}}[f(t)]^{(1-n)/(p-1)}dt\left\{\int_{2^{-j-1}}^{2^{-j}}[f(t)]^{(1-n)/(p-1)}dt\right\}^{-1}$$

for $x\in G_j\backslash G_{j+1}$. It is clear that

$$c_p(G_j\backslash \mathrm{clos}_\Omega G_{j+1})\leqslant \int_{G_j\backslash G_{j+1}}|\nabla u_j|^p dx\leqslant c\left(\int_{2^{-j-1}}^{2^{-j}}[f(t)]^{(1-n)/(p-1)}dt\right)^{1-p}.$$

Consequently, for large N

$$[\mathfrak{B}_{p,\alpha}(M)]^{p/(\alpha p-1)}\geqslant c\sum_{j=-\infty}^{-N}\left\{\int_{2^{-j}}^{\infty}[f(t)]^{n-1}dt\right\}^{\alpha p/(\alpha p-1)}$$
$$\times\left\{\int_{2^{-j-1}}^{2^{-j}}[f(t)]^{(1-n)/(p-1)}dt\right\}^{(p-1)/(\alpha p-1)}.$$

By (2) the right-hand term majorizes

$$c\sum_{j=-\infty}^{-N}f(2^{-j})2^{-j(1+p/(\alpha p-1))}\,.$$

So the finiteness of $\mathfrak{B}_{p,\alpha}(M)$ implies the convergence of the integral (3).

Example 2. Consider the spiral Ω in Examples 3.3.3/3 and 4.3.5/3. We assume in addition that

$$\delta(2\theta)\geqslant c\delta(\theta)\,,\qquad \int_\theta^\infty \delta(\varphi)d\varphi\leqslant c\theta\delta(\theta)$$

for large θ. Then, using the same arguments as in Example 1 we can show that $\Omega\in\mathscr{H}_{p,\alpha}$ if and only if

$$\int_0^\infty \delta(\varphi)\varphi^{p/(\alpha p-1)}d\varphi<\infty\,. \tag{4}$$

A more complicated example of a domain contained in $\mathscr{H}_{p,\alpha}$ is given in the following section.

4.4.7. Other Descriptions of the Classes $\mathscr{I}_{p,\alpha}$ and $\mathscr{H}_{p,\alpha}$

We show that the class of conductors $K = G\backslash F$ used in Definition 4.3.1/1 of $\mathscr{I}_{p,\alpha}$ can be made essentially narrower.

Theorem 1. *Let Ω be a bounded domain and let ω be a fixed open set with $\bar{\omega} \subset \Omega$. The domain Ω belongs to $\mathscr{I}_{p,\alpha}(p \geqslant 1, \alpha > 0, \alpha \geqslant p^{-1} - n^{-1})$ if and only if*

$$\text{(1)} \qquad \sup_{\{F\}} \frac{[m_n(F)]^\alpha}{[c_p(G\backslash F)]^{1/p}} < \infty ,$$

where $G = \Omega\backslash\bar{\omega}$ and $\{F\}$ is the collection of closed (in Ω) subsets of G.

Proof. Let $S(\omega)$ denote the left-hand side in (1). The *necessity* of (1) is obvious since

$$S(\omega) \leqslant \mathfrak{A}_{p,\alpha}(m_n(\Omega\backslash\bar{\omega})) .$$

We prove the *sufficiency*. Let D be a domain with smooth boundary and such that $\bar{\omega} \subset D \subset \bar{D} \subset \Omega$. Further, let η be a smooth function, $\eta = 1$ on $\Omega\backslash D$, $\eta = 0$ on ω and $0 \leqslant \eta \leqslant 1$.

For any $u \in L^1_p(\Omega)$ we have

$$\int_0^\infty [m_n(\{x\colon (\eta|u|)(x) \geqslant t\})]^{\alpha p} d(t^p) \leqslant [S(\omega)]^p \int_0^\infty c_p(K_t^{(1)}) d(t^p) ,$$

where $K_t^{(1)}$ is the conductor $(\Omega\backslash\bar{\omega})\backslash\{x \in \Omega\colon (\eta|u|)(x) \geqslant t\}$. The preceding inequality and Lemma 4.1.3/3 imply

$$\text{(2)} \quad \int_0^\infty [m_n(\{x\colon (\eta|u|)(x) \geqslant t\})]^{\alpha p} d(t^p) \leqslant c[S(\omega)]^p \int_\Omega |\nabla(\eta|u|)|^p dx$$
$$+ c\int_0^\infty [m_n(\{x\colon (1-\eta(x))|u(x)| \geqslant t\}) d(t^p) .$$

Since $\operatorname{supp}(1-\eta)|u| \subset \bar{D}$ and D has a smooth boundary, then

$$[m_n(\{x\colon (1-\eta(x))|u(x)| \geqslant t\})]^\alpha \leqslant \text{const}\, c_p(K_t^{(2)}) ,$$

where $K_t^{(2)}$ is the conductor $D\backslash\{x\colon (1-\eta(x))|u(x)| \geqslant t\}$. Hence from (2) and Lemma 4.1.3/3 we obtain

$$\int_0^\infty [m_n(\{x\colon |u(x)| \geqslant t\})]^{\alpha p} d(t^p) \leqslant \text{const}\left(\int_\Omega |\nabla(\eta|u|)|^p dx + \int_\Omega |\nabla((1-\eta)|u|)|^p dx\right)$$
$$\leqslant \text{const}\left(\int_\Omega |\nabla u|^p dx + \int_D |u|^p dx\right).$$

Let $M = \frac{1}{2} m_n(D)$ and $m_n(\operatorname{supp} u) \leqslant M$. Then

$$\int_D |u|^p dx \leqslant \text{const} \int_D |\nabla u|^p dx$$

and so

$$\int_0^\infty [m_n(\{x: |u(x)| \geqslant t\})]^{\alpha p} d(t^p) \leqslant \text{const} \int_\Omega |\nabla u|^p dx . \tag{3}$$

Consider the conductor $K^* = G^* \backslash F^*$ in Ω subject to the condition $m_n(G^*) \leqslant M$. We insert $u \in T_\Omega(K^*)$ into (3). Then we arrive at

$$[m_n(F^*)]^{\alpha p} \leqslant \text{const}\, c_p(K^*) ,$$

which is equivalent to the inclusion $\Omega \in \mathscr{I}_{p,\alpha}$.

Remark. The assertion we just proved remains valid for $p=1$ provided $S(\omega)$ designates the supremum of $[m_n(g)]^\alpha / s(\partial_i g)$ taken over all admissible sets g contained in Ω with $\operatorname{clos}_\Omega g \subset \Omega \backslash \bar{\omega}$.

Following the same argument as in the proof of Theorem 1, we can establish that the inclusion $\Omega \in \mathscr{H}_{p,\alpha}$ is equivalent to the finiteness of $\mathfrak{B}_G^{(p,\alpha)}$ where $G = \Omega \backslash \bar{\omega}$ (cf. 4.4.1).

We can give a different description of the class $\mathscr{I}_{p,\alpha}$ for $\alpha p < 1$ replacing G by $\Omega_\varrho(x) = \Omega \cap B_\varrho(x)$, $x \in \partial\Omega$. Namely, we introduce the function

$$[0,1] \ni \varrho \to a_{p,\alpha}(\varrho) = \sup_{x \in \partial\Omega} \sup_{\{F\}} \frac{[m_n(F)]^\alpha}{[c_p(\Omega_\varrho(x) \backslash F)]^{1/p}} ,$$

where $\{F\}$ is the collection of closed in Ω subsets of $\Omega_\varrho(x)$.

Theorem 2. *Let Ω be a bounded domain and let $\alpha p < 1$. Then $\Omega \in \mathscr{I}_{p,\alpha}$ if and only if $a_{p,\alpha}(\varrho) < \infty$ for some ϱ.*

Proof. Necessity does not require proof. Let $a_{p,\alpha}(\varrho) < \infty$. We construct a finite covering of $\bar{\Omega}$ by open balls with radius ϱ and take a partition of unity $\{\eta_i\}$ subordinate to it. By Lemma 4.2

$$\| u \eta_i \|_{L_{q^*}(\Omega)} \leqslant c a_{p,\alpha}(\varrho) \, \| \nabla (u \eta_i) \|_{L_p(\Omega)} ,$$

where $q^* = \alpha^{-1}$. Summing over i, we conclude that $W_p^1(\Omega) \subset L_{q^*}(\Omega)$. Consequently, by Theorem 4.3.3 (part 2)) $\Omega \in \mathscr{I}_{p,\alpha}$.

4.4.8. Integral Inequalities for Domains with Power Cusps

Let us consider in more detail the domain

$$\Omega^{(\lambda)} = \{x = (x', x_n) \colon |x'| < a x_n^\lambda,\ 0 < x_n < 1\} ,$$

presented in Example 4.3.5/1. There we showed that $\Omega^{(\lambda)} \in \mathscr{I}_{p,\alpha}$ provided $n > p$, $\lambda > (p-1)/(n-1)$, $\alpha = [\lambda(n-1)+1-p]/p[\lambda(n-1)+1]$. By Theorem

4.4.3/2 the latter is equivalent to the inclusion $L^1_p(\Omega^{(\lambda)}) \subset L_{q^*}(\Omega^{(\lambda)})$ with $q^* = p[\lambda(n-1)+1]/[\lambda(n-1)+1-p]$. Although here the exponent q^* is the best possible, it is natural to try to refine the stated result by using spaces with weighted norms (cf. Remark 3.3.3).

Let

$$\|u\|_{L_r(\sigma,\Omega^{(\lambda)})} = \left(\int_{\Omega^{(\lambda)}} |u(x)|^r x_n^{r\sigma} dx \right)^{1/r}.$$

The coordinate transformation $\varkappa: x \to \xi$ defined by $\xi_i = x_i$, $1 \leqslant i \leqslant n-1$, $\xi_n = x_n^\lambda$, maps $\Omega^{(\lambda)}$ onto $\Omega^{(1)}$. Since $\Omega^{(1)}$ is a domain of the class $C^{0,1}$, then from Corollary 2.1.6/2 it easily follows that

$$\|v\|_{L_q(\beta,\Omega^{(1)})} \leqslant c(\|\nabla v\|_{L_p(\alpha,\Omega^{(1)})} + \|v\|_{L(\varkappa(\omega))}),$$

where $n > p \geqslant 1$, $p \leqslant q \leqslant pn/(n-p)$, $\beta = \alpha - 1 + n(p^{-1} - q^{-1}) > -n/q$ and ω is a nonempty domain, $\bar{\omega} \subset \Omega^{(\lambda)}$. Returning to the variable x, we obtain

$$\|u\|_{L_q(\lambda\beta + (\lambda-1)/q,\, \Omega^{(\lambda)})}$$
$$\leqslant c(\|\nabla_{x'} u\|_{L_p(\alpha\lambda + (\lambda-1)/p,\, \Omega^{(\lambda)})} + \|\partial u/\partial x_n\|_{L_p(\alpha\lambda - (\lambda-1)(p-1)/p,\, \Omega^{(\lambda)})} + \|u\|_{L(\omega)}),$$

where $\nabla_{x'} = (\partial/\partial x_1, \ldots, \partial/\partial x_{n-1})$. Putting $\alpha = (\lambda-1)(p-1)/\lambda p$, we obtain

(1) $$\|u\|_{L_q(\lambda\beta + (\lambda-1)/q,\, \Omega^{(\lambda)})} \leqslant c(\|\nabla_{x'} u\|_{L_p(\lambda-1,\, \Omega^{(\lambda)})} + \|\partial u/\partial x_n\|_{L_p(\Omega^{(\lambda)})} + \|u\|_{L(\omega)}).$$

Choosing q to eliminate the weight in the left-hand side, we arrive at

$$\|u\|_{L_{q^*}(\Omega^{(\lambda)})} \leqslant c(\|\nabla_{x'} u\|_{L_p(\lambda-1,\, \Omega^{(\lambda)})} + \|\partial u/\partial x_n\|_{L_p(\Omega^{(\lambda)})} + \|u\|_{L(\omega)}),$$

where, as before, $q^* = p[\lambda(n-1)+1]/[\lambda(n-1)+1-p]$. Since $\lambda > 1$, the preceding result is better than the imbedding $L^1_p(\Omega^{(\lambda)}) \subset L_{q^*}(\Omega^{(\lambda)})$.

For $\lambda > 1$ we can take q to be the limit exponent $pn/(n-p)$ in Sobolev's theorem. Then (1) becomes

$$\|u\|_{L_{pn/(n-p)}((\lambda-1)(n-1)/n,\, \Omega^{(\lambda)})}$$
$$\leqslant c(\|\nabla_{x'} u\|_{L_p(\lambda-1,\, \Omega^{(\lambda)})} + \|\partial u/\partial x_n\|_{L_p(\Omega^{(\lambda)})} + \|u\|_{L(\omega)}),$$

which, in particular, guarantees the inclusion $L^1_p(\Omega) \subset L_{pn/(n-p)}((\lambda-1)(n-1)/n, \Omega^{(\lambda)})$. We can readily check by the example of the function x_n^τ with $\tau = 1 + \varepsilon - [\lambda(n-1)+1]/p$ (ε is a small positive number) that the power exponent of the weight is exact.

In conclusion we remark that we can obtain an integral representation similar to (1.1.10/1) for the domain $\Omega^{(\lambda)}$.

By (1.1.10/1), for any $v \in C^1(\Omega^{(1)}) \cap L_1^1(\Omega^{(1)})$ we have

$$v(\xi) = \int_{\Omega^{(1)}} \varphi(\eta) v(\eta) d\eta + \sum_{i=1}^{n} \int_{\Omega^{(1)}} \frac{f_i(\xi, \eta)}{|\xi - \eta|^{n-1}} \frac{\partial v}{\partial \eta_i}(\eta) d\eta ,$$

where $\varphi \in \mathscr{D}(\Omega^{(1)})$ and $f_i \in L_\infty(\Omega^{(1)} \times \Omega^{(1)})$. Therefore the function $u = v \circ \varkappa$ has the integral representation

(2)

$$u(x) = \int_{\Omega^{(\lambda)}} \Phi(y) u(y) dy + \sum_{i=1}^{n-1} \int_{\Omega^{(\lambda)}} \frac{F_i(x, y) y_n^{\lambda - 1}}{(|x' - y'|^2 + (x_n^\lambda - y_n^\lambda)^2)^{(n-1)/2}} \frac{\partial u}{\partial y_i}(y) dy$$

$$+ \int_{\Omega^{(\lambda)}} \frac{F_n(x, y)}{(|x' - y'|^2 + (x_n^\lambda - y_n^\lambda)^2)^{(n-1)/2}} \frac{\partial u}{\partial y_n}(y) dy ,$$

where $\Phi \in \mathscr{D}(\Omega^{(\lambda)})$ and $F_i \in L_\infty(\Omega^{(\lambda)} \times \Omega^{(\lambda)})$. It is easily seen that we can take u to be an arbitrary function in $C^1(\overline{\Omega^{(\lambda)}})$. Since by Theorem 1.1.6/1 the space $C^1(\bar{\Omega}^{(\lambda)})$ is dense in $L_1^1(\Omega^{(\lambda)})$ then (2) is valid for all $u \in L_1^1(\Omega^{(\lambda)})$.

§ 4.5. More on the Nikodým Example

In this section we consider the domain described in Example 1.1.4/1 (cf. also § 4.3) with $\varepsilon_m = \delta(2^{-m-1})$ where δ is a nondecreasing function such that $2\delta(t) < t$. Here we show that *the convergence of the integral*

(1)
$$\int_0^1 \left[\frac{t}{\delta(t)}\right]^{1/(\alpha p - 1)} dt$$

is necessary and sufficient for Ω *to belong to* $\mathscr{H}_{p,\alpha}$ *for* $\alpha p > 1$.

Lemma. (The inverse Minkowski inequality) *If* g_m *are nonnegative measurable functions on* $[0, 1]$, *then*

(2)
$$\left\{ \int_0^1 \frac{dt}{\left[\sum_m g_m(t)\right]^{1/(p-1)}} \right\}^{1-p} \geqslant \sum_m \left\{ \int_0^1 \frac{dt}{[g_m(t)]^{1/(p-1)}} \right\}^{1-p} .$$

Proof. Let λ be an absolutely continuous nondecreasing function on $[0, 1]$ with $\lambda(0) = 0$ and $\lambda(1) = 1$. We put $g(t) = \sum_m g_m(t)$. Then

$$\int_0^1 (\lambda')^p g \, dt = \sum_m \int_0^1 (\lambda')^p g_m dt .$$

By Hölder's inequality,

$$\sum_m \int_0^1 (\lambda')^p g_m dt \geqslant \sum_m \frac{\left(\int_0^1 \lambda' dt\right)^p}{\left(\int_0^1 g_m^{1/(1-p)} dt\right)^{p-1}} = \sum_m \left(\int_0^1 \frac{dt}{g_m^{1/(p-1)}}\right)^{1-p}.$$

Finally, by Lemma 2.2.2/2,

$$\inf_\lambda \int_0^1 (\lambda')^p g\, dt = \left\{\int_0^1 \frac{dt}{g^{1/(p-1)}}\right\}^{1-p}.$$

Hence (2) holds.

Next we prove that $\Omega \in \mathscr{H}_{p,\alpha}$ provided (1) is finite.

Consider an arbitrary nonnegative function $u \in L_p^1(\Omega)$ that is infinitely differentiable in $A_m \cup B_m$ for any m and vanishes in the rectangle C.

We fix an arbitrary number m and note that each level set $\mathscr{E}_t^{(m)} = \{(x, y): u(x, y) = t\} \cap (A_m \cup B_m)$ consists of a finite number of smooth homeomorphic images of a circle and simple arcs with end points on $\partial(A_m \cup B_m) \backslash \{y = 2/3\}$ for almost all levels $t \in (0, \infty)$ (cf. Corollary 1.2.2). Henceforth we shall always consider only such levels.

If t satisfies

$$s(\mathscr{E}_t^{(m)}) \geqslant 2^{-m-3}, \tag{3}$$

then

$$m_2(\mathscr{N}_t^{(m)}) \leqslant \tfrac{1}{3}[1 + 2^{m+1}\delta(2^{-m-1})]2^{-m-1} < s(\mathscr{E}_t^{(m)}), \tag{4}$$

where $\mathscr{N}_t^{(m)} = \{(x, y): u \geqslant t\} \cap (A_m \cup B_m)$. Let $\mathfrak{B}_m$ denote the collection of all levels t for which (3) is valid. We show that for $t \notin \mathfrak{B}_m$ one of the following three cases occurs:

$$\begin{cases} s(\mathscr{E}_t^{(m)}) \geqslant \delta(2^{-m-1}), & (5)\\ m_2(\mathscr{N}_t^{(m)}) \leqslant k\delta(2^{-m-1}), & (6)\end{cases}$$

where k is a constant that depends on integral (1);

$$\begin{cases} s(\mathscr{E}_t^{(m)}) \geqslant \delta(2^{-m-1}), & (7)\\ m_2(\mathscr{L}_t^{(m)}) \leqslant k\delta(2^{-m-1}), & (8)\end{cases}$$

where $\mathscr{L}_t^{(m)} = (A_m \cup B_m) \backslash \mathscr{N}_t^{(m)}$;

$$\begin{cases} s(\mathscr{E}_t^{(m)}) < \delta(2^{-m-1}), & (9)\\ m_2(\mathscr{N}_t^{(m)}) \leqslant k s(\mathscr{E}_t^{(m)}). & (10)\end{cases}$$

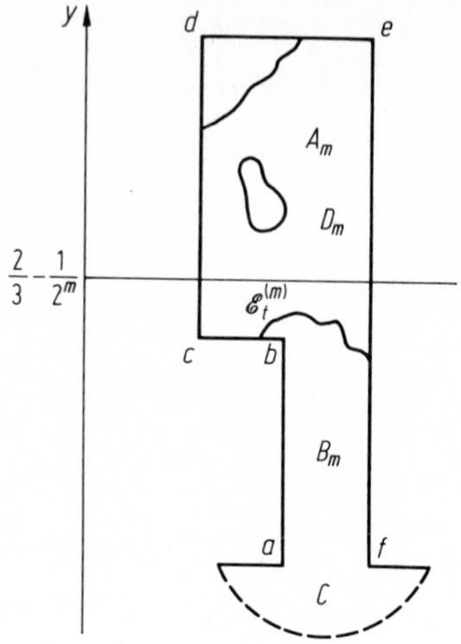

Fig. 16

We note that there are no components of $\mathscr{E}_t^{(m)}$ joining cd and ef since $t \notin \mathfrak{B}_m$ (cf. Fig. 16). Besides, the set $\mathscr{E}_t^{(m)}$ $(t>0)$ is disjoint with the line $y=\frac{2}{3}$ because $u=0$ in C.

a) Assume (5) is valid. Let $\tilde{\mathscr{E}}_t^{(m)}$ denote the upper component of $\mathscr{E}_t^{(m)}$ which joins the polygonal line abc with fe. The set $\tilde{\mathscr{E}}_t^{(m)}$ divides $A_m \cup B_m$ into components; the component containing de will be denoted by D_m. Since $t \notin \mathfrak{B}_m$ then $\tilde{\mathscr{E}}_t^{(m)}$ is placed below the line $y=\frac{2}{3}+2^{-m}$ and hence

$$m_2(\mathscr{N}_t^{(m)} \backslash D_m) \leqslant (2^{-2m-1}+\tfrac{1}{3}\delta(2^{-m-1}))\,,$$

$$m_2(\mathscr{L}_t^{(m)} \backslash D_m) \leqslant (2^{-2m-1}+\tfrac{1}{3}\delta(2^{-m-1}))\,.$$

Taking into account that δ increases and $2\delta(t)<t$, we obtain

$$\text{(11)} \qquad \int_0^{2^{-m-1}} \left[\frac{t}{\delta(t)}\right]^{\gamma} dt \geqslant 2^{\gamma-1} \int_0^{2^{-m-1}} \frac{t\,dt}{\delta(t)} \geqslant 2^{\gamma-2} \frac{2^{-2(m+1)}}{\delta(2^{-m-1})}$$

with $\gamma=(\alpha p-1)^{-1}$. Consequently,

$$\text{(12)} \qquad m_2(\mathscr{N}_t^{(m)} \backslash D_m) \leqslant k_1\delta(2^{-m-1})\,, \quad m_2(\mathscr{L}_t^{(m)} \backslash D_m) \leqslant k_1\delta(2^{-m-1})\,,$$

where

$$k_1=\tfrac{1}{3}+2^{\gamma-1}\int_0^1 (t/\delta(t))^{\gamma} dt\,.$$

The set $\mathscr{E}_t^{(m)} \backslash D_m$ divides $\Omega \backslash D_m$ into components. Let $\tilde{D}_m$ denote one of them with boundary containing $\tilde{\mathscr{E}}_t^{(m)}$ and the end points of the segment de. Suppose $\tilde{D}_m \subset \mathscr{L}_t^{(m)}$. We estimate $m_2(\mathscr{N}_t^{(m)} \cap D_m)$. First we note that $\mathscr{N}_t^{(m)}$

$\cap D_m$ is bounded by the components of $\mathscr{E}_t^{(m)}$ which (with the exception of $\tilde{\mathscr{E}}_t^{(m)}$) are either closed in $A_m \cup B_m$ or join points of the polygonal lines $abcde$ or def. This implies

$$s(\partial(A_m \cup B_m) \cap \overline{\mathscr{N}_t^{(m)}} \cap D_m) \leqslant 2s(\mathscr{E}_t^{(m)} \cap D_m) .$$

Using the isoperimetric inequality we obtain

$$[m_2(\mathscr{N}_t^{(m)} \cap D_m)]^{1/2} \leqslant \frac{3}{2\sqrt{\pi}} s(\mathscr{E}_t^{(m)} \cap D_m) . \tag{13}$$

Since $t \notin \mathfrak{B}_m$, the latter and (11) yield

$$m_2(\mathscr{N}_t^{(m)} \cap D_m) \leqslant \frac{9}{4\pi} 2^{-2(m+1)} \leqslant \frac{9 \cdot 2^{2-\gamma}}{4\pi} \delta(2^{-m-1}) \int_0^1 \left(\frac{t}{\delta(t)}\right)^{\gamma} dt ,$$

which together with (12) leads to (6).

b) Inequality (8) can be derived in the same way provided we assume that $\tilde{D}_m \subset \mathscr{N}_t^{(m)}$.

c) Suppose (9) is valid. Then $\mathscr{E}_t^{(m)}$ does not contain components which join $abcd$ and ef. So following the same argument as in the derivation of (13), we obtain

$$[m_2(\mathscr{N}_t^{(m)})]^{1/2} \leqslant \frac{3}{2\sqrt{\pi}} s(\mathscr{E}_t^{(m)}) .$$

The preceding inequality and (9) imply (10).

Thus, one of the following cases is possible: either (10) is valid, or (5) and (6), or (7) and (8). Let $\mathfrak{B}_m'$ denote the set of levels t for which (10) is valid. Let $\mathfrak{B}_m''$ and $\mathfrak{B}_m'''$ be the sets of levels satisfying (5), (6) or (7), (8) respectively.

Let $\psi_m(t)$ be defined by

$$\psi_m(t) = \int_0^t \left(\int_{\mathscr{E}_t^{(m)}} |\nabla u|^{p-1} ds \right)^{1/(1-p)} .$$

We have

$$\psi_m(t) \leqslant -\int_0^t \frac{d}{d\tau} [m_2(\mathscr{N}_\tau^{(m)})] \frac{d\tau}{[s(\mathscr{E}_\tau^{(m)})]^{p/(p-1)}}$$

(cf. Corollary 4.1.3/1). We express the right integral as the sum

$$\int_{\mathfrak{B}_m'} + \int_{\mathfrak{B}_m''} + \int_{\mathfrak{B}_m'''} .$$

By (10)

$$\int_{\mathfrak{B}_m'} \leqslant -\int_0^1 \frac{d}{d\tau} [m_2(\mathscr{N}_\tau^{(m)})] \frac{d\tau}{[m_2(\mathscr{N}_\tau^{(m)})]^{p/(p-1)}} \leqslant \frac{p-1}{[m_2(\mathscr{N}_t^{(m)})]^{1/(p-1)}} .$$

Using (5) and (6) we obtain

$$\int_{\mathfrak{B}''_m} \leqslant [\delta(2^{-m-1})]^{p/(1-p)} \sup_{\tau\in\mathfrak{B}''_m} m_2(\mathcal{N}_\tau^{(m)}) \leqslant k[\delta(2^{-m-1})]^{1/(1-p)}.$$

We note that

$$-\frac{d}{d\tau} m_2(\mathcal{N}_\tau^{(m)}) = \frac{d}{d\tau} m_2(\mathcal{L}_\tau^{(m)})$$

and make use of (7) and (8). Then

$$\int_{\mathfrak{B}'''_m} \leqslant \int_{\mathfrak{B}'''_m} \frac{d}{d\tau} m_2(\mathcal{L}_\tau^{(m)}) \frac{d\tau}{[s(\mathcal{E}_\tau^{(m)})]^{p/(p-1)}} \sup_{\tau\in\mathfrak{B}'''_m} m_2(\mathcal{L}_t^{(m)}) \leqslant k[\delta(2^{-m-1})]^{1/(1-p)}.$$

Consequently,

(14) $$\psi_m(t) \leqslant 2k[\delta(2^{-m-1})]^{1/(1-p)} + [m_2(\mathcal{N}_t^{(m)})]^{1/(1-p)}.$$

Let l denote the smallest number for which

$$m_2(\mathcal{N}_t^{(l)}) \geqslant (2c)^{1-p}\delta(2^{-l-1}).$$

Then (14) implies

(15) $$\psi_l(t) \leqslant 4k[\delta(2^{-l-1})]^{1/(1-p)}.$$

Next, taking into account that

$$m_2(\mathcal{N}_t^{(m)}) < \tfrac{1}{3}\cdot 2^{-m},$$

we obtain

$$\delta\left[\tfrac{3}{4} m_2\left(\bigcup_{m=l}^{\infty} \mathcal{N}_t^{(m)}\right)\right] \leqslant \delta(2^{-l-1}),$$

which together with (15) yields

(16) $$\delta\left[\tfrac{3}{4} m_2\left(\bigcup_{m=l}^{\infty} \mathcal{N}_t^{(m)}\right)\right] \leqslant [4k/\psi_l(t)]^{p-1}.$$

Since

$$m_2(\mathcal{N}_t^{(m)}) < (2c)^{1-p}\delta(2^{-m-1})$$

for $m < l$, then by (14) for $m < l$

$$\psi_m(t) \leqslant 2[m_2(\mathcal{N}_t^{(m)})]^{1/(1-p)}.$$

Consequently,

$$m_2\left(\bigcup_{m=1}^{l-1} \mathcal{N}_t^{(m)}\right) \leqslant 2^{p-1} \sum_{m=1}^{l-1} [\psi_m(t)]^{1-p}$$

and so

$$\delta\left[m_2\left(\bigcup_{m=1}^{l-1} \mathcal{N}_t^{(m)}\right)\right] \leqslant 2^{p-2} \sum_{m=1}^{l-1} [\psi_m(t)]^{1-p} \tag{17}$$

because $\delta(t) < t/2$. If

$$m_2\left(\bigcup_{m=1}^{l-1} \mathcal{N}_t^{(m)}\right) < \tfrac{3}{4} m_2\left(\bigcup_{m=l}^{\infty} \mathcal{N}_t^{(m)}\right), \tag{18}$$

then by (16)

$$\delta[\tfrac{3}{8} m_2(\mathcal{N}_t)] \leqslant [4k/\psi_l(t)]^{p-1}.$$

Otherwise, if the reverse of (18) is valid, then by (17)

$$\delta[\tfrac{3}{8} m_2(\mathcal{N}_t)] \leqslant 2^{p-2} \sum_{m=1}^{l-1} [\psi_m(t)]^{1-p}.$$

Thus, we always have

$$\delta[\tfrac{3}{8} m_2(\mathcal{N}_t)] \leqslant k' \sum_{m=1}^{\infty} [\psi_m(t)]^{1-p}, \tag{19}$$

where k' is the larger of $(4k)^{p-1}$ and 2^{p-2}.

Let $\psi(t)$ be defined by

$$\psi(t) = \int_0^t \left(\int_{\mathscr{E}_\tau} |\nabla u|^{p-1} ds \right)^{1/(1-p)} d\tau .$$

Since by Lemma

$$[\psi(t)]^{1-p} \geqslant \sum_{m \geqslant 1} [\psi_m(t)]^{1-p},$$

then (19) implies

$$\delta[\tfrac{3}{8} m_2(\mathcal{N}_t)] \leqslant k' [\psi(t)]^{1-p}. \tag{20}$$

Let F be an arbitrary subset of $G = \Omega \backslash \bar{C}$ that is closed in Ω and let u be an arbitrary function in $V_\Omega(K)$, $K = G \backslash F$. By (20) we have

$$\delta[\tfrac{3}{8} m_2(F)] \leqslant k' [\psi(1)]^{1-p},$$

which together with Lemma 4.1.3/1 yields

$$\delta(\tfrac{3}{8} m_2(F)) \leqslant k' c_p(K) .$$

Consequently,

$$\delta(\tfrac{3}{8} t) \leqslant k' \nu_G^{(p)}(t) , \tag{21}$$

where $\nu_G^{(p)}$ is the function introduced in Remark 4.4.4.

Taking into account the convergence of the integral (1) as well as Remark 4.4.4 from (21) we obtain that there exists a constant Q such that

$$\|u\|_{L_q(\Omega)} \leqslant Q \|\nabla u\|_{L_p(\Omega)} \tag{22}$$

for all $u \in C^{0,1}(\Omega)$ that vanish in C with $q = \alpha^{-1}$.

Now let u be an arbitrary function in $C^{0,1}(\Omega)$ and let η be continuous in Ω, vanish in C, equal to unity in $\bigcup_{m \geqslant 1} A_m$ and linear in $B_m (m = 1, 2, \ldots)$. Then

$$\|u\|_{L_q(\Omega)} \leqslant \|u\eta\|_{L_q(\Omega \setminus C)} + \|u\|_{L_q(\Omega \setminus \bigcup_{m \geqslant 1} A_m)}. \tag{23}$$

Using (22), we obtain

$$\|u\eta\|_{L_q(\Omega \setminus C)} \leqslant Q_1(\|\nabla u\|_{L_p(\Omega)} + \|u\|_{L_p(\bigcup_{m \geqslant 1} B_m)}).$$

The latter and (23) imply

$$\|u\|_{L_q(\Omega)} \leqslant Q_2(\|\nabla u\|_{L_p(\Omega)} + \|u\|_{L_p(\Omega \setminus \bigcup_{m \geqslant 1} A_m)}). \tag{24}$$

We estimate the second norm on the right in (24). Let $(x, y) \in \Omega \setminus \bigcup_{m \geqslant 1} A_m$ and $(x, z) \in C$. Obviously,

$$|u(x, y)|^p \leqslant Q_3(|u(x, z)|^p + \int |\nabla u(x, \bar{y})|^p d\bar{y}),$$

where the integral is taken over the vertical segment contained in Ω and passing through the point $(x, 0)$. By integrating in x, y and z, we obtain

$$\iint_{\Omega \setminus \bigcup_{m \geqslant 1} A_m} |u|^p dx\,dy \leqslant Q_4\left(\iint_C |u|^p dx\,dy + \iint_{\Omega \setminus \bigcup_{m \geqslant 1} A_m} |\nabla u|^p dx\,dy\right).$$

Therefore

$$\|u\|_{L_q(\Omega)} \leqslant Q_5(\|\nabla u\|_{L_p(\Omega)} + \|u\|_{L_p(C)}).$$

Hence

$$\inf_{c \in R^1} \|u - c\|_{L_q(\Omega)} \leqslant Q_5(\|\nabla u\|_{L_p(\Omega)} + \inf_{c \in R^1} \|u - c\|_{L_p(C)}).$$

Using the Poincaré inequality for the rectangle C, we obtain

$$\inf_{c \in R^1} \|u - c\|_{L_q(\Omega)} \leqslant Q_6 \|\nabla u\|_{L_p(\Omega)},$$

which according to Theorem 4.3.3/2 is equivalent to $\Omega \in \mathscr{H}_{p,\alpha}$ with $\alpha = q^{-1}$.

Next we show that the convergence of the integral (1) is necessary for Ω to be contained in $\mathscr{H}_{p,\alpha}$. Let

$$\int_0^1 [t/\delta(t)]^\gamma dt = \infty,$$

where $\gamma = q/(p-q)$, $q = \alpha^{-1}$. Then

$$\sum_{m \geqslant 1} \frac{\lambda_m^{\gamma+1}}{\delta(\lambda_m)} = \infty\,, \tag{25}$$

where $\lambda_m = 2^{-m-1}$. Consider a continuous function u_m in Ω that vanishes in C, is linear in B_m and equal to

$$[\lambda_m/\delta(\lambda_m)]^{(\gamma+1)/p}$$

in A_m, $m \geqslant 1$. For $v_N = \sum_{1 \leqslant m \leqslant N} u_m$ we have

$$\iint_\Omega v_N^{p\gamma/(\gamma+1)} dx\,dy \geqslant \tfrac{1}{3} \sum_{m=1}^{N} u_m^{p\gamma/(\gamma+1)} \lambda_m = \sum_{m=1}^{N} \lambda_m^{\gamma+1} [\delta(\lambda_m)]^{-\gamma}.$$

On the other hand,

$$\iint_\Omega |\nabla v_N|^p dx\,dy = 3^p \sum_{m=1}^{N} u_m^p \delta(\lambda_m) = 3^p \sum_{m=1}^{N} \lambda_m^{\gamma+1} [\delta(\lambda_m)]^{-\gamma}.$$

If Ω were contained in $\mathscr{H}_{p,\alpha}$, then for all $u \in C^{0,1}(\Omega)$ that vanish in C

$$\|u\|^p_{L_{p\gamma/(\gamma+1)}(\Omega)} \leqslant Q \iint_\Omega |\nabla u|^p dx\,dy\,, \tag{26}$$

where Q does not depend on u. From (26) we obtain

$$\left(\sum_{m=1}^{N} \frac{\lambda_m^{\gamma+1}}{[\delta(\lambda_m)]^\gamma} \right)^{(\gamma+1)/\gamma} \leqslant Q \sum_{m=1}^{N} \frac{\lambda_m^{\gamma+1}}{[\delta(\lambda_m)]^\gamma}\,.$$

Hence

$$\sum_{m=1}^{N} \frac{\lambda_m^{\gamma+1}}{[\delta(\lambda_m)]^\gamma} \leqslant Q^\gamma\,,$$

which contradicts (25).

Remark 1. From (2) and Lemma 4.1.3/2 it follows that

$$\int_0^\infty \delta(\tfrac{3}{8} m_2(\mathscr{N}_t))\, d(t^p) \leqslant Q \iint_\Omega |\nabla u|^p dx\,dy \tag{27}$$

for all $u \in C^\infty(\Omega)$, $u = 0$ in C. Further let $\delta \in C^{0,1}[0,1]$ and $\delta(2t) \leqslant \mathrm{const}\, \delta(t)$. Then, following the same argument as in the proof of Proposition 3.4, from (2) we obtain $\nu_p(t) \geqslant k\,\delta(t)$. The reverse estimate follows by considering the sequence of conductors $\{G_m \backslash F_m\}$ where G_m is the interior of $A_m \cup B_m$ and $F_m = \mathrm{clos}_\Omega A_m$. In fact, for a piecewise linear function u_m that vanishes in C and is equal to 1 in A_m we have

$$c_p(G_m \backslash F_m) \leqslant \iint_{\Omega} |\nabla u_m|^p dx\, dy = 3^p \delta(2^{-m-1}) \leqslant k\delta(m_2(F))\,.$$

Thus, for the Nikodým domain and for any $p \geqslant 1$,

(28) $$\nu_p(t) \sim \delta(t)$$

and so $\Omega \in \mathscr{I}_{p,\alpha}$ if and only if

(29) $$\liminf_{t \to +0} t^{-\alpha p} \delta(t) > 0$$

(since $\delta(t) \leqslant t$, then $\alpha p \geqslant 1$).

Remark 2. The domain considered in the present section is interesting in the following respect. Whereas the conditions for the domains in the examples of subsection 4.3.5 to belong to $\mathscr{J}_{\alpha+1-1/p}$ and $\mathscr{I}_{p,\alpha}$ coincide (i.e. Proposition 4.3.4/2 is exact), the Nikodým domain is simultaneously contained in $\mathscr{J}_{p,\alpha}$ and $\mathscr{I}_{p,\alpha}$ by virtue of (29). This means that if, for example, $\delta(t) = t^\beta$, $\beta > 1$, then the sufficient conditions for the imbedding $L_p^1(\Omega) \subset L_q(\Omega)$ $(p > 1)$, being formulated in terms of the function λ, give an incorrect value of the limit exponent $q^* = p/(1 + p(\beta - 1))$.

The actual maximal value of q^*, obtained here by the direct estimate of ν_p, is equal to p/β.

§ 4.6. Some Generalizations

The spaces $L_s(\Omega)$, $L_r(\Omega)$, $L_q(\Omega)$ can be replaced by the spaces $L_s(\Omega, \sigma)$, $L_r(\Omega, \sigma)$, $L_q(\Omega, \sigma)$ of functions that are summable of order s, r, q respectively with respect to the measure σ in Ω; we just need to replace the Lebesgue measure by σ in corresponding necessary and sufficient conditions. As an example, we pause for a moment to present a generalization of Lemma 4.2.

Let G be an open bounded subset of Ω. For $p > 1$ we put

$$\mathfrak{A}_{G,\sigma}^{(p,\alpha)} = \sup_{\{F\}} \frac{[\sigma(F)]^\alpha}{[c_p(G \backslash F)]^{1/p}}\,,$$

where $\{F\}$ is the collection of subsets of G that are closed in Ω. Further, let

$$\mathfrak{A}_{G,\sigma}^{(1,\alpha)} = \sup_{\{g\}} \frac{[\sigma(g)]^\alpha}{s(\partial_i g)}\,,$$

where $\{g\}$ is the collection of admissible subsets of G. Thus, by definition, $\mathfrak{A}_{G,m_n}^{(p,\alpha)} = \mathfrak{A}_G^{(p,\alpha)}$.

Theorem. *Let $p \geqslant 1$ and let G be an open bounded subset of Ω.*

1) *If $\mathfrak{A}_{G,\sigma}^{(p,\alpha)} < \infty$ and the numbers q, α, p are related by either one of the following conditions:*

(i) $q \leqslant q^* = \alpha^{-1}$ *for* $\alpha p \leqslant 1$, (ii) $q < q^* = \alpha^{-1}$ *for* $\alpha p > 1$, *then, for all $u \in C^{0,1}(\Omega)$ that vanish outside G, we have*

$$\|u\|_{L_q(\Omega,\sigma)} \leqslant C \|\nabla u\|_{L_p(\Omega)}^{1-\varkappa} \|u\|_{L_r(\Omega,\sigma)}^{\varkappa}, \tag{1}$$

with $r \in (0,q)$, $\varkappa = r(q^*-q)/(q^*-r)q$, $C \leqslant c[\mathfrak{A}_{G,\sigma}^{(p,\alpha)}]^{1-\varkappa}$.

2) *Let $q^* > 0$, $r \in (0, q^*)$ and let (1) be valid for some $q \in (0,q^*)$ and for any $u \in C^{0,1}(\Omega)$ that vanishes outside G with $\varkappa = r(q^*-q)/(q^*-r)q$ and with a constant C that is independent of u. Then $C \geqslant c[\mathfrak{A}_{G,\sigma}^{(p,\alpha)}]^{1-\varkappa}$.*

The proof does not differ from that of Lemma 4.2.

Next we present a sufficient condition for the finiteness of $\mathfrak{A}_{G,\sigma}^{(p,\gamma)}$.

Proposition. *We have*

$$\mathfrak{A}_{G,\sigma}^{(p,\gamma)} \leqslant c(\mathfrak{A}_{G}^{(p,\beta)})^{1-\gamma/\alpha}(\mathfrak{A}_{G,\sigma}^{(1,\alpha)})^{\gamma/\alpha}, \tag{2}$$

where $\gamma = \alpha\beta p(p-1+p\beta)^{-1}$.

Proof. Let $K = G \backslash F$ and let u be any function in $V_\Omega(K)$. We put

$$\psi(t) = \int_0^t \left(\int_{\mathscr{E}_\tau} |\nabla u|^{p-1} ds \right)^{1/(1-p)} d\tau .$$

The definition of $\mathfrak{A}_{G}^{(p,\beta)}$ and (4.1.3/1) imply

$$\psi(t) \leqslant [c_p(G\backslash \mathscr{N}_t)]^{1/(1-p)} \leqslant (\mathfrak{A}_{G}^{(p,\beta)}[m_n(\mathscr{N}_t)]^{-\beta})^{p/(p-1)}, \tag{3}$$

where $t \in [0,1)$. Thus, if $\mathfrak{A}_{G}^{(p,\beta)} < \infty$ then $\psi(t)$ is finite and hence absolutely continuous on any segment $[0,1-\varepsilon]$, $\varepsilon > 0$. Let $t(\psi)$ be the inverse of $\psi(t)$. Since the function $\psi \to \sigma(\mathscr{N}_{t(\psi)})$ does not increase then by Lemma 1.3.3/3

$$\psi^{\alpha/\gamma}[\sigma(\mathscr{N}_{t(\psi)})]^{\alpha p/(p-1)} \leqslant c \sup_{\psi} \psi^{(p-1)/p\beta} \int_{\psi}^{\psi(1-\varepsilon)} [\sigma(\mathscr{N}_{t(\psi)})]^{\alpha p/(p-1)} d\psi$$

for $t(\psi) \in [0, 1-\varepsilon]$. The right-hand side is equal to

$$c \sup_{t \in [0,1-\varepsilon]} [\psi(t)]^{(p-1)/p\beta} \int_t^{1-\varepsilon} \frac{[\sigma(\mathscr{N}_\tau)]^{\alpha p/(p-1)} d\tau}{\|\nabla u\|_{L_{p-1}(\mathscr{E}_\tau)}} .$$

(The change of variable $\psi = \psi(t)$ is possible since $\psi(t)$ is absolutely continuous on $[0,1-\varepsilon]$.) The latter, (3) and Lemma 4.1.3/2 imply

(4)
$$\psi^{\alpha/\gamma}[\sigma(\mathcal{N}_{t(\psi)})]^{\alpha p/(p-1)}$$
$$\leqslant c(\mathfrak{A}_G^{(p,\beta)})^{1/\beta} \sup_{t\in[0,1-\varepsilon]} \frac{1}{m_n(\mathcal{N}_t)} \int_t^{1-\varepsilon} \left(\frac{[\sigma(\mathcal{N}_\tau)]^\alpha}{s(\mathscr{E}_\tau)}\right)^{p/(p-1)} \left(-\frac{d}{d\tau} m_n(\mathcal{N}_\tau)\right) d\tau .$$

Taking into account that

$$[\sigma(\mathcal{N}_\tau)]^\alpha \leqslant \mathfrak{A}_{G,\sigma}^{(1,\alpha)} s(\mathscr{E}_\tau)$$

for almost all $\tau\in(0,1)$, from (4) we obtain

$$[\psi(t)]^{\alpha/\gamma}[\sigma(\mathcal{N}_t)]^{\alpha p/(p-1)} \leqslant c(\mathfrak{A}_G^{(p,\beta)})^{1/\beta}(\mathfrak{A}_{G,\sigma}^{(1,\alpha)})^{p/(p-1)}$$
$$\times \sup_{t\in[0,1-\varepsilon]} \frac{1}{m_n(\mathcal{N}_t)} \int_t^{1-\varepsilon} \left(-\frac{d}{d\tau} m_n(\mathcal{N}_\tau)\right) d\tau$$
$$\leqslant c(\mathfrak{A}_G^{(p,\beta)})^{1/\beta}(\mathfrak{A}_{G,\sigma}^{(1,\alpha)})^{p/(p-1)} .$$

Passing to the limit as $t\to 1-0$ we arrive at

$$[\sigma(F)]^\gamma \leqslant c(\mathfrak{A}_G^{(p,\beta)})^{1-\sigma/\alpha}(\mathfrak{A}_{G,\sigma}^{(1,\alpha)})^{\gamma/\alpha}[\psi(1)]^{(1-p)/p} .$$

Minimizing the right-hand side over $V_\Omega(K)$, we obtain

$$[\sigma(F)]^\gamma \leqslant c(\mathfrak{A}_G^{(p,\beta)})^{1-\gamma/\alpha}(\mathfrak{A}_{G,\sigma}^{(1,\alpha)})^{\gamma/\alpha}[c_p(G\backslash F)]^{1/p} .$$

The result follows.

Now we give an example of the application of the preceding proposition in a concrete situation.

Example. Let

$$\Omega = \{x: |x'| < x_n^\lambda,\ 0 < x_n < \infty\} ,$$

where $\lambda > 1$, $x' = (x_1, \ldots, x_{n-1})$ and let $G = \{x\in\Omega: 0 < x_n < 1\}$. Here the role of the measure σ is played by $(n-1)$-dimensional measure s on the set $\Pi = \{x\in\Omega: x_1 = 0\}$. We show that $\mathfrak{A}_{G,s}^{(p,\gamma)}$ is finite and the value of γ is the best possible provided $\lambda(n-1)+1 > p \geqslant 1$ and $\gamma = (\lambda(n-1)+1-p)/(\lambda(n-2)+1)$.

First let $p = 1$. In Example 3.3.3/1 it was shown that the mapping

$$x \to \xi = (x_1, \ldots, x_{n-1}, x_n^\lambda)$$

of Ω onto the cone $\xi\Omega = \{\xi: |\xi'| < \xi_n, 0 < \xi_n < \infty\}$ is subareal. Hence

(5)
$$s(\partial_i g) \geqslant c s(\partial_i \xi g)$$

for any admissible set g with $\operatorname{clos}_\Omega g \subset G$. Since $\xi\Omega$ is a cone and $\xi\Pi$ is its cross section by a hyperplane, then by Theorem 1.4.5 we have

$$\|u\|_{L(\xi\Pi)} \leqslant c \|\nabla_\xi u\|_{L(\xi\Omega)} \tag{6}$$

for all $u \in L_p^1(\xi\Omega)$ that vanish outside ξG. Therefore,

$$cs(\partial_i \xi g) \geqslant s(\xi\Pi \cap \xi g) . \tag{7}$$

(The latter estimate results from the substitution of the sequence $\{w_m\}$ constructed in Lemma 3.2.2 into (6).)

It is clear that

$$s(\xi\Pi \cap \xi g) = \lambda \int_{\Pi \cap g} x_n^{\lambda-1} dx_2 \ldots dx_n . \tag{8}$$

Since $\lambda > 1$, the infimum of the integral on the right in (8), taken over all sets $\Pi \cap g$ with the fixed measure $s(\Pi \cap g)$, is attained at $\{x \in \Pi: 0 < x_n < a\}$, where a is the number defined by

$$v_{n-2}(\lambda(n-2)+1)^{-1} a^{\lambda(n-2)+1} = s(\Pi \cap g) .$$

Therefore,

$$s(\xi\Pi \cap \xi g) \geqslant c[s(\Pi \cap g)]^{\lambda(n-1)/(\lambda(n-2)+1)}$$

which together with (5) and (7) yields

$$s(\partial_i g) \geqslant c[s(\Pi \cap g)]^{\alpha} ,$$

where $\alpha = \lambda(n-1)/(\lambda(n-2)+1)$. Thus, $\mathfrak{A}_{G,s}^{(1,\alpha)} < \infty$. On the other hand, since $\Omega \in \mathscr{I}_{p,\beta}$ with $\beta = (\lambda(n-1)+1-p)p/(\lambda(n-1)+1)$ (cf. Example 4.3.1/1) then $\mathfrak{A}_G^{(p,\beta)} < \infty$. Now (2) implies $\mathfrak{A}_{G,s}^{(p,\gamma)} < \infty$ with

$$\begin{aligned} \gamma &= \frac{\lambda(n-1)}{\lambda(n-2)+1} \cdot \frac{\lambda(n-1)+1-p}{p(\lambda(n-1)+1)} p \left(p-1+\frac{\lambda(n-1)+1-p}{\lambda(n-1)+1}\right)^{-1} \\ &= \frac{\lambda(n-1)+1-p}{p(\lambda(n-2)+1)} . \end{aligned}$$

This value of γ is best possible; this may be verified using the sequence $F_m = \{x \in \Omega: 0 < x_n < m^{-1}\}$, $m = 1, 2, \ldots$. In fact,

$$c_p(G \backslash F_m) \leqslant c \left(\int_{m^{-1}}^{1} \tau^{\lambda(1-n)/(p-1)} d\tau \right)^{1-p} \leqslant c m^{p-1-\lambda(n-1)}$$

(cf. Example 4.3.1/1) and $s(F_m \cap \Pi) = c m^{-1-\lambda(n-2)}$. So the estimate

$$[s(F_m \cap \Pi)]^{\gamma} \leqslant \text{const}\,[c_p(G \setminus F_m)]^{1/p}$$

implies $\gamma \geqslant (\lambda(n-1)+1-p)/p(\lambda(n-2)+1)$.

In conclusion we consider briefly some other generalizations of the above results.

Following Chapter 2 with minor modifications in the proofs, we can generalize the results of the present and the previous chapters to encompass functions with the finite integral

$$\int_\Omega [\Phi(x, \nabla u)]^p dx$$

and even those satisfying the following more general condition

$$\int_\Omega \Psi(x, u, \nabla u)\, dx < \infty$$

(cf. Remark 2.3.2).

Another possible generalization, which needs no essential changes in the proofs, is the replacement of $L_q(\Omega)$ by the Orlicz space (cf. Theorem 2.3.2).

§ 4.7. The Inclusion $W_{p,r}^1(\Omega) \subset L_q(\Omega)\,(r > q)$ for Domains with Infinite Volume

4.7.1. The Classes $\overset{\infty}{\mathcal{J}}_\alpha$ and $\overset{\infty}{\mathcal{I}}_{p,\alpha}$

The classes $\mathcal{J}_\alpha$, $\mathcal{I}_{p,\alpha}$ introduced above characterize the domains "in the small". In the present section we shall be interested in the structure of domains at infinity.

Consider for example the unbounded plane domain

$$\Omega = \{(x, y)\colon 0 < x < \infty, |y| < x^{1/2}\}.$$

We have

$$\|u\|_{L_2(\Omega)} \leqslant C(\|\nabla u\|_{L_1(\Omega)} + \|u\|_{L_r(\Omega)}), \tag{1}$$

where r is an arbitrary positive number which does not exceed 2.

The latter can be proved in the following way. Let $Q_{m,n}$ be an arbitrary square of the integral coordinate grid. Each of the domains $\Omega_{m,n} = \Omega \cap Q_{m,n}$ can be mapped onto $Q_{0,0}$ by a quasi-isometric mapping so that the Lipschitz constants of the mapping functions are uniformly bounded and the Jacobian determinants are uniformly separated from zero. This and Theorem 1.4.5 imply the sequence of inequalities

$$\int_{\Omega_{m,n}} u^2 dx \leqslant c(\|\nabla u\|^2_{L_1(\Omega_{m,n})} + \|u\|^2_{L_r(\Omega_{m,n})})$$

with constant c that is independent of m, n. Summing over m, n and using $(\sum_i a_i^\alpha)^{1/\alpha} \leqslant \sum_i a_i$ with $\alpha \geqslant 1$, $a_i > 0$ we arrive at (1).

The condition $r \leqslant 2$ is essential for the validity of (1). In fact, for $u(x,y) = (x+1)^{-\gamma}$ with $3r/2 < \gamma < \frac{3}{4}$, $2 < r < 3$, the right-hand side in (1) is finite whereas $u \notin L_2(\Omega)$.

In a sense estimate (1) is unsatisfactory: the norm in $L_r(\Omega)$ is not weaker than that in $L_2(\Omega)$ (contrary to the case $m_n(\Omega) < \infty$). If we discuss the rate of decrease of a function at infinity then the finiteness of the norm in $L_r(\Omega)(r<2)$ is a more restrictive condition than that of the norm in $L_2(\Omega)$.

So we may pose the following question. Let $m_n(\Omega) = \infty$. What is the space $L_q(\Omega)$ containing $W^1_{p,r}(\Omega)$ for large r?

To this end we introduce classes similar to $\mathscr{J}_\alpha$, $\mathscr{I}_{p,\alpha}$.

Definition 1. The set Ω is contained in *the class* $\overset{\infty}{\mathscr{J}}_\alpha$ if there exists a constant $M > 0$ such that

$$\sup_{\{g\}} \frac{[m_n(g)]^\alpha}{s(\partial_i g)} < \infty, \tag{2}$$

where the supremum is taken over all admissible sets $g \subset \Omega$ with $m_n(g) \geqslant M$.

We note, for the time being without proof, that the domain Ω inside the parabola, mentioned at the beginning of the section, is in the class $\overset{\infty}{\mathscr{J}}_{1/3}$ and that

$$\|u\|_{L_3(\Omega)} \leqslant C(\|\nabla u\|_{L_1(\Omega)} + \|u\|_{L_r(\Omega)}) \tag{3}$$

for any $r \geqslant 3$. The exponent 3 in the left-hand side of the above inequality cannot be reduced.

Let F be a bounded subset of Ω that is closed in Ω and let $\Omega_R = \Omega \cap B_R$. By the p-capacity of F relative to Ω we mean the limit of $c_p(\Omega_R \backslash F)$ as $R \to \infty$. We denote it by $p\text{-cap}_\Omega(F)$.

Definition 2. The domain Ω is contained in *the class* $\overset{\infty}{\mathscr{I}}_{p,\alpha}$ if there exists a constant $M > 0$ such that

$$\overset{\infty}{\mathfrak{A}}_{p,\alpha}(M) \overset{\text{def}}{=} \sup_{\{F\}} \frac{[m_n(F)]^\alpha}{[p\text{-cap}_\Omega(F)]^{1/p}} < \infty. \tag{4}$$

Here the supremum is taken over all F with $m_n(F) \geqslant M$, $p\text{-cap}_\Omega(F) > 0$.

Similarly to Lemma 4.3.2/1 we can prove that the classes $\overset{\infty}{\mathscr{I}}_{1,\alpha}$ and $\overset{\infty}{\mathscr{J}}_\alpha$ coincide and that

$$\overset{\infty}{\mathfrak{A}}_{1,\alpha}(M) = \sup_{\{g\}} \frac{[m_n(g)]^\alpha}{s(\partial_i g)},$$

where $\{g\}$ has the same meaning as in (2).

Proposition 1. *The class* $\overset{\infty}{\mathscr{I}}_{p,\alpha}$ *is empty provided* $\alpha > 1/p - 1/n$.

Proof. Let $\Omega \in \overset{\infty}{\mathscr{I}}_{p,\alpha}$. If ϱ is a large enough positive number such that $m_n(\Omega_\varrho) \geqslant M$ and $R > \varrho$ then by (4)

$$[m_n(\Omega_\varrho)]^\alpha \leqslant K[c_p(\Omega_R \backslash \operatorname{clos}_\Omega \Omega_\varrho)]^{1/p}, \qquad K = \text{const}.$$

Let $u(x) = \eta(|x|)$ where η is a piecewise linear continuous function that vanishes for $t > R$ and is equal to unity for $t < \varrho$. Since $u \in U_\Omega(\Omega_R \backslash \operatorname{clos}_\Omega \Omega_\varrho)$, then

$$c_p(\Omega_R \backslash \operatorname{clos}_\Omega \Omega_\varrho) \leqslant (R-\varrho)^{-p} m_n(\Omega_R \backslash \Omega_\varrho).$$

Consequently,

$$R - \varrho \leqslant K[m_n(\Omega_R) - m_n(\Omega_\varrho)]^{1/p}[m_n(\Omega_\varrho)]^{-\alpha}.$$

We define a sequence of numbers $\{\varrho_j\}_{j\geqslant 1}$ by $m_n(\Omega_{\varrho_j}) = 2^j M$. Then $\varrho_{j+1} - \varrho_j \leqslant K 2^{j(p^{-1}-\alpha)}$. Summing, we get $\varrho_j \leqslant \varrho_1 + cK 2^{j(p^{-1}-\alpha)}$ which together with the definition of the sequence $\{\varrho_j\}$ yields

$$\varrho_j \leqslant \varrho_1 + cK(m_n(\Omega_{\varrho_j}))^{p^{-1}-\alpha}.$$

Since $\varrho_j \to \infty$ then $\alpha < p^{-1}$. Further we have

$$\varrho_j \leqslant \varrho_1 + cK(v_n \varrho_j^n)^{p^{-1}-\alpha}$$

and hence $\alpha \leqslant p^{-1} - n^{-1}$. The result follows.

Let F be a bounded subset of Ω that is closed in Ω and let $\Lambda_F(\sigma) = \inf s(\partial_i g)$ over all admissible subsets g of Ω which contain F and with $m_n(g) \geqslant \sigma$.

An immediate corollary of inequality (4.1.3/3) is the next proposition.

Proposition 2. *The inequality*

$$p\text{-cap}_\Omega(F) \geqslant \left(\int_{m_n(F)}^{\infty} [\Lambda_F(\sigma)]^{-p/(p-1)} d\sigma \right)^{1-p} \tag{5}$$

is valid.

Proposition 3. *If* $\Omega \in \overset{\infty}{\mathscr{I}}_{\alpha+(p-1)/p}$, *then* $\Omega \in \overset{\infty}{\mathscr{I}}_{p,\alpha}$ *and*

$$\overset{\infty}{\mathfrak{A}}_{p,\alpha}(M) \leqslant \left(\frac{p-1}{p\alpha}\right)^{(p-1)/p} \overset{\infty}{\mathfrak{A}}_{1,\alpha+(p-1)/p}(M). \tag{6}$$

Proof. If $m_n(F) \geqslant M$ then by (5) we obtain

$$p\text{-cap}_\Omega(F) \geqslant [\overset{\infty}{\mathfrak{A}}_{1,\alpha+(p-1)/p}(M)]^{-p} \left(\int_{m_n(F)}^{\infty} \sigma^{-(\alpha+1-1/p)p/(p-1)} d\sigma \right)^{1-p},$$

which is equivalent to (6).

4.7.2. The Imbedding $W^1_{p,r}(\Omega) \subset L_q(\Omega)(r>q)$

The proof of the following theorem is carried out using a device similar to that used to prove Theorem 4.3.3. However, we present it for the reader's convenience since it differs in details.

Theorem. 1) *If* $\Omega \in \overset{\infty}{\mathscr{I}}_{p,\alpha}$ *and* $r>q=\alpha^{-1}$, *then for any* $u \in W^1_{p,r}(\Omega)$

$$\|u\|_{L_q(\Omega)} \leqslant C_1 \|\nabla u\|_{L_p(\Omega)} + C_2 \|u\|_{L_r(\Omega)}, \tag{1}$$

where $C_2 = M^{(r-q)/rq}$, $C_1 \leqslant p(p-1)^{(1-p)/p} \overset{\infty}{\mathfrak{A}}_{p,\alpha}(M)$.

2) *If* (1) *is valid with* $r>q$ *then* $\Omega \in \overset{\infty}{\mathscr{I}}_{p,\alpha}$ *with* $\alpha = q^{-1}$. *Moreover,* $M^{(r-q)/rq} = \varepsilon^{-1} C_2$, $\overset{\infty}{\mathfrak{A}}_{p,\alpha}(M) \leqslant (1-\varepsilon)^{-1} C_1$, *where* ε *is an arbitrary number in* $(0,1)$.

Proof. 1) By virtue of Lemma 3.1.2/2 it suffices to prove (1) for functions in $C^\infty(\Omega)$ with supports in Ω_R for some $R<\infty$. We choose a number T so that

$$m_n(\mathscr{L}_T) \leqslant M \leqslant m_n(\mathscr{N}_T).$$

It can be readily checked that

$$\int_\Omega |u|^q dx = \int_{\mathscr{L}_T} |u|^q dx + \int_0^T m_n(\mathscr{N}_t \backslash \mathscr{L}_T) d(t^p). \tag{2}$$

The first summand on the right is estimated by Hölder's inequality

$$\int_{\mathscr{L}_T} |u|^q dx \leqslant M^{1-q/r} \left(\int_\Omega |u|^r dx \right)^{q/r}.$$

By (1.3.3/1) the second integral in (2) does not exceed

$$\left\{ \int_0^T [m_n(\mathscr{N}_t \backslash \mathscr{L}_T)]^{p/q} d(t^p) \right\}^{q/p}.$$

Therefore,

$$\|u\|_{L_q(\Omega)} \leqslant M^{1/q-1/r} \|u\|_{L_r(\Omega)} + \left\{ \int_0^T [m_n(\mathscr{N}_t)]^{p/q} d(t^p) \right\}^{1/p}.$$

Since $m_n(\mathscr{N}_t) \geqslant M$ for $t \in (0,T)$, then

$$(3) \quad [m_n(\mathcal{N}_t)]^{1/q} \leqslant \overset{\infty}{\mathfrak{A}}_{p,\alpha}(M)[p\text{-cap}_\Omega(\mathcal{N}_t)]^{1/p} \leqslant \overset{\infty}{\mathfrak{A}}_{p,\alpha}(M)[c_p(\Omega_R \backslash \mathcal{N}_t)]^{1/p}.$$

Applying (3) and Lemma 4.1.3/2, we obtain

$$\|u\|_{L_q(M)} \leqslant M^{1/q-1/r}\|u\|_{L_r(\Omega)} + \overset{\infty}{\mathfrak{A}}_{p,\alpha}(M)\left[\int_0^\infty c_p(\Omega_R \backslash \mathcal{N}_t)\, d(t^p)\right]^{1/p}$$

$$\leqslant M^{1/q-1/r}\|u\|_{L_r(\Omega)} + \overset{\infty}{\mathfrak{A}}_{p,\alpha}(M)\frac{p}{(p-1)^{(p-1)/p}}\|\nabla u\|_{L_p(\Omega)}.$$

2) We put $M = (C_2\varepsilon^{-1})^{rq/(r-q)}$ and consider an arbitrary bounded $F \subset \Omega$ that is closed in Ω with $m_n(F) \geqslant M$. Let u be any function in $C^{0,1}(\Omega)$ that vanishes outside some ball and is equal to unity on F. It is clear that

$$\int_\Omega |u|^r dx = \int_0^1 m_n(\mathcal{N}_t)\, d(t^r).$$

Since $m_n(\mathcal{N}_t)$ does not increase and $q < r$, then by (1.3.3/1)

$$\int_\Omega |u|^r dx \leqslant \left(\int_0^1 [m_n(\mathcal{N}_t)]^{q/r} d(t^q)\right)^{r/q}.$$

Taking into account that $m_n(\mathcal{N}_t) \geqslant m_n(F) \geqslant M$, we obtain

$$\|u\|_{L_r(\Omega)} \leqslant M^{1/r-1/q}\left(\int_0^1 m_n(\mathcal{N}_t)\, d(t^q)\right)^{r/q} = \varepsilon C_2^{-1}\|u\|_{L_q(\Omega)}.$$

So (1) and the preceding inequality imply that

$$\|u\|_{L_q(\Omega)} \leqslant C_1(1-\varepsilon)^{-1}\|\nabla u\|_{L_p(\Omega)}.$$

Having in mind that $u = 1$ on F and minimizing $\|\nabla u\|_{L_p(\Omega)}$, we finally obtain

$$[m_n(F)]^{1/q} \leqslant C_1(1-\varepsilon)^{-1}[p\text{-cap}_\Omega(F)]^{1/p}.$$

The theorem is proved.

The first part of Theorem and Proposition 4.7.1/3 imply the next corollary.

Corollary. *If* $\Omega \in \overset{\infty}{\mathcal{J}}_\alpha$, $\alpha \leqslant 1$, $p \geqslant 1$, $r > q$, $p(1-\alpha) < 1$, $q = p/[1-p(1-\alpha)]$ *then* (1) *is valid for any* $u \in W_{p,r}^1(\Omega)$.

4.7.3. Example of a Domain in the Class $\overset{\infty}{\mathcal{J}}_{p,\alpha}$

Example. Consider the "paraboloid"

$$\Omega = \{x \in R^n\colon x_1^2 + \cdots + x_{n-1}^2 < a x_n^{2\beta},\ 0 < x_n < \infty\}\,, \tag{1}$$

where $1 > \beta > 0$ and $a = \text{const} > 0$ (Fig. 17).

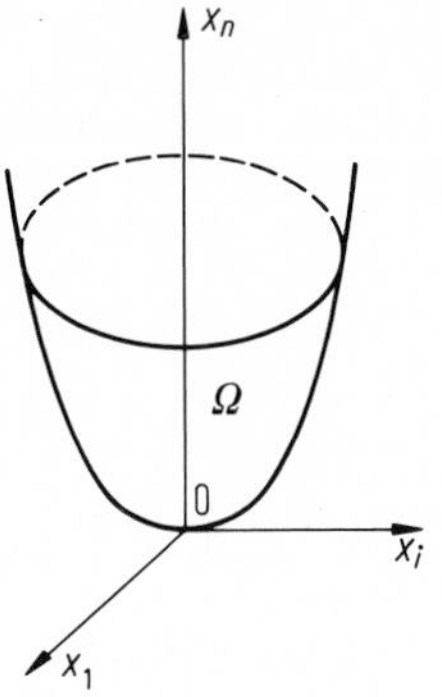

Fig. 17

First we show that

$$0 < \limsup_{M\to\infty} \frac{[m_n(g)]^\alpha}{s(\partial_i g)} < \infty\,, \tag{2}$$

where the supremum is taken over all admissible subsets g of the domain Ω with $m_n(g) \geqslant M$ and $\alpha = \beta(n-1)/(\beta(n-1)+1)$. Taking the symmetrization of g with respect to the ray Ox_n and repeating the proof of Lemma 3.2.1/1 we obtain that the ball B, orthogonal to $\partial\Omega$, has the smallest area $\partial_i g$ among all sets g with the fixed volume M. After a routine calculation we obtain

$$\lim_{M\to\infty} \frac{[m_n(B)]^\alpha}{s(\partial_i B)} = \frac{(1-\alpha)^\alpha}{v_{n-1}^{1-\alpha}}\,.$$

So (2) follows.

Thus, $\Omega \in \overset{\infty}{\mathcal{J}}_{\beta(n-1)/(\beta(n-1)+1)}$ and by Corollary 4.7.2 and the second part of Theorem 4.7.2 we have $\Omega \in \overset{\infty}{\mathcal{J}}_{p,\alpha}$ with $p < \beta(n-1)+1$ and $\alpha = p^{-1} - (\beta(n-1)+1)^{-1}$. We show that this value of α is the largest possible. In fact, let $\Omega(\mathcal{X}) = \{x \in \Omega\colon x_n \leqslant \mathcal{X}\}$. It is clear that

$$p\text{-cap}_\Omega(\Omega(\mathcal{X})) \leqslant \int\limits_{\Omega\setminus\Omega(\mathcal{X})} |\nabla\,[(\mathcal{X}/x_n)^{\beta(n-1)}]\,|^p dx = c\,\mathcal{X}^{\beta(n-1)+1-p}$$

and hence

$$\frac{[m_n(\Omega(\mathscr{X}))]^\alpha}{[p\text{-cap}_\Omega(\Omega(\mathscr{X}))]^{1/p}} \geqslant c\,\mathscr{X}^{[\beta(n-1)+1](\alpha-\gamma)} \xrightarrow[\mathscr{X}\to\infty]{} \infty$$

for $\alpha > p^{-1} - [\beta(n-1)+1]^{-1} = \gamma$.

Thus, for the domain (1) and for $\beta(n-1) > p-1 \geqslant 0$, the inequality (4.7.2/1) is valid with $r > q = [\beta(n-1)+1]p/[\beta(n-1)+1-p]$. This value of q can not be reduced. We note that it exceeds the limit exponent $np/(n-p)$ in the Sobolev theorem for $\beta < 1$.

4.7.4. The Space $\overset{(0)}{L}{}_p^1(\Omega)$ and Its Imbedding into $L_q(\Omega)$

Let $\overset{(0)}{L}{}_p^1(\Omega)$ denote the completion of the set of functions in $C^\infty(\Omega) \cap L_p^1(\Omega)$ with bounded supports with respect to the norm $\|\nabla u\|_{L_p(\Omega)}$. (Here and elsewhere in this section $m_n(\Omega) = \infty$.)

According to Lemma 3.1.2/3, the space $\overset{(0)}{L}{}_p^1(\Omega)$ coincides with the completion of $W_{p,r}^1(\Omega)$ (r is an arbitrary positive number) with respect to the norm $\|\nabla u\|_{L_p(\Omega)}$.

Removing the conditions $m_n(g) \geqslant M$, $m_n(F) \geqslant M$ in the definitions of the classes $\overset{\infty}{\mathscr{J}}_\alpha$, $\overset{\infty}{\mathscr{I}}_{p,\alpha}$ (i.e. putting $M = 0$) we obtain the definitions of the classes $\overset{\infty}{\mathscr{J}}_\alpha(0)$, $\overset{\infty}{\mathscr{I}}_{p,\alpha}(0)$.

Remark 4.3.1 implies $\alpha \geqslant 1/p - 1/n$ provided $n \geqslant p$ and $\Omega \in \overset{\infty}{\mathscr{I}}_{p,\alpha}$. On the other hand, according to Proposition 4.6, $\alpha \leqslant 1/p - 1/n$. So only the class $\overset{\infty}{\mathscr{I}}_{p,1/p-1/n}(0)$ is not empty. (For example, the domain (4.7.3/1) with $\beta = 1$ and the space R^n are contained in this class.)

Taking the latter into account and mimicking the proof of Theorem 2.3.2 with minor modifications we arrive at the following theorem.

Theorem. *The inequality*

$$\|u\|_{L_q(\Omega)} \leqslant C\|\nabla u\|_{L_p(\Omega)}, \quad p \geqslant 1, \tag{1}$$

is valid for all $u \in \overset{(0)}{L}{}_p^1(\Omega)$ *if and only if* $n > p, q = pn/(n-p)$ *and* $\Omega \in \overset{\infty}{\mathscr{I}}_{p,1/p-1/n}(0)$.

The best constant in (1) *satisfies*

$$\overset{\infty}{\mathfrak{A}}_{p,1/p-1/n}(0) \leqslant C \leqslant p(p-1)^{(1-p)/p}\overset{\infty}{\mathfrak{A}}_{p,1/p-1/n}(0)\,.$$

Remark. We note that the inclusion $\Omega \in \overset{\infty}{\mathscr{I}}_{p,1/p-1/n}(0), n > p$, does not imply the Poincaré type inequality

$$\inf_{c\in R^1} \|u-c\|_{L_{pn/(n-p)}(\Omega)} \leqslant C\|\nabla u\|_{L_p(\Omega)}, \quad u \in L_p^1(\Omega)\,. \tag{2}$$

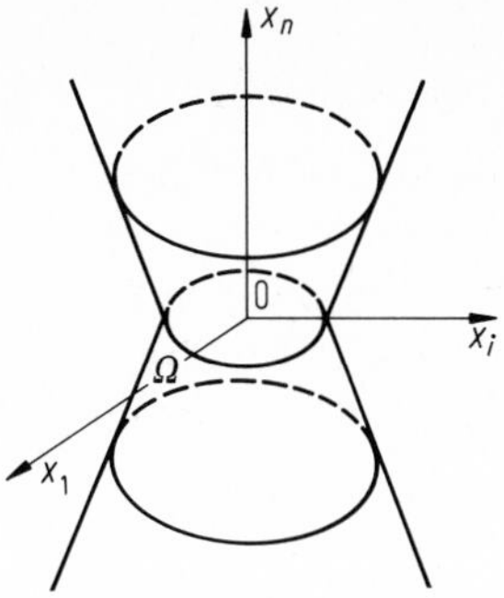

Fig. 18

In fact, consider the domain in Fig. 18, which is the union of the two cones $\{x: |x'| < x_n + 1\}$ and $\{x: |x'| < 1 - x_n\}$, $x' = (x_1, \ldots, x_{n-1})$. Each of the cones is in the class $\overset{\infty}{\mathscr{I}}_{p,1/p-1/n}(0)$. So their union Ω is in the same class (cf. Proposition 4.3.1/1). However, the left-hand side in (2) is infinite for a smooth function that is odd in x_n, vanishes for $0 < x_n < 1$ and is equal to unity for $x_n > 2$, and which, obviously, belongs to $L^1_p(\Omega)$.

At the same time, by Theorem, the inclusion $\Omega \in \overset{\infty}{\mathscr{I}}_{p,1/p-1/n}(0)$ is equivalent to the inequality

(3) $$\|u\|_{L_{pn/(n-p)}(\Omega)} \leqslant C \|\nabla u\|_{L_p(\Omega)}, \quad u \in W^1_{p,pn/(n-p)}(\Omega).$$

In particular, from this it follows that (2) implies $\Omega \in \overset{\infty}{\mathscr{I}}_{p,1/p-1/n}(0)$.

The preceding Theorem shows as well that the norm in $L_{pn/(n-p)}(\Omega)$ can not be replaced by the norm in $L_q(\Omega)$ with $q \neq pn/(n-p)$ in (2).

4.7.5. On the Poincaré Inequality for Domains with Infinite Volume

The following assertion gives a description of domains for which (4.7.4/2) is valid.

Here (and only here) we shall assume that the condition of boundedness of the sets G and F is omitted in the definition of p-conductivity.

Theorem. *Let $m_n(\Omega) = \infty$. Inequality* (4.7.4/2) *is valid for all $u \in L^1_p(\Omega)$, $p \geqslant 1$, if and only if Ω is a connected open set in $\overset{\infty}{\mathscr{I}}_{p,1/p-1/n}(0)$ and*

(1) *the finiteness of the p-conductivity of the conductor $K = G \backslash F$ in Ω implies either $m_n(F) < \infty$ or $m_n(\Omega \backslash G) < \infty$.*

For $p = 1$ the condition (1) *is equivalent to the following:*

(2) *if G is an open subset of Ω such that $\partial_i G$ is a smooth manifold and $s(\partial_i G) < \infty$ then either $m_n(G) < \infty$ or $m_n(\Omega \backslash G) < \infty$.*

(We recall that $\overset{\infty}{\mathscr{I}}_{1,1-1/n}(0)=\overset{\infty}{\mathscr{J}}_{1-1/n}(0)$.)

Proof. The necessity of the inclusion $\Omega\in\overset{\infty}{\mathscr{I}}_{p,1/p-1/n}(0)$ was noted at the end of Remark 4.7.4. The necessity of the connectedness of Ω is obvious.

We prove that (4.7.4/2) implies (1). Let v be an arbitrary function in $U_\Omega(K)$, where K is the conductor $G\backslash F$ with $c_p(K)<\infty$. We put $u=\max\{0,\min\{v,1\}\}$ in (4.7.4/2). Then

$$[|c|^q m_n(\Omega\backslash G)+|1-c|^q m_n(F)]^{1/q}\leqslant C\|\nabla u\|_{L_p(\Omega)},$$

with $q=pn/(n-p)$. Therefore, either $m_n(\Omega\backslash G)<\infty$ or $m_n(F)<\infty$.

Now let $p=1$. We prove the necessity of (2). First we note that the condition that G is bounded was not used in the proof of Lemma 3.2.2. Let G be an open subset of Ω such that $\partial_i G$ is a smooth manifold and $s(\partial_i G)<\infty$. We insert any function w_m from the sequence constructed in Lemma 3.2.2 in (4.7.4/2) in place of u. Then, starting with some index m, for any compactum $e\subset G$, we have

$$(|c_m|^{n/(n-1)}m_n(\Omega\backslash G)+|1-c_m|^{n/(n-1)}m_n(e))^{(n-1)/n}\leqslant C\|\nabla w_m\|_{L(\Omega)},$$

where $c_m=\text{const}$. Since

$$\limsup_{m\to\infty}\|\nabla w_m\|_{L(\Omega)}=s(\partial_i G)<\infty,$$

then either $m_n(\Omega\backslash G)<\infty$ or $c_m=0$ and

$$[m_n(e)]^{(n-1)/n}\leqslant Cs(\partial_i G).$$

Consequently, (2) is valid.

The sufficiency is proved in several steps.

Lemma 1. 1) *Let $\Omega\in\overset{\infty}{\mathscr{I}}_{p,q}(0)$ with $q=pn/(n-p)$, $n>p$. Then*

$$[m_n(F)]^{1-p/n}\leqslant \text{const}\, c_p(K) \tag{3}$$

is valid for all conductors $K=G\backslash F$ where G is an open subset of Ω and F is a subset of Ω with finite volume that is closed in Ω.

2) *Let $\Omega\in\overset{\infty}{\mathscr{J}}_{1-1/n}(0)$. Then*

$$[m_n(G)]^{1-1/n}\leqslant \text{const}\, s(\partial_i G) \tag{4}$$

is valid for all open sets $G\subset\Omega$ such that $\partial_i G$ is a smooth manifold and $m_n(G)<\infty$.

Proof. 1) Since $\Omega\in\overset{\infty}{\mathscr{I}}_{p,q}(0)$, then

$$[m_n(H)]^{1-p/n}\leqslant \text{const}\, c_p(G\backslash H)$$

for any bounded set $H \subset F$ that is closed in Ω. Now (3) follows from $c_p(G\backslash H) \leqslant c_p(G\backslash F)$ and $m_n(F)=\sup_H m_n(H)$.

2) Let $\Omega \in \overset{\infty}{\mathscr{J}}_{1-1/n}(0)$, $m_n(G)<\infty$, $s(\partial_i G)<\infty$. We note that we did not use the boundedness of G in the proof of Lemma 3.2.2 and insert the sequence constructed in this lemma into (4.7.4/3). Passing to the limit as $m\to\infty$, we obtain

$$[m_n(e)]^{1-1/n} \leqslant \mathrm{const}\, s(\partial_i G)$$

for any compactum $e \subset G$.

Lemma 2. 1) *If* $\Omega \in \overset{\infty}{\mathscr{J}}_{p,q}(0)$ *with* $q=pn/(n-p)$, $n>p$, *and* (1) *is valid, then for any* $u \in C^\infty(\Omega) \cap L^1_p(\Omega)$ *there exists a unique number c such that*

$$m_n(\{x\colon |u(x)-c| \geqslant \varepsilon\})<\infty \quad \textit{for all } \varepsilon>0\,. \tag{5}$$

2) *The same is true for* $p=1$ *provided* $\Omega \in \overset{\infty}{\mathscr{J}}_{1-1/n}(0)$ *and* (2) *is valid.*

Proof. 1) We introduce the sets $A_t=\{x\colon u(x)>t\}$, $B_t=\{x\colon u(x)\geqslant t\}$, $C_t=\Omega\backslash A_t$, $D_t=\Omega\backslash B_t$ and put

$$c=\inf\{t\colon m_n(A_t)<\infty\}\,. \tag{6}$$

Suppose $c=+\infty$. Then $m_n(A_t)=\infty$ for all $t\in R^1$ and $m_n(C_t)<\infty$ for all t by virtue of

$$(T-t)^p c_p(A_t\backslash B_T) \leqslant \|\nabla u\|^p_{L_p(\Omega)} \tag{7}$$

and (1). According to (3) we have

$$[m_n(C_t)]^{1-p/n} \leqslant \mathrm{const}\, c_p(D_T\backslash C_t) \tag{8}$$

for all $T>t$. Since

$$(T-t)^p c_p(D_T\backslash C_t) \leqslant \|\nabla u\|^p_{L_p(\Omega)}$$

then the right-hand side in (8) tends to zero as $T\to+\infty$. Consequently, $m_n(C_t)=0$ for all t and $c<+\infty$.

Now let $c=-\infty$. Then $m_n(A_t)<\infty$ for all $t\in R^1$. Applying (3) to the conductor $A_t\backslash B_T$ with $T>t$, we arrive at

$$[m_n(B_T)]^{1-p/n} \leqslant \mathrm{const}\, c_p(A_t\backslash B_T)\,.$$

Since by (7) the right-hand side tends to zero as $t\to-\infty$ then $m_n(B_T)=0$ for all T. So $c>-\infty$.

Now we prove (5). From definition (6) it follows that

(9) $$m_n(\{x\colon u-c\geqslant\varepsilon\})<\infty$$

for $\varepsilon>0$. On the other hand, (6) gives $m_n(\{x\colon u-c\geqslant-\varepsilon/2\})=\infty$.

Since the p-conductivity of the conductor $A_{c-\varepsilon/2}\backslash B_{c-\varepsilon}$ is finite (cf. (7)), then (1) implies

(10) $$m_n(\{x\colon u<c-\varepsilon\})<\infty\,.$$

Inequalities (9) and (10) are equivalent to (5). The uniqueness of the constant c is an obvious corollary of the condition (1) and the finiteness of the conductivity of any conductor $A_t\backslash B_T$, $t>T$. The first part of the lemma is proved.

2) Now let $p=1$. The identity

$$\int_\Omega|\nabla u|\,dx=\int_{-\infty}^{+\infty}s(\partial A_t)\,dt\,,\qquad u\in C^\infty(\Omega)\cap L_1^1(\Omega)$$

implies

(11) $$s(\partial A_t)<\infty\qquad\text{for almost all } t$$

and

(12) $$\liminf_{t\to-\infty}s(\partial A_t)=\liminf_{t\to+\infty}s(\partial A_t)=0\,.$$

Further, it suffices to duplicate the argument in the proof of the first part of Theorem using (11) in place of the finiteness of the conductivity of the conductor $A_t\backslash B_T=D_T\backslash C_t$, and (12) in place of the convergence to zero of $c_p(A_t\backslash B_T)$ as $t\to+\infty$ or $T\to-\infty$. The lemma is proved.

We proceed to the proof of sufficiency in Theorem. Let $u\in C^\infty(\Omega)\cap L_p^1(\Omega)$. According to Lemma 4.1.1/1 we may in addition assume that $u\in L_\infty(\Omega)$.

We put

$$u_\varepsilon(x)=\begin{cases}u(x)-c-\varepsilon & \text{if } u(x)>c+\varepsilon\,,\\ 0 & \text{if } |u(x)-c|\leqslant\varepsilon\,,\\ u(x)-c+\varepsilon & \text{if } u(x)<c-\varepsilon\,,\end{cases}$$

where c is the constant specified in Lemma 2. From (5) and the boundedness of u it follows that $u\in L_{pn/(n-p)}(\Omega)$. So u_ε can be inserted into (4.2.4/3). Passing to the limit as $\varepsilon\to+0$, we arrive at (4.7.4/2). The theorem is proved.

§ 4.8. On the Compactness of the Imbedding $L_p^1(\Omega)\subset L_q(\Omega)$

In this section we obtain necessary and sufficient conditions for sets bounded in $L_p^1(\Omega)$ to be compact in $L_q(\Omega)$. Here Ω is *a domain with finite volume.*

4.8.1. The Classes $\mathring{\mathscr{I}}_{p,\alpha}$, $\mathring{\mathscr{H}}_{p,\alpha}$

As before, by $\mathfrak{A}_{p,\alpha}(M)$ and $\mathfrak{B}_{p,\alpha}(M)$ we mean the constants in the definitions of the classes $\mathscr{I}_{p,\alpha}$ and $\mathscr{H}_{p,\alpha}$.

Definition. The domain Ω is contained in *the class* $\mathring{\mathscr{I}}_{p,\alpha}(\mathring{\mathscr{H}}_{p,\alpha})$ provided $\mathfrak{A}_{p,\alpha}(M) \to 0$ as $M \to 0$ ($\mathfrak{B}_{p,\alpha}(M) \to 0$ as $M \to 0$).

The equality (4.3.2/1) implies that $\Omega \in \mathring{\mathscr{I}}_{1,\alpha}$ if and only if

(1) $$\lim_{M \to 0} \sup_{\{g:\, m_n(g) \leqslant M\}} \frac{[m_n(g)]^{\alpha}}{s(\partial_i g)} = 0$$

(as before, here g designates an admissible subset of Ω).

The value α in the definition of $\mathring{\mathscr{I}}_{p,\alpha}$ exceeds $1/p - 1/n$ since

$$c_p(B_{2\varrho} \backslash \bar{B}_{\varrho}) = \text{const}\, \varrho^{n-p}$$

and hence

$$\frac{[m_n(B_\varrho)]^{1/p-1/n}}{[c_p(B_{2\varrho} \backslash \bar{B}_\varrho)]^{1/p}} = \text{const} > 0\,.$$

4.8.2. A Criterion for Compactness

Theorem. *The imbedding operator of $L_p^1(\Omega)$ into $L_{q^*}(\Omega)$, $1 \leqslant q^* < \infty$, is compact if and only if $\Omega \in \mathring{\mathscr{I}}_{p,\alpha}$ for $p\alpha \leqslant 1$ or $\Omega \in \mathring{\mathscr{H}}_{p,\alpha}$ for $p\alpha > 1$, where $\alpha^{-1} = q^*$.*

Proof. Sufficiency. Let u be an arbitrary function in $C^\infty(\Omega) \cap L_p^1(\Omega) \cap L_\infty(\Omega)$ with bounded support. (According to Corollary 3.1.2 the set of such functions is dense in $L_p^1(\Omega)$.) Let

$$T = \inf\{t:\, m_n(\mathscr{N}_t) \leqslant M\}\,.$$

Obviously,

$$\| u \|_{L_{q^*}(\Omega)} \leqslant c(\| (|u| - T)_+ \|_{L_{q^*}(\Omega)} + T[m_n(\Omega)]^{1/q^*})\,.$$

By Corollary 4.3.3 and Corollary 4.4.2/1 we have

$$\| (|u| - T)_+ \|_{L_{q^*}(\Omega)} \leqslant \delta(M) \| \nabla u \|_{L_p(\Omega)}\,,$$

where $\delta(M) = c\mathfrak{A}_{p,\alpha}(M)$ for $p\alpha \leqslant 1$ and $\delta(M) = c\mathfrak{B}_{p,\alpha}(M)$ for $p\alpha > 1$.

Let Ω_M denote a bounded subdomain of Ω with $C^{0,1}$ boundary and with $m_n(\Omega \backslash \Omega_M) < M/2$. Since $m_n(\mathscr{N}_T) \geqslant M$, then $m_n(\mathscr{N}_T \cap \Omega_M) \geqslant M/2$. Consequently,

$$\| u \|_{L_r(\Omega_M)} \geqslant 2^{-1/r} T M^{1/r}$$

and we arrive at

(1) $$\|u\|_{L_{q^*}(\Omega)} \leqslant c\delta(M)\|\nabla u\|_{L_p(\Omega)} + cM^{-1/r}[m_n(\Omega)]^{1/q^*}\|u\|_{L_r(\Omega_M)}.$$

By Corollary 3.1.2 the latter is valid for all $u \in L_p^1(\Omega)$.

Since Ω_M is a domain with smooth boundary and compact closure, the imbedding operator of $L_p^1(\Omega_M)$ into $L_r(\Omega_M)$ is compact. Let $\{u_m\}_{m\geqslant 1}$ with $\|u_m\|_{L_p^1(\Omega)} = 1$ be a Cauchy sequence in $L_r(\Omega_M)$. Then (1) implies

(2) $$\|u_m - u_l\|_{L_{q^*}(\Omega)} \leqslant c\delta(M) + cM^{-1/r}[m_n(\Omega)]^{1/q^*}\|u_m - u\|_{L_r(\Omega_M)}.$$

Given any $\varepsilon > 0$ we can find an M such that $c\delta(M) < \varepsilon/2$. Next we choose a large enough number N_ε so that the second summand in (2) does not exceed $\varepsilon/2$ for $m, l > N_\varepsilon$. Then $\|u_m - u_l\|_{L_{q^*}(\Omega)} < \varepsilon$ for $m, l > N_\varepsilon$ and hence $\{u_m\}$ is a Cauchy sequence in $L_{q^*}(\Omega)$.

Necessity. Suppose the imbedding operator of $L_p^1(\Omega)$ into $L_{q^*}(\Omega)$ is compact. Then the elements of the unit sphere in $L_p^1(\Omega)$ have absolutely equicontinuous norms in $L_{q^*}(\Omega)$. So, for all $u \in L_p^1(\Omega)$

$$\|u\|_{L_{q^*}(G)} \leqslant \varepsilon(M)(\|\nabla u\|_{L_p(\Omega)} + \|u\|_{L_1(\omega)}),$$

where ω is a bounded subdomain of Ω, $\bar{\omega} \subset \Omega$, G is an arbitrary open subset of Ω with $m_n(G) \leqslant M$ and $\varepsilon(M)$ tends to zero as $M \to 0$.

Suppose the function $u \in L_p^1(\Omega)$ vanishes outside G. Then

$$\|u\|_{L_{q^*}(\Omega)} \leqslant \varepsilon(M)[1 - \varepsilon(M)M^{1-1/q^*}]^{-1}\|\nabla u\|_{L_p(\Omega)}.$$

It remains to use the second part of Corollary 4.3.3 for $\alpha p \leqslant 1$ and the second part of Corollary 4.4.2/1 for $\alpha p > 1$. The theorem is proved.

4.8.3. Sufficient Conditions for Compactness of the Imbedding $L_p^1(\Omega) \subset L_{q^*}(\Omega)$

The inequalities

$$\mathfrak{A}_{p_1,\alpha_1}(M) \leqslant c\mathfrak{A}_{p,\alpha}(M), \quad \mathfrak{B}_{p_1,\alpha_1}(M) \leqslant c\mathfrak{B}_{p,\alpha}(M)$$

with $p_1 > p \geqslant 1$, $\alpha_1 - p_1^{-1} = \alpha - p^{-1}$ imply the imbeddings

$$\mathring{\mathscr{I}}_{p,\alpha} \subset \mathring{\mathscr{I}}_{p_1,\alpha_1}, \quad \mathring{\mathscr{H}}_{p,\alpha} \subset \mathring{\mathscr{H}}_{p_1,\alpha_1}.$$

In particular,

$$\mathring{\mathscr{J}}_{\alpha+1-p^{-1}} \overset{\text{def}}{=} \mathring{\mathscr{I}}_{1,\alpha+1-p^{-1}} \subset \mathring{\mathscr{I}}_{p,\alpha}.$$

The preceding leads to the following corollary.

Corollary 1. *If $\Omega \subset \mathring{\mathscr{J}}_\alpha$ and $p(1-\alpha) < 1$, $1 \leqslant p \leqslant q^* = p/[1 + p(1-\alpha)]$ then the imbedding operator of $L_p^1(\Omega)$ into $L_{q^*}(\Omega)$ is compact.*

By virtue of Propositions 4.4.4/1 and 4.4.4/2 the condition

$$\int_0^M \left(\frac{\tau}{\nu_{M,p}(\tau)}\right)^{1/(\alpha p-1)} d\tau < \infty \tag{1}$$

and *a fortiori* the requirement

$$\int_0^M \left(\frac{\tau}{\lambda_M(\tau)}\right)^{p/(\alpha p-1)} d\tau < \infty \tag{2}$$

imply $\mathfrak{B}_{p,\alpha}(M) \to 0$ as $M \to 0$. Therefore we have the next corollary.

Corollary 2. *If integral* (2) (*integral* (1)) *converges then the imbedding operator of* $L_p^1(\Omega)$ *into* $L_{q^*}(\Omega)$ $(q^* = \alpha^{-1}, \alpha p > 1)$ *is compact.*

Corollaries 1 and 2 immediately imply the following coarser assertion.

Corollary 3. *If* $\Omega \in \mathcal{J}_\alpha$ *and* $p(1-\alpha) \leqslant 1, p \geqslant 1, 1 \leqslant q < p/[1+p(\alpha-1)]$ *then the imbedding operator of* $L_p^1(\Omega)$ *into* $L_q(\Omega)$ *is compact.*

Clearly, the space $L_p^1(\Omega)$ can be replaced by $W_{p,r}^1(\Omega)$ with $r \leqslant q^*$ in Theorem 4.8.2 and Corollaries 1–3.

4.8.4. A Compactness Theorem for an Arbitrary Domain with Finite Volume

The positiveness of the function λ_M (cf. Lemma 3.2.4) and the estimate (4.3.4/1) imply $\nu_{M,p}(t) > 0$ for $t > 0$. So there exists a nondecreasing positive continuous function φ on $(0, m_n(\Omega)]$ such that $\varphi(t)/\nu_{M,p}(t)$ tends to zero as $t \to +0$.

Theorem. *Let* Ω *be an arbitrary domain with finite volume. Then from any bounded sequence in* $L_p^1(\Omega)$ *we can select a subsequence* $\{u_m\}_{m \geqslant 1}$ *with*

$$\int_0^\infty \varphi[m_n\{x: |u_m(x) - u_k(x)| \geqslant t\}]\, d(t^p) \xrightarrow[m,k\to\infty]{} 0$$

and therefore any bounded subset of $L_p^1(\Omega)$ *is compact in n-dimensional Lebesgue measure.*

Proof. Let u be a function in $C^\infty(\Omega) \cap L_p^1(\Omega) \cap L_\infty(\Omega)$ with bounded support. Obviously,

$$\int_0^\infty \varphi[m_n(\mathcal{N}_t)]\, d(t^p) \leqslant \int_T^\infty \varphi[m_n(\mathcal{N}_t)]\, d(t^p) + T^p \varphi[m_n(\Omega)]\,. \tag{1}$$

Here $T = \inf\{t: m_n(\mathcal{N}_t) \leqslant \mu\}$, where μ is a sufficiently small positive number that is independent of u. The right-hand side in (1) does not exceed

$$\sup_{0<\tau\leqslant\mu}\frac{\varphi(\tau)}{\nu_{M,p}(\tau)}\int_T^\infty c_p(\mathscr{L}_T\backslash\mathscr{N}_t)\,d(t^p)+c\varphi[m_n(\Omega)]\mu^{-p}\left(\int_{\Omega_\mu}|u|\,dx\right)^p,$$

where Ω_μ is the domain specified in the proof of Theorem 4.8.2 with M replaced by μ. By Lemma 4.1.3/3 we have

(2) $$\int_0^\infty\varphi[m_n(\mathscr{N}_t)]\,d(t^p)\leqslant\sup_{0\leqslant\tau\leqslant\mu}\frac{\varphi(\tau)}{\nu_{M,p}(\tau)}\|\nabla u\|^p_{L_p(\Omega)}+c\varphi[m_n(\Omega)]\mu^{-p}\|u\|^p_{L(\Omega_\mu)}.$$

By Corollary 3.1.2 the latter inequality extends to encompass all functions in $L_p^1(\Omega)$. It remains to apply the arguments used at the end of the proof of sufficiency in Theorem 4.8.2.

4.8.5. Examples of Domains in the Class $\mathring{\mathscr{I}}_{p,\alpha}$

Example 1. Estimates (4.3.5/1) imply that the domain

$$\Omega=\{x\colon(x_1^2+\cdots+x_{n-1}^2)^{1/2}<f(x_n),\ 0<x_n<a\}$$

in Example 4.3.5/1 is contained in $\mathring{\mathscr{I}}_{p,\alpha}$ if and only if

$$\lim_{x\to+0}\left(\int_0^x[f(t)]^{n-1}dt\right)^{\alpha p/(p-1)}\int_x^a[f(t)]^{(1-n)/(p-1)}dt=0\,.$$

By (3.3.3/1) and Corollary 4.8.3/1 a sufficient condition for Ω to belong to $\mathring{\mathscr{I}}_{p,\alpha}$ is

(1) $$\lim_{x\to+0}[f(x)]^{1-n}\left(\int_0^x[f(t)]^{n-1}dt\right)^{\alpha+1-1/p}=0\,.$$

Since f does not decrease, then (1) holds for $\alpha p=1$ and also for $\alpha p<1$ provided $\lim_{x\to+0}x^\sigma f(x)=0$, $\sigma=(p\alpha+p-1)/(n-1)(\alpha p-1)$.

Example 2. The domain $\Omega=\{x\colon 0<x_n<\infty,\ (x_1^2+\ldots+x_{n-1}^2)^{1/2}<f(x_n)\}$ in Example 4.3.5/2 is contained in $\mathring{\mathscr{I}}_{p,\alpha}$ if and only if

(2) $$\lim_{x\to+\infty}\left(\int_x^{+\infty}[f(\tau)]^{n-1}d\tau\right)^{\alpha p/(p-1)}\int_0^x[f(\tau)]^{(1-n)/(p-1)}d\tau=0$$

(cf. estimates (4.3.5/3)). By (3.3.3/4) and (4.3.4/1) the latter is valid if

(3) $$\lim_{x\to+\infty}[f(x)]^{1-n}\left(\int_x^\infty[f(\tau)]^{n-1}d\tau\right)^{\alpha+1-1/p}=0\,.$$

In particular, $\Omega \in \mathring{\mathscr{I}}_{p,1/p}$ provided

$$f(\tau) = e^{-\beta(\tau)}, \quad \beta'(\tau) \to +\infty \quad \text{as } \tau \to +\infty .$$

In case $f(\tau) = e^{-c\tau}$, the domain under consideration is contained in $\mathscr{I}_{p,1/p}$ and does not belong to $\mathring{\mathscr{I}}_{p,1/p}$.

Similarly, a necessary and sufficient condition for the spiral in Examples 3.3.3/3 and 4.3.5/3 to be in $\mathring{\mathscr{I}}_{p,\alpha}$ is that

$$\lim_{\theta \to +\infty} \left(\int_\theta^\infty \delta(\varphi)\, d\varphi \right)^{\alpha p/(p-1)} \int_0^\theta [\delta(\varphi)]^{1/(1-p)} d\varphi = 0 .$$

A simpler sufficient condition is that

$$\left(\int_\theta^{+\infty} \delta(\varphi)\, d\varphi \right)^{\alpha + 1 - 1/p} = o(\delta(\theta)) \quad \text{as } \theta \to +\infty .$$

In particular, $\Omega \in \mathring{\mathscr{I}}_{p,1/p}$ if $\delta(\varphi) = e^{-\beta(\varphi)}, \beta'(\varphi) \to +\infty$ as $\varphi \to +\infty$ and $\Omega \in \mathscr{I}_{p,1/p} \setminus \mathring{\mathscr{I}}_{p,1/p}$ if $\delta(\varphi) = e^{-c\varphi}$.

§ 4.9. On the Imbedding $L_p^l(\Omega) \subset L_q(\Omega)$

We present sufficient conditions for the boundedness and the compactness of the imbedding operators of $L_p^l(\Omega)$ into $L_{q^*}(\Omega)$ which are simple corollaries of Theorems 4.3.3 and 4.4.2.

Theorem 1. *If $\Omega \in \mathscr{I}_{p,\alpha}$, $1 - 1/l < p\alpha \leqslant 1$ or $\Omega \in \mathscr{H}_{p,\alpha}$, $p\alpha > 1$ then the imbedding operator of $L_p^l(\Omega)$ into $L_{q^*}(\Omega)$, $q^* = p/(1 - l + pl\alpha)$, is bounded.*

The proof is by induction on the number of derivatives l. In addition, we must use the imbeddings

$$\mathscr{I}_{p,\alpha} \subset \mathscr{I}_{p_1,\alpha_1}, \qquad \mathscr{H}_{p,\alpha} \subset \mathscr{H}_{p_1,\alpha_1}$$

with $p_1 > p \geqslant 1$, $\alpha_1 - p_1^{-1} = \alpha - p^{-1}$ (cf. Corollaries 4.2 and 4.4.2/2).

In particular, Theorem 1 guarantees the continuity of the imbedding operator of $L_p^l(\Omega)$ $(lp < n)$ into $L_{q^*}(\Omega)$ with the same $q^* = pn/(n - lp)$ as in the Sobolev theorem for domains of the class $\mathscr{I}_{p,1/p-1/n}$.

Theorem 1 and Proposition 4.3.4/2 imply the following corollary.

Corollary 1. *Let $\Omega \in \mathscr{J}_\alpha$, $1 - 1/n \leqslant \alpha \leqslant 1$, $lp(1-\alpha) \leqslant 1$. Then $L_p^l(\Omega) \subset L_{q^*}(\Omega)$, where $q^* = p/(1 - pl(1-\alpha))$ for $pl(1-\alpha) < 1$ and q^* is arbitrary for $pl(1-\alpha) = 1$.* (Then exponent $q^* = pn/(n - pl)$ corresponds to $\alpha = 1 - 1/n$.)

Example 1. Since the domain

$$\Omega^{(\lambda)} = \{x: x_1^2 + \cdots + x_{n-1}^2 < x_n^{2\lambda}, 0 < x_n < 1\}, \qquad \lambda \geqslant 1,$$

belongs to the class $\mathcal{J}_\alpha$ with $\alpha = \lambda(n-1)/(\lambda(n-1)+1)$ (cf. Example 3.3.3/1), we have $L_p^l(\Omega^{(\lambda)}) \subset L_{q^*}(\Omega^{(\lambda)})$, where $1 + \lambda(n-1) > pl$ and

$$q^* = p(\lambda(n-1)+1)/(1+\lambda(n-1)-pl). \tag{1}$$

The example of the function $u(x) = x_n^\nu$ with $\nu = l + \varepsilon - (1+\lambda(n-1))/p$ (ε is a small positive number) shows that the exponent q^* cannot be increased.

Similarly to Theorem 1 we obtain the following theorem stating some conditions for the compactness of the imbedding $L_p^l(\Omega) \subset L_{q^*}(\Omega)$ for domains with finite measure m_n.

Theorem 2. *If $\Omega \in \mathring{\mathcal{J}}_{p,\alpha}$, $1 - 1/l < p\alpha \leqslant 1$, or $\Omega \in \mathring{\mathcal{H}}_{p,\alpha}$, $p\alpha > 1$, then the imbedding operator of $L_p^l(\Omega)$ into $L_{q^*}(\Omega)$, $q^* = p/(1-pl(1-\alpha))$, is compact.*

This theorem and Corollary 4.8.3/1 imply the next corollary.

Corollary 2. *If $m_n(\Omega) < \infty$ and $\Omega \in \mathring{\mathcal{J}}_\alpha$, where $1 - 1/n < \alpha \leqslant 1$, $lp(1-\alpha) < 1$, then the imbedding operator of $L_p^l(\Omega)$ into $L_q(\Omega)$, $q < p/(1-pl(1-\alpha))$, is compact.*

From this we immediately obtain the following coarser sufficient condition in terms of $\mathcal{J}_\alpha$.

Corollary 3. *If $m_n(\Omega) < \infty$ and $\Omega \in \mathcal{J}_\alpha$, $1 - 1/n \leqslant \alpha \leqslant 1$, $lp(1-\alpha) \leqslant 1$, then the imbedding operator of $L_p^l(\Omega)$ into $L_q(\Omega)$, $q < p/(1-pl(1-\alpha))$ is compact.*

Example 2. Consider the domain in Example 1. According to Corollary 3 the imbedding operator of $L_p^l(\Omega^{(\lambda)})$ into $L_q(\Omega^{(\lambda)})$ is compact provided

$$q < p(\lambda(n-1)+1)/(1+\lambda(n-1)-pl) \tag{2}$$

(we suppose $1 + \lambda(n-1) \geqslant pl$). We can not put the equality sign in (2). In fact, let $\eta \in C_0^\infty(0,3)$, $\eta = 1$ on $(1,2)$. Obviously, the family of functions $\{u_\varepsilon\}_{\varepsilon>0}$, where

$$u_\varepsilon(x) = \varepsilon^{l-(\lambda(n-1)+1)/p}\eta(x/\varepsilon),$$

is bounded in $L_p^l(\Omega^{(\lambda)})$ but not compact in $L_{q^*}(\Omega^{(\lambda)})$ with q^* specified by (1).

§ 4.10. Application to the Neumann Problem for Strongly Elliptic Operators

Here we present some applications of the above results to the study of the solvability and the discreteness of the spectrum of the Neumann problem in domains with irregular boundaries.

4.10.1. Second Order Operators

Let Ω be a domain with finite volume in R^n and let a_{ij} $(i, j = 1, \dots, n)$ be real measurable functions in Ω, $a_{ij} = a_{ji}$. Suppose there exists a constant $c \geqslant 1$ such that

$$c^{-1}|\xi|^2 \leqslant a_{ij}\xi_i\xi_j \leqslant c|\xi|^2$$

for almost all $x \in \Omega$ and for all vectors $\xi = (\xi_1, \dots, \xi_n)$.

We define the operator A_q, $1 \leqslant q < \infty$ of the Neumann problem for the differential operator

$$u \to -\partial/\partial x_i(a_{ij}\partial u/\partial x_j)$$

by the following conditions: 1) $u \in W^1_{2,q}(\Omega)$, $A_q u \in L_{q'}(\Omega)$, $1/q' + 1/q = 1$; 2) for all $v \in W^1_{2,q}(\Omega)$ the equality

$$\int_\Omega v A_q u \, dx = \int_\Omega a_{ij} \frac{\partial u}{\partial x_i} \frac{\partial v}{\partial x_j} dx \tag{1}$$

is valid. The mapping $u \to A_q u$ is closed. It is clear that the range $R(A_q)$ is contained in the set $L_{q'}(\Omega) \ominus 1$ of functions in $L_{q'}(\Omega)$ that are orthogonal to unity in Ω.

Lemma. *$R(A_q) = L_{q'}(\Omega) \ominus 1$ if and only if for all $v \in W^1_{2,q}(\Omega)$ the "generalized Poincaré inequality"*

$$\inf_{c \in R^1} \|v - c\|_{L_q(\Omega)} \leqslant k \|\nabla v\|_{L_2(\Omega)} \tag{2}$$

is valid.

Proof. Sufficiency. According to Lemma 3.1.2/2, the set $W^1_{2,q}(\Omega)$ is dense in $L^1_2(\Omega)$. Thus, if (2) holds for all $v \in W^1_{2,q}(\Omega)$ then it also holds for all $v \in L^1_2(\Omega)$. Therefore, the functional $v \to \int_\Omega v f \, dx$ is bounded in $L^1_2(\Omega)$ and can be expressed in the form

$$\int_\Omega a_{ij}(\partial v/\partial x_j)(\partial u/\partial x_i) \, dx, \quad u \in L^1_2(\Omega), \tag{3}$$

for arbitrary function $f \in L_{q'}(\Omega)$. Since by (2) $L^1_2(\Omega) \subset L_q(\Omega)$, then $u \in W^1_{2,q}(\Omega)$ and so $A_q u = f$.

Necessity. Let $f \in L_{q'}(\Omega) \ominus 1$, $v \in L_2^1(\Omega) \cap L_q(\Omega)$, $\|\nabla v\|_{L_2(\Omega)} = 1$. Since $R(A_q) = L_{q'}(\Omega) \ominus 1$, the functional $f \to v(f) = \int_\Omega f v\, dx$, defined on $L_{q'} \ominus 1$; can be expressed in the form (3). Therefore, $|v(f)| \leqslant C \|\nabla u\|_{L_2(\Omega)}$ and the functionals $v(f)$ are bounded for each $f \in L_{q'}(\Omega)$. Thus, they are totally bounded, i.e. (2) holds for all $v \in W_{2,q}^1(\Omega)$. The lemma is proved.

Theorems 4.3.3, 4.4.2 and the above lemma imply the following criterion for the solvability of the problem $A_q u = f$ for all $f \in L_{q'}(\Omega) \ominus 1$.

Theorem 1. *$R(A_q) = L_{q'}(\Omega) \ominus 1$ if and only if $\Omega \in \mathscr{I}_{2,1/q}$ for $q \geqslant 2$ and $\Omega \in \mathscr{H}_{2,1/q}$ for $q < 2$.*

Let a be a real function in $L_\infty(\Omega)$ such that $a(x) \geqslant \text{const} > 0$ for almost all $x \in \Omega$. Then the operator $u \to A_q u + a u$ has the same domain as A_q. Consider the Neumann problem $A_q u + a u = f$ where $f \in L_{q'}(\Omega)$. If $q' \geqslant 2$ then its solvability is a trivial consequence of the continuity of the functional $\int_\Omega f v\, dx$ in the space $W_2^1(\Omega)$ with inner product

$$\int_\Omega (a_{ij}(\partial v/\partial x_j)(\partial u/\partial x_i) + a v u)\, dx\,.$$

If $q' < 2$ then a necessary and sufficient condition for solvability is

$$\|v\|_{L_q(\Omega)} \leqslant C \|v\|_{W_2^1(\Omega)}$$

for all $v \in W_2^1(\Omega)$.

The preceding theorem together with Theorem 4.3.3 imply the next result.

Theorem 2. *$R(A_q + aI) = L_{q'}(\Omega)$ with $q' < 2$ if and only if $\Omega \in \mathscr{I}_{2,1/q}$.*

By virtue of Rellich's lemma the problem of requirements on Ω for the discreteness of the spectrum of the operator $A \overset{\text{def}}{=} A_2$ is equivalent to the study of the compactness of the imbedding $W_2^1(\Omega) \subset L_2(\Omega)$. Therefore, from Theorem 4.8.2 we obtain the next theorem.

Theorem 3. *The spectrum of the operator A is discrete if and only if $\Omega \in \mathring{\mathscr{I}}_{2,1/2}$.*

The sufficient conditions for a set to be in $\mathscr{I}_{2,1/q}$, $\mathscr{H}_{2,1/q}$, $\mathring{\mathscr{I}}_{2,1/2}$ as well as examples of domains belonging to these classes were presented in previous sections of this chapter.

4.10.2. The Neumann Problem for Operators of Arbitrary Order

In this subsection we limit consideration to operators with range in $L_2(\Omega)$.

Let Ω be a bounded subdomain of R^n. Let i, j denote multi-indices of order not higher than l, $l \geqslant 1$, and let a_{ij} denote bounded complex-valued measurable functions in Ω.

Suppose for all $u \in L_2^l(\Omega)$

(1) $$\operatorname{Re} \int_\Omega \sum_{|i|=|j|=l} a_{ij} D^i u \overline{D^j u}\, dx \geqslant C \| \nabla_l u \|^2_{L_2(\Omega)},$$

where $D^i = \{\partial^{|i|}/\partial x_1^{i_1} \ldots \partial x_n^{i_n}\}$. Let the operator A of the Neumann problem for the differential operator

$$u \to (-1)^l \sum_{|i|=|j|=l} D^i (a_{ij} D^j u)$$

be defined by the following conditions: 1) $u \in W_2^l(\Omega)$, $Au \in L_2(\Omega)$, 2) for all $v \in W_2^l(\Omega)$

$$\int_\Omega \bar{v} A u\, dx = \int_\Omega \sum_{|i|=|j|=l} a_{ij} D^j u \overline{D^i v}\, dx .$$

It is clear that the range $R(A)$ is contained in the orthogonal complement $L_2(\Omega) \ominus \mathscr{P}_{l-1}$ where $\mathscr{P}_{l-1}$ is the space of polynomials of degree not higher than $l-1$.

If for all $v \in L_2^l(\Omega)$

(2) $$\inf_{\Pi \in \mathscr{P}_{l-1}} \| v - \Pi \|_{L_2(\Omega)} \leqslant k \| \nabla_l v \|_{L_2(\Omega)}$$

then $R(A) = L_2(\Omega) \ominus \mathscr{P}_{l-1}$ (cf. Lions and Magenes [132], 9.1., Ch. 2).

By a simple argument using induction on the number of derivatives, we show that (2) follows from the Poincaré inequality

$$\inf_{c \in R^1} \| u - c \|_{L_2(\Omega)} \leqslant k \| \nabla v \|_{L_2(\Omega)} .$$

Thus we have the following assertion.

Theorem 1. *If $\Omega \in \mathscr{J}_{2,1/2}$ then $R(A) = L_2(\Omega) \ominus \mathscr{P}_{l-1}$; i.e. the Neumann problem $Au = f$ is solvable for all $f \in L_2(\Omega) \ominus \mathscr{P}_{l-1}$.*

We can pose the Neumann problem for the more general operator

$$u \to (-1)^l \sum_{|i|, |j| \leqslant l} D^i (a_{ij} D^j u)$$

in a similar way. We define the operator B of this problem by the conditions:
1) $u \in V_2^l(\Omega)$, $Bu \in L_2(\Omega)$;
2) for all $v \in V_2^l(\Omega)$

(3) $$\int_\Omega \bar{v} B u\, dx = \int_\Omega \sum_{|i|, |j| \leqslant l} a_{ij} D^j u \overline{D^i v}\, dx .$$

Theorem 2. *If $\Omega \in \mathring{\mathscr{J}}_{2,1/2}$ then $R(B + \lambda I) = L_2(\Omega)$ for sufficiently large values of* $\operatorname{Re} \lambda$. *Moreover, the operator $(B + \lambda I)^{-1}$: $L_2(\Omega) \to V_2^l(\Omega)$ is compact.*

To prove the theorem we need the following lemma.

Lemma. *If* $\Omega \in \mathring{\mathscr{I}}_{2,1/2}$ *then for all* $u \in W_2^l(\Omega)$ *and for any* $\varepsilon > 0$

$$\sum_{k=0}^{l-1} \| \nabla_k u \|_{L_2(\Omega)} \leqslant \varepsilon \| \nabla_l u \|_{L_2(\Omega)} + C(\varepsilon) \| u \|_{L_2(\Omega)}, \tag{4}$$

Proof. By inequality (4.8.2/1) we have

$$\| u \|_{L_2(\Omega)} \leqslant c \mathfrak{A}_{2,1/2}(M) \| \nabla u \|_{L_2(\Omega)} + c \left(\frac{m_n(\Omega)}{M} \right)^{1/2} \| u \|_{L_2(\Omega_M)} .$$

where Ω_M is a subdomain of Ω with boundary of the class C^1 and such that $2 m_n(\Omega \setminus \Omega_M) < M$. Therefore

$$\| \nabla_k u \|_{L_2(\Omega)} \leqslant c \mathfrak{A}_{2,1/2}(M) \| \nabla_{k+1} u \|_{L_2(\Omega)} + c \left(\frac{m_n(\Omega)}{M} \right)^{1/2} \| \nabla_k u \|_{L_2(\Omega_M)}$$

for all $k = 0, 1, \ldots, l-1$. Since the boundary of Ω_M is smooth, then

$$\| \nabla_k u \|_{L_2(\Omega_M)} \leqslant \varepsilon \| \nabla_{k+1} u \|_{L_2(\Omega_M)} + C^{(0)}(\varepsilon) \| u \|_{L_2(\Omega_M)}$$

for all $\varepsilon > 0$. Therefore

$$\| \nabla_k u \|_{L_2(\Omega)} \leqslant c \mathfrak{A}_{2,1/2}(M) \| \nabla_{k+1} u \|_{L_2(\Omega)} + C^{(1)}(M) \| u \|_{L_2(\Omega_M)} .$$

Applying this inequality with indices $k, k+1, \ldots, l-1$, we obtain

$$\| \nabla_k u \|_{L_2(\Omega)} \leqslant c [\mathfrak{A}_{2,1/2}(M)]^{l-k} \| \nabla_l u \|_{L_2(\Omega)} + C^{(2)}(M) \| u \|_{L_2(\Omega_M)} .$$

It remains to note that $\mathfrak{A}_{2,1/2}(M) \to 0$ as $M \to 0$. The lemma is proved.

We established, incidentally, that (4) is valid for some $\varepsilon > 0$ provided $\Omega \in \mathscr{I}_{2,1/2}$, i.e. $\mathfrak{A}_{2,1/2}(M) < \infty$.

The proof of Theorem 2. By virtue of (1) we have

$$\operatorname{Re} \int_\Omega \sum_{|i|, |j| \leqslant l} a_{ij} D^i u \overline{D^j u} \, dx \geqslant C \| \nabla_l u \|^2_{L_2(\Omega)} - C_1 \sum_{k=0}^{l-1} \| \nabla_k u \|^2_{L_2(\Omega)} .$$

Applying (4) with $\varepsilon = C/2 C_1$ we obtain

$$\operatorname{Re} \int_\Omega \left(\sum_{|i|, |j| \leqslant l} a_{ij} D^i u \overline{D^j u} + \lambda |u|^2 \right) dx \geqslant \tfrac{1}{2} C_1 \| \nabla_l u \|^2_{L_2(\Omega)} + (\operatorname{Re} \lambda - C_2) \| u \|^2_{L_2(\Omega)} .$$

Thus the "coercive inequality"

$$\sum_{k=0}^{l} \| \nabla_k u \|^2_{L_2(\Omega)} \leqslant \text{const Re} \int_{\Omega} \left(\sum_{|i|, |j| \leqslant l} a_{ij} D^i u \overline{D^j u} + \lambda |u|^2 \right) dx$$

is valid for $\text{Re}\,\lambda > C_2$. This implies (cf., for instance, Lions and Magenes [132], Ch. 2, 9.1) the unique solvability of the equation $Bu + \lambda u = f$ for all $f \in L_2(\Omega)$. The compactness of $(B + \lambda I)^{-1}$ results from Theorem 4.9/2. The proof is complete.

4.10.3. The Neumann Problem for a Special Domain

The monograph by Courant and Hilbert [47] contains the following example of a domain for which the Poincaré inequality is false.

Let Ω be the union of the square

$$Q = \{(x, y) \colon 0 < x < 2, \ -1 < y < 1\}$$

and the sequence of symmetrically situated squares Q_m, Q_{-m}, $m = 1, 2, \ldots$ connected with Q by necks S_m, S_{-m} (Fig. 19). Let the side lengths of the squares Q_m, Q_{-m} as well as the heights of the necks be equal to $\varepsilon_m = 2^{-m}$. Let the widths of the necks be ε_m^α.

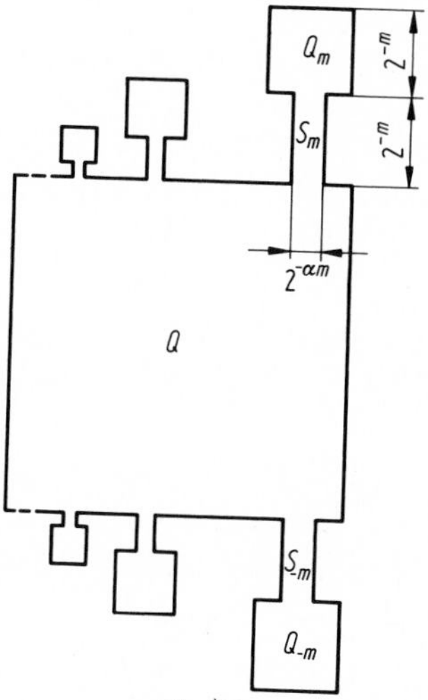

Fig. 19

We introduce the sequence of functions $\{u_m\}_{m \geqslant 1}$ defined by $u_m = \pm \varepsilon_m^{-1}$ on $Q_{\pm m}$, $u_m(x, y) = \varepsilon_m^{-2}(y \mp 1)$ on $S_{\pm m}$, $u_m = 0$ outside $S_m \cup S_{-m} \cup Q_m \cup Q_{-m}$. This sequence satisfies

$$\iint_\Omega u_m dx\,dy = 0\,, \quad \iint_\Omega (\nabla u_m)^2 dx\,dy = 2\varepsilon_m^{\alpha-3}\,, \quad \iint_\Omega u_m^2 dx\,dy > 2\,.$$

Thus the Poincaré inequality is false for Ω if $\alpha > 3$ and the imbedding operator of $W_2^1(\Omega)$ into $L_2(\Omega)$ is not compact if $\alpha \geqslant 3$.

In this subsection we show that the Poincaré inequality is valid for $\alpha \leqslant 3$ and the Rellich lemma holds for $\alpha < 3$. Hence the Neumann problem considered in 4.10.1 is solvable in $L_2^1(\Omega)$ for any right-hand side in $L_2^1(\Omega) \ominus 1$ for $\alpha \leqslant 3$ and the spectrum of this problem is discrete for $\alpha < 3$.

Consider a nonnegative function u equal to zero outside $Q_m \cup S_m$ (m is a fixed positive number) and infinitely differentiable in $\overline{Q_m \cup S_m}$. We introduce the notation:

$$\mathscr{E}_t = \{(x,y)\colon u = t\}\,, \quad \mathscr{H}_t = \{(x,y)\colon u < t\}\,, \quad \mathscr{N}_t = \{(x,y)\colon u \geqslant t\}\,.$$

If $t \in (0, \infty)$ satisfies

(1) $$s(\mathscr{E}_t) \geqslant 2^{-(\alpha+1)m/2}\,,$$

then

(2) $$m_2(\mathscr{N}_t) \leqslant c2^{-(3-\alpha)m/2} s(\mathscr{E}_t)\,.$$

The set of levels t for which (1) is valid will be denoted by $\mathfrak{P}$. Duplicating with minor modification the arguments presented in § 4.5, we can show that one of the following cases occurs for $t \in C\mathfrak{P}$:

(3) $$s(\mathscr{E}_t) \geqslant 2^{-\alpha m}\,,$$

(4) $$m_2(\mathscr{N}_t) < c2^{-(1+\alpha)m}\,;$$

(5) $$s(\mathscr{E}_t) \geqslant 2^{-\alpha m}\,,$$

(6) $$m_2(\mathscr{H}_t) < c2^{-(1+\alpha)m}\,;$$

(7) $$s(\mathscr{E}_t) < 2^{-\alpha m}\,,$$

(8) $$m_2(\mathscr{N}_t) \leqslant c2^{-(3-\alpha)m/2} s(\mathscr{E}_t)\,.$$

This implies that the set of all levels t (up to a set of measure zero) can be represented as the union $\mathfrak{R}' \cup \mathfrak{R}'' \cup \mathfrak{R}'''$ where $\mathfrak{R}'$ is the set of those t for which (7), (8) are valid, $\mathfrak{R}''$ and $\mathfrak{R}'''$ are the sets of levels for which (3), (4) and (5), (6) are valid, respectively.

The function

$$t \to \psi(t) = \int_0^t \left(\int_{\mathscr{E}_\tau} |\nabla u|\, ds \right)^{-1} d\tau$$

admits the estimate

$$\psi(t) \leqslant -\int_0^t \frac{d}{d\tau}\, m_2(\mathscr{N}_\tau)\, \frac{d\tau}{[s(\mathscr{E}_\tau)]^2}$$

(cf. Lemma 4.1.3/2). We express the right hand side as the sum $\int_{\mathfrak{R}'}+\int_{\mathfrak{R}''}+\int_{\mathfrak{R}'''}$. Inequality (8) implies

$$\int_{\mathfrak{R}'}\leqslant -c2^{-(3-\alpha)m}\int_0^t [m_2(\mathcal{N}_\tau)]^{-2}\frac{d}{d\tau}m_2(\mathcal{N}_\tau)\,d\tau\leqslant c2^{-(3-\alpha)m}/m_2(\mathcal{N}_t)\,.$$

Using (3) and (4) we obtain

$$\int_{\mathfrak{R}''}\leqslant 2^{\alpha m}\sup_{\tau\in\mathfrak{R}''} m_2(\mathcal{N}_\tau)\leqslant 2^{(\alpha-1)m}\,.$$

Similarly, by (5) and (6),

$$\int_{\mathfrak{R}'''}\leqslant 2^{\alpha m}\sup_{\tau\in\mathfrak{R}'''} m_2(\mathcal{H}_\tau)\leqslant 2^{(\alpha-1)m}\,.$$

Consequently,

$$\psi(t)\leqslant c\left(2^{(\alpha-1)m}+\frac{2^{-(3-\alpha)m}}{m_2(\mathcal{N}_t)}\right). \tag{9}$$

Since $m_2(\mathcal{N}_t)\leqslant 2^{-2m}$, then (9) yields

$$m_2(\mathcal{N}_t)\,\psi(t)\leqslant c2^{-(3-\alpha)m}\,. \tag{10}$$

Therefore,

$$\iint_{Q_m\cup S_m} u^2dx\,dy=2\int_0^\infty t\,t'_\psi m_2(\mathcal{N}_{t(\psi)})\,d\psi\leqslant c2^{-(3-\alpha)m}\int_0^\infty t\,t'_\psi\frac{d\psi}{\psi}\,.$$

The integral on the right does not exceed

$$\left(\int_0^\infty t^2\frac{d\psi}{\psi^2}\right)^{1/2}\left(\int_0^\infty (t'_\psi)^2d\psi\right)^{1/2}\leqslant 2\int_0^\infty (t'_\psi)^2d\psi=2\iint_{Q_m\cup S_m}(\nabla u)^2dx\,dy\,.$$

Hence

$$\iint_{Q_m\cup S_m} u^2dx\,dy\leqslant c2^{-(3-\alpha)m}\iint_{Q_m\cup S_m}(\nabla u)^2dx\,dy\,. \tag{11}$$

It is clear that this inequality is valid for any function $u\in L_2^1(\Omega)$ that is equal to zero outside $Q_m\cup S_m$ and that a similar estimate holds for negative indices m.

Now let v be an arbitrary function in $L_2^1(\Omega)$ and let η be a "truncating" function equal to zero in Q, to unity in Q_m and in Q_{-m}, and linear in S_m and S_{-m} $(m=1,2,\dots)$. Then

$$\iint_\Omega v^2dx\,dy\leqslant\sum_{|k|\geqslant N}\left(\iint_{Q_k\cup S_k}(v\eta)^2dx\,dy+\iint_{S_k}v^2dx\,dy\right)+\iint_{\Omega_N}v^2dx\,dy\,, \tag{12}$$

where $\Omega_N = \Omega \setminus \bigcup_{|k|\geq N} (Q_k \cup S_k)$ and N is an arbitrary positive integer. From (11) we obtain

$$(13) \quad \iint_{Q_m \cup S_m} (v\eta)^2 dx dy \leqslant c 2^{-(3-\alpha)m} \left[\iint_{Q_m \cup S_m} (\nabla v)^2 dx dy + 2^{2m} \iint_{S_m} v^2 dx dy \right].$$

We estimate the second integral on the right. We can easily check that

$$\iint_{S_m} |v| dx dy \leqslant 2^{-m} \iint_{S_m} |\nabla v| dx dy + 2^{-m} \int_{\partial S_m \cap \partial Q} |v| dx .$$

Hence

$$\iint_{S_m} v^2 dx dy \leqslant \tfrac{1}{2} \iint_{S_m} v^2 dx dy + 2^{-2m-1} \iint_{S_m} (\nabla v)^2 dx dy + 2^{-m} \int_{\partial S_m \cup \partial Q} v^2 dx .$$

Since $s(\partial S_m \cap \partial Q) = 2^{-\alpha m}$, then by Hölder's inequality

$$(14) \quad \iint_{S_m} v^2 dx dy \leqslant c 2^{-2m} \iint_{S_m} (\nabla v)^2 dx dy + c 2^{-2m} \| v \|^2_{L_{2\alpha/(\alpha-1)}(\partial S_m \cap \partial Q)} .$$

Therefore (13) implies

$$(15) \quad \iint_{Q_m \cup S_m} (v\eta)^2 dx dy \leqslant c 2^{-(3-\alpha)m} \left[\iint_{Q_m \cup S_m} (\nabla v)^2 dx dy + \| v \|^2_{L_{2\alpha/(\alpha-1)}(\partial S_m \cap \partial Q)} \right].$$

Using (14), (15) from (12) we obtain

$$\iint_{\Omega} v^2 dx dy \leqslant c 2^{-(3-\alpha)N} \sum_{|k|\geqslant N} \left[\iint_{Q_k \cup S_k} (\nabla v)^2 dx dy + \| v \|^2_{L_{2\alpha/(\alpha-1)}(\partial S_k \cap \partial Q)} \right] + \iint_{\Omega_N} v^2 dx dy .$$

Again by virtue of Hölder's inequality

$$\begin{aligned} \sum_{|k|\geqslant N} \| v \|^2_{L_{2\alpha/(\alpha-1)}(\partial S_k \cap \partial Q)} &\leqslant \sum_{|k|\geqslant N} 2^{-(\alpha-1)|k|/2} \| v \|^2_{L_{4\alpha/(\alpha-1)}(\partial S_k \cap \partial Q)} \\ &\leqslant \left(\sum_{|k|\geqslant N} 2^{-|k|(\alpha-1)\alpha/(\alpha+1)} \right)^{(\alpha+1)/2\alpha} \\ &\quad \times \left(\sum_{|k|\geqslant N} \int_{\partial S_k \cap \partial Q} |v|^{4\alpha/(\alpha-1)} dx \right)^{(\alpha-1)/2\alpha} \\ &\leqslant c \| v \|^2_{L_{4\alpha/(\alpha-1)}(\partial Q)} . \end{aligned}$$

Thus

$$(16) \quad \iint_{\Omega} v^2 dx dy \leqslant c 2^{-(3-\alpha)N} \iint_{\Omega} (\nabla v)^2 dx dy + c \| v \|^2_{L_{4\alpha/(\alpha-1)}(\partial Q)} + c \| v \|^2_{L_2(\Omega_N)} .$$

Since for any $r \in (1, \infty)$

$$\|v\|_{L_r(\partial Q)} \leqslant c(\|\nabla v\|_{L_2(\Omega)} + \|v\|_{L_2(\Omega)}),$$

then (16) yields

$$\|v\|_{L_2(\Omega)} \leqslant c2^{-(3-\alpha)N/2}\|\nabla v\|_{L_2(\Omega)} + c\|v\|_{L_2(\Omega_N)}. \tag{17}$$

The boundary of Ω_N is of the class $C^{0,1}$ and so the imbedding operator of $W_2^1(\Omega_N)$ into $L_2(\Omega_N)$ is compact. This and (17) imply the compactness of the imbedding operator of $W_2^1(\Omega)$ into $L_2(\Omega)$ for $\alpha<3$. Finally, for $\alpha \leqslant 3$ from (17) we get the Poincaré inequality

$$\inf_{\gamma \in R^1} \|v-\gamma\|_{L_2(\Omega)} \leqslant c(\|\nabla v\|_{L_2(\Omega)} + \inf_{\gamma \in R^1} \|v-\gamma\|_{L_2(\Omega_1)}) \leqslant c\|\nabla v\|_{L_2(\Omega)}.$$

4.10.4. A Counterexample to Inequality (4.10.2/4)

We shall show that the validity of inequality (4.10.2/4) for some $\varepsilon>0$ does not imply its validity for all $\varepsilon>0$.

Let Ω be the domain considered in 4.10.3. Suppose the width of the necks S_m and S_{-m} is equal to 2^{-3m}. In 4.10.3 we showed that in this case $\Omega \in \mathscr{I}_{2,1/2}$. So (4.10.2/4) holds for some $\varepsilon>0$.

Consider the sequence of functions $\{u_m\}_{m\geqslant 1}$ defined by $u_m=0$ outside $Q_m \cup S_m$, $u_m(x,y)=4^m(y-1)^2$ on S_m, $u_m(x,y)=2^{m+1}(y-1)-1$ in Q_m. We can easily see that

$$\iint_\Omega |\nabla u_m|^2 dx\,dy \leqslant 4(1+4^{-m}), \qquad \iint_\Omega |\nabla_2 u_m|^2 dx\,dy = 4, \qquad \iint_\Omega u_m^2 dx\,dy \geqslant 4^{-m}.$$

By (4.10.2/4) with $l=2$ we have

$$2(1+4^{-m})^{1/2} \leqslant 2\varepsilon + k(\varepsilon)2^{-m}, \qquad m=1,2,\ldots,$$

which fails for small $\varepsilon>0$.

§ 4.11. Inequalities Containing Integrals over the Boundary

4.11.1. The Imbedding $W_{p,r}^1(\Omega, \partial\Omega) \subset L_q(\Omega)$

The content of the present subsection is related to that of § 3.6 where the case $p=1$ is considered. The space $W_{p,r}^1(\Omega, \partial\Omega)$ and the class $K_{\alpha,\beta}$ are defined in 3.6.1.

Theorem 3.6.3 implies the following sufficient condition for the continuity of the imbedding $W_{p,r}^1(\Omega, \partial\Omega) \subset L_q(\Omega)$ for $p>1$.

Theorem 1. *If* $\Omega \in K_{\alpha,\beta}$ *with* $\alpha \leqslant 1$, $p(1-\alpha)<1$, $\beta \geqslant \alpha$, *then for all* $u \in W^1_{p,r}(\Omega, \partial\Omega)$

$$\|u\|_{L_q(\Omega)} \leqslant c\|u\|_{W^1_{p,r}(\Omega,\partial\Omega)}, \tag{1}$$

where $q = p/(1-p(1-\alpha))$, $r = p\alpha/\beta(1-p(1-\alpha))$.

Proof. By Theorem 3.6.3 for all $v \in C^\infty(\Omega) \cap C(\bar{\Omega})$ with bounded supports we have

$$\left(\int_\Omega |v|^{1/\alpha} dx\right)^\alpha \leqslant C\left(\|\nabla v\|_{L(\Omega)} + \left(\int_{\partial\Omega} |v|^{1/\beta} ds\right)^\beta\right).$$

We put $v = |u|^{q\alpha}$ and see that by Hölder's inequality

$$\int_\Omega |u|^{(p-1)/(1-p(1-\alpha))} |\nabla u| dx \leqslant \|\nabla u\|_{L_p(\Omega)} \left(\int_\Omega |u|^{p/(1-p(1-\alpha))} dx\right)^{1-1/p}.$$

Hence

$$\|u\|_{L_q(\Omega)} \leqslant C_1(\|\nabla u\|_{L_p(\Omega)}^{1/p\alpha - 1/\alpha + 1} \|u\|_{L_q(\Omega)}^{(p-1)/p\alpha} + \|u\|_{L_r(\partial\Omega)}),$$

and (1) follows.

Since any set Ω is contained in $K_{1-1/n,1}$, we obtain the following corollary.

Corollary 1. *The inequality*

$$\|u\|_{L_{pn/(n-p)}(\Omega)} \leqslant c(\|\nabla u\|_{L_p(\Omega)} + \|u\|_{L_{p(n-1)/(n-p)}(\partial\Omega)}) \tag{2}$$

is valid for all $u \in W^1_{p,p(n-1)/(n-p)}(\Omega, \partial\Omega)$ *with* $p<n$ *for arbitrary open set* Ω.

Replacing u by $|u|^r$ and applying Hölder's inequality in (3.6.3/7) we arrive at the next corollary.

Corollary 2. *The following sharpened Friedrichs inequality*

$$\|u\|_{L_q(\Omega)} \leqslant C(\|\nabla u\|_{L_p(\Omega)} + \|u\|_{L_r(\partial\Omega)}) \tag{3}$$

is valid for $(n-p)r \leqslant p(n-1)$, $r \geqslant 1$, $q = rn/(n-1)$ *for arbitrary open set* Ω *with finite volume.*

We show that the exponent $q = rn/(n-1)$ on the left in (3) cannot be improved provided Ω is not subject to additional conditions.

Example. Let the domain Ω be the union of the semiball $B^- = \{x: x_n < 0, |x| < 1\}$, the sequence of balls $\mathscr{B}_m$ $(m = 1, 2, \ldots)$ and thin pipes $\mathscr{C}_m$ connecting $\mathscr{B}_m$ with B^- (Fig. 20). Let ϱ_m be the radius of the ball $\mathscr{B}_m$ and let h_m be the height of $\mathscr{C}_m$. Let u_m denote a piecewise linear function equal to unity in $\mathscr{B}_m$ and to zero outside $\mathscr{B}_m \cup \mathscr{C}_m$. Suppose there exists a constant Q such that

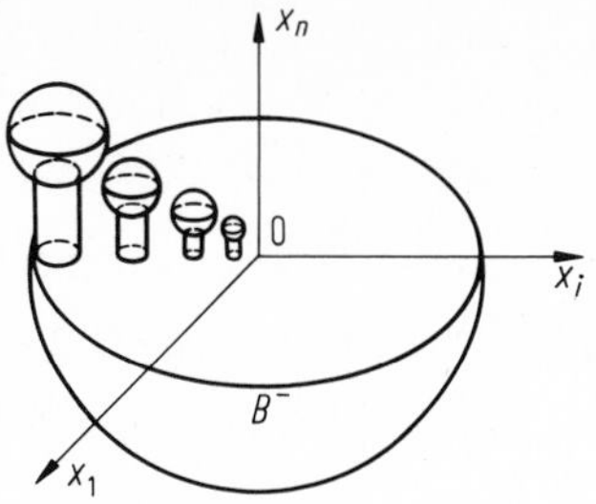

Fig. 20

$$\|u_m\|_{L_q(\Omega)} \leqslant Q(\|\nabla u_m\|_{L_p(\Omega)} + \|u_m\|_{L_r(\partial\Omega)})$$

for all u_m. This implies the estimate

$$[m_n(\mathscr{B}_m)]^{1/q} \leqslant Q(h_m^{-1}[m_n(\mathscr{C}_m)]^{1/p} + [s(\partial\mathscr{B}_m \cup \partial\mathscr{C}_m)]^{1/r}) .$$

Since the first summand on the right can be made arbitrarily small by diminishing the width of $\mathscr{C}_m$, then $\varrho_m^{n/q} = O(\varrho_m^{(n-1)r})$. Hence $q \leqslant rn/(n-1)$.

To formulate a necessary and sufficient condition for the validity of (1) we need the following kind of p-conductivity.

Let K be a conductor in Ω. We put

(4)
$$\tilde{c}_p(K) = \inf\left\{ \int_\Omega |\nabla f|^p dx : f \in C^\infty(\Omega) \cap C(\bar{\Omega}), f \geqslant 1 \text{ on } F, f \leqslant 0 \text{ on } \Omega\backslash G \right\} .$$

Similarly to Lemma 4.1.1/2 we can prove that $\tilde{c}_p(K)$ can be expressed as follows:

(5)
$$\tilde{c}_p(K) = \inf\left\{ \int_\Omega |\nabla f|^p dx : f \in C^\infty(\Omega) \cap C(\bar{\Omega}), f = 1 \text{ on } F, f = 0 \text{ on } \Omega\backslash G \right\} .$$

Theorem 2. *A necessary and sufficient condition for the validity of* (1) *with* $p > 1$, $q \geqslant p \geqslant r$ *is*

$$[m_n(F)]^{1/q} \leqslant \text{const}\,([\tilde{c}_p(K)]^{1/p} + [s(\partial_e G)]^{1/r}),$$

where K is any conductor $G\backslash F$ in Ω.

This assertion can be proved similarly to Theorem 2.3.7.

The same argument as in the proof of Theorem 4.8.2 leads to the following criterion for compactness.

Theorem 3. *A necessary and sufficient condition for compactness of the imbedding operator of $W^1_{p,r}(\Omega, \partial\Omega)$ into $L_q(\Omega)$ with $m_n(\Omega) < \infty$ and $q \geqslant p \geqslant r$ is that*

(6) $$\limsup_{M \to 0} \left\{ \frac{[m_n(F)]^{1/q}}{[\tilde{c}_p(K)]^{1/p} + [s(\partial_e G)]^{1/r}} : m_n(G) \leqslant M \right\} = 0 \,.$$

This and Corollary 2 imply the next corollary.

Corollary 3. *Let* $(n-p)r \leqslant p(n-1)$, $r \geqslant 1$, $q < rn/(n-1)$. *Then the imbedding operator of* $W_{p,r}^1(\Omega, \partial\Omega)$ *into* $L_q(\Omega)$ *is compact for arbitrary open set* Ω *with finite volume.*

The example of the present subsection shows that there exist domains with finite volume for which the imbedding $W_{p,r}^1(\Omega, \partial\Omega) \subset L_{rn/(n-1)}(\Omega)$ is not compact.

4.11.2. The Classes $\mathscr{I}_{p,\alpha}^{(n-1)}$, $\mathscr{J}_\alpha^{(n-1)}$

Definition 1. Let $\tilde{W}_p^1(\Omega)$ be the completion of the set of functions in $C^\infty(\Omega) \cap C(\bar{\Omega})$ with bounded supports with respect to the norm in $W_p^1(\Omega)$.

Definition 2. We say that Ω is contained in *the class* $\mathscr{I}_{p,\alpha}^{(n-1)}$, $p \geqslant 1$, $\alpha \geqslant (n-p)/p(n-1)$, if there exists a constant $R > 0$ such that

$$\mathfrak{M}_{p,\alpha}(R) \overset{\text{def}}{=} \sup \frac{[s(\partial_e F)]^\alpha}{[\tilde{c}_p(K)]^{1/p}} < \infty \,.$$

Here $\partial_e F = \partial F \cap \partial\Omega$ and the supremum is taken over the set of all conductors $K = G \backslash F$ in Ω with $G = \Omega \cap B_R(x)$, $x \in \partial\Omega$.

The restriction $\alpha \geqslant (n-p)/p(n-1)$ is due to the fact that the class $\mathscr{I}_{p,\alpha}^{(n-1)}$ contains only sets Ω with boundary having Hausdorff measure zero provided $\alpha < (n-p)/p(n-1)$.

Proposition 1. *If* $\alpha < (n-p)/p(n-1)$ *then either* $\mathfrak{M}_{p,\alpha}(R) \equiv \infty$ *or* $s(\partial\Omega) = 0$.

Proof. Let $\Omega \in \mathscr{I}_{p,\alpha}^{(n-1)}$, $s(\partial\Omega) > 0$ and let ε be a small enough positive number. We construct a covering of $\partial\Omega$ by open balls $B_{r_j}(x_j)$ with $r_j < \varepsilon$ and

$$\sum_j r_j^{n-1} \leqslant cs(\partial\Omega) \,.$$

Then

$$\sum_j r_j^{n-1} \leqslant c \sum_j s(B_{r_j}(x_j) \cap \partial\Omega)$$

and hence for at least one ball we have

(1) $$r_j^{n-1} \leqslant cs(B_{r_j}(x_j) \cap \partial\Omega) \,.$$

Consider the conductor $K_j = G_j \backslash F_j$ where $G_j = \Omega \cap B_{2r_j}(x_j)$ and $F_j = \Omega \cap \overline{B_{r_j}(x_j)}$. Since $c_p(K_j) \leqslant p\text{-cap}(\overline{B_{r_j}(x_j)}, B_{2r_j}(x_j)) = cr_j^{n-p}$ (cf. 2.2.4), then by definition of the class $\mathscr{I}_{p,\alpha}^{(n-1)}$ and by estimate (1) we obtain $r_j^{(n-1)p\alpha}$

$\leqslant \mathrm{const}\, r_j^{n-p}$. Noting that $r_j < \varepsilon$ and ε is small we obtain $(n-1)p\alpha \geqslant n-p$. The proposition is proved.

Definition 3. The set Ω is contained in *the class* $\mathscr{J}_\alpha^{(n-1)}$ if there exists a constant $M \in (0, m_n(\Omega))$ such that

$$\mathfrak{R}_\alpha(M) \overset{\text{def}}{=} \sup\left\{\frac{[s(\partial_e g)]^\alpha}{s(\partial_i g)} : g \text{ is an admissible subset of } \Omega \text{ with } m_n(g) \leqslant M\right\} < \infty .$$

We introduce the function

$$\mathfrak{P}_{p,\alpha}(M) = \sup \frac{[s(\partial_e F)]^\alpha}{[\tilde{c}_p(K)]^{1/p}},$$

where the supremum is taken over the collection of all conductors $K = G \backslash F$ in Ω with $m_n(G) \leqslant M$.

In the same way as we proved Proposition 4.6 we can prove the following assertion.

Proposition 2. *The inequality*

$$\mathfrak{P}_{p,\gamma}(M) \leqslant c[\mathfrak{A}_{p,\beta}(M)]^{1-\gamma/\alpha}[\mathfrak{R}_\alpha(M)]^{\gamma/\alpha}$$

is valid for $\gamma = \alpha\beta p/(p-1+p\beta)$ *where* $\mathfrak{A}_{p,\beta}$ *is the function in the definition of the class* $\mathscr{J}_{p,\beta}$ *(cf.* 4.3.1*).*

From this proposition it follows that

$$\mathscr{J}_\alpha^{(n-1)} \cap \mathscr{J}_{p,\beta} \subset \mathscr{J}_{p,\gamma}^{(n-1)} . \tag{2}$$

4.11.3. Examples of Domains in $\mathscr{J}_{p,\alpha}^{(n-1)}$, $\mathscr{J}_\alpha^{(n-1)}$

Example 1. Let $x' = (x_1, \ldots, x_{n-1})$ and let

$$\Omega = \{x \colon x' \in R^{n-1},\ -\infty < x_n < |x'|^{-\lambda}\}, \qquad 0 < \lambda < n-2 .$$

Let g denote an arbitrary admissible subset of Ω with $s(\partial_i g) < 1$. We have

$$s(\partial_e g) = \int_{\mathrm{Pr}(\partial_e g)} (1 + \lambda^2 |x'|^{-2(\lambda+1)})^{1/2} dx' ,$$

where Pr is the projection mapping onto the plane $x_n = 0$. It is clear that the supremum of the integral

$$\int_{\mathscr{E}} (1 + \lambda^2 |x'|^{-2(\lambda+1)})^{1/2} dx'$$

taken over all subsets $\mathscr{E}$ of the plane $x_n = 0$ with a fixed $(n-1)$-dimensional measure, is attained at the $(n-1)$-dimensional ball centered at the origin. Therefore

$$s(\partial_e \mathscr{g}) \leqslant c \int_0^{\varrho} r^{n-2}(1 + \lambda^2 r^{-2(\lambda+1)})^{1/2} dr ,$$

where

$$\varrho = [v_{n-1}^{-1} s(\Pr(\partial_e \mathscr{g}))]^{1/(n-1)} .$$

This implies

$$s(\partial_e \mathscr{g}) \leqslant c s(\Pr(\partial_e \mathscr{g}))^{(n-2-\lambda)/(n-1)} .$$

However, since

$$s(\Pr(\partial_e \mathscr{g})) \leqslant s(\partial_i \mathscr{g}) ,$$

then

$$[s(\partial_e \mathscr{g})]^{(n-1)/(n-2-\lambda)} \leqslant c s(\partial_i \mathscr{g}) .$$

In Example 4.3.5/2 we showed that Ω is contained in $\mathscr{I}_{p,\beta}$ with $\beta = (n-1 + (p-1)\lambda)/(n-1-\lambda)p$. So using (4.11.2/2) we obtain that $\Omega \in \mathscr{I}_{p,\gamma}^{(n-1)}$ with $\gamma = (n-1+(p-1)\lambda)/p(n-2-\lambda)$.

This value of γ is best possible; this is checked using the sequence of conductors $K_m = G_m \backslash F_m$, where $G_m = \{x \in \Omega: \ 0 < x_n < 2m^{-1}\}$ and $F_m = \{x \in \Omega: 0 < x_n < m^{-1}\}$ (cf. Example 4.6).

Example 2. A similar argument shows that the set

$$\Omega = \{x: |x'| < x_n^{\lambda}, 0 < x_n < \infty\}$$

with $\lambda \geqslant 1$ is contained in $\mathscr{I}_{\lambda(n-1)/(\lambda(n-2)+1)}^{(n-1)}$. Since, according to Example 4.3.5/1, $\Omega \in \mathscr{I}_{p,\beta}$ with $\beta = (\lambda(n-1)+1-p)/p(\lambda(n-1)+1)$, then (4.11.2/2) implies $\Omega \in \mathscr{I}_{p,\gamma}^{(n-1)}$ with $\gamma = (\lambda(n-1)+1-p)/p(\lambda(n-2)+1)$.

4.11.4. Estimates for the Norm in $L_q(\partial\Omega)$

Theorem 1. *Let $s(\partial\Omega) < \infty$.*

1) If $\Omega \in \mathscr{I}_{p,\alpha}^{(n-1)}$ with $\alpha p \leqslant 1$, then for all functions $u \in C^{\infty}(\Omega) \cap C(\bar{\Omega})$ with bounded supports the inequality

$$(1) \qquad\qquad \|u\|_{L_q(\partial\Omega)} \leqslant C \|u\|_{W_p^1(\Omega)}$$

is valid with $q = \alpha^{-1}$ and with constant C that is independent of u.

2) If for the same set of functions u inequality (1) is valid with $1/q \geqslant (n-p)/p(n-1)$, then $\Omega \in \mathscr{I}_{p,1/q}^{(n-1)}$.

Proof. 1) We construct the covering of $\partial\Omega$ by equal open balls $B_R(x_i)$, $x_i \in \partial\Omega$, such that the multiplicity of the covering is finite and depends only on n. Let $\{\eta_i\}$ be the partition of unity subordinate to this covering with $|\nabla \eta_i| \leqslant cR^{-1}$.

Duplicating with obvious modifications the proof of Theorem 2.3.2, we obtain

$$\|u\eta_i\|^q_{L_q(\partial\Omega)} \leqslant c \sup_{F\subset \Omega\cap B_R(x_i)} \frac{s(\partial_e F)}{[\tilde{c}_p(G\backslash F)]^{q/p}} \|\nabla(u\eta_i)\|^q_{L_p(\Omega)},$$

where $G = \Omega \cap B_R(x_i)$. Summing over i we arrive at

(2) $$\|u\|_{L_q(\partial\Omega)} \leqslant c\mathfrak{M}_{p,1/q}(R)(\|\nabla u\|_{L_p(\Omega)} + R^{-1}\|u\|_{L_p(\Omega)}).$$

2) We show that $\mathfrak{P}_{p,1/q}(M)$ is bounded for some small $M>0$.

Consider an arbitrary conductor $K = G\backslash F$ in Ω with $m_n(G) \leqslant M$ where M is a constant which will be chosen at the end of the proof.

We insert any function f of the class specified in (4.11.1/5) into (1). Then

(3) $$\begin{aligned}\|f\|_{L_q(\partial\Omega)} &\leqslant C(\|\nabla f\|_{L_p(\Omega)} + \|f\|_{L_p(\Omega)})\\ &\leqslant C(\|\nabla f\|_{L_p(\Omega)} + M^{1/p-(n-1)/nq}\|f\|_{L_{qn/(n-1)}(\Omega)}).\end{aligned}$$

According to Corollary 4.11.1/1

(4) $$\|f\|_{L_{qn/(n-1)}(\Omega)} \leqslant C(\|\nabla f\|_{L_p(\Omega)} + \|f\|_{L_q(\partial\Omega)}).$$

Inequalities (3) and (4) imply

$$\|f\|_{L_q(\partial\Omega)} \leqslant C(\|\nabla f\|_{L_p(\Omega)} + M^{1/p-(n-1)/nq}\|f\|_{L_q(\partial\Omega)}).$$

If from the very beginning the constant M is chosen to be so small that

$$2CM^{1/p-(n-1)/nq} < 1$$

then

$$\|f\|_{L_q(\partial\Omega)} \leqslant 2C\|\nabla f\|_{L_p(\Omega)}.$$

Minimizing the right-hand side we obtain

$$[s(\partial_e F)]^{1/q} \leqslant 2C[\tilde{c}_p(K)]^{1/p}.$$

The proof of Theorem 1 implies the next corollary.

Corollary. *Let $s(\partial\Omega) < \infty$ and $p\alpha \leqslant 1$. The class $\mathscr{I}^{(n-1)}_{p,\alpha}$ can be defined by the condition: $\mathfrak{P}_{p,\alpha}(M)$ is finite for some $M>0$.*

Theorem 2. *Let $s(\partial\Omega) < \infty$, $m_n(\Omega) < \infty$.*

1) If $\Omega \in \mathscr{I}^{(n-1)}_{p,\alpha}$, $p\alpha < 1$, then for all functions $u \in C^\infty(\Omega) \cap C(\bar{\Omega})$ with bounded supports the inequality

(5) $$\|u\|_{L_q(\partial\Omega)} \leqslant C\|u\|_{W^1_{p,p}(\Omega,\partial\Omega)}$$

is valid with $q = \alpha^{-1}$ and with a constant C that is independent of u.

2) *If for any u of the same class* (5) *is valid with* $q>p$ *then* $\Omega \in \mathscr{I}_{p,\alpha}^{(n-1)}$, $\alpha = q^{-1}$.

The first part of the theorem follows from (4.11.1/3) and Theorem 1, the proof of the second part is similar to that of the second part of Theorem 1.

Theorem 3. *Let* Ω *be a domain with* $s(\partial\Omega) < \infty$, $m_n(\Omega) < \infty$ *and let* $q \geqslant p$. *The inequality*

(6)
$$\inf_{c \in R^1} \| u - c \|_{L_q(\partial\Omega)} \leqslant C \| \nabla u \|_{L_p(\Omega)}$$

is valid for any function u in $C^\infty(\Omega) \cap C(\bar{\Omega})$ *with bounded support and with* $q \geqslant p$ *if and only if* $\Omega \in \mathscr{I}_{p,1/q}^{(n-1)}$.

Proof. Sufficiency. Let $K = G \backslash F$, $m_n(G) \leqslant M$. By virtue of Theorem 4.11.1/2 and Corollary 4.11.1/3 we have

$$m_n(F) \leqslant \text{const}\,(\tilde{c}_p(K) + s(\partial_e G)) \; .$$

This and the corollary of the present subsection imply

$$m_n(F) \leqslant \text{const}\, \tilde{c}_p(K) \; .$$

In other words, Ω is contained in $\mathscr{I}_{p,1/p}$. By Theorem 4.4.3/2 and Lemma 3.2.3/1, for all $u \in L_p^1(\Omega)$ we have

$$\inf_{c \in R^1} \| u - c \|_{L_p(\Omega)} \leqslant C \| \nabla u \|_{L_p(\Omega)} \; .$$

It remains to refer to Theorem 1.

Necessity. Substituting any function f of the class specified in (4.11.1/5) into (6), we obtain

$$\min_{c \in R^1} \{ |1-c|^q s(\partial_e F) + |c|^q s(\partial\Omega \backslash \partial_e G) \} \leqslant C^q [\tilde{c}_p(K)]^{q/p} \, .$$

This leads to the estimate

$$\frac{s(\partial_e F)\, s(\partial\Omega \backslash \partial_e G)}{\{ [s(\partial_e F)]^{1/(q-1)} + [s(\partial\Omega \backslash \partial_e G)]^{1/(q-1)} \}^{q-1}} \leqslant C^q [\tilde{c}_p(K)]^{q/p} \, .$$

Therefore,

$$s(\partial_e F) \leqslant 2^{q-1} C^q [\tilde{c}_p(K)]^{q/p}$$

provided $2s(\partial_e G) \leqslant s(\partial\Omega)$. It remains to take any ball of sufficiently small radius with center at $\partial\Omega$ as G. The theorem is proved.

4.11.5. The Class $\mathring{\mathscr{I}}_{p,\alpha}^{(n-1)}$ and Theorems on Compactness

Definition. The set Ω is contained in *the class* $\mathring{\mathscr{I}}_{p,\alpha}^{(n-1)}$ if

$$\lim_{R \to 0} \mathfrak{M}_{p,\alpha}(R) = 0 \; .$$

In the proof of Proposition 4.11.2/1 we showed that $\alpha > (n-p)/p(n-1)$ provided $s(\partial\Omega) > 0$ and the class $\mathring{\mathscr{I}}_{p,\alpha}^{(n-1)}$ is not empty.

Example. Consider the domains

$$\Omega_1 = \{x: |x'| < 1,\ 1 < x_n < |x'|^{-\lambda}\}, \quad 0 < \lambda < n-2,$$

$$\Omega_2 = \{x: |x'| < x_n^\lambda,\ 0 < x_n < 1\}, \quad \lambda \geqslant 1.$$

In Examples 4.11.3/1 and 4.11.3/2 we actually showed that $\Omega_1 \in \mathscr{I}_{p,\gamma_1}^{(n-1)}$ and $\Omega_2 \in \mathscr{I}_{p,\gamma_2}^{(n-1)}$, where $\gamma_1 = (n-1+(p-1)\lambda)/(n-2-\lambda)p$ and $\gamma_2 = (\lambda(n-1)+1-p)/(\lambda(n-2)+1)p$ as well as that $\Omega_i \notin \mathring{\mathscr{I}}_{p,\gamma_i}$. Consequently, $\Omega_i \in \mathring{\mathscr{I}}_{p,\alpha_i}$ $(i=1,2)$ if and only if $\alpha_i > \gamma_i$.

Theorem 1. *Let $s(\partial\Omega) < \infty$ and $m_n(\Omega) < \infty$. The set of functions in $C^\infty(\Omega) \cap C(\bar\Omega)$ having bounded supports and contained in the unit ball of the space $W_p^1(\Omega)$ is relatively compact in $L_q(\partial\Omega)$, $q \geqslant p$, if and only if $\Omega \in \mathring{\mathscr{I}}_{p,1/q}^{(n-1)}$.*

Proof. Sufficiency. Let $\Omega \in \mathring{\mathscr{I}}_{p,1/q}^{(n-1)}$, $q \geqslant p$. If $\|u\|_{W_p^1(\Omega)} \leqslant 1$ then by Theorem 4.11.4/1 we have

$$\|\nabla u\|_{L_p(\Omega)} + \|u\|_{L_p(\partial\Omega)} \leqslant \text{const}.$$

According to Corollary 4.11.1/3 the imbedding operator of $W_{p,p}^1(\Omega, \partial\Omega)$ into $L_p(\Omega)$ is compact and the unit ball in $W_p^1(\Omega)$ is a compact subset of $L_p(\Omega)$.

Given any positive number ε we can find an R such that $\mathfrak{M}_{p,1/q}(R) < \varepsilon$. So by (4.11.4/2), for all $u \in C^\infty(\Omega) \cap C(\bar\Omega)$ with bounded supports we have

$$\|u\|_{L_q(\partial\Omega)} \leqslant \varepsilon \|\nabla u\|_{L_p(\Omega)} + C(\varepsilon)\|u\|_{L_p(\Omega)}.$$

Now the result follows by a standard argument.

Necessity. Let Θ be the set of functions specified in the statement of the theorem. Since the traces on $\partial\Omega$ of functions in Θ form a compact subset of $L_q(\partial\Omega)$, then given any $\varepsilon > 0$ we can find an R such that

$$\left(\int_{B_R(x)\cap\partial\Omega} |u|^q ds\right)^{1/q} \leqslant \varepsilon$$

for all $u \in \Theta$ and for all balls $B_R(x)$. Let u be an arbitrary function in $C^\infty(\Omega) \cap C(\bar\Omega)$ with support in $B_R(x)$. We have

$$\|u\|_{L_q(B_R(x)\cap\partial\Omega)} \leqslant \varepsilon(\|\nabla u\|_{L_p(\Omega)} + \|u\|_{L_p(\Omega)}).$$

Since by Corollary 4.11.1/2

$$\|u\|_{L_p(\Omega)} \leqslant C(\|\nabla u\|_{L_p(\Omega)} + \|u\|_{L_p(\partial\Omega)}),$$

then

$$\left(\int_{B_R(x)\cap\partial\Omega} |u|^q ds\right)^{1/q} \leqslant \varepsilon C\left(\|\nabla u\|_{L_p(\Omega)} + \left(\int_{B_R(x)\cap\partial\Omega} |u|^p ds\right)^{1/p}\right).$$

Thus, if ε is small enough, then

$$\left(\int_{B_R(x)\cap\partial\Omega} |u|^q ds\right)^{1/q} \leqslant 2\varepsilon C\|\nabla u\|_{L_p(\Omega)}.$$

Let K be the conductor $(B_R(x)\cap\Omega)\backslash F$. Substituting any function f of the class specified by the formula (4.11.1/5) into the latter inequality, we obtain

$$[s(\partial_e F)]^{1/q} \leqslant 2\varepsilon C[\tilde{c}_p(K)]^{1/p}.$$

While proving Theorem 1 we also obtained the following result.

Theorem 2. *Let $s(\partial\Omega)<\infty$ and $m_n(\Omega)<\infty$. The set of functions in $C^\infty(\Omega)\cap C(\bar{\Omega})$ having bounded supports and contained in the unit ball of the space $W_{p,p}^1(\Omega,\partial\Omega)$ is relatively compact in $L_q(\partial\Omega)$, $q\geqslant p$, if and only if $\Omega\in\mathcal{I}_{p,1/q}^{(n-1)}$.*

4.11.6. Application to Boundary Value Problems for Second Order Elliptic Equations

In 4.10.1 we established necessary and sufficient conditions for the solvability of the Neumann problem with homogeneous boundary data for uniformly elliptic second order equations in the energy space as well as criteria for the discreteness of the spectrum of this problem. The theorems of the present section enable us to obtain similar results for the problem

(1)
$$Lu \equiv -\frac{\partial}{\partial x_i}\left(a_{ij}\frac{\partial u}{\partial x_j}\right) + au = f \quad \text{in } \Omega,$$
$$Mu \equiv a_{ij}\frac{\partial u}{\partial x_i}\cos(\nu, x_j) + bu = \varphi \quad \text{on } \partial\Omega,$$

where ν is an outward normal to $\partial\Omega$. Here a and b are real functions, $a\in L_\infty(\Omega)$, $b\in L_\infty(\partial\Omega)$ and $a_{ij}=a_{ji}$.

In what follows we assume that $s(\partial\Omega)<\infty$, $m_n(\Omega)<\infty$ and that either both a and b are separated from zero and positive or they vanish identically. We assume for the moment that $f\in L(\Omega)$ and $\varphi\in L(\partial\Omega)$. The exact formulation of the problem is the following.

We require a function in $W_2^1(\Omega,\partial\Omega)$ such that

(2)
$$\int_\Omega\left(a_{ij}\frac{\partial u}{\partial x_j}\frac{\partial v}{\partial x_i} + auv\right)dx + \int_{\partial\Omega} buv\,ds = \int_\Omega fv\,dx + \int_{\partial\Omega}\varphi v\,ds,$$

where v is an arbitrary function in $C(\bar{\Omega}) \cap W_2^1(\Omega, \partial\Omega)$ with bounded support.

This formulation is correct since by definition of the space $W_2^1(\Omega, \partial\Omega)$ and (4.11.1/3) the integrals on the left in (2) converge.

The case $b=0$, $\varphi=0$ was studied in 4.10.1. The same argument as in 4.10.1 together with Theorems 4.11.1/1 – 4.11.1/3, 4.11.4/1 – 4.11.4/3, 4.11.5/1 and 4.11.5/2 leads to the following result.

Theorem 1. (1) *If* $a=0$, $b=0$, $f=0$, $q'=q/(q-1)\leqslant 2$, *then the problem* (1) *is solvable for all* $\varphi \in L_{q'}(\partial\Omega)$, *orthogonal to unity on* $\partial\Omega$, *if and only if* $\Omega \in \mathscr{I}_{2,1/q}^{(n-1)}$.

(2) *If* $\inf a>0$, $b=0$ *and* $f=0$, *then the problem* (1) *is solvable for all* $\varphi \in L_{q'}(\partial\Omega)$, $q'\leqslant 2$, *if and only if* $\Omega \in \mathscr{I}_{2,1/q}^{(n-1)}$.

(3) *If* $a=0$, $\inf b>0$ *and* $f=0$ *then the problem* (1) *is solvable for all* $\varphi \in L_2(\partial\Omega)$ *for arbitrary* Ω. *Under the same assumptions on* a, b, f *a necessary and sufficient condition for the solvability of the problem* (1) *for all* $\varphi \in L_{q'}(\partial\Omega)$, $q'<2$, *is the inclusion* $\Omega \in \mathscr{I}_{2,1/q}^{(n-1)}$.

In each of these three cases the solution of the problem (1) *is contained in* $W_{2,q}^1(\Omega, \partial\Omega)$.

(4) *Let* $\varphi=0$ *and* $\inf b>0$. *The problem* (1) *is solvable for all* $f \in L_{q'}(\Omega)$, $q'\geqslant 2n/(n+1)$, *for arbitrary set* Ω. *A necessary and sufficient condition for the solvability of this problem for all* $f \in L_{q'}(\Omega)$, $q'<2n/(n+1)$, *is the condition of Theorem* 4.11.1/2 *with* $p=r=2$.

Theorem 2. (1) *Assume the assumptions* (1) – (3) *of the previous theorem are valid. A necessary and sufficient condition for the compactness of the inverse operator*

$$L_q(\partial\Omega) \to W_{2,2}^1(\Omega, \partial\Omega)\,, \quad q\leqslant 2\,,$$

of the problem (1) *is that* $\Omega \in \mathring{\mathscr{I}}_{2,1/q}^{(n-1)}$.

(2) *Assume the assumption (4) of Theorem* 1 *is valid. Then the inverse operator*

$$L_q(\partial\Omega) \to W_{2,2}^1(\Omega, \partial\Omega)$$

of the problem (1) *is compact for any set* Ω *provided* $q'>2n/(n+1)$.

A necessary and sufficient condition for the compactness of this operator for $q'\leqslant 2n/(n+1)$ *is the condition of Theorem* 4.11.1/3 *with* $p=r=2$.

In the case $q=2$. Theorem 2 yields necessary and sufficient conditions for the discreteness of the spectrum of the problems

$$Lu=0 \quad \text{in } \Omega\,, \qquad Mu=\lambda u \quad \text{on } \partial\Omega\,,$$

$$Lu=\lambda u \quad \text{in } \Omega\,, \qquad Mu=0 \quad \text{on } \partial\Omega\,.$$

An extension of the results of the present subsection to the mixed boundary problem

$$Lu=f \quad \text{on } \Omega\backslash E\,, \qquad Mu=\varphi \quad \text{on } \partial\Omega\backslash E\,, \qquad u=0 \quad \text{on } E\,,$$

where E is a subset of $\bar{\Omega}$, is a simple exercise.

§ 4.12. Comments to Chapter 4

§ **4.1.** Conductivity (i.e. 2-conductivity) was studied by Pólya and Szegö [213]. This notion was applied to imbedding theorems by the author [142]. Here the presentation follows the author's paper [159]. Concerning the content of subsection 4.1.3 see the comments to § 2.2. Corollary 4.1.3/2 was heuristically obtained for $p=2$ by Pólya and Szegö [213]. Lemma 4.1.3/3 is due to the author [159].

§§ **4.2 – 4.4.** The content of these sections except subsections 4.4.5, 4.4.7 is taken from the author's paper [159].

§ **4.5.** The result of this section for $p=2$ was obtained by the author [149].

§ **4.6** was first published in the author's book [165].

§ **4.7.** Most of this section (4.7.1 – 4.7.4 except Proposition 4.7.1/1) is borrowed from the author's paper [159]. Proposition 4.7.1/1 as well as the content of subsection 4.7.5 follow the author's book [165]. In connection with Proposition 4.7.1/1 we note the paper by Andersson [15] where, in particular, the impossibility of the imbedding $L_p^1(\Omega) \subset L_q(\Omega)$ for $1/p \neq 1/q+1/n$ and for domains with infinite volume is proved.

§§ **4.8 – 4.9** are a part of the author's paper [159].

§ **4.10** is partly contained in the author's paper [149]. Subsections 4.10.2, 4.10.4, 4.10.5 were published in the author's book [165]. The equivalence of the Poincaré inequality and the solvability of the Neumann problem is well known. The same pertains to the interconnection of conditions for the discreteness of the spectrum and the theorems on compactness (cf. Deny and Lions [51], Lions and Magenes [132], Nečas [197], and others).

§ **4.11** is borrowed from the author's book [165].

There are a number of papers where for special classes of domains (without the cone property or unbounded) theorems on the continuity and the compactness of the imbedding operator $W_p^l(\Omega) \to L_q(\Omega)$ as well as necessary conditions for these properties are proved (cf. Lions [131], Björup [32], Stampacchia [236], Globenko [75], Campanato [42], Andersson [15, 16], Hurd [101], and R.A. Adams [12]). Similar problems for the "anisotropic" space $W_p^l(\Omega)$ are considered in the book by Besov, Il'in and Nikol'skiĭ ([27], § 12, Ch. 3).

We also note the papers by Fraenkel [66], Amick [14] and Edmunds [55] where different classes of domains connected with imbedding theorems are considered. In particular, in the paper by Amick just mentioned the decomposition of the space $[L_2(\Omega)]^N$ into two orthogonal subspaces of solenoidal vector fields and of gradients of functions in $W_2^1(\Omega)$ are studied. This decomposition plays an important role in the mathematical theory of viscous fluids (cf. Ladyženskaja [122]). According to the Amick theorem [14], this decomposition is possible for a bounded domain Ω if and only if the spaces $W_2^1(\Omega)$ and $L_2^1(\Omega)$ coincide. By virtue of Theorem 4.4.3/2 of the present book the latter is equivalent to the inclusion $\Omega \in \mathscr{I}_{2,1/2}$.

Chapter 5. On Continuity and Boundedness of Functions in Sobolev Spaces

If a domain Ω has the cone property, then by the Sobolev theorem any function u in $W_p^l(\Omega)$, $pl>n$, coincides almost everywhere with a continuous function in Ω, and

$$\|u\|_{L_\infty(\Omega)} \leqslant C\|u\|_{W_p^l(\Omega)} ,$$

where the constant C does not depend of u.

The simple example of the function $u(x)=x_1^\mu$, $\mu>0$, defined on the plane domain $\Omega=\{x: 0<x_1<1, 0<x_2<x_1^\nu\}$, $\nu>1$, shows that the cone property is essential for the validity of Sobolev's theorem. We can naturally expect that for sets with "bad" boundaries the imbedding $W_p^l(\Omega)\subset L_\infty(\Omega)\cap C(\Omega)$ is valid in some cases under stronger requirements on p and l.

In the present chapter we study the classes of domains Ω for which the imbedding operator of $W_p^l(\Omega)$ into $L_\infty(\Omega)\cap C(\Omega)$ is bounded or compact. Some theorems that we prove give necessary and sufficient conditions and they are stated in terms of the p-conductivity. Other results contain easily checked sufficient conditions for the validity of the imbedding $W_p^l(\Omega)\subset L_\infty(\Omega)\cap C(\Omega)$. We also present examples that illustrate the properties of "bad" domains.

The greater part of the results in this chapter were stated by the author in [142] and the detailed exposition is given in [157].

§ 5.1. On the Imbedding $W_p^1(\Omega)\subset C(\Omega)\cap L_\infty(\Omega)$

5.1.1. Criteria for the Continuity of the Imbedding Operators of $W_p^1(\Omega)$ and $L_p^1(\Omega)$ into $C(\Omega)\cap L_\infty(\Omega)$

Let y be an arbitrary point in the domain Ω and let $\varrho>0$.

Here and in the next two subsections we consider only conductors of the form $\Omega_\varrho(y)\backslash y$. Further, we introduce the function

$$\gamma_p(\varrho)=\inf_{y\in\Omega} c_p(\Omega_\varrho(y)\backslash y) , \quad p>n , \tag{1}$$

on $(0, +\infty)$. Obviously, γ_p does not increase and vanishes for $\varrho > \mathrm{diam}(\Omega)$. The condition $p > n$ in the definition of γ_p is justified by the fact that the infimum on the right in (1) equals zero for $p \leqslant n$ by (2.2.4/1) and (2.2.4/2).

Noting that the function $u(x) = (1-\varrho^{-1}|x-y|)_+$ is contained in the class $U_\Omega(\Omega_\varrho(y)\backslash y)$ we obtain $\gamma_p(\varrho) \leqslant c\varrho^{n-p}$.

Theorem 1. *The imbedding operator of $W_p^1(\Omega)$ into $C(\Omega) \cap L_\infty(\Omega)$ is bounded if and only if $\gamma_p(\varrho) \not\equiv 0$.*

Proof. Sufficiency. Let u be any function in $C^\infty(\Omega) \cap W_p^1(\Omega)$ and let y be a point in Ω such that $u(y) \neq 0$. Let R denote a number for which $\gamma_p(R) > 0$ and let ϱ denote an arbitrary number in $(0, R]$. We put $v(x) = \eta((x-y)/\varrho) \times u(x)/u(y)$ where $\eta \in C_0^\infty(B_1), \eta(0) = 1$. Since $v(y) = 1$ and $v(x) = 0$ outside $\Omega_\varrho(y)$ then

$$c_p(\Omega_\varrho(y)\backslash y) \leqslant \int_\Omega |\nabla v|^p dx$$

and therefore

$$|u(y)|^p c_p(\Omega_\varrho(y)\backslash y) \leqslant c\left(\int_{\Omega_\varrho(y)} |\nabla u|^p dx + \varrho^{-p} \int_{\Omega_\varrho(y)} |u|^p dx\right). \tag{2}$$

Thus the sufficiency of $\gamma_p \not\equiv 0$ follows.

Necessity. For all $u \in W_p^1(\Omega)$, let

$$\|u\|_{L_\infty(\Omega)} \leqslant C\|u\|_{W_p^1(\Omega)}. \tag{3}$$

Inserting an arbitrary $u \in T_\Omega(\Omega_\varrho(y)\backslash y)$ into (3) we obtain

$$1 \leqslant C(\|\nabla u\|_{L_p(\Omega)} + v_n^{1/p}\varrho^{n/p}).$$

If ϱ is small enough then

$$(2C)^{-p} \leqslant \int_\Omega |\nabla u|^p dx.$$

Minimizing the preceding integral over $T_\Omega(\Omega_\varrho(y)\backslash y)$ we obtain

$$c_p(\Omega_\varrho(y)\backslash y) \geqslant (2C)^{-p}.$$

The theorem is proved.

An assertion similar to Theorem 1 is valid for the space $L_p^1(\Omega)$.

Theorem 2. *Let $m_n(\Omega) < \infty$. The imbedding operator of $L_p^1(\Omega)$ into $C(\Omega) \cap L_\infty(\Omega)$ is bounded if and only if $\gamma_p \not\equiv 0$.*

We only need to prove the sufficiency of $\gamma_p \not\equiv 0$. By virtue of Lemma 3.1.2/2 we need to derive the inequality

$$\|u\|_{L_\infty(\Omega)} \leqslant C\|u\|_{L_p^1(\Omega)} \tag{4}$$

for functions in $L_p^1(\Omega) \cap L_\infty(\Omega)$. Let ω denote a bounded set with $\bar{\omega} \subset \Omega$. The estimate (3) implies

$$\|u\|_{L_\infty(\Omega)} \leqslant C(\|\nabla u\|_{L_p(\Omega)} + \|u\|_{L_\infty(\Omega)}(m_n(\Omega\setminus\omega))^{1/p}).$$

Choosing ω to satisfy $2C(m_n(\Omega\setminus\omega))^{1/p} < 1$, we arrive at (4). The theorem is proved.

Remark. Let $\tilde{L}_p^l(\Omega)$ and $\tilde{W}_p^l(\Omega)$ denote the completions of the spaces $C^\infty(\Omega) \cap C(\bar{\Omega}) \cap L_p^l(\Omega)$ and $C^\infty(\Omega) \cap C(\bar{\Omega}) \cap W_p^l(\Omega)$ with respect to the norms in $L_p^l(\Omega)$ and $W_p^l(\Omega)$.

If we replace $\gamma_p(\varrho)$ in Theorems 1 and 2 by

$$\tilde{\gamma}_p(\varrho) = \inf_{y\in\Omega} \tilde{c}_p(\Omega_\varrho(y)\setminus y),$$

where $\tilde{c}_p$ is the p-conductivity defined by (4.11.1/5), then we obtain analogous assertions for the spaces $\tilde{W}_p^1(\Omega)$ and $\tilde{L}_p^1(\Omega)$.

The following theorem contains two-sided estimates for the constants in inequality (5) below.

Let $\sigma_p(\mu)$ denote the infimum of $c_p(K)$ taken over the set of conductors $K = G\setminus F$ in Ω with $m_n(G) \leqslant \mu$.

Since $c_p(K)$ is a nondecreasing function of F, we may assume F to be a point.

Theorem 3. 1) *If $\sigma_p(\mu) \neq 0$ for some $\mu < m_n(\Omega)$ then for all $u \in L_p^1(\Omega) \cap L_q(\Omega)$*

$$\|u\|_{L_\infty(\Omega)} \leqslant k_1 \|\nabla u\|_{L_p(\Omega)} + k_2 \|u\|_{L_q(\Omega)}, \tag{5}$$

where $k_1 \leqslant [\sigma_p(\mu)]^{-1/p}$, $k_2 \leqslant \mu^{-1/q}$.

2) *If for any $u \in L_p^1(\Omega) \cap L_q(\Omega)$ inequality* (5) *is valid then $\sigma_p(\mu) \geqslant (2k_1)^{-p}$ with $\mu = (2k_2)^{-q}$.*

Proof. 1) It suffices to derive (5) for functions in $C^\infty(\Omega) \cap L_p^1(\Omega) \cap L_q(\Omega)$. We choose a positive number t such that

$$m_n(\{x: |u(x)| > t\}) \leqslant \mu,\ m_n(\{x: |u(x)| \geqslant t\}) \geqslant \mu.$$

Let $T > t$ and $\{x: |u(x)| \geqslant T\} \neq \varnothing$. By the definition of p-conductivity, for the conductor

$$K_{t,T} = \{x: |u(x)| > t\}\setminus\{x: |u(x)| \geqslant T\}$$

we have

$$(T-t)^p c_p(K_{t,T}) \leqslant \int_\Omega |\nabla |u||^p dx = \int_\Omega |\nabla u|^p dx.$$

Consequently,

$$(T-t)^p \sigma_p(\mu) \leqslant \int_\Omega |\nabla u|^p dx.$$

Hence

$$T \leqslant [\sigma_p(\mu)]^{-1/p} \| \nabla u \|_{L_p(\Omega)} + \mu^{-1/q} \| u \|_{L_q(\{x: |u(x)| \geqslant t\})}$$

and (5) follows.

2) Suppose (5) is valid. We put $\mu = (2k_2)^{-q}$ and consider an arbitrary conductor $K = G \backslash F$ with $m_n(G) \leqslant \mu$. Let $\{u_m\}$ be a sequence of functions in $T_\Omega(K)$ such that

$$\| \nabla u_m \|^p_{L_p(\Omega)} \to c_p(K) .$$

Clearly,

$$k_2 \| u_m \|_{L_q(\Omega)} \leqslant k_2 [m_n(G)]^{1/q} \leqslant k_2 \mu^{1/q} = \tfrac{1}{2} .$$

Moreover, by (5) we have

$$1 \leqslant 2k_1 \| \nabla u_m \|_{L_p(K)} \to 2k_1 [c_p(K)]^{1/p} .$$

Consequently, $\sigma_p(\mu) \geqslant (2k_1)^{-p}$. The theorem is proved.

Remark 2. Theorems 1 and 3 imply that the conditions $\gamma_p \equiv 0$ and $\sigma_p \equiv 0$ are equivalent.

5.1.2. A Sufficient Condition in Terms of λ_M for the Imbedding $W_p^1(\Omega) \subset C(\Omega) \cap L_\infty(\Omega)$

From Corollary 4.1.3/2 and the definition of the functions σ_p and λ_M it immediately follows that

$$\sigma_p(\mu) \geqslant \left(\int_0^\mu \frac{d\tau}{[\lambda_M(\tau)]^{p/(p-1)}} \right)^{1-p} , \tag{1}$$

where $\mu \leqslant M$, which together with Theorem 5.1.1/3 yields the following sufficient condition for the imbedding $W_p^1(\Omega) \subset C(\Omega) \cap L_\infty(\Omega)$.

Theorem 1. *If for some* $M < m_n(\Omega)$

$$\int_0^M \frac{d\mu}{[\lambda_M(\mu)]^{p/(p-1)}} < \infty , \tag{2}$$

then the imbedding operator of $W_p^1(\Omega)$ *into* $C(\Omega) \cap L_\infty(\Omega)$ *is bounded.*

This implies an obvious corollary.

Corollary. *If* $\Omega \in \mathcal{J}_\alpha$ *and* $p(1-\alpha) > 1$ *then the imbedding operator of* $W_p^1(\Omega)$ *into* $C(\Omega) \cap L_\infty(\Omega)$ *is bounded.*

Example. Consider the domain

$$\Omega = \{x: (x_1^2 + \cdots + x_{n-1}^2)^{1/2} < f(x_n),\ 0 < x_n < a\} \tag{3}$$

in Example 3.3.3/1. From (3.3.3/1) it follows that the convergence of integral (2) is equivalent to the condition

$$\int_0^a \frac{d\tau}{[f(\tau)]^{(n-1)/(p-1)}} < \infty . \tag{4}$$

We show that $\sigma_p(\mu) \equiv 0$, i.e. $W_p^1(\Omega)$ is not imbedded in $C(\Omega) \cap L_\infty(\Omega)$ if (4) fails.

Let

$$F = \Omega \cap \{0 < x_n \leqslant \varepsilon\} , \qquad G = \Omega \cap \{x\colon 0 < x_n < \delta\} ,$$

where $\delta > \varepsilon$ and K is the conductor $G \backslash F$. We introduce the function $u \in U_\Omega(K)$ that vanishes outside G, is equal to unity on F and to

$$\int_{x_n}^{\delta} \frac{d\xi}{[f(\xi)]^{(n-1)/(p-1)}} \left(\int_{\varepsilon}^{\delta} \frac{d\xi}{[f(\xi)]^{(n-1)/(p-1)}} \right)^{-1}$$

on $G \backslash F$. Obviously,

$$c_p(K) \leqslant \int_\Omega |\nabla u|^p dx = c \left(\int_\varepsilon^\delta \frac{d\xi}{[f(\xi)]^{(n-1)/(p-1)}} \right)^{1-p} . \tag{5}$$

Therefore $c_p(K) \to 0$ as $\varepsilon \to 0$ and hence $\sigma_p \equiv 0$ provided (4) diverges.

If $f(\tau) = c\tau^\beta$, $\beta \geqslant 1$, then Ω is contained in $\mathscr{J}_\alpha$ with $\alpha = \beta(n-1)/(\beta(n-1)+1)$ (cf., for instance, Example 3.3.3/1) and consequently $W_p^1(\Omega) \subset C(\Omega) \cap L_\infty(\Omega)$ for $p > 1 + \beta(n-1)$.

The condition (4) implies that the imbedding operator of $W_p^1(\Omega)$ into $C(\Omega) \cap L_\infty(\Omega)$ is bounded for all $p > n$ if for small τ the function f is defined as

$$f(\tau) = \tau h(\log(1/\tau)) ,$$

where $h(s) \to 0$ and $s^{-1} \log h(s) \to 0$ as $s \to +\infty$. (Of course, this domain does not have the cone property.)

If for any point P in Ω we can construct a "quasiconic body" situated in Ω and specified in some coordinate system with the origin at P by inequalities (3) where f is subject to (4), then, obviously, $\gamma_p(\varrho) \not\equiv 0$ and the imbedding operator of $W_p^1(\Omega)$ into $C(\Omega) \cap L_\infty(\Omega)$ is bounded.

§ 5.2. On a Multiplicative Estimate for the Modulus of a Function in $W_p^1(\Omega)$

5.2.1. Conditions for the Validity of a Multiplicative Inequality

It is well known that the estimate

$$\|u\|_{L_\infty(\Omega)} \leqslant C \|u\|_{W_p^1(\Omega)}^{n/p} \|u\|_{L_p(\Omega)}^{1-n/p} \tag{1}$$

is valid for $p>n$ provided the domain Ω has the cone property. This is a particular case of the general multiplicative Gagliardo-Nirenberg inequalities (cf. 1.4.7, 1.4.8). The following theorem contains a necessary and sufficient condition for the validity of the estimate

$$\|u\|_{L_\infty(\Omega)} \leqslant C\|u\|_{W_p^1(\Omega)}^{1/(r+1)} \|u\|_{L_p(\Omega)}^{r/(r+1)}, \tag{2}$$

where r is a positive number.

Theorem 1. *If for some* $r>0$

$$\liminf_{\mu\to+0} \mu^r \sigma_p(\mu) > 0, \tag{3}$$

then (2) *is valid for all* $u\in W_p^1(\Omega)$.

Conversely, if for all $u\in W_p^1(\Omega)$ *inequality* (2) *is valid, then* Ω *satisfies* (3).

Proof. Sufficiency. By (3) there exists a constant M such that

$$\mu^r\sigma_p(\mu) \geqslant \varkappa = \text{const} > 0$$

for $\mu\in(0,M]$. Therefore, according to Theorem 5.1.1/3,

$$\|u\|_{L_\infty(\Omega)} \leqslant \mu^{r/p}\varkappa^{-1/p}\|\nabla u\|_{L_p(\Omega)} + \mu^{-1/p}\|u\|_{L_p(\Omega)}. \tag{4}$$

The minimum value of the right-hand side over μ is attained for $\mu^* = (\varkappa^{1/p} r^{-1} \cdot \|u\|_{L_p(\Omega)}/\|\nabla u\|_{L_p(\Omega)})^{p/(r+1)}$ and it is equal to

$$c\varkappa^{-1/p(r+1)}\|\nabla u\|_{L_p(\Omega)}^{1/(r+1)}\|u\|_{L_p(\Omega)}^{r/(r+1)}.$$

If $\mu^*\leqslant M$ then (2) follows. If $\mu^*>M$, then

$$\varkappa^{1/p} r^{-1}\|u\|_{L_p(\Omega)} \geqslant M^{1+1/r}\|\nabla u\|_{L_p(\Omega)}$$

and (4) implies

$$\|u\|_{L_\infty(\Omega)} \leqslant c_1\varkappa^{-1/p(r+1)}\|\nabla u\|_{L_p(\Omega)}^{1/(r+1)}\|u\|_{L_p(\Omega)}^{r/(r+1)} + cM^{-1/p}\|u\|_{L_p(\Omega)}.$$

Inequality (2) is proved.

Necessity. We put $M=(2C^{r+1})^{-p/(r+1)}$. We may assume that the constant C in (2) is so large that $M<m_n(\Omega)$. Consider an arbitrary conductor $K=G\backslash F$ with $m_n(G)\leqslant\mu\leqslant M$. From (2), for any $u\in T_\Omega(K)$, we have

$$1\leqslant C\mu^{1/p(r+1)}(\|\nabla u\|_{L_p(\Omega)}+M^{1/p})^{1/(r+1)}.$$

Therefore, $2C^{r+1}\mu^{r/p}\|\nabla u\|_{L_p(\Omega)}\geqslant 1$. Minimizing the left-hand side over $T_\Omega(K)$ we obtain

$$(2C^{r+1})^p\mu^r\sigma_p(\mu)\geqslant 1.$$

The theorem is proved.

Theorems 1 and 5.1.2/1 imply the following sufficient condition for the validity of inequality (2).

Corollary. *If* $\Omega \in \mathscr{J}_\alpha$ *with* $1 > \alpha \geqslant 1 - 1/n$ *and* $p(1-\alpha) > 1$, *then for any* $u \in W_p^1(\Omega)$ *inequality* (2) *is valid with* $r = p(1-\alpha) - 1$.

Proof. Since $\Omega \in \mathscr{J}_\alpha$, then $\lambda_M(\mu) \geqslant C_M \mu^\alpha$ for $\mu < M$ where C_M is a positive constant. This and (5.1.2/1) imply

$$\sigma_p(\mu) \geqslant C_M^p (1 - p\alpha/(p-1))^{p-1} \mu^{1-p(1-\alpha)} .$$

The result follows.

Example. For $f(x_n) = c x_n^\beta$, $\beta \geqslant 1$, the domain (5.1.2/3) is in the class $\mathscr{J}_{\beta(n-1)/(\beta(n-1)+1)}$ and hence by Corollary inequality (2) is valid for $p > 1 + \beta(n-1)$ with $r = (p - 1 - \beta(n-1))/(1 + \beta(n-1))$. This exponent is best possible since (5.1.2/5) implies

$$\sigma_p(\delta^{\beta(n-1)+1}) \leqslant c_1 \left(\int_0^{c\delta} \xi^{-\beta(n-1)/(p-1)} d\xi \right)^{1-p} = c_2 \delta^{1+\beta(n-1)-p} ,$$

where δ is any sufficiently small positive number.

5.2.2. On the Multiplicative Inequality in the Limit Case $r = (p-n)/n$

Inequality (5.2.1/2) becomes (5.2.1/1) for $r = (p-n)/n$. In this particular case a necessary and sufficient condition can be expressed in terms of the function γ_p.

Theorem. *Inequality* (5.2.1/1) *is true for all* $u \in W_p^1(\Omega)$ *if and only if*

$$\liminf_{\varrho \to +0} \varrho^{p-n} \gamma_p(\varrho) > 0 . \tag{1}$$

Proof. Sufficiency. Let r be so small that $\varrho^{p-n} \gamma_p(\varrho) > \delta > 0$ for $\varrho < r$. By virtue of (5.1.1/2) we have

$$c\delta^{1/p} \|u\|_{L_\infty(\Omega)} \leqslant \varrho^{1-n/p} \|\nabla u\|_{L_p(\Omega)} + \varrho^{-n/p} \|u\|_{L_p(\Omega)} \tag{2}$$

for $\varrho \leqslant r$ with $c > 0$. The minimum of the right-hand side in (2) over $\varrho > 0$ is attained at

$$\varrho^* = n(p-n)^{-1} \|u\|_{L_p(\Omega)} / \|\nabla u\|_{L_p(\Omega)}$$

and is equal to

$$c \|\nabla u\|_{L_p(\Omega)}^{n/p} \|u\|_{L_p(\Omega)}^{1-n/p} .$$

If $\varrho^* \leqslant r$ then (5.2.1/1) follows. If $\varrho^* > r$ then

$$\|u\|_{L_p(\Omega)} \geqslant (p-n)rn^{-1}\|\nabla u\|_{L_p(\Omega)}$$

and (2) implies

$$c\delta^{1/p}\|u\|_{L_\infty(\Omega)} \leqslant \|\nabla u\|_{L_p(\Omega)}^{n/p}\|u\|_{L_p(\Omega)}^{1-n/p} + r^{-n/p}\|u\|_{L_p(\Omega)}.$$

Thus the sufficiency of the condition (1) is proved.

Necessity. We insert an arbitrary $u \in T_\Omega(\Omega_\varrho(y)\backslash y)$ into (5.2.1/1). Since

$$\|u\|_{L_p(\Omega)}^p \leqslant c\varrho^n, \qquad \|u\|_{W_p^1(\Omega)}^p \leqslant c(c_p(\Omega_\varrho(y)\backslash y) + \varrho^n),$$

then by (5.2.1/1)

$$C^{-p} \leqslant c(c_p(\Omega_\varrho(y)\backslash y) + \varrho^n)^{n/p}\varrho^{n(p-n)/p}.$$

Consequently,

$$C^{-p^2/n} \leqslant c(\varrho^{p-n}\gamma_p(\varrho) + \varrho^p).$$

It remains to pass to the lower limit as $\varrho \to +0$.

In the next proposition we give a sufficient condition for (2) which generalizes the cone property. Let $y \in \Omega$ and let $S_\varrho(y)$ denote the "sector" $\{x: |x-y| < \varrho, |x-y|^{-1}(x-y) \in \omega(y)\}$, where $\omega(y)$ is a measurable subset of the $(n-1)$-dimensional unit sphere.

Proposition. *Suppose there exist positive constants R and δ such that any point y in the set Ω can be placed at the vertex of the sector $S_R(y)$ contained in Ω and satisfying the condition $s(\omega(y)) > \delta$. Then* (1) *is valid.*

Proof. Let $0 < \varrho < R$ and let (r, θ) be spherical coordinates centered at y. Obviously,

$$c_p(\Omega_\varrho(y)\backslash y) \geqslant \inf \int_{S_\varrho(y)} |\nabla u|^p dx,$$

where the infimum is taken over all functions $u \in C^{0,1}(\overline{S_\varrho(y)})$ with $u(y) = 1$, $u(\varrho, \theta) = 0$ for $\theta \in \omega(y)$. It remains to note that

$$\int_{S_\varrho(y)} |\nabla u|^p dx \geqslant \int_{\omega(y)} d\theta \int_0^\varrho \left|\frac{\partial u}{\partial r}\right|^p r^{n-1} dr$$

$$\geqslant \int_{\omega(y)} d\theta \left|\int_0^\varrho \frac{\partial u}{\partial r} dr\right|^p \left(\int_0^\varrho r^{(1-n)/(p-1)} dr\right)^{1-p} > \left(\frac{p-n}{p-1}\right)^{p-1} \delta\varrho^{n-p}.$$

Let us consider a domain which does not satisfy the condition of Proposition and for which (1) is nevertheless true.

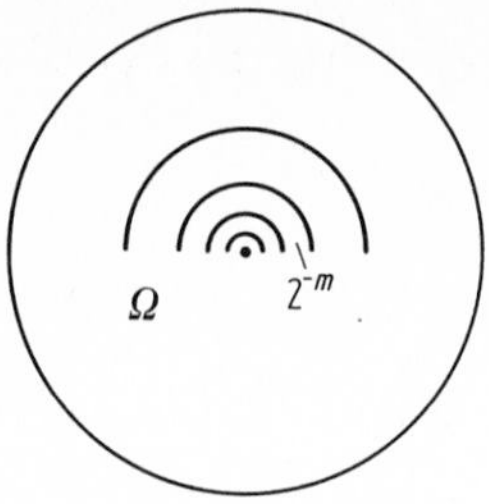

Fig. 21

Example. Let Ω be the domain in Fig. 21. Further, let $\delta_m = 2^{-m}$, $Q_m = \{x\colon \delta_{m+1} < |x| < \delta_m\} \cap \Omega$, $y \in Q_m$. Let u denote a function in $T_\Omega(\Omega_\varrho(y)\backslash y)$ such that

$$\int_\Omega |\nabla u|^p dx \leqslant c_p(\Omega_\varrho(y)\backslash y) + \varepsilon\,, \qquad \varepsilon > 0\,.$$

We note that

$$|u(\xi) - u(\eta)|^p \leqslant c\,|\xi - \eta|^{p-2} \int_{Q_j} |\nabla u|^p dx \tag{3}$$

for any points $\xi, \eta \in Q_j$, $j = 1, 2, \ldots$. (This estimate is invariant with respect to a similarity transformation and so it suffices to limit consideration to Q_1. However, inequality (3) for Q_1 is contained in Theorem 1.4.5, part (*f*).) We begin with the case $\varrho < \delta_m$ when $Q_m \cap \partial B_\varrho(y) \neq \varnothing$. Let $j = m$, $\xi = y$ and $\eta \in Q_m \cap \partial B_\varrho(y)$ in (3). Then

$$1 \leqslant c\varrho^{p-2}(c_p(\Omega_\varrho(y)\backslash y) + \varepsilon)\,.$$

Next suppose $\varrho \geqslant \delta_m$. For all $\xi \in Q_j \cap \{x = (x_1, x_2)\colon x_2 < 0\}$ we have

$$|u(\xi) - u(0)|^p \leqslant c\,|\xi|^{p-2} \int_\Omega |\nabla u|^p dx\,.$$

Taking (3) into account we find that the latter inequality is valid for all $\xi \in Q_j$. Consequently,

$$\Big(\operatorname*{osc}_{\Omega_{2\varrho}(0)} u\Big)^p \leqslant c\varrho^{p-2} \int_\Omega |\nabla u|^p dx\,.$$

Noting that $\Omega_{2\varrho}(0) \supset \Omega_\varrho(y)$, we finally obtain

$$1 = \Big(\operatorname*{osc}_{\Omega_\varrho(y)} u\Big)^p \leqslant c\varrho^{p-2}(c_p(\Omega_\varrho(y)\backslash y) + \varepsilon)\,.$$

§ 5.3. On the Modulus of Continuity of Functions in $L_p^1(\Omega)$

The following assertion is an obvious corollary of the definition of p-conductivity.

Theorem 1. *Let $m_n(\Omega) < \infty$, Λ be a nondecreasing continuous function on $[0, \infty)$ and let u be an arbitrary function in $L_p^1(\Omega)$. In order that for almost all $x, y \in \Omega$ the inequality*

$$|u(x) - u(y)| \leqslant \Lambda(|x-y|) \, \|\nabla u\|_{L_p(\Omega)} \tag{1}$$

be valid it is necessary and sufficient that

$$c_p(K) \geqslant [\Lambda(\operatorname{dist}(\partial_i F, \partial_i G))]^{-p} \tag{2}$$

for any conductor $K = G \backslash F$.

Since the conductivity is a nonincreasing function of G and a nondecreasing function of F, the last condition is equivalent to

$$c_p[(\Omega \backslash x) \backslash y] \geqslant [\Lambda(|x-y|)]^{-p}, \quad x, y \in \Omega . \tag{3}$$

We say that the class $\dot{u} = \{u + \text{const}\}$ is contained in the space $C_\Lambda(\Omega)$ if

$$\sup_{x, y \in \Omega} \frac{|u(x) - u(y)|}{\Lambda(|x-y|)} < \infty .$$

Thus the imbedding operator of $\dot{L}_p^1(\Omega)$ into $C_\Lambda(\Omega)$ is continuous if and only if (3) is valid.

Example. Farther in this section we consider the domain Ω already studied in Examples 3.3.3/1, 3.5.2, 4.3.5/1 and 5.1.2. Here we show that for this domain the imbedding operator of $L_p^1(\Omega)$ into $C_\Lambda(\Omega)$ is continuous if and only if

$$\Lambda(t) \geqslant k \left(\int_0^t \frac{d\xi}{[f(\xi)]^{(n-1)/(p-1)}} \right)^{1-1/p}, \quad k = \text{const} > 0 . \tag{4}$$

Proof. Necessity. Into (1) we insert the function u equal to unity for $x_n < \varepsilon$, to zero for $x_n > t$ and to

$$\int_{x_n}^t \frac{d\xi}{[f(\xi)]^{(n-1)/(p-1)}} \left(\int_\varepsilon^t \frac{d\xi}{[f(\xi)]^{(n-1)/(p-1)}} \right)^{-1}$$

for $\varepsilon \leqslant x_n \leqslant t$. (Here $\varepsilon > 0$ and $t \in (\varepsilon, a)$.) Then

$$1 \leqslant v_{n-1} [\Lambda(t)]^p \left(\int_\varepsilon^t \frac{d\xi}{[f(\xi)]^{(n-1)/(p-1)}} \right)^{p-1},$$

which becomes (4) as $\varepsilon \to +0$.

The *sufficiency* of the condition (4) is a simple corollary of the inequality

$$|u(x)-u(0)| \leqslant k\left(\int_0^{x_n} \frac{d\xi}{[f(\xi)]^{(n-1)/(p-1)}}\right)^{1-1/p} \|\nabla u\|_{L_p(\Omega)}. \tag{5}$$

(We note that Theorem 1.1.6/1 implies the density of $C^\infty(\bar{\Omega})$ in $L_p^1(\Omega)$ for the Ω under consideration.)

To prove (5) we need the following lemma.

Lemma. *Let*

$$\Omega_b = \{x=(x', x_n): |x'| < f(x_n),\ 0 < x_n < b\}$$

and let u be a function in $C^\infty(\bar{\Omega}_b)$ *with* $u(0)=0$ *and* $u(x) \geqslant 1$ *for* $x_n = b$. *Then*

$$\int_{\Omega_b} |\nabla u|^p dx \geqslant k\left(\int_0^b \frac{d\xi}{[f(\xi)]^{(n-1)/(p-1)}}\right)^{1-p}. \tag{6}$$

Proof. It suffices to establish (6) under the assumption that $u=0$ for $x_n < \varepsilon$, $u=1$ for $x_n > b-\varepsilon$ where ε is a small positive number. Then

$$\int_{\Omega_b} |\nabla u|^p dx \geqslant c_p(K_\varepsilon),$$

where $K_\varepsilon = G_\varepsilon \backslash F_\varepsilon$, $F_\varepsilon = \operatorname{clos}_\Omega \Omega_\varepsilon$, $G_\varepsilon = \Omega_{b-\varepsilon}$. To estimate $c_p(K_\varepsilon)$ from below we make use of (5.1.2/1) and (3.3.3/1). These inequalities are applicable despite the fact that the measure of the set G_ε is large. In fact, extending f to $[b, 2b]$ we obtain the enlarged domain Ω_{2b} such that $2m_n(G_\varepsilon) \leqslant m_n(\Omega_{2b})$ with no modification of the conductor K_ε. We have

$$c_p(K_\varepsilon) \geqslant k\left(\int_\varepsilon^{b-\varepsilon} \frac{d\xi}{[f(\xi)]^{(n-1)/(p-1)}}\right)^{1-p}, \tag{7}$$

which together with (6) completes the proof of the lemma.

Proof of inequality (5). First we note that smooth functions in the closure of the domain

$$g_x = \{y \in \Omega: x_n - [2f'(a)]^{-1} f(x_n) < y_n < x_n,\ x_n < a\}$$

satisfy the inequality

$$|u(z)-u(y)| \leqslant C|z-y|^{1-n/p} \|\nabla u\|_{L_p(g_x)}, \tag{8}$$

where z, y are arbitrary points in g_x and C is a constant that is independent of x. The latter is a corollary of the Sobolev theorem on the imbedding of L_p^1 into $C^{1-n/p}$ for domains with smooth boundaries.

Let $u \in C^\infty(\bar{\Omega}_a)$, $u(0)=0$, $u(x)=1$ at some $x \in \bar{\Omega}_a$. By virtue of (8)

$$C[f(x_n)]^{n-p} \max_{y \in \bar{g}_x} |1-u(y)|^p \leqslant \int_{\Omega_a} |\nabla u|^p dx .$$

Therefore

$$\int_{\Omega_a} |\nabla u|^p dx \geqslant C x_n^{n-p}$$

provided $2 \min u < 1$ in g_x. This and the obvious estimate

$$\left(\int_0^{x_n} \frac{d\xi}{[f(\xi)]^{(n-1)/(p-1)}} \right)^{p-1} \geqslant k \left(\int_0^{x_n} \xi^{(1-n)/(p-1)} d\xi \right)^{p-1} = k_1 x_n^{p-n}$$

imply (5).

Next we assume that $2u(y) \geqslant 1$ for all $y \in g_x$. Then the function $2u$ satisfies the conditions of Lemma with

$$b = x_n - [2f'(a)]^{-1} f(x_n)$$

and so

$$\int_{\Omega_a} |\nabla u|^p dx \geqslant k \left(\int_0^b \frac{d\xi}{[f(\xi)]^{(n-1)/(p-1)}} \right)^{1-p} \geqslant k \left(\int_0^{x_n} \frac{d\xi}{[f(\xi)]^{(n-1)/(p-1)}} \right)^{1-p} .$$

Inequality (5) follows.

§ 5.4. On the Boundedness of Functions with Derivatives in Orlicz Classes

Most of the results of the previous sections in this chapter can be generalized to the space of functions with the finite integral

$$\int_\Omega \Phi(|\nabla u|)\, dx , \tag{1}$$

where Φ is a convex function. For this purpose we must introduce the conductivity generated by integral (1).

Here we consider only a sufficient condition for the boundedness of functions with the finite integral (1) which is formulated in terms of the function λ. We also state some corollaries of this condition.

Lemma. *If $u \in C^\infty(\Omega)$ then for almost all t*

$$\int_{\mathscr{E}_t} \frac{ds}{|\nabla u|} = -\frac{d}{dt} m_n(\mathscr{L}_t) , \tag{2}$$

where $\mathscr{E}_t = \{x\colon u(x) = t\}$, $\mathscr{L}_t = \{x\colon u(x) > t\}$.

Proof. Equality (2) follows from the identity

$$\int_{\tau \geqslant u > t} dx = \int_t^\tau d\xi \int_{\mathscr{E}_\xi} \frac{ds}{|\nabla u|},$$

which in turn results from Theorem 1.2.4.

Theorem. *Let Φ be a convex nonnegative function with $\Phi(0)=0$ and let Ψ be the complementary function of Φ (cf. 2.3.2). If Ω has a finite volume and*

$$\int_0^{m_n(\Omega)/2} \Psi(1/\lambda(\mu))\, d\mu < \infty, \tag{3}$$

then any function $u \in C^\infty(\Omega)$ with the finite integral (1) *is bounded.*

Proof. Let τ denote a number such that

$$2m_n(\mathscr{N}_\tau) \geqslant m_n(\Omega), \qquad 2m_n(\mathscr{L}_\tau) \leqslant m_n(\Omega),$$

where $\mathscr{N}_\tau = \{x\colon u(x) \geqslant \tau\}$. We introduce the notation

$$m(t) = m_n(\mathscr{L}_t), \qquad h(t) = s(\mathscr{E}_t).$$

By the inequality $\alpha\beta \leqslant \Phi(\alpha) + \Psi(\beta)$ with $\alpha, \beta > 0$ for $u(x) \geqslant \tau$ we have

$$u(x) - \tau = \int_\tau^{u(x)} \frac{h(t)}{m'(t)} \frac{m'(t)}{h(t)} dt$$

$$\leqslant -\int_\tau^{u(x)} \Phi\left(\frac{h(t)}{-m'(t)}\right) m'(t)\, dt - \int_\tau^{u(x)} \Psi\left(\frac{1}{h(t)}\right) m'(t)\, dt.$$

Using (2) together with Jensen's inequality, we obtain

$$-\Phi\left(\frac{h(t)}{-m'(t)}\right) m'(t) = \Phi\left[\frac{1}{\int_{\mathscr{E}_t} \frac{ds}{|\nabla u|}} \int_{\mathscr{E}_t} |\nabla u| \frac{ds}{|\nabla u|}\right] \int_{\mathscr{E}_t} \frac{ds}{|\nabla u|}$$

$$\leqslant \int_{\mathscr{E}_t} \Phi(|\nabla u|) \frac{ds}{|\nabla u|}.$$

Consequently,

$$(u(x) - \tau)_+ \leqslant \int_{\mathscr{N}_\tau} \Phi(|\nabla u|)\, dx + \int_0^{m_n(\Omega)/2} \Psi(1/\lambda(\mu))\, d\mu.$$

The similar estimate is valid for $(\tau - u(x))_+$. Therefore u is bounded and

$$\operatorname{osc} u \leqslant \int_\Omega \Phi(|\nabla u|)\, dx + 2 \int_0^{m_n(\Omega)/2} \Psi(1/\lambda(\mu))\, d\mu.$$

The next corollary follows from the theorem just proved.

Corollary. *If $\Omega \in \mathscr{J}_\alpha$, $\alpha < 1$, and*

$$\int_1^\infty \Psi(t)\, t^{-1-1/\alpha} dt < \infty ,$$

then any function $u \in C^\infty(\Omega)$ with the finite integral (1) *is bounded.*
In particular, $u \in L_\infty(\Omega)$ if

$$\int_\Omega |\nabla u|^{1/(1-\alpha)} \left(\prod_{k=1}^m \log_+^k |\nabla u| \right)^{\alpha/(1-\alpha)} (\log_+^{m+1} |\nabla u|)^r dx < \infty , \tag{4}$$

where $m \geqslant 0$, $r > \alpha/(1-\alpha)$ and $\log_+^k$ is the k-times iterated $\log_+$. (For $m = 0$ the expression in the first parentheses in (4) *is absent.)*

To prove the second assertion we must use the fact that the convex function

$$\Psi(t) = \alpha t^{1/\alpha} \left(\prod_{k=1}^m \log^k t \right)^{-1} (\log^{m+1} t)^{-r(1-\alpha)/\alpha}$$

is equivalent to the complementary function of

$$(1-\alpha)\, t^{1/(1-\alpha)} \left(\prod_{k=1}^m \log^k t \right)^{\alpha/(1-\alpha)} (\log^{m+1} t)^r$$

for large t (see Krasnosel'skiĭ and Rutickiĭ [43]).

The Sobolev theorem on the imbedding $W_p^1(\Omega) \subset C(\Omega) \cap L_\infty(\Omega)$ for $p > n$ can be refined for domains having the cone property on the basis of Corollary. Namely, if $\Omega \in \mathscr{J}_{1-1/n}$ then the continuity and the boundedness of functions in Ω result from the convergence of the integral

$$\int_\Omega |\nabla u|^n \left(\prod_{k=1}^m \log_+^k |\nabla u| \right)^{n-1} (\log_+^{m+1} |\nabla u|)^{n-1+\varepsilon} dx , \qquad \varepsilon > 0 .$$

We show that we cannot put $r = \alpha/(1-\alpha)$ in (4).

Example. Consider the domain Ω in Examples 3.3.3/1, 3.5.2, and others. By virtue of (3.3.3/1), condition (3) is equivalent to

$$\int_0^1 \Psi([f(\tau)]^{1-n}) [f(\tau)]^{n-1} d\tau < \infty .$$

Let $f(\tau) = c\tau^\beta$, $\beta \geqslant 1$. As already noted, $\Omega \in \mathscr{J}_\alpha$ with $\alpha = \beta(n-1)/(\beta(n-1)+1)$. The function $u(x) = \log_+^{m+3} x_n^{-1}$, $m \geqslant 0$, is unbounded in Ω. On the other hand, for small $x_n > 0$ we have

$$|\nabla u|^{\beta(n-1)+1}\left(\prod_{k=1}^{m+1}\log_+^k|\nabla u|\right)^{\beta(n-1)}$$

$$\leqslant c x_n^{-\beta(n-1)-1}(\log x_n^{-1})^{-1}(\log^2 x_n^{-1})^{-1}\dots(\log^{m+1}x_n^{-1})^{-1}(\log^{m+2}x_n^{-1})^{-\beta(n-1)-1};$$

therefore

$$\int_\Omega|\nabla u|^{1/(1-\alpha)}\left(\prod_{k=1}^{m+1}\log_+^k|\nabla u|\right)^{\alpha/(1-\alpha)}dx<\infty .$$

§ 5.5. On the Compactness of the Imbedding $W_p^1(\Omega)\subset C(\Omega)\cap L_\infty(\Omega)$

5.5.1. A Criterion for Compactness

Let γ_p be the function defined by (5.1.1/1) and let Ω be a domain with finite volume.

Theorem. *The condition*

(1) $$\lim_{\varrho\to+0}\gamma_p(\varrho)=\infty$$

is necessary and sufficient for the compactness of the imbedding operator of $W_p^1(\Omega)$ into $C(\Omega)\cap L_\infty(\Omega)$.

Proof. Sufficiency. From estimate (5.1.1/2) for small $\varrho>0$ it follows that

$$\|u\|^p_{L_\infty(\Omega)}\leqslant c[\gamma_p(\varrho)]^{-1}\|\nabla u\|^p_{L_p(\Omega)}+C(\varrho)\|u\|^p_{L_p(\Omega)},$$

where $C(\varrho)<\infty$ for each $\varrho>0$. We fix a small number $\varrho>0$ and we denote an open set such that $\bar\omega_\varrho\subset\Omega$, $2C(\varrho)m_n(\Omega\backslash\omega_\varrho)<1$ by ω_ϱ. Then

$$\|u\|^p_{L_\infty(\Omega)}\leqslant 2c[\gamma_p(\varrho)]^{-1}\|\nabla u\|^p_{L_p(\Omega)}+2C(\varrho)\|u\|^p_{L_p(\omega_\varrho)}\,.$$

Consider the unit ball in $W_p^1(\Omega)$ and select a sequence $\{u_m\}$ in this ball that converges in $L_p(\omega_\varrho)$. Then

(2) $$\limsup_{k,l\to\infty}\|u_k-u_l\|^p_{L_\infty(\Omega)}\leqslant 2c[\gamma_p(\varrho)]^{-1}\,.$$

Taking into account that $\gamma_p(\varrho)\to\infty$ as $\varrho\to 0$ and passing to the subsequence $\{u_{m_k}\}$ we obtain a sequence that is convergent in $L_\infty(\Omega)\cap C(\Omega)$.

Necessity. Let the imbedding operator of $W_p^1(\Omega)$ into $C(\Omega)\cap L_\infty(\Omega)$ be compact and let

(3) $$\gamma_p(\varrho)=\inf_{y\in\Omega}c_p(\Omega_\varrho(y)\backslash y)<A\,.$$

We construct a sequence ϱ_k that converges to zero and a sequence of points $y_k \in \Omega$ such that

(4) $$c_p(\Omega_{\varrho_k}(y_k) \backslash y_k) < A\,, \qquad k = 1, 2, \ldots\,.$$

Since

$$\lim_{\varrho \to 0} c_p(B_\varrho(y) \backslash y) = \infty$$

for $p > n$ (cf. 2.2.4), the limit points of the sequence $\{y_k\}$ are located on $\partial\Omega$. From (4) it follows that there exists a sequence of functions $u_k \in T_\Omega(\Omega_{\varrho_k}(y_k) \backslash y_k)$ with

$$\int_\Omega |\nabla u_k|^p dx < A\,.$$

Since $0 \leqslant u_k \leqslant 1$, this sequence is bounded in $W_p^1(\Omega)$ and hence it is compact in $C(\Omega) \cap L_\infty(\Omega)$. Therefore, given any $\varepsilon > 0$ we can find a number N such that $\|u_m - u_k\|_{L_\infty(\Omega)} < \varepsilon$ for all $m, k \geqslant N$. In particular, $|u_N(y_N) - u_k(y_N)| < \varepsilon$ for all $k > N$. On the other hand, since y_N is not a limit point of $\{y_k\}$ and $u_k(x) = 0$ outside $\Omega_{\varrho k}(y_k)$, $u_N(y_N) = 1$, then $|u_N(y_N) - u_k(y_N)| = 1$ for sufficiently large k. Thus assumption (3) is false. The theorem is proved.

Remark. Replacing $\gamma_p(\varrho)$ by $\tilde{\gamma}_p(\varrho)$, defined in Remark 5.1.1/1, in the last theorem, we obtain a necessary and sufficient condition for the compactness of the imbedding $\tilde{W}_p^1(\Omega) \subset C(\bar{\Omega})$. We actually proved in the theorem that (1) is necessary and sufficient for the compactness of the imbedding $L_p^1(\Omega) \subset C(\Omega) \cap L_\infty(\Omega)$.

5.5.2. A Sufficient Condition for Compactness in Terms of the Function λ_M

Theorem. *If integral* (5.1.2/2) *converges for some M then the imbedding operator of $W_p^1(\Omega)$ into $C(\Omega) \cap L_\infty(\Omega)$ is compact.*

Proof. The definition of the function σ_p implies

$$c_p(\Omega_\varrho(y) \backslash y) \geqslant \sigma_p(m_n(\Omega_\varrho(y)))$$

for all $y \in \Omega$. This and (5.1.2/1) yield

$$c_p(\Omega_\varrho(y) \backslash y) \geqslant \left(\int_0^{m_n(\Omega_\varrho(y))} \frac{d\tau}{[\lambda_M(\tau)]^{p/(p-1)}} \right)^{1-p}.$$

Since $m_n(\Omega_\varrho(y)) \leqslant v_n \varrho^n$, then from the definition of γ_p we obtain

$$\gamma_p(\varrho) \geqslant \left(\int_0^{v_n \varrho^n} \frac{d\tau}{[\lambda_M(\tau)]^{p/(p-1)}} \right)^{1-p}.$$

Now the required assertion follows from Theorem 5.5.1.

Example. In Example 5.1.2 we noted that for

$$\Omega = \{x: |x'| < f(x_n),\ 0 < x_n < a\}$$

condition (5.1.2/2) is equivalent to convergence of the integral (5.1.2/4). Therefore for Ω the imbedding operator of $W_p^1(\Omega)$ into $C(\Omega) \cap L_\infty(\Omega)$ is compact if and only if (5.1.2/4) is valid.

5.5.3. A Domain for Which the Imbedding Operator of $W_p^1(\Omega)$ into $C(\Omega) \cap L_\infty(\Omega)$ is Bounded but not Compact

The imbedding operator of $W_p^1(\Omega)$ into $C(\Omega) \cap L_\infty(\Omega)$ is simultaneously bounded and compact for the domain in Example 5.5.2. According to Theorems 1.4.5 and 1.4.6/2 this is also valid if Ω has the cone property.

The situation can be different with domains having "bad" boundaries. As an example we shall consider a domain for which the function γ_p is not identically zero and is bounded. Theorems 5.1.2/1 and 5.5.1 imply that for such a domain the imbedding operator of $W_p^1(\Omega)$ into $C(\Omega) \cap L_\infty(\Omega)$ is bounded without being compact.

Example. First we show that the domain depicted in Fig. 22 satisfies $\gamma_p(\varrho) \not\equiv 0$ for $p > 2$. Consider the conductor $\Omega_\varrho(y) \backslash y$ where ϱ is small enough and $y \in \Omega$. If $y \in Q$ then

$$c_p(Q_\varrho(y) \backslash y) \geqslant c\varrho^{2-p},$$

where $Q_\varrho(y) = B_\varrho(y) \cap Q$ (cf. Proposition 5.2.2) and hence

$$c_p(\Omega_\varrho(y) \backslash y) \geqslant c\varrho^{2-p}. \tag{1}$$

Let y be in the rectangle R_m and let $G = B_\varrho(y) \cap (Q \cup R_m)$. By the definition of p-conductivity,

$$c_p(\Omega_\varrho(y) \backslash y) \geqslant c_p(G \backslash y). \tag{2}$$

Take an arbitrary function $u \in T_\Omega(G \backslash y)$. Let

$$\mathscr{N}_t = \{x \in \Omega: u(x) \geqslant t\}, \qquad \mathscr{E}_t = \{x \in \Omega: u(x) = t\}.$$

We only need to consider those levels t for which $\mathscr{E}_t$ is a smooth curve. If $m_2(\mathscr{N}_t) \geqslant 2\varepsilon_m^{p'}$, where $p' = p/(p-1)$, then

$$m_2(\mathscr{N}_t \cap Q) \geqslant \varepsilon_m^{p'} \geqslant m_2(\mathscr{N}_t \cap R_m).$$

Since $Q \in \mathscr{J}_{1/2}$, then in the case $m_2(\mathscr{N}_t) \geqslant 2\varepsilon_m^{p'}$ we have

$$[s(\mathscr{E}_t)]^2 \geqslant c m_2(\mathscr{N}_t \cap Q) \geqslant \tfrac{1}{2} c m_2(\mathscr{N}_t). \tag{3}$$

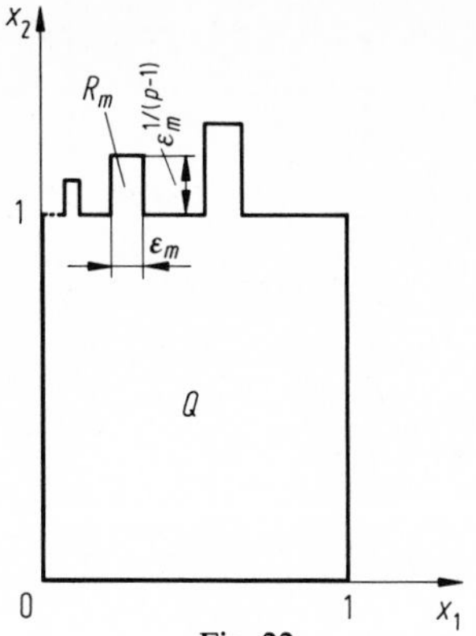

Fig. 22

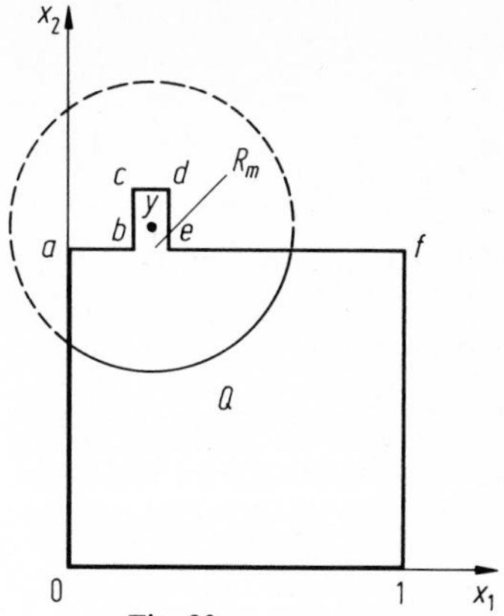

Fig. 23

Let $m_2(\mathcal{N}_t) < 2\varepsilon_m^{p'}$. If the set $\mathscr{E}_t$ contains a component connecting points of polygonal lines abc and def (Fig. 23) then we can easily see that $2s(\mathscr{E}_t) \geqslant s(\partial\Omega \cap \bar{\mathcal{N}}_t)$ and by the isoperimetric inequality we have

$$2\pi^{1/2}[m_2(\mathcal{N}_t)]^{1/2} \leqslant s(\partial\Omega \cap \bar{\mathcal{N}}_t) + s(\mathscr{E}_t) \leqslant 3s(\mathscr{E}_t)\,. \tag{4}$$

Thus either $s(\mathscr{E}_t) \geqslant \varepsilon_m$ or $[m_2(\mathcal{N}_t)]^{1/2} \leqslant c_0 s(\mathscr{E}_t)$ provided $m_2(\mathcal{N}_t) < 2\varepsilon_m^{p'}$.

Next we proceed to the estimate of $c_p(G\backslash y)$. By Corollary 4.1.3 we obtain

$$c_p(G\backslash y) \geqslant \inf\left[-\int_0^1 \frac{d}{dt} m_2(\mathcal{N}_t)\frac{dt}{[s(\mathscr{E}_t)]^{p'}}\right]^{1-p}. \tag{5}$$

We express the integral in the right-hand side of (5) as the sum of integrals over the sets A_1, A_2, A_3, where

$$A_1 = \{t\colon m_2(\mathcal{N}_t) \geqslant 2\varepsilon_m^{p'}\}\,,$$
$$A_2 = \{t\colon s(\mathscr{E}_t) \geqslant \varepsilon_m\}\backslash A_1\,,$$
$$A_3 = \{t\colon [m_2(\mathcal{N}_t)]^{1/2} \leqslant c_0 s(\mathscr{E}_t)\}\backslash A_1\,.$$

From (3) it follows that

$$\int_{A_1} \leqslant \left(\frac{c}{2}\right)^{p/2}\left[-\int_0^1 \frac{d}{dt} m_2(\mathcal{N}_t)\frac{dt}{[m_2(\mathcal{N}_t)]^{p'/2}}\right] \leqslant c_1[m_2(G)]^{(p-2)/2(p-1)}\,.$$

The integral over A_2 admits the obvious estimate

$$\int_{A_2} \leqslant \varepsilon_m^{p/(1-p)}\left[-\int_{A_2} \frac{d}{dt} m_2(\mathcal{N}_t)\,dt\right] \leqslant 2$$

and the integral over A_3 is estimated by virtue of (4) as follows:

$$\int_{A_3} \leqslant \left(\frac{3}{2\sqrt{\pi}}\right)^{p'} \left[-\int_0^1 \frac{d}{dt} m_2(\mathcal{N}_t) \frac{dt}{[m_2(\mathcal{N}_t)]^{p'/2}}\right] \leqslant c_2[m_2(G)]^{(p-2)/2(p-1)} .$$

The last three inequalities and (5) lead to $c_p(G\backslash y) \geqslant \text{const}$, which together with (2) and (1) yields the required result.

We show that the imbedding operator of $W_p^1(\Omega)$ into $C(\Omega) \cap L_\infty(\Omega)$ is not compact. We define the sequence of functions $\{u_m\}_{m\geqslant 1}$ as follows: $u_m(x_1,x_2) = \varepsilon_m^{1/(1-p)}(x_2-1)$ if $(x_1,x_2)\in R_m$, $u_m(x_1,x_2) = 0$ if $(x_1,x_2)\in Q$. These functions are uniformly bounded in $W_p^1(\Omega)$ since

$$\| \nabla u_m \|_{L_p(\Omega)} = 1 , \quad \| u_m \|_{L_p(\Omega)} = c\,\varepsilon_m^{1/(p-1)} .$$

However $\|u_m - u_k\|_{L_\infty(\Omega)} = 2$ for $m \neq k$ and the sequence $\{u_m\}$ is not compact in $C(\Omega) \cap L_\infty(\Omega)$.

§ 5.6. Generalizations to Sobolev Spaces of an Arbitrary Integer Order

5.6.1. On the (p,l)-conductivity

Let G be an open subset of the set Ω and let F be a subset of G that is closed in Ω. We define the (p,l)-conductivity of the conductor $G\backslash F$ by

$$c_{p,l}(G\backslash F) = \inf \| \nabla_l u \|_{L_p(\Omega)}^p , \tag{1}$$

where the infimum is taken over all functions $u\in C^\infty(\Omega)$ that are equal to zero on $\Omega\backslash G$ and to unity on F.

Proposition 1. *If $pl>n$, $p>1$, or $l\geqslant n$, $p=1$, then*

$$c_{p,l}(B_R\backslash \bar{B}_\varrho) \sim R^{n-pl} \tag{2}$$

for $R>2\varrho$.

Proof. If $R=1$ then (2) follows from the Sobolev inequality

$$\| u \|_{L_\infty(B_1)} \leqslant c \| \nabla_l u \|_{L_p(B_1)} , \quad u\in C_0^\infty(B_1) .$$

The general case can be reduced to $R=1$ by a similarity transformation.

Proposition 2. *If $n=pl$ and $p>1$, then*

$$c_{p,l}(B_R\backslash \bar{B}_\varrho) \sim \left(\log \frac{R}{\varrho}\right)^{1-p} \tag{3}$$

for $R>2\varrho$.

We shall establish (3) in the proof of Proposition 9.1.2/2 below.

Proposition 3. *If $pl \leqslant n$, $p>1$ or $l<n$, $p=1$ then for $R>2\varrho$,*

(4) $$c_{p,l}(B_R \backslash \bar{B}_\varrho) \sim \varrho^{n-pl} .$$

Proof. It is clear that

$$c_{p,l}(R^n \backslash \bar{B}_\varrho) \leqslant c_{p,l}^{\bullet}(B_R \backslash \bar{B}_\varrho) \leqslant c_{p,l}(B_{2\varrho} \backslash B_\varrho) .$$

It suffices to show that the rightmost and the leftmost of these functions are equivalent to ϱ^{n-pl}. A similarity transformation reduces the proof to the case $\varrho=1$ where the required assertion follows from the Sobolev inequality

$$\| u \|_{L_{pn/(n-pl)}} \leqslant c \| \nabla_l u \|_{L_p}, \quad u \in C_0^\infty .$$

In the present section we shall consider only conductors of the form $G\backslash y$ with $y \in G$. Propositions 2 and 3 along with the definition of the (p,l)-conductivity imply that $c_{p,l}(G\backslash y)$ is identically zero provided $pl \leqslant n$, $p>1$ or $l<n$, $p=1$. According to Proposition 1,

$$c_{p,l}(B_\varrho(y)\backslash y) = c\varrho^{n-pl}, \qquad c = \text{const} > 0$$

for $pl>n$, $p>1$ or for $l \geqslant n$, $p=1$.

5.6.2. The Imbedding $L_p^l(\Omega) \subset C(\Omega) \cap L_\infty(\Omega)$

Theorem. *Let Ω be a domain. The imbedding operator of $L_p^l(\Omega)$ into $C(\Omega) \cap L_\infty(\Omega)$ is continuous if and only if*

(1) $$\inf_{y \in \Omega \backslash \bar{\omega}} c_{p,l}((\Omega \backslash \bar{\omega}) \backslash y) > 0$$

for some open set ω with compact closure $\bar{\omega} \subset \Omega$.

Proof. Sufficiency. Let ω' be a bounded open set with smooth boundary and such that $\bar{\omega} \subset \omega'$, $\overline{\omega'} \subset \Omega$. Let η denote a function in $C^\infty(\Omega)$ which is equal to unity outside ω' and to zero on ω. Further, let u be any function in $C^\infty(\Omega) \cap L_p^l(\Omega)$.

We fix an arbitrary point $y \in \Omega \backslash \omega'$ for which $u(y) \neq 0$ and put $v(x) = \eta(x) u(x)/u(y)$, $x \in \Omega$. Since $v(y)=1$ and $v(x)=0$ outside the set $G = \Omega \backslash \bar{\omega}$ then

$$c_{p,l}(G \backslash y) \leqslant \| \nabla_l v \|_{L_p(\Omega)}^p .$$

Therefore

$$|u(y)|^p c_{p,l}(G\backslash y) \leqslant c \sum_{k=0}^{l} \|\nabla_l(u\eta)\|^p_{L_p(\Omega)}$$

$$\leqslant c\|\nabla_l u\|^p_{L_p(\Omega)} + C\|u\|^p_{W_p^{l-1}(\omega')} .$$

So

(2) $$\sup_{\Omega\backslash\omega'} |u|^p \leqslant c\left(\inf_{y\in G} c_{p,l}(G\backslash y)\right)^{-1} (\|\nabla_l u\|^p_{L_p(\Omega)} + C\|u\|^p_{W_p^{l-1}(\omega')}) .$$

The estimate for $|u|$ in $\overline{\omega'}$ follows from the Sobolev theorem on the imbedding of W_p^l into C for domains with smooth boundaries.

Necessity. For all $u \in C^\infty(\Omega) \cap L_p^l(\Omega)$ let the inequality

(3) $$\sup_{\Omega} |u| \leqslant C(\|\nabla_l u\|_{L_p(\Omega)} + \|u\|_{L_p(\omega)})$$

be valid, where ω is a domain with compact closure $\bar{\omega}$, $\bar{\omega} \subset \Omega$. Consider any conductor $G\backslash y$ where $G = \Omega\backslash\bar{\omega}$ and $y \in G$. The insertion of an arbitrary function $u \in C^\infty(\Omega) \cap L_p^1(\Omega)$, equal to unity at y and to zero outside G, into (3) yields

$$1 \leqslant \sup_{\Omega} |u| \leqslant c\|\nabla u\|_{L_p(\Omega)} .$$

Minimizing the last norm we obtain $c_{p,l}(G\backslash y) \geqslant C^{-p}$.

5.6.3. The Imbedding $V_p^l(\Omega) \subset C(\Omega) \cap L_\infty(\Omega)$

Now we present a direct extension of Theorem 5.1.2/1 to the space $V_p^l(\Omega)$.

Let $y \in \Omega$ and let ϱ be a positive number. Consider the conductor $\Omega_\varrho(y)\backslash y$. Further, let $pl > n$ or $l = n$, $p = 1$ and

(1) $$c^*_{p,l}(\Omega_\varrho(y)\backslash y) = \inf \sum_{k=1}^{l} \|\nabla_k u\|^p_{L_p(\Omega)} ,$$

where the infimum is taken over all infinitely differentiable functions in the class $V_p^l(\Omega)$ that are equal to zero in $\Omega\backslash B_\varrho(y)$ and to unity at y.

Theorem. *The imbedding operator of $V_p^l(\Omega)$ into $C(\Omega) \cap L_\infty(\Omega)$ is continuous if and only if*

(2) $$\inf_{y\in\Omega} c^*_{p,l}(\Omega_\varrho(y)\backslash y) \neq 0 .$$

Proof. Sufficiency. Let u be an arbitrary function in $C^\infty(\Omega) \cap V_p^l(\Omega)$ and let $y \in \Omega$ be such that $u(y) \neq 0$. Further, let

$$\inf_{y\in\Omega} c^*_{p,l}(\Omega_\varrho(y)\backslash y) > 0$$

for some ϱ and let $\eta \in C_0^\infty(B_1)$. Consider the function $v(x) = \eta((x-y)/\varrho) \cdot u(x)/u(y)$. Since $v(y) = 1$ and $v(x) = 0$ outside $\Omega_\varrho(y)$, then

$$c^*_{p,l}(\Omega_\varrho(y)\backslash y) \leqslant \sum_{k=1}^{l} \varrho^{p(k-l)} \| \nabla_k v \|^p_{L_p(\Omega)} .$$

Consequently,

$$|u(y)|^p \inf_{y\in\Omega} c^*_{p,l}(\Omega_\varrho(y)\backslash y) \leqslant c \sum_{k=0}^{l} \varrho^{p(k-l)} \| \nabla_k u \|^p_{L_p(\Omega)} .$$

Necessity. For all infinitely differentiable functions in $V^l_p(\Omega)$, let the inequality

(3) $$\sup_{\Omega} |u| \leqslant C \sum_{k=0}^{l} \| \nabla_k u \|_{L_p(\Omega)}$$

be valid. Consider any conductor $\Omega_\varrho(y)\backslash y$ with $y\in\Omega$. We insert an arbitrary function in the definition of $c^*_{p,l}(\Omega_\varrho(y)\backslash y)$ into (3). Obviously,

$$\| u \|_{L_p(\Omega)} \leqslant (v_n \varrho^n)^{1/p} \sup_{\Omega_\varrho(y)} |u| .$$

Therefore, if $\varrho < v_n^{-1/n}(2C)^{-p/n}$ then

$$\sup_{\Omega_\varrho(y)} |u| \leqslant 2C \sum_{k=1}^{l} \| \nabla_k u \|_{L_p(\Omega_\varrho(y))}$$

and so

$$1 \leqslant 2C \sum_{k=1}^{l} \| \nabla_k u \|_{L_p(\Omega_\varrho(y))} .$$

Minimizing the right-hand side over $V_\Omega(\Omega_\varrho(y)\backslash y)$ we obtain

$$c^*_{p,l}(\Omega_\varrho(y)\backslash y) \geqslant cC^{-p} .$$

The theorem is proved.

5.6.4. The Compactness of the Imbedding $L^l_p(\Omega) \subset C(\Omega) \cap L_\infty(\Omega)$

Now we present a criterion for the compactness of the imbedding $L^l_p(\Omega) \subset C(\Omega) \cap L_\infty(\Omega)$.

Theorem. *Let $m_n(\Omega) < \infty$. The imbedding operator of $L^l_p(\Omega)$ into $C(\Omega) \cap L_\infty(\Omega)$ is compact if and only if*

(1) $$\lim_{v\to\infty} \inf_{y\in G_v} c_{p,l}(G_v\backslash y) = \infty$$

for some monotone sequence of bounded open sets $\{\omega_v\}_{v\geqslant 1}$ such that $\bar\omega_v \subset \Omega$ and $\omega_v \to \Omega$. Here $G_v = \Omega\backslash\bar\omega_v$.

Proof. Sufficiency. Let ω'_v be an open set with $\bar\omega_v \subset \omega'_v$, $\overline{\omega'_v} \subset \Omega$. By (5.6.2/2) we have

$$\sup_{\Omega} |u|^p \leqslant c\left(\inf_{y\in G_\nu} c_{p,l}(G_\nu\backslash y)\right)^{-1} (\|\nabla_l u\|^p_{L_p(\Omega)} + C\|u\|^p_{W_p^{l-1}(\omega'_\nu)}) + \sup_{\omega'_\nu} |u|^p .$$

It remains to use the compactness of the imbedding of $L_p^l(\Omega)$ into $W_p^{l-1}(\omega'_\nu)$ and into $C(\overline{\omega'_\nu})$ along with the condition (1) (see the proof of sufficiency in Theorem 5.5.1).

Necessity. Suppose

$$\lim_{\nu\to\infty} \inf_{y\in G_\nu} c_{p,l}(G_\nu\backslash y) < A = \text{const} \tag{2}$$

for an increasing sequence of open sets $\{\omega_\nu\}_{\nu\geqslant 1}$. We equip $L_p^l(\Omega)$ with the norm

$$\|u\|_{L_p^l(\Omega)} = \|\nabla_l u\|_{L_p(\Omega)} + \|u\|_{L_p(\omega_1)} .$$

By (2) there exist sequences $\{y_\nu\}$ and $\{u_\nu\}$, $u_\nu \in V_\Omega(G_\nu\backslash y_\nu)$, such that $\|\nabla_l u_\nu\|_{L_p(\Omega)} < A^{1/p}$. Since the sequence $\{u_\nu\}_{\nu\geqslant 1}$ is compact in $C(\Omega)\cap L_\infty(\Omega)$ then given $\varepsilon > 0$ there exists a number N such that $\sup_\Omega |u_\mu - u_\nu| < \varepsilon$ for all $\mu, \nu > N$. Using $u_\nu(y_\nu) = 1$ we obtain

$$|u_\mu(y_\nu) - 1| < \varepsilon , \quad \mu, \nu > N . \tag{3}$$

Further, since $\omega_\mu \uparrow \Omega$, the point y_ν is contained in ω_μ for a fixed $\nu > N$ and for all large enough μ. Therefore $u_\mu(y_\nu) = 0$ which contradicts (3). The theorem is proved.

We note that we derived (1) in the proof of necessity for any monotone sequence of bounded open sets ω_ν with $\bar{\omega}_\nu \subset \Omega, \bigcup_\nu \omega_\nu = \Omega$.

5.6.5. Sufficient Conditions for the Continuity and the Compactness of the Imbedding $L_p^l(\Omega) \subset C(\Omega)\cap L_\infty(\Omega)$

We present a sufficient condition for the boundedness and the compactness of the imbedding operator of $L_p^l(\Omega)$ into $C(\Omega)\cap L_\infty(\Omega)$ which generalizes (5.1.2/2).

Theorem 1. *Let $m_n(\Omega) < \infty$, $p \geqslant 1$, l a positive number and let Ω satisfy*

$$\int_0 [\lambda(\mu)]^{pl/(1-pl)} d\mu < \infty . \tag{1}$$

Then

$$\|u\|_{L_\infty(\Omega)} \leqslant C\|u\|_{L_p^l(\Omega)} \tag{2}$$

and the imbedding operator of $L_p^l(\Omega)$ into $C(\Omega)\cap L_\infty(\Omega)$ is compact.

Proof. By Theorem 5.1.2/1

$$\|u\|_{L_\infty(\Omega)} \leqslant C(\|\nabla u\|_{L_{pl}(\Omega)} + \|u\|_{L_p(\omega)}) , \tag{3}$$

where ω is an open set, $\bar{\omega} \subset \Omega$ and C is a constant that is independent of u. From (1) it follows that $\Omega \in \mathcal{J}_\alpha$ with $1-\alpha = 1/pl$. Since $p(l-1)(1-\alpha) < 1$ and $pl = p/[1-p(l-1)(1-\alpha)]$, then according to Corollary 4.9/1

$$\text{(4)} \qquad \sum_{i=1}^{n} \left\| \frac{\partial u}{\partial x_i} \right\|_{L_{pl}(\Omega)} \leqslant C \sum_{i=1}^{n} \left(\left\| \nabla_{l-1} \frac{\partial u}{\partial x_i} \right\|_{L_p(\Omega)} + \left\| \frac{\partial u}{\partial x_i} \right\|_{L_p(\omega)} \right)$$

$$\leqslant C_1 (\| \nabla_l u \|_{L_p(\Omega)} + \| u \|_{L_p(\omega)}) \, .$$

Combining (3) and (4) we arrive at (2).

The compactness of the imbedding $L_p^l(\Omega) \subset C(\Omega) \cap L_\infty(\Omega)$ follows from (4) and Theorem 5.5.2 in which p is replaced by pl and the condition (5.1.2/1) is replaced by (1).

Theorem 2. *If Ω is a domain with finite volume contained in $\mathcal{J}_\alpha$ with $1 > \alpha > (n-1)/n$ and $pl(1-\alpha) > 1$, then for all $u \in W_p^l(\Omega)$*

$$\| u \|_{L_\infty(\Omega)} \leqslant C \| u \|_{W_p^l(\Omega)}^{1/(r+1)} \| u \|_{L_p(\Omega)}^{r/(r+1)}, \qquad r = pl(1-\alpha) - 1 \, .$$

For the proof it suffices to use Corollary 5.2.1 with p replaced by pl and then to apply (4).

Example. Let Ω be the domain in Examples 3.3.3/1, 5.1.2 and others. Then condition (1) is equivalent to

$$\int_0 [f(\tau)]^{(n-1)/(1-pl)} d\tau < \infty$$

by virtue of (3.3.3/1). In particular, for $f(\tau) = c\tau^\beta$, $\beta \geqslant 1$, the imbedding operator of $L_p^l(\Omega)$ into $C(\Omega) \cap L_\infty(\Omega)$ is compact provided $pl > \beta(n-1)+1$. If the inequality sign is replaced here by equality then the operator fails to be bounded. In fact, the function $u(x) = \log|\log x_n|$ is not in $L_\infty(\Omega)$ and belongs to $L_p^l(\Omega)$ for $pl = \beta(n-1)+1$.

5.6.6. On Imbedding Operators for the Space $W_p^l(\Omega) \cap \mathring{W}_p^k(\Omega)$, $l > 2k$

In § 1.6 we showed that for $l \leqslant 2k$ the space $W_p^l(\Omega) \cap \mathring{W}_p^k(\Omega)$ satisfies the Sobolev type theorems for arbitrary bounded domains. Here we consider the case $l > 2k$ where, according to 1.6.4, some additional requirements on Ω are necessary.

By Corollary 4.9/1 and Theorem 5.6.5/2 the inclusion $\Omega \in \mathcal{J}_\alpha$ with $(n-1)/n \leqslant \alpha < 1$ implies the compactness of the imbedding $W_p^l(\Omega) \subset W_q^m(\Omega)$ where $q^{-1} = p^{-1} - (l-m)(1-\alpha)$ if $1 > p(l-m)(1-\alpha)$, q is an arbitrary positive number if $1 = p(l-m)(1-\alpha)$ and $q = \infty$ if $1 < p(l-m)(1-\alpha)$.

Below we show that in the case $m \geqslant 2k$ the preceding result is also the best possible for the space $W_p^l(\Omega) \cap \mathring{W}_p^k(\Omega)$. We present an example of a domain

$\Omega \in \mathcal{J}_\alpha$ for which the compactness of the imbedding $W_p^l(\Omega) \cap \mathring{W}_p^k(\Omega) \subset W_q^m(\Omega)$ implies the inequality $q^{-1} \geqslant p^{-1} - (l-m)(1-\alpha)$.

Let Ω be the union of the semiball $B^- = \{x = (y, z): z < 0, |x| < 2\}$ and the sequence of disjoint semi-ellipsoids

$$e_i^+ = \{x = (y, z): z > 0,\ \delta_i^{-2\gamma} z^2 + \delta_i^{-2} |y - O_i|^2 < 1\},$$

where $0 < \gamma < 1$, $\delta_i = 2^{-i-1}$, $|O - O_i| = 3 \cdot 2^{-i}$ (see Fig. 24).

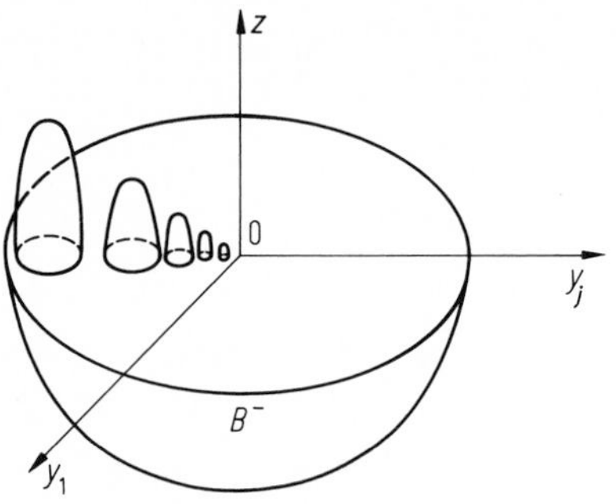

Fig. 24

In e_i^+ we define the function

$$w_i(x) = (1 - \delta_i^{-2\gamma} z^2 - \delta_i^{-2} |y - O_i|^2)^k \eta(z/\delta^\gamma),$$

where η is a smooth function on $(0, +\infty)$, $\eta(z) = 0$ near $z = 0$ and $\eta = 1$ on the halfaxis $(\frac{1}{2}, +\infty)$. We shall assume that each w_i, $i = 1, 2, \ldots$, is extended to $\Omega \backslash e_i^+$.

We can easily check that

$$\| \nabla_s w_i \|_{L_q(\Omega)} \sim \begin{cases} \delta_i^{-s+(n-1+\gamma)/q}, & s < 2k, \\ \delta_i^{2k(\gamma-1) - s\gamma + (n-1+\gamma)/q}, & s \geqslant 2k. \end{cases}$$

Let the space $W_p^l(\Omega) \cap \mathring{W}_p^k(\Omega)$ be continuously imbedded into $W_q^m(\Omega)$, $m \geqslant 2k$. Then

$$\| \nabla_m w_i \|_{L_q(\Omega)} \leqslant C \| w_i \|_{W_p^l(\Omega)},$$

or, equivalently,

$$\delta_i^{\gamma(m-l) + (1/p - 1/q)(n-1+\gamma)} \geqslant c C^{-1}.$$

Consequently, $1/q \geqslant 1/p - (l-m)(1-\alpha)$ for $\alpha = (n-1)/(n-1+\gamma)$.

Next we show that $\Omega \in \mathscr{J}_\alpha$. We introduce the sets

$$e^+ = \{\xi = (\eta, \zeta) \in R^n \colon \zeta > 0, \ \zeta^2 + \eta^2 < 1\},$$
$$\gamma^+ = e^+ \cap \{\xi \colon \zeta < \delta_i^{1-\gamma}\}.$$

Since the imbedding operator of $W_1^1(e^+)$ into $L_s(e^+)$ with $s = 1/\alpha$ is continuous then for all $v \in W_1^1(e^+)$

$$\| v \|_{L_s(e^+)} \leqslant c(\| \nabla v \|_{L(e^+)} + \delta_i^{\gamma-1} \| v \|_{L(\gamma^+)}).$$

Let $u \in W_1^1(\Omega)$. Applying the latter inequality to the function $v(\zeta) = u(\delta_i \eta + O_i, \ \delta_i^\gamma \zeta)$ we obtain

$$\|u\|_{L(e_i^+)} \leqslant c(\| \nabla u \|_{L(e_i^+)} + \delta_i^{-1} \|u\|_{L(\gamma_i^+)}),$$

where $\gamma_i^+ = \{x \in e_i^+ \colon z < \delta_i\}$. Consequently

$$\text{(1)} \qquad \|u\|_{L_s(\Omega)} \leqslant c\left(\sum_{i=1}^{\infty} \delta_i^{-1} \|u\|_{L(\gamma_i^+)} + \| \nabla u \|_{L(\Omega)} + \|u\|_{L(B^-)} \right).$$

Let γ_i^- denote the mirror image of γ_i^+ with respect to the plane $z = 0$. It is clear that

$$\delta_i^{-1} \int_{\gamma_i^+} |u| dx \leqslant \int_{\gamma_i^+ \cup \gamma_i^-} |\nabla u| dx + \delta_i^{-1} \int_{\gamma_i^-} |u| dx.$$

This and (1) imply

$$\|u\|_{L_s(\Omega)} \leqslant c\left(\| \nabla u \|_{L(\Omega)} + \int_{B^-} |u| \frac{dx}{|x|} \right).$$

Since the second summand on the right does not exceed $c \| u \|_{W_1^1(B^-)}$ then

$$\inf_{c \in R^1} \|u - c\|_{L_s(\Omega)} \leqslant c \| \nabla u \|_{L(\Omega)}$$

and the inclusion $\Omega \in \mathscr{J}_\alpha$ follows from Theorem 3.2.3.

Chapter 6. On Functions in the Space $BV(\Omega)$

In the present chapter, written together with Ju. D. Burago, we consider the space $BV(\Omega)$ of functions whose generalized derivatives are measures in the open set $\Omega \subset R^n$. We study the connection between the properties of functions in $BV(\Omega)$ and the geometric characteristics of the boundary of Ω. We find requirements on Ω in terms of "isoperimetric inequalities" which are necessary and sufficient for any function in $BV(\Omega)$ to admit an extension to R^n in the class $BV(\Omega)$ and for the boundedness of the extension operator.

We define the notion of a "trace" on the boundary for a function in $BV(\Omega)$ and give conditions for the summability of the trace. We establish some results on the relation between the "isoperimetric inequalities" and the integral inequalities (of the imbedding theorem type) for $BV(\Omega)$.

We also consider conditions for the validity of the Gauss-Green formula for functions in $BV(\Omega)$.

§ 6.1. Properties of the Set Perimeter and of Functions in $BV(\Omega)$

6.1.1. Definitions of the Space $BV(\Omega)$ and of the Relative Perimeter

The space of functions u that are locally summable in Ω, whose gradients $\nabla_\Omega u$ (in the sense of distribution theory) are charges in Ω, is called the space $BV(\Omega)$. We denote the variation of the charge over the whole domain Ω by $\|u\|_{BV(\Omega)}$. The perimeter of a set $\mathscr{E}$ relative to Ω is defined by

(1) $$P_\Omega(\mathscr{E}) = \|\chi_{\mathscr{E}\cap\Omega}\|_{BV(\Omega)},$$

where $\chi_{\mathscr{A}}$ is the characteristic function of the set $\mathscr{A}$. (We put $P_\Omega(\mathscr{E}) = \infty$ provided $\chi_{\mathscr{E}\cap\Omega} \notin BV(\Omega)$.)

Further we introduce the perimeter of $\mathscr{E}$ relative to the closed set $C\Omega = R^n \backslash \Omega$. Namely, $P_{C\Omega}(\mathscr{E}) = \inf_{G \supset C\Omega} P_G(\mathscr{E})$ where G is an open set.

If $P_{R^n}(\mathscr{E}) < \infty$ then obviously

(2) $$P_\Omega(\mathscr{E}) = \operatorname{var} \nabla_{R^n} \chi_{\mathscr{E}}(\Omega), \qquad P_{C\Omega}(\mathscr{E}) = \operatorname{var} \nabla_{R^n} \chi_{\mathscr{E}}(C\Omega),$$
$$P_\Omega(\mathscr{E}) + P_{C\Omega}(\mathscr{E}) = P_{R^n}(\mathscr{E}).$$

We also note that

$$P_\Omega(\mathscr{E}_1) = P_\Omega(\mathscr{E}_2) \tag{3}$$

if $\mathscr{E}_1 \cap \Omega = \mathscr{E}_2 \cap \Omega$.

Henceforth, whenever it causes no ambiguity, we write ∇u instead of $\nabla_\Omega u$, $\nabla_{R^n} u$ and $P(\mathscr{E})$ instead of $P_{R^n}(\mathscr{E})$.

6.1.2. Approximation of Functions in $BV(\Omega)$

The definition of the mollification operator $\mathscr{M}_h$ (cf. 1.1.5) immediately implies the following lemma.

Lemma 1. *If $u \in BV(\Omega)$ and G is an open subset of Ω with $[G]_h \subset \Omega$, where $[G]_h$ is the h-neighborhood of G, then*

$$\| \nabla \mathscr{M}_h u \|_{L(\Omega)} \leqslant \operatorname{var} \nabla u([G]_h) \,. \tag{1}$$

Lemma 2. *If $u_i \in BV(\Omega)$ and $u_i \to u$ in $L(\Omega, \text{loc})$ then*

$$\| u \|_{BV(\Omega)} \leqslant \liminf_{i \to \infty} \| u_i \|_{BV(\Omega)} \,. \tag{2}$$

Proof. It suffices to consider the case

$$\liminf_{i \to \infty} \| u_i \|_{BV(\Omega)} < \infty \,.$$

For any vector-function φ with components in $\mathscr{D}(\Omega)$ we have

$$\int_\Omega \varphi \nabla u_i dx = -\int_\Omega u_i \operatorname{div} \varphi \, dx \to -\int_\Omega u \operatorname{div} \varphi \, dx \,. \tag{3}$$

Therefore

$$\left| \int_\Omega u \operatorname{div} \varphi \, dx \right| \leqslant \sup |\varphi| \liminf_{i \to \infty} \| u_i \|_{BV(\Omega)} \,,$$

i.e., $\nabla_\Omega u$ is a charge and inequality (2) is valid.

By definition, the sequence $\{\mu_k\}_{k \geqslant 1}$ of finite charges converges to a charge μ locally weakly in Ω if, for any function $\varphi \in C(\Omega)$ with compact support,

$$\lim_{k \to \infty} \int_\Omega \varphi \mu_k(dx) = \int_\Omega \varphi \mu(dx) \,.$$

Lemma 3. *If $u_i \in BV(\Omega)$, $u_i \to u$ in $L(\Omega, \text{loc})$ and $\sup_i \| u_i \|_{BV(\Omega)} < \infty$ then*

$$\nabla_\Omega u_i \xrightarrow{\text{loc. weak.}} \nabla_\Omega u \,.$$

Proof. By Lemma 2 we have $u \in BV(\Omega)$. It remains to refer to (3) and to use the density of $\mathscr{D}(\Omega)$ in the space of continuous functions with compact supports in Ω.

Theorem. *Let $u \in BV(\Omega)$. Then there exists a sequence of functions $\{u_m\}_{m \geqslant 1}$ in $C^\infty(\Omega)$ such that $u_m \to u$ in $L(\Omega, \text{loc})$ and*

$$\lim_{m \to \infty} \int_\Omega |\nabla u_m| \, dx = \|u\|_{BV(\Omega)} .$$

If, in addition, $u \in L(\Omega)$ then $u_m \to u$ in $L(\Omega)$.

Proof. Let $\{\Omega_i\}_{i \geqslant 0}$ be a sequence of open sets with compact closures $\bar{\Omega}_i \in \Omega_{i+1}$ and such that $\bigcup_i \Omega_i = \Omega$, $\Omega_0 = \varnothing$. We choose Ω_i so that

$$\operatorname{var} \nabla u \left(\bigcup_i \partial \Omega_i \right) = 0 .$$

This can be done, for instance, in the following way. Let $\{\Omega_i'\}$ be an arbitrary sequence of open sets with compact closures such that $\bigcup_i \Omega_i' = \Omega$, $\bar{\Omega}_i' \subset \Omega$, $\partial \Omega_i' \cap \partial \Omega_j' = \varnothing$ for $i \neq j$, $\partial \Omega_i' \in C^\infty$. Let Ω_i^t denote the t-neighborhood of Ω_i'. For small t the surface $\partial \Omega_i^t$ is smooth. The set of t for which $\operatorname{var} \nabla u(\partial \Omega_i^t) \neq 0$ is finite or countable as the collection of jumps of a monotonic function. Therefore, for any i we can find an arbitrarily small number t_i such that $\operatorname{var} \nabla u(\partial \Omega_i^{t_i}) = 0$. It remains to put $\Omega_i = \Omega_i^{t_i}$.

We fix a positive integer m and choose bounded open sets D_i, G_i such that $G_i \supset \bar{D}_i \supset (\bar{\Omega}_{i+1} \backslash \Omega_i)$ and

$$\sum_i \operatorname{var} \nabla u(G_i \backslash (\bar{\Omega}_{i+1} \backslash \Omega_i)) < m^{-1} .$$

Let $\{\alpha_i\}$ be a partition of unity subordinate to the covering $\{D_i\}$ of Ω. We can find small numbers $h_i > 0$ so that $\bar{G}_i \subset [D_i]_{h_i}$ and

$$\|u - \mathcal{M}_{h_i} u\|_{L(D_i)} \max |\nabla \alpha_i| \leqslant m^{-1} 2^{-i} . \tag{4}$$

We put $u_m = \sum \alpha_i \mathcal{M}_{h_i} u$. Then $u_m \to u$ in $L(\Omega, \text{loc})$. Besides,

$$\|\nabla u_m\|_{L(\Omega)} \leqslant \sum_i \|\alpha_i \nabla \mathcal{M}_{h_i} u\|_{L(\Omega)} + \|\sum_i \mathcal{M}_{h_i} u \nabla \alpha_i\|_{L(\Omega)} . \tag{5}$$

Since $\operatorname{supp} \alpha_i \subset D_i$ then by Lemma 1 the first summand does not exceed

$$\sum_i \|\nabla \mathcal{M}_{h_i} u\|_{L(D_i)} \leqslant \sum_i \operatorname{var} \nabla u(G_i) \leqslant \sum_i \operatorname{var} \nabla u(\Omega) + m^{-1} .$$

In virtue of the equality $\sum_i \nabla \alpha_i = 0$ and (4), for the second summand on the right in (5) we have

$$\left\| \sum_i \mathcal{M}_{h_i} u \nabla \alpha_i \right\|_{L(\Omega)} = \left\| \sum_i (\mathcal{M}_{h_i} u - u) \nabla \alpha_i \right\|_{L(\Omega)}$$
$$\leqslant \sum_i \|\mathcal{M}_{h_i} u - u\|_{L(D_i)} \max_{\bar{D}_i} |\nabla \alpha_i| \leqslant \sum_{i=1}^\infty m^{-1} 2^{-i} = m^{-1} .$$

Consequently,

$$\|\nabla u_m\|_{L(\Omega)} \leqslant \operatorname{var} \nabla u(\Omega) + 2m^{-1}$$

and

$$\limsup_{m\to\infty} \|\nabla u_m\|_{L(\Omega)} \leqslant \operatorname{var} \nabla u(\Omega) .$$

The result follows from the latter inequality together with Lemma 2.

Corollary. *If $u \in BV(\Omega)$ then the functions u^+, u^-, $|u|$ are also contained in $BV(\Omega)$ and*

$$\|u^+\|_{BV(\Omega)} + \|u^-\|_{BV(\Omega)} = \||u|\|_{BV(\Omega)} = \|u\|_{BV(\Omega)} . \tag{6}$$

In fact, let $\{u_m\}$ be the sequence of functions in $C^\infty(\Omega)$ introduced in Theorem. Then $u_m^+ \to u^+$, $u_m^- \to u^-$ in $L(\Omega, \mathrm{loc})$ and

$$\|u_m^+\|_{BV(\Omega)} + \|u_m^-\|_{BV(\Omega)} = \||u_m|\|_{BV(\Omega)} = \|u_m\|_{BV(\Omega)} . \tag{7}$$

This and Lemma 6.1.2/1 imply

$$\|u^+\|_{BV(\Omega)} + \|u^-\|_{BV(\Omega)} \leqslant \|u\|_{BV(\Omega)} . \tag{8}$$

Consequently, $u^+, u^- \in BV(\Omega)$. The reverse inequality of (8) is obvious. Passing to the limit in (7) we arrive at (6).

6.1.3. Approximation of Sets with Finite Perimeter

By definition, the sequence $\{\mathscr{E}_i\}$ of sets $\mathscr{E}_i \subset \Omega$ converges to $\mathscr{E} \subset \Omega$ if $\chi_{\mathscr{E}_i} \to \chi_{\mathscr{E}}$ in $L(\Omega, \mathrm{loc})$.

Lemmas 6.1.2/2 and 6.1.2/3 imply the next lemma.

Lemma 1. *If $\mathscr{E}_k \to \mathscr{E}$ then $P_\Omega(\mathscr{E}) \leqslant \liminf_{k\to\infty} P_\Omega(\mathscr{E}_k)$ and if $\sup_k P_\Omega(\mathscr{E}_k) < \infty$ then $\nabla_\Omega \chi_{\mathscr{E}_k} \xrightarrow{\text{loc. weak.}} \nabla_\Omega \chi_{\mathscr{E}}$.*

Lemma 2. *Let $u \in L(\Omega)$ and let $\chi_{\mathscr{E}}$ be the characteristic function of the set $\mathscr{E} \subset \Omega$. Further let $\|\chi_{\mathscr{E}} - u\|_{L(\Omega)} \leqslant \varepsilon$. Then for any $t \in [\gamma, 1-\gamma]$, $\gamma > 0$, the inequality*

$$\|\chi_{\mathscr{E}} - \chi_{\mathscr{N}_t}\|_{L(\Omega)} \leqslant \varepsilon\gamma^{-1} ,$$

where $\mathscr{N}_t = \{x \colon u(x) \geqslant t\}$, is valid.

Proof. Obviously,

$$\varepsilon \geqslant \|\chi_{\mathscr{E}} - u\|_{L(\mathscr{E}\setminus\mathscr{N}_t)} + \|u - \chi_{\mathscr{E}}\|_{L(\mathscr{N}_t\setminus\mathscr{E})} \geqslant \int_{\mathscr{E}\setminus\mathscr{N}_t} (1-u(x))\,dx + \int_{\mathscr{N}_t\setminus\mathscr{E}} u(x)\,dx .$$

Since $u(x) < t$ for $x \in \mathscr{E}\setminus\mathscr{N}_t$ and $u(x) \geqslant t$ for $x \in \mathscr{N}_t\setminus\mathscr{E}$ then

$$\varepsilon \geqslant (1-t)\,m_n(\mathscr{E}\setminus\mathscr{N}_t) + t\,m_n(\mathscr{N}_t\setminus\mathscr{E}) \geqslant \gamma\|\chi_{\mathscr{E}} - \chi_{\mathscr{N}_t}\|_{L(\Omega)} .$$

Theorem. *For any measurable set $\mathscr{E} \subset \Omega$ having finite measure m_n there exists a sequence of sets $\mathscr{E}_i \subset \Omega$ for which $\partial\mathscr{E}_i \backslash \partial\Omega$ is a C^∞-smooth submanifold of R^n (however, not compact in general). Moreover, $\chi_{\mathscr{E}_i} \to \chi_{\mathscr{E}}$ in $L(\Omega)$ and $P_\Omega(\mathscr{E}_i) \to P_\Omega(\mathscr{E})$.*

Proof. If $P(\mathscr{E}) = \infty$ then the result follows. Let $P(\mathscr{E}) < \infty$. Let u_m denote the sequence constructed in Theorem 6.1.2 for $u = \chi_{\mathscr{E}}$. Since $0 \leqslant \chi_{\mathscr{E}} \leqslant 1$, the definition of u_m implies $0 \leqslant u_m \leqslant 1$. Therefore, according to Theorem 1.2.4 we have

$$\|\nabla u_m\|_{L(\Omega)} = \int_0^1 s(\mathscr{E}_t^{(m)})\,dt\,, \tag{1}$$

where $\mathscr{E}_t^{(m)} = \{x: u_m(x) = t\}$. The sets $\mathscr{E}_t^{(m)}$ are C^∞-manifolds for almost all $t \in (0,1)$ (see Corollary 1.2.2). In what follows we consider only such levels t.

Let $\varepsilon > 0$. We choose $m = m(\varepsilon)$ so large that

$$\|\chi_{\mathscr{E}} - u_m\|_{L(\Omega)} < \varepsilon\,.$$

Then by Lemma 1

$$\|\chi_{\mathscr{E}} - \chi_{\mathscr{N}_t^{(m)}}\|_{L(\Omega)} \leqslant \varepsilon^{1/2}\,, \tag{2}$$

where $\mathscr{N}_t^{(m)} = \{x: u_m(t) \geqslant t\}$ and $t \in [\varepsilon^{1/2}, 1-\varepsilon^{1/2}]$. Furthermore, for any m there exists a $t = t_m \in (\varepsilon^{1/2}, 1-\varepsilon^{1/2})$ such that

$$(1-2\varepsilon^{1/2})\,s(\mathscr{E}_{t_m}^{(m)}) \leqslant \int_0^1 s(\mathscr{E}_t^{(m)})\,dt\,. \tag{3}$$

Inequalities (2), (3) together with the equality

$$P_\Omega(\mathscr{E}) = \lim_{m\to\infty} \int_0^1 s(\mathscr{E}_t^{(m)})\,dt\,,$$

which follows from (1) and Theorem 6.1.2, imply $\chi_{\mathscr{N}_{t_m}^{(m)}} \to \chi_{\mathscr{E}}$ in $L(\Omega)$ and

$$\limsup_{\varepsilon\to 0} s(\mathscr{E}_{t_m}^{(m)}) \leqslant P_\Omega(\mathscr{E})\,.$$

Remark. If $\mathscr{E}$ is a set with compact closure $\bar{\mathscr{E}} \subset \Omega$ then the smooth manifolds constructed in the preceding theorem are compact.

6.1.4. Compactness of the Family of Sets with Uniformly Bounded Relative Perimeters

Theorem. *The collection of sets $\mathscr{E}_\alpha \subset \Omega$ with uniformly bounded relative perimeters $P_\Omega(\mathscr{E}_\alpha)$ is compact.*

Proof. By virtue of Theorem 6.1.2, for any $\mathscr{E}_\alpha$ there exists a sequence u_{α_m} that converges to $\chi_{\mathscr{E}_\alpha}$ in $L(\Omega, \text{loc})$ and is such that

$$\lim_{m\to\infty} \|\nabla u_{\alpha_m}\|_{L(\Omega)} = P_\Omega(\mathscr{E}_\alpha)\,.$$

Lemma 1.4.6 implies that the family $\{u_{\alpha_m}\}$ is compact in $L(\omega)$ where ω is an arbitrary open set with compact closure $\bar{\omega} \subset \Omega$ and with smooth boundary. Therefore the family $\{\chi_{\mathscr{E}_\alpha}\}$ is compact in $L(\omega)$.

6.1.5. Isoperimetric Inequality

Theorem. *If $\mathscr{E}$ is a measurable subset of R^n and $m_n(\Omega) < \infty$ then*

$$m_n(\mathscr{E})^{(n-1)/n} \leqslant n^{-1} v_n^{-1/n} P(\mathscr{E})\,. \tag{1}$$

Proof. It suffices to consider the case $P(\mathscr{E}) < \infty$. By Theorem 6.1.3 there exists a sequence of open sets $\mathscr{E}_i$ with C^∞-smooth boundaries $\partial\mathscr{E}_i$ such that $m_n(\mathscr{E}_i) \to m_n(\mathscr{E})$ and $s(\partial\mathscr{E}_i) \to P(\mathscr{E})$ where s is the $(n-1)$-dimensional area. Inequality (1) is valid for the sets $\mathscr{E}_i$ (cf. Ljusternik [140] and others). Passing to the limit we arrive at (1).

6.1.6. An Integral Formula for the Norm in $BV(\Omega)$

Lemma. *If u_1, u_2 are nonnegative functions in $L(\Omega)$ then*

$$\int_\Omega |u_1 - u_2|\,dx = \int_0^\infty m_n((\mathscr{L}_t^1 \setminus \mathscr{L}_t^2) \cup (\mathscr{L}_t^2 \setminus \mathscr{L}_t^1))\,dt\,,$$

where $\mathscr{L}_t^i = \{x\colon x \in \Omega,\ u_i(x) > t\}$.

Proof. It is clear that

$$\int_\Omega |u_1 - u_2|\,dx = \int_A (u_1 - u_2)\,dx + \int_{\Omega\setminus A} (u_2 - u_1)\,dx = \mathscr{I}_1 + \mathscr{I}_2\,,$$

where $A = \{x \in \Omega\colon u_1 > u_2\}$. By Theorem 1.2.3

$$\mathscr{I}_1 = \int_0^\infty m_n(\mathscr{L}_t^1 \cap A)\,dt - \int_0^\infty m_n(\mathscr{L}_t^2 \cap A)\,dt\,.$$

We note that $u_1(x) > u_2(x)$ if $x \in \mathscr{L}_t^1 \setminus \mathscr{L}_t^2$. Therefore $(\mathscr{L}_t^1 \setminus \mathscr{L}_t^2) \cap A = \mathscr{L}_t^1 \setminus \mathscr{L}_t^2$ and, similarly, $(\mathscr{L}_t^2 \setminus \mathscr{L}_t^1) \cap (\Omega\setminus A) = \mathscr{L}_t^2 \setminus \mathscr{L}_t^1$. Hence

$$\mathscr{I}_1 = \int_0^\infty m_n(\mathscr{L}_t^1 \setminus \mathscr{L}_t^2)\,dt\,.$$

In the same way we obtain

$$\mathscr{I}_2 = \int_0^\infty m_n(\mathscr{L}_t^2 \setminus \mathscr{L}_t^1)\,dt\,.$$

This completes the proof.

Theorem. *For any function u that is locally integrable in Ω we have*

(1) $$\|u\|_{BV(\Omega)} = \int_{-\infty}^{+\infty} P_\Omega(\mathscr{L}_t)\,dt\,,$$

where $\mathscr{L}_t = \{x\colon u(x) > t\}$.

Proof. By virtue of Corollary 6.1.2 we may assume $u \geqslant 0$. According to Theorem 1.2.3 for any smooth vector-function φ with compact support in Ω,

$$\int_\Omega u \operatorname{div}\varphi\,dx = \int_0^\infty dt \left(\int_\Omega \chi_{\mathscr{L}_t} \operatorname{div}\varphi\,dx \right).$$

Therefore

$$\left| \int_\Omega u \operatorname{div}\varphi\,dx \right| \leqslant \max|\varphi| \,{}_*\!\int_0^\infty P_\Omega(\mathscr{L}_t)\,dt\,,$$

where ${}_*\!\int$ is the lower Lebesgue integral. Hence

(2) $$\|u\|_{BV(\Omega)} \leqslant {}_*\!\int_0^\infty P_\Omega(\mathscr{L}_t)\,dt\,.$$

If $\|u\|_{BV(\Omega)} = \infty$ then (1) follows. Let $u \in BV(\Omega)$. Consider the sequence $\{u_m\}$ constructed in the proof of Theorem 6.1.2. Note that $u_m \geqslant 0$. Let $\{\omega_i\}$ be a sequence of open sets ω_i with compact closures $\bar{\omega}_i \subset \Omega$ and such that $\bigcup_i \omega_i = \Omega$. Since $u_m \to u$ in $L(\Omega, \mathrm{loc})$ then by Lemma we obtain

$$\int_{\omega_i} |u_m - u|\,dx = \int_0^\infty m_n(((\mathscr{L}_t^m \backslash \mathscr{L}_t) \cup (\mathscr{L}_t \backslash \mathscr{L}_t^m)) \cap \omega_i)\,dt \to 0\,,$$

where $\mathscr{L}_t^m = \{x \in \Omega\colon u_m(x) > t\}$. Therefore for almost all t and for all i

$$m_n(((\mathscr{L}_t^m \backslash \mathscr{L}_t) \cup (\mathscr{L}_t \backslash \mathscr{L}_t^m)) \cap \omega_i) \xrightarrow[m \to \infty]{} 0\,.$$

The latter means that $\mathscr{L}_t^m \to \mathscr{L}_t$ for almost all t. Hence by Lemma 6.1.3/1 we have

$${}^*\!\int_0^\infty P_\Omega(\mathscr{L}_t)\,dt \leqslant {}^*\!\int_0^\infty \liminf_{m\to\infty} P_\Omega(\mathscr{L}_t^m)\,dt \leqslant \liminf_{m\to\infty} {}^*\!\int_0^\infty P_\Omega(\mathscr{L}_t^m)\,dt\,,$$

where ${}^*\!\int$ is the upper Lebesgue integral. According to formula (1.2.4/1) the last integral is equal to $\|\nabla u_m\|_{L(\Omega)}$ and so

$${}^*\!\int_0^\infty P_\Omega(\mathscr{L}_t)\,dt \leqslant \liminf_{m\to\infty} \|\nabla u_m\|_{L(\Omega)} = \|u\|_{BV(\Omega)}\,,$$

which together with (2) completes the proof.

6.1.7. On the Imbedding $BV(\Omega) \subset L_q(\Omega)$

The contents of the present subsection are closely connected with Chapter 3. First we note that by Theorem 6.1.2 the inequality

$$\inf_{c\in R^1} \|u-c\|_{L_q(\Omega)} \leqslant C\|\nabla u\|_{L(\Omega)}, \qquad u\in L_1(\Omega),$$

implies

$$\inf_{c\in R^1} \|u-c\|_{L_q(\Omega)} \leqslant C\|u\|_{BV(\Omega)}, \qquad u\in BV(\Omega).$$

Therefore, for the domain Ω with finite volume, by Theorem 3.2.3 the last inequality (for $q\geqslant 1$) is valid for $u\in BV(\Omega)$ if and only if $\Omega\in\mathscr{J}_\alpha$, $\alpha=q^{-1}$.

In the same way we can establish theorems similar to Theorems 3.5.2/1 and 4.3.3/1 for the space $BV(\Omega)$.

By virtue of Theorem 6.1.3 the definitions of the classes $\mathscr{J}_\alpha$ and $\mathring{\mathscr{J}}_\alpha$ can be formulated in terms of the ratio

$$[m_n(\mathscr{E})]^\alpha / P_\Omega(\mathscr{E}),$$

where $\mathscr{E}$ is a measurable subset of Ω. The function λ_M introduced in 3.2.4 can be defined as the infimum of the numbers $P_\Omega(\mathscr{E})$ taken over the collection of measurable sets $\mathscr{E}\subset\Omega$ with $\mu\leqslant m_n(\mathscr{E})\leqslant M$.

Further we note that according to Lemma 3.2.1/1 for the unit ball Ω and for any $\mathscr{E}\subset\Omega$ the inequality

$$\min[m_n(\mathscr{E}), m_n(\Omega\backslash\mathscr{E})] \leqslant \tfrac{1}{2} v_n v_{n-1}^{n/(1-n)} [P_\Omega(\mathscr{E})]^{n/(n-1)} \tag{1}$$

is valid with the best possible constant.

§ 6.2. The Gauss-Green Formula for Lipschitz Functions

6.2.1. The Normal in the Sense of Federer and the Reduced Boundary

For fixed $x, \nu\in R^n$, $\nu\neq 0$ we put

$$A^+=\{y\colon (y-x)\nu>0\}, \qquad A^-=\{y\colon (y-x)\nu<0\},$$
$$A^0=\{y\colon (y-x)\nu=0\}.$$

Definition 1. The unit vector ν is called *the (outward) normal in the sense of Federer to the set* $\mathscr{E}$ *at the point* x if

$$\lim_{\varrho\to 0}\varrho^{-n} m_n(\mathscr{E}\cap B_\varrho(x)\cap A^+)=0, \tag{1}$$
$$\lim_{\varrho\to 0}\varrho^{-n} m_n(C\mathscr{E}\cap B_\varrho(x)\cap A^-)=0.$$

Definition 2. The set of those points $x\in\partial\mathscr{E}$ for which normals to $\mathscr{E}$ exist is called *the reduced boundary* $\partial^*\mathscr{E}$ *of* $\mathscr{E}$.

6.2.2. The Gauss-Green Formula

The remainder of section 6.2 contains the proof of the following assertion.

Theorem 1. *If $P(\mathscr{E}) < \infty$ then the set $\partial^*\mathscr{E}$ is measurable with respect to s and* var $\nabla\chi_{\mathscr{E}}$. *Moreover,* var $\nabla\chi_{\mathscr{E}}(\partial\mathscr{E}\backslash\partial^*\mathscr{E}) = 0$ *and for any $\mathfrak{B} \subset \partial^*\mathscr{E}$*

(1) $$\nabla\chi_{\mathscr{E}}(\mathfrak{B}) = -\int_{\mathfrak{B}} \nu(x)s(dx), \qquad \operatorname{var}\nabla\chi_{\mathscr{E}}(\mathfrak{B}) = s(\mathfrak{B}) .$$

This immediately implies the next theorem.

Theorem 2 (The Gauss-Green formula). *If $P(\mathscr{E}) < \infty$ and u is a Lipschitz function in R^n with compact support then*

(2) $$\int_{\mathscr{E}} \nabla u(x)\,dx = \int_{\partial^*\mathscr{E}} u(x)\,\nu(x)s(dx) .$$

It suffices to prove (2) for smooth functions. By the definition of $\nabla\chi_{\mathscr{E}}$ we have

$$\int_{R^n} \chi_{\mathscr{E}}\nabla u\,dx = -\int_{R^n} u\nabla\chi_{\mathscr{E}}(dx) ,$$

which together with (1) implies the result.

Remark. In particular, from Theorem 1 it follows that $P(\mathscr{E}) \leqslant s(\partial\mathscr{E})$. The case $P(\mathscr{E}) < s(\partial\mathscr{E})$ is not excluded. Moreover, the perimeter can be finite whereas $s(\partial\mathscr{E}) = \infty$. As an example it suffices to consider the plane disk B_1 from which a sequence of segments of infinite total length has been removed. In this case $\partial^*\mathscr{E} = \partial B_1$.

6.2.3. Several Auxiliary Assertions

Lemma 1. *Let the vector-charge μ concentrated on $\mathscr{E} \subset R^n$ satisfy the condition $|\mu(\mathscr{E})| =$* var $\mu(\mathscr{E})$. *Then $\mu = a\varphi$ where a is a constant vector and φ is a scalar nonnegative measure.*

Proof. Since the charge μ is absolutely continuous with respect to $\nu = \operatorname{var}\mu$ then the derivative $d\mu/d\nu = f = (f_1, \ldots, f_n)$ exists ν-almost everywhere. The equality $|\mu(\mathscr{E})| = \operatorname{var}\mu(\mathscr{E})$ implies that $|f| < 1$ is impossible on a set of positive measure ν. In fact, then we have $|\mu(E)| < \operatorname{var}\mu(E)$ for some E with $\nu(E) > 0$. Since $|\mu(\mathscr{E}\backslash E)| \leqslant \operatorname{var}\mu(\mathscr{E}\backslash E)$ then

$$|\mu(\mathscr{E})| \leqslant |\mu(E)| + |\mu(\mathscr{E}\backslash E)| < \operatorname{var}\mu(E) + \operatorname{var}\mu(\mathscr{E}\backslash E) = \operatorname{var}\mu(\mathscr{E})$$

and we arrive at a contradiction. Since $|f| \leqslant 1$ ν-almost everywhere then $|f| = 1$ ν-almost everywhere and since $|d\mu_i/d\nu| \leqslant 1$ then

$$\mu_i(\mathscr{E}) = \int \frac{d\mu_i}{d\nu}\,d\nu$$

by the absolute continuity of μ_i with respect to ν. Therefore,

$$|\mu(\mathscr{E})| = \left[\sum_i \mu_i(\mathscr{E})^2\right]^{1/2} = \left[\sum_i \left(\int_{\mathscr{E}} \frac{d\mu_i}{d\nu}\, d\nu\right)^2\right]^{1/2} = \left[\sum_i \left(\int f_i\, d\nu\right)^2\right]^{1/2}.$$

The condition $\nu(\mathscr{E}) = |\mu(\mathscr{E})|$ means that the Minkowski inequality

$$\left[\sum_i \left(\int f_i\, d\nu\right)^2\right]^{1/2} \leqslant \int \left(\sum_i f_i^2\right)^{1/2} d\nu$$

holds with the equality sign. Then the functions $x \to f_i(x)$ do not change sign and are proportional with coefficients independent of x for ν-almost all x.

Lemma 2. *If $P(\mathscr{E}) < \infty$ and the equality $\nabla \chi_{\mathscr{E}} = a\varphi$ is valid in the ball B_ϱ, where a is a constant vector and φ is a scalar measure, then, up to a set of the measure m_n zero, we have*

$$B_\varrho \cap \mathscr{E} = \{x \in B_\varrho \colon (x-y)a > 0\},$$

where y is a point in B_ϱ.

Proof. We may assume that $a = (1, 0, \ldots, 0)$. Mollifying $\chi_{\mathscr{E}}$ with radius ε we obtain

$$\frac{\partial}{\partial x_1} \mathscr{M}_\varepsilon \chi_{\mathscr{E}} \geqslant 0, \qquad \frac{\partial}{\partial x_i} \mathscr{M}_\varepsilon \chi_{\mathscr{E}} = 0 \qquad (i = 2, \ldots, m)$$

in the ball $B_{\varrho-\varepsilon}$. Hence the function $\mathscr{M}_\varepsilon \chi_{\mathscr{E}}$ does not depend on $x_2, \ldots, x_n$ and does not decrease in x_1 in $B_{\varrho-\varepsilon}$. Therefore the same is true for the limit function $\chi_{\mathscr{E}}$.

Lemma 3. *If $P(\mathscr{E}) < \infty$ then for almost all $\varrho > 0$*

$$\nabla_{B_\varrho} \chi_{\mathscr{E}}(B_\varrho) = -\frac{1}{\varrho} \int_{\mathscr{E} \cap \partial B_\varrho} x\, ds(x).$$

Proof. For all $\varrho > 0$ except at most a countable set we have $\operatorname{var} \nabla \chi_{\mathscr{E}}(\partial B_\varrho) = 0$. Suppose ϱ is not contained in that exceptional set. Let $\eta_\varepsilon(t)$ denote a piecewise linear continuous function on $(0, \infty)$ that is equal to 1 for $t \leqslant \varrho$ and vanishes for $t > \varrho + \varepsilon$, $\varepsilon > 0$.

Since

$$\int_{R^n} \chi_{\mathscr{E}}(x) [\eta_\varepsilon(|x|)]\, dx = -\int_{R^n} \eta_\varepsilon(|x|) \nabla \chi_{\mathscr{E}}(dx),$$

then

$$(1) \qquad \frac{1}{\varepsilon} \int_{B_{\varrho+\varepsilon} \setminus B_\varrho} \chi_{\mathscr{E}}(x) \frac{x}{|x|}\, dx = -\nabla \chi_{\mathscr{E}}(B_\varrho) - \int_{B_{\varrho+\varepsilon} \setminus B_\varrho} \eta_\varepsilon(|x|) \nabla \chi_{\mathscr{E}}(dx).$$

By virtue of $\operatorname{var} \nabla \chi_{\mathscr{E}}(\partial B_\varrho) = 0$ the latter integral converges to zero as $\varepsilon \to +0$. The left-hand side in (1) has limit equal to

$$\varrho^{-1} \int_{\partial B_\varrho} x s(dx)$$

for almost all ϱ. The result follows.

Lemma 4. *If $P(\mathscr{E}) < \infty$ then $P(\mathscr{E} \cap B_r(x)) < \infty$ for any $x \in R^n$ and for almost all $r > 0$. Moreover,*

$$P(\mathscr{E} \cap B_r(x)) = P_{B_r(x)}(\mathscr{E}) + s(\mathscr{E} \cap \partial B_r(x)) .$$

Proof. We assume that x is located at the origin. By Theorem 6.1.3 there exists a sequence of polyhedra Π_i such that $\Pi_i \to \mathscr{E}$ and $P(\Pi_i) \to P(\mathscr{E})$. Using the Fubini theorem we obtain $s(\Pi_i \cap \partial B_r) \to s(\mathscr{E} \cap \partial B_r)$ for almost all $r > 0$. Then

$$\limsup_{i\to\infty} P(\Pi_i \cap B_r) \leqslant \lim_{i\to\infty} P(\Pi_i) + \lim_{i\to\infty} s(\Pi_i \cap \partial B_r) = P(\mathscr{E}) + s(\mathscr{E} \cap \partial B_r)$$

and thus $P(\mathscr{E} \cap B_r) < \infty$. According to Lemma 6.1.3/1 there exists a sequence of polyhedra $\{\Pi_i\}$ such that

$$\nabla \chi_{\Pi_i \cap B_r} \to \nabla \chi_{\mathscr{E} \cap B_r}, \qquad \nabla \chi_{\Pi_i} \to \nabla \chi_{\mathscr{E}} . \tag{2}$$

Let the number r satisfy the equality

$$\limsup_{i\to\infty} \operatorname{var} \nabla \chi_{\Pi_i}(\partial B_r) = 0$$

(which can fail only for a countable set of values r). Then (2) implies

$$\nabla_{B_r} \chi_{\Pi_i} \to \nabla_{B_r} \chi_{\mathscr{E}} . \tag{3}$$

By the convergence $s(\Pi_i \cap \partial B_r) \to s(\mathscr{E} \cap \partial B_r)$ we find that the set functions μ_i defined by

$$\mu_i(\mathfrak{B}) = \int_{\partial B_r} \chi_{\mathfrak{B} \cap \Pi_i} \nu \, ds ,$$

where ν is the outward normal to B_r, weakly converge to μ, where

$$\mu(\mathfrak{B}) = \int_{\partial B_r} \chi_{\mathfrak{B} \cap \mathscr{E}} \nu \, ds .$$

Obviously, $\nabla \chi_{\Pi_i \cap B_r} = \nabla_{B_r} \chi_{\Pi_i} + \mu_i$. Passing here to the limit and taking into account (2), (3) and the weak convergence of μ_i to μ we arrive at $\nabla \chi_{\mathscr{E} \cap B_r} = \nabla_{B_r} \chi_{\mathscr{E}} + \mu$. Since the set function $\nabla_{B_r} \chi_{\mathscr{E}}$ is supported on B_r and $\operatorname{supp} \mu \subset \partial B_r$, the result follows from the latter identity.

6.2.4. The Study of the Set N

Let N denote the set of points $x \in \partial \mathscr{E}$ that satisfy the following conditions:
a) $\operatorname{var} \nabla \chi_{\mathscr{E}}(B_\varrho(x)) > 0$ for all $\varrho > 0$, b) the limit

$$\xi = \lim_{\varrho \to 0} \frac{\nabla \chi_{\mathscr{E}}(B_\varrho(x))}{\operatorname{var} \nabla \chi_{\mathscr{E}}(B_\varrho(x))}$$

exists and $|\xi| = 1$.

We at once note that the vector $\xi(x)$ exists and that $|\xi(x)| = 1$ almost everywhere with respect to the measure $\operatorname{var} \nabla \chi_{\mathscr{E}}$. Moreover,

(1) $$\nabla \chi_{\mathscr{E}}(\mathfrak{B}) = \int_{\mathfrak{B} \cap N} \xi(x) \operatorname{var} \nabla \chi_{\mathscr{E}}(dx) .$$

Lemma. *If $P(\mathscr{E}) < \infty$ and $x \in N$ then*

(2) $$\liminf_{\varrho \to 0} \varrho^{-n} m_n(\mathscr{E} \cap B_\varrho(x)) > 0 ,$$

(3) $$\liminf_{\varrho \to 0} \varrho^{-n} m_n(C\mathscr{E} \cap B_\varrho(x)) > 0 ,$$

(4) $$\limsup_{\varrho \to 0} \varrho^{1-n} P_{B_\varrho(x)}(\mathscr{E}) < \infty .$$

Proof. By the definition of ξ

$$P_{B_\varrho(x)}(\mathscr{E}) = \operatorname{var} \nabla \chi_{\mathscr{E}}(B_\varrho(x)) \leqslant 2 |\nabla \chi_{\mathscr{E}}(B_\varrho(x))|$$

for sufficiently small ϱ. By Lemma 6.2.3/3 the right-hand side of this inequality does not exceed $2s(\mathscr{E} \cap \partial B_\varrho(x))$. According to Lemma 6.2.3/1 we have

$$P(\mathscr{E} \cap B_\varrho(x)) = P_{B_\varrho(x)}(\mathscr{E}) + s(\mathscr{E} \cap \partial B_\varrho(x)) .$$

Hence

(5) $$P(\mathscr{E} \cap B_\varrho(x)) \leqslant 3s(\mathscr{E} \cap \partial B_\varrho(x)) .$$

The latter estimate together with the isoperimetric inequality (6.1.5/1) shows that

(6) $$m_n(\mathscr{E} \cap B_\varrho(x))^{(n-1)/n} \leqslant c \frac{d}{d\varrho} m_n(\mathscr{E} \cap B_\varrho(x))$$

for sufficiently small ϱ. The property a) of the set N and Lemma 6.2.3/4 imply $P(\mathscr{E} \cap B_\varrho(x)) > 0$; therefore,

$$m_n(\mathscr{E} \cap B_\varrho(x)) > 0 .$$

Since the function $\varrho \to m_n(\mathscr{E} \cap B_\varrho(x))$ is absolutely continuous then from (6) it follows that $c_1 \varrho^n \leqslant m_n(\mathscr{E} \cap B_\varrho(x))$ for almost all ϱ.

It is clear that the latter inequality is actually true for all ϱ. Thus (2) follows. Replacing $\mathscr{E}$ by $C\mathscr{E}$ in the above arguments we arrive at (3).

From (5) we have

$$P(\mathscr{E} \cap B_\varrho(x)) \leqslant c\varrho^{n-1}$$

for almost all ϱ which together with Lemma 6.2.3/1 yields

$$P_{B_\varrho(x)}(\mathscr{E}) \leqslant c\varrho^{n-1}$$

for all ϱ.

Theorem. *If $P(\mathscr{E}) < \infty$ and $x \in N$ then the normal ν at x exists and $\nu = \xi$. Moreover, for any $\varepsilon > 0$*

$$\lim_{\varrho \to 0} \varrho^{1-n} \operatorname{var} \nabla \chi_{\mathscr{E}}(B_\varrho(x) \cap [A^0]_{\varrho\varepsilon}) = v_{n-1}, \tag{7}$$

where $A^0 = \{y: (y-x)\nu = 0\}$ and $[\ ]_\varepsilon$ is the ε-neighborhood.

Proof. It suffices to check that any sequence $\varrho > 0$ contains a subsequence such that equalities (6.2.1/1) and (7) are valid. Let $\delta\mathscr{E}$ denote the set obtained from $\mathscr{E}$ by the similarity transformation with center x and coefficient δ. We may assume that x is located at the origin. Clearly, $P_{B_\varrho}(\mathscr{E}) = \varrho^{n-1} P_{B_1}(\varrho^{-1}\mathscr{E})$. By Lemma the relative perimeters $P_{B_1}(\varrho^{-1}\mathscr{E})$ are uniformly bounded. Consequently, by Theorem 6.1.4 there exists a sequence $\varrho_i > 0$ such that the sequence of sets $B_1 \cap \varrho_i^{-1}\mathscr{E}$ converges to some set D.

Moreover, Lemma 6.1.3/1 yields

$$\nabla_{B_1} \chi_{\varrho_i^{-1}\mathscr{E}} \to \nabla_{B_1} \chi_D .$$

Thus, for all $r \in (0,1)$ except at most a countable set we have

$$\nabla_{B_1} \chi_{\varrho_i^{-1}\mathscr{E}}(B_r) = \nabla \chi_{\varrho_i^{-1}\mathscr{E}}(B_r) \xrightarrow[i\to\infty]{} \nabla \chi_D(B_r) . \tag{8}$$

By definition of the set N we obtain

$$\lim_{i\to\infty} \frac{|\nabla \chi_{\varrho_i^{-1}\mathscr{E}}(B_r)|}{\operatorname{var} \nabla \chi_{\varrho_i^{-1}\mathscr{E}}(B_r)} = \lim_{i\to\infty} \frac{|\nabla \chi_{\mathscr{E}}(B_{\varrho_i r})|}{\operatorname{var} \nabla \chi_{\mathscr{E}}(B_{\varrho_i r})} = 1 .$$

Comparing the latter equalities with (8) and taking into account the semicontinuity of the variation under the weak convergence we obtain

$$|\nabla \chi_D(B_r)| = \lim_{i\to\infty} |\nabla \chi_{\varrho_i^{-1}\mathscr{E}}(B_r)| = \lim_{i\to\infty} \operatorname{var} \nabla \chi_{\varrho_i^{-1}\mathscr{E}}(B_r) \geqslant \operatorname{var} \nabla \chi_D(B_r) . \tag{9}$$

Hence by virtue of Lemmas 6.2.3/1, 6.2.3/2 we conclude that the set $D \cap B_r$ coincides with $\{y \in B_r: y\nu < b\}$ up to a set of measure m_n zero.

We show that $b = 0$. In fact, if $b < 0$ then

$$0 = m_n(D \cap B_{|b|}) = \lim_{i\to\infty} m_n(\varrho_i^{-1}\mathscr{E} \cap B_{|b|}) = \lim_{i\to\infty} \varrho_i^{-1} m_n(\mathscr{E} \cap B_{|b|}) ,$$

which contradicts (2). Similarly, $b > 0$ contradicts (3). From the convergence

$$B_r \cap \varrho_i^{-1}\mathscr{E} \to B_r \cap D = B_r \cap A^-$$

it follows that equalities of the form (6.2.1/1) are valid for the sequence $\{\varrho_i r\}$, where $\{\varrho_i\}$ is a subsequence of any given sequence $\varrho\to 0$, and r is arbitrarily close to unity. Hence (6.2.1/1) is true.

It remains to prove (7). We choose a subsequence ϱ_i such that

$$\operatorname{var} \nabla \chi_{\varrho_i^{-1}\mathscr{E}} \to \mu ,$$

where μ satisfies the inequality

$$\mu(\mathfrak{B}) \geqslant \operatorname{var} \nabla \chi_D(\mathfrak{B})$$

for any $\mathfrak{B} \subset B_1$. On the other hand, (9) implies the existence of numbers $r<1$ arbitrarily close to unity such that

$$\mu(B_r) = |\nabla \chi_D(B_r)| \leqslant \operatorname{var} \nabla \chi_D(B_r) .$$

Therefore $\mu = \operatorname{var} \nabla \chi_D$. Now for almost all $\varepsilon>0$ and $r\in(0,1)$ we have

$$\begin{aligned}\lim_{i\to\infty} (\varrho_i r)^{1-n} \operatorname{var} \nabla \chi_{\mathscr{E}}(B_{\varrho_i r} \cap [A^0]_{\varrho_i \varepsilon}) &= \lim_{i\to\infty} \operatorname{var} \nabla \chi_{\varrho_i^{-1}\mathscr{E}}(B_r \cap [A^0]_\varepsilon)\\ &= \operatorname{var} \nabla \chi_D(B_r \cap [A^0]_\varepsilon) = r^{n-1} v_{n-1}\end{aligned}$$

and (7) follows.

6.2.5. The Relations Between var $\nabla \chi_{\mathscr{E}}$ and s on $\partial\mathscr{E}$

Theorem 6.2.4 implies $\partial^*\mathscr{E} \supset N$. Moreover, since $\operatorname{var} \nabla \chi_{\mathscr{E}}(R^n \backslash N) = 0$, then $\operatorname{var} \nabla \chi_{\mathscr{E}}(R^n \backslash \partial^*\mathscr{E}) = 0$ and thus the sets $N, \partial^*\mathscr{E}$ are measurable relative to $\operatorname{var} \nabla \chi_{\mathscr{E}}$.

Next we need the following well-known assertion.

Lemma 1. *Let μ be a measure in R^n and, for all points x in the μ-measurable set $\mathfrak{B}$, suppose the following inequality is valid:*

$$\limsup_{\varrho\to 0} \varrho^{1-n} \mu(B_\varrho(x)) \geqslant \beta > 0 ,$$

where β does not depend on x. Then $\beta s(\mathfrak{B}) \leqslant c(n)\mu(\mathfrak{B})$.

Proof. For any $\varepsilon>0$ there exists an open set G such that $\mu(G\backslash\mathfrak{B}) + \mu(\mathfrak{B}\backslash G) < \varepsilon$. By the definition of Hausdorff measure, given $\varepsilon>0$ there exists a $\delta>0$ such that

(1) $$s(G) \leqslant c_1(n) \sum \varrho_i^{n-1} + \varepsilon$$

for any covering of G by balls B_{ϱ_i}, $\varrho_i < \delta$. For any $x\in\mathfrak{B}\cap G$ consider the family of balls $B_\varrho(x) \subset G$, $3\varrho<\delta$, such that

(2) $$\varrho^{1-n} \mu(B_\varrho(x)) \geqslant \beta/2 .$$

According to Theorem 1.2.1/1 there exists a sequence of mutually disjoint balls $B_{\varrho_i}(x_i)$ satisfying the condition $\bigcup_i B_{3\varrho_i}(x_i) \supset \mathfrak{B} \cap G$. Then

$$\sum \mu(B_{\varrho_i}(x_i)) \leqslant \mu(G) \leqslant \mu(\mathfrak{B}) + \varepsilon .$$

By virtue of (1) and (2) we have

$$s(G) \leqslant c_1(n) \sum (3\varrho_i)^{n-1} + \varepsilon \leqslant c_2(n) \sum \varrho_i^{n-1} + \varepsilon$$
$$\leqslant c_2(n)\,\beta^{-1} \sum \mu(B_{\varrho_i}(x_i)) + \varepsilon \leqslant c_3(n)\,\beta^{-1}(\mu(\mathfrak{B}) + \varepsilon) + \varepsilon .$$

The definition 6.2.1/1 and the Fubini theorem imply the following lemma.

Lemma 2. *If $P(\mathscr{E}) < \infty$ and $x \in \partial^* \mathscr{E}$ then*

$$\liminf_{\varrho \to 0} \varrho^{1-n} s(\mathscr{E} \cap \partial B_\varrho(x) \cap A^+) = 0 ,$$

where the lower limit is taken over any subset of measure 1 *in the interval* $0 < \varrho < 1$.

Lemma 3. *If $P(\mathscr{E}) < \infty$ and $x \in \partial^* \mathscr{E}$ then*

$$\limsup_{\varrho \to 0} \varrho^{1-n} \operatorname{var} \nabla \chi_{\mathscr{E}}(B_\varrho(x)) \geqslant v_{n-1} .$$

Proof. Let Q be a subset of the interval $0 < \varrho < 1$ on which the identity in Lemma 6.2.3/3 is valid. By Lemmas 6.2.3/3 and 2 we have

$$\limsup_{\varrho \to 0} \varrho^{1-n} \operatorname{var} \nabla \chi_{\mathscr{E}}(B_\varrho(x)) \geqslant \limsup_{\varrho \to 0} \varrho^{1-n} |\nabla \chi_{\mathscr{E}}(B_\varrho(x))|$$
$$\geqslant \limsup_{Q \ni \varrho \to 0} \varrho^{-n} \Big| \int_{\mathscr{E} \cap \partial B_\varrho(x)} x\, ds \Big|$$
$$= \lim_{\varrho \to 0} \varrho^{-n} \Big| \int_{A^- \cap \partial B_\varrho(x)} x\, ds \Big| = v_{n-1} .$$

The result follows.

Taking into account the equality $\operatorname{var} \nabla \chi_{\mathscr{E}}(\partial^* \mathscr{E} \backslash N) = 0$, from Lemmas 1 and 3 we obtain the next assertion.

Lemma 4. *If $P(\mathscr{E}) < \infty$ then $s(\partial^* \mathscr{E} \backslash N) = 0$.*

Now to prove Theorem 6.2.2/1 it suffices to verify that the vector-measures $v\, ds$ and $\operatorname{var} \nabla \chi_{\mathscr{E}}(dx)$ coincide on N.

Lemma 5. *Let $P(\mathscr{E}) < \infty$ and let the set $\mathfrak{B} \cap N$ be measurable relative to* $\operatorname{var} \nabla \chi_{\mathscr{E}}$. *Then $s(\mathfrak{B}) \geqslant \operatorname{var} \nabla \chi_{\mathscr{E}}(\mathfrak{B})$.*

Proof. The function

$$x \to f_\varrho(x) = v_{n-1}^{-1} \varrho^{1-n} \operatorname{var} \nabla \chi_{\mathscr{E}}(B_\varrho(x))$$

is lower semicontinuous. This is a consequence of the relation

$$B_\varrho(x)\setminus B_\varrho(x_1)\to\varnothing \qquad \text{as } x_1\to x\,.$$

Therefore $f_\varrho(x)$ is measurable. Let $\varrho_i\to 0$. By Theorem 6.2.4 the sequence f_{ϱ_i} converges to $f(x)\equiv 1$ on N. By the Egorov theorem, for any $\varepsilon>0$ there exists a set $N_\varepsilon\subset N$ such that $\operatorname{var}\nabla\chi_{\mathscr{E}}(N_\varepsilon)<\varepsilon$ and the sequence f_{ϱ_i} converges uniformly on $N\setminus N_\varepsilon$. Therefore there exists a $\delta>0$ such that

$$\operatorname{var}\nabla\chi_{\mathscr{E}}(B_r(x))\leqslant(1+\varepsilon)\,v_{n-1}r^{n-1} \tag{3}$$

for all $x\in N\setminus N_\varepsilon$ and $r\in(0,\delta)$.

By definition of the measure s there exists a finite covering of $N\setminus N_\varepsilon$ by balls $B_{r_i}(x_i)$, $r_i<\delta$, such that

$$(1+\varepsilon)\,s(\mathfrak{B}\cap(N\setminus N_\varepsilon))\geqslant v_{n-1}\sum r_i^{n-1}\,.$$

This and (3) imply

$$\begin{aligned}\operatorname{var}\nabla\chi_{\mathscr{E}}(\mathfrak{B})&\leqslant\varepsilon+\operatorname{var}\nabla\chi_{\mathscr{E}}(\mathfrak{B}\cap(N\setminus N_\varepsilon))\\&\leqslant\varepsilon+\sum_i\operatorname{var}\nabla\chi_{\mathscr{E}}(B_{r_i}(x))\leqslant\varepsilon+(1+\varepsilon)\,v_{n-1}\sum_i r_i^{n-1}\\&\leqslant\varepsilon+(1+\varepsilon)^2 s(\mathfrak{B}\cap(N\setminus N_\varepsilon))\leqslant\varepsilon+(1+\varepsilon)^2 s(\mathfrak{B})\,.\end{aligned}$$

The result follows since ε is arbitrary.

The next assertion is a modification of the classical Vitali-Carathéodory covering theorem.

Lemma 6. *Let μ be a finite measure in R^n concentrated on a set $\mathscr{E}$. Further, let $\mathfrak{M}$ be a family of closed balls having the following property: for each point $x\in\mathscr{E}$ there exists a $\delta(x)>0$ such that $B_r(x)\in\mathfrak{M}$ for all $r<\delta(x)$ and*

$$\alpha r^k<\mu(B_r(x))\leqslant\beta r^k \tag{4}$$

for some $k>0$, where $B_r(x)$ is any ball in $\mathfrak{M}$ and α, β are positive constants that are independent of r and x. Then there exists at most a countable family of mutually disjoint balls $\mathscr{B}^{(i)}\in\mathfrak{M}$ such that $\mu(\mathscr{E}\setminus\bigcup_i\mathscr{B}^{(i)})=0$.

Proof. We fix a number $a>1$ and construct a sequence of balls $\mathscr{B}^{(i)}\in\mathfrak{M}$ in the following way.

Suppose that $\mathscr{B}^{(1)},\dots,\mathscr{B}^{(j-1)}$ have already been specified. Then we choose $\mathscr{B}^{(j)}$ to satisfy

$$\mathscr{B}^{(j)}\cap\mathscr{B}^{(i)}=\varnothing \qquad \text{for } i<j\,,$$

$$a\mu(\mathscr{B}^{(j)})\geqslant\sup\{\mu(B_r(x)\colon B_r(x)\cap\mathscr{B}^{(i)}=\varnothing,\ 1\leqslant i<j\}.$$

If the process breaks at some j then $\mathscr{E} \subset \bigcup_{i=1}^{j} \mathscr{B}^{(i)}$ and the lemma is proved.

Suppose the sequence $\{\mathscr{B}^{(i)}\}$ is infinite. Let $\mathscr{C}^{(i)}$ denote the closed ball concentric to $\mathscr{B}^{(i)}$ with radius $R_i = Qr_i$ where r_i is the radius of $\mathscr{B}^{(i)}$ and the constant $Q \in (1, \infty)$ will be specified later. Note that from the very beginning we could have constructed the sequence $\{\mathscr{B}^{(i)}\}$ so that $\mathscr{C}^{(i)}$ is contained in $\mathfrak{M}$ simultaneously with $\mathscr{B}^{(i)}$.

We show that

(5)
$$\mathscr{E} \subset \mathscr{E} \cap \left[\left(\bigcup_{i=1}^{j-1} \mathscr{B}^{(i)}\right) \cup \left(\bigcup_{i=j}^{\infty} \mathscr{C}^{(i)}\right)\right]$$

for some Q and for all j. In fact, let $x \in \mathscr{E} \setminus \bigcup_{i=1}^{j-1} \mathscr{B}^{(i)}$. Then there exists a ball $\mathscr{B} \in \mathfrak{M}$ centered at x such that $\mathscr{B} \cap \mathscr{B}^{(i)} = \varnothing$ for $i < j$. Note that we have $\mathscr{B} \cap \mathscr{B}^{(p)} \neq \varnothing$ for some $p \geqslant j$. Indeed, if $\mathscr{B} \cap \mathscr{B}^{(p)} = \varnothing$ for all p then the constructed sequence $\{\mathscr{B}^{(i)}\}$ satisfies $\mu(\mathscr{B}) \leqslant a\mu(\mathscr{B}^{(p)})$. Since the balls $\mathscr{B}^{(p)}$ are mutually disjoint, the latter inequality contradicts the finiteness of the measure μ.

Let the number p be such that $\mathscr{B} \cap \mathscr{B}^{(i)} = \varnothing$ for $i < p$ and $\mathscr{B} \cap \mathscr{B}^{(p)} \neq \varnothing$. Inequalities $\mu(\mathscr{B}) \leqslant a\mu(\mathscr{B}^{(p)})$ and (4) imply the estimates

$$\alpha r^k \leqslant \mu(\mathscr{B}) \leqslant a\mu(\mathscr{B}^{(p)}) \leqslant a\beta r_p^k ,$$

where r is the radius of $\mathscr{B}$. Since the balls $\mathscr{B}$ and $\mathscr{B}^{(p)}$ are disjoint, the distance between their centers satisfies

$$d \leqslant r + r_p \leqslant r_p(1 + (a\beta/\alpha)^{1/k}) .$$

Let the constant Q be equal to $1 + (a\beta/\alpha)^{1/k}$. Then $d \leqslant R_p$ and hence $x \in \mathscr{C}^{(p)}$. The inclusion (5) follows.

It remains to note that

$$\mu\left(\mathscr{E} \setminus \bigcup_{i=1}^{j-1} \mathscr{B}^{(i)}\right) \leqslant \sum_{i=j}^{\infty} \mu(\mathscr{C}^{(i)}) \leqslant \beta \sum_{i=j}^{\infty} R_i^k \leqslant \beta Q^k \sum_{i=j}^{\infty} r_i^k \leqslant \frac{\beta Q^k}{\alpha} \sum_{i=j}^{\infty} \mu(\mathscr{B}^{(i)}) .$$

Since the series $\sum_{i=1}^{\infty} \mu(\mathscr{B}^{(i)})$ converges then

$$\mu\left(\mathscr{E} \setminus \bigcup_{i=1}^{j-1} \mathscr{B}^{(i)}\right) \to 0 \quad \text{as } j \to \infty .$$

Lemma 7. *If $P(\mathscr{E}) < \infty$ and $\mathfrak{B}$ is a subset of N that is measurable with respect to* var $\nabla \chi_{\mathscr{E}}$, *then $\mathfrak{B}$ is s-measurable and*

(6)
$$s(\mathfrak{B}) \leqslant \operatorname{var} \nabla \chi_{\mathscr{E}}(\mathfrak{B}) .$$

Proof. By Theorem 6.2.4, for any $\varepsilon \in (0,1)$ the measure $\mu = \operatorname{var} \nabla \chi_{\mathscr{E}}$ satisfies the conditions of Lemma 6 with $\alpha = v_{n-1}(1-\varepsilon)$, $\beta = v_{n-1}(1+\varepsilon)$, $k = n-1$.

By the definition of Hausdorff measure, given any ε there exists a $\delta > 0$ such that

$$s(\mathfrak{B}) \leqslant v_{n-1} \sum r_i^{n-1} + \varepsilon$$

for any finite covering of $\mathfrak{B}$ by balls $B_{r_i}(x_i)$ with $r_i < \delta$.

Let $\{\mathscr{B}^{(i)}\}$ be the sequence of closed balls in Lemma 6. We assume their radii to be less than δ. We choose a finite subsequence $\{\mathscr{B}^{(i)}\}_{i=1}^{q}$ such that

$$\mu\left(\mathfrak{B} \setminus \bigcup_{i=1}^{q} \mathscr{B}^{(i)}\right) < \varepsilon .$$

As was shown in the proof of Lemma 1, there exists a finite collection of disjoint open balls $\mathscr{C}^{(j)}$ with radii $\varrho_j < \delta$ such that $\mu\left(\bigcup_j \mathscr{C}^{(j)}\right) < \varepsilon$ and the concentric balls $3\,\mathscr{C}^{(j)}$ with radii $3\varrho_j$ form a covering of $\mathfrak{B} \setminus \bigcup_{i \leqslant q} \mathscr{B}^{(i)}$. Thus

$$\bigcup_j 3\,\mathscr{C}^{(j)} \cup \left(\bigcup_{i \leqslant q} \mathscr{B}^{(i)}\right) \supset \mathfrak{B} .$$

Now we have

$$s(\mathfrak{B}) \leqslant v_{n-1}\left(3 \sum_j \varrho_j^{n-1} + \sum_{i \leqslant q} r_i^{n-1}\right) + \varepsilon ,$$

where r_i is the radius of $\mathscr{B}^{(i)}$. Hence

$$s(\mathfrak{B}) \leqslant (1+\varepsilon)\left[c \sum_j \mu(\mathscr{B}^{(j)}) + \sum_{i \leqslant q} \mu(\mathscr{C}^{(i)})\right] + \varepsilon \leqslant (1+\varepsilon)(c\varepsilon + \mu(\mathfrak{B})) + \varepsilon$$

and (6.2.5/6) follows because ε is arbitrary.

Since inequality (6.2.5/6) is valid for all μ-measurable sets, this implies that $\mathfrak{B}$ is s-measurable.

Combining Lemmas 4, 5, 7, we arrive at Theorem 6.2.2/1.

§ 6.3. On the Extension of Functions in $BV(\Omega)$ onto the Whole Space

With any set $\mathscr{E} \subset \Omega$ we associate the value

$$\tau_\Omega(\mathscr{E}) = \inf_{\mathfrak{B} \cap \Omega = \mathscr{E}} P_{C\Omega}(\mathfrak{B}) .$$

It is clear that $\tau_\Omega(\mathscr{E}) = \tau_\Omega(\Omega \setminus \mathscr{E})$.

Theorem. a) *If for any function $u \in BV(\Omega)$ there exists an extension $\hat{u} \in BV(R^n)$ such that*

(1) $$\|\hat{u}\|_{BV(R^n)} \leqslant C \|u\|_{BV(\Omega)},$$

where C is a constant that is independent of u, then

(2) $$\tau_\Omega(\mathscr{E}) \leqslant (C-1) P_\Omega(\mathscr{E})$$

for any set $\mathscr{E} \subset \Omega$.

b) *Conversely, if for any $\mathscr{E} \subset \Omega$ inequality* (2) *is valid with a constant C that is independent of $\mathscr{E}$, then for any $u \in BV(\Omega)$ there exists an extension $\hat{u} \in BV(R^n)$ for which* (1) *is true.*

6.3.1. Proof of the Necessity of Condition (6.3/2)

Inequality (6.3/2) is trivial provided $P_\Omega(\mathscr{E}) = \infty$. Let $P_\Omega(\mathscr{E}) < \infty$. By hypothesis there exists an extension $\hat{\chi}_{\mathscr{E}}$ of the characteristic function $\chi_{\mathscr{E}}$ such that

$$\|\hat{\chi}_{\mathscr{E}}\|_{BV(R^n)} \leqslant C P_\Omega(\mathscr{E}).$$

This and formula (6.1.6/1) imply

$$C P_\Omega(\mathscr{E}) \geqslant \int_{-\infty}^{\infty} P_{R^n}(\{x: \hat{\chi}_{\mathscr{E}} > t\})\, dt \geqslant \int_0^1 P_{R^n}(\{x: \hat{\chi}_{\mathscr{E}} > t\})\, dt.$$

Since $\{x: \hat{\chi}_{\mathscr{E}}(x) > t\} \cap \Omega = \mathscr{E}$ for $t \in (0,1)$ then, taking (6.1.1/2) and (6.1.1/3) into account, we obtain

$$C P_\Omega(\mathscr{E}) \geqslant \inf_{\mathfrak{B} \cap \Omega = \mathscr{E}} P_{R^n}(\mathfrak{B}) \geqslant \inf_{\mathfrak{B} \cap \Omega = \mathscr{E}} P_\Omega(\mathfrak{B}) + \inf_{\mathfrak{B} \cap \Omega = \mathscr{E}} P_{C\Omega}(\mathfrak{B}) \geqslant P_\Omega(\mathscr{E}) + \tau_\Omega(\mathscr{E});$$

hence (6.3/2) follows.

6.3.2. Three Lemmas on $P_{C\Omega}(\mathscr{E})$

To prove the sufficiency of (6.3/2) we need the following three auxiliary assertions.

Lemma 1. *If $\mathfrak{B} \subset \Omega$, $\tau_\Omega(\mathfrak{B}) < \infty$, $P_\Omega(\mathfrak{B}) < \infty$ then there exists a set $\mathscr{E} \subset R^n$ such that $\mathscr{E} \cap \Omega = \mathfrak{B}$ and*

(1) $$P_{C\Omega}(\mathscr{E}) = \tau_\Omega(\mathfrak{B}).$$

Proof. Let $\{\mathscr{E}_i\}$ be a sequence of subsets of R^n such that $\mathscr{E}_i \cap \Omega = \mathfrak{B}$ and

(2) $$\lim_{i\to\infty} P_{C\Omega}(\mathscr{E}_i) = \tau_\Omega(\mathfrak{B}) .$$

By virtue of (2) $\sup_i P_{C\Omega}(\mathscr{E}_i) < \infty$ and, since $P_\Omega(\mathscr{E}_i) = P_\Omega(\mathfrak{B}) < \infty$ then $\sup_i P_{R^n}(\mathscr{E}_i) < \infty$. Hence from Theorem 6.1.4 it follows that there exists a subsequence (for which we retain the notation $\{\mathscr{E}_i\}$) that converges to some set $\mathscr{E}$. By Lemma 6.1.3/1 we have $P(\mathscr{E}) \leqslant \liminf_{i\to\infty} P(\mathscr{E}_i)$. Taking into account that $\mathscr{E} \cap \Omega = \mathfrak{B}$ as well as equalities (6.1.1/2) and (6.1.1/3), we obtain

(3) $$P_{C\Omega}(\mathscr{E}) \leqslant \lim_{i\to\infty} P_{C\Omega}(\mathscr{E}_i) = \tau_\Omega(\mathfrak{B}) .$$

By comparing (6.3.2/3) with the definition of $\tau_\Omega(\mathfrak{B})$ we arrive at (6.3.2/1).

Lemma 2. *Let $\mathscr{E}_1, \mathscr{E}_2$ be measurable subsets of R^n. Then*

(4) $$P_{C\Omega}(\mathscr{E}_1 \cap \mathscr{E}_2) + P_{C\Omega}(\mathscr{E}_1 \cup \mathscr{E}_2) \leqslant P_{C\Omega}(\mathscr{E}_1) + P_{C\Omega}(\mathscr{E}_2) .$$

Proof. Let G be an open set, $G \supset C\Omega$. Then by (6.1.6/1)

(5) $$\begin{aligned} P_G(\mathscr{E}_1) + P_G(\mathscr{E}_2) &\geqslant \|(\chi_{\mathscr{E}_1} + \chi_{\mathscr{E}_2})\|_{BV(G)} \\ &= \int_{-\infty}^{\infty} P_G(\{x: \chi_{\mathscr{E}_1} + \chi_{\mathscr{E}_2} > t\})\, dt \\ &= \int_0^1 P_G(\{\chi_{\mathscr{E}_1} + \chi_{\mathscr{E}_2} > t\})\, dt + \int_1^2 P_G(\{\chi_{\mathscr{E}_1} + \chi_{\mathscr{E}_2} > t\})\, dt \\ &= P_G(\mathscr{E}_1 \cup \mathscr{E}_2) + P_G(\mathscr{E}_1 \cap \mathscr{E}_2) . \end{aligned}$$

Consider the sequence of open sets G_i such that $G_{i+1} \subset G_i$ and $\bigcap_i G_i = C\Omega$. Since $P_{C\Omega}(\mathscr{E}_k) = \lim_{i\to\infty} P_{G_i}(\mathscr{E}_k)$, $k = 1, 2$, then applying (5) we obtain (4).

Lemma 3. *Let $P_{C\Omega}(\mathscr{E}_k) < \infty$, $k = 1, 2$. We put $\mathfrak{B}_k = \mathscr{E}_k \cap \Omega$. Then*

$$P_{C\Omega}(\mathscr{E}_1 \cap \mathscr{E}_2) = P_{C\Omega}(\mathscr{E}_1) , \qquad P_{C\Omega}(\mathscr{E}_1 \cup \mathscr{E}_2) = P_{C\Omega}(\mathscr{E}_2)$$

provided $\mathfrak{B}_1 \subset \mathfrak{B}_2$ and

(6) $$P_{C\Omega}(\mathscr{E}_k) = \tau_\Omega(\mathfrak{B}_k) , \qquad k = 1, 2 .$$

Proof. Since $\mathscr{E}_1 \cap \mathscr{E}_2 \cap \Omega = \mathfrak{B}_1$ and $(\mathscr{E}_1 \cup \mathscr{E}_2) \cap \Omega = \mathfrak{B}_2$ then by the definition of τ_Ω we have

(7) $$\tau_\Omega(\mathfrak{B}_1) \leqslant P_{C\Omega}(\mathscr{E}_1 \cap \mathscr{E}_2) , \qquad \tau_\Omega(\mathfrak{B}_2) \leqslant P_{C\Omega}(\mathscr{E}_1 \cup \mathscr{E}_2) .$$

Using (6) we can rewrite (4) as

$$P_{C\Omega}(\mathscr{E}_1 \cap \mathscr{E}_2) + P_{C\Omega}(\mathscr{E}_1 \cup \mathscr{E}_2) \leqslant \tau_\Omega(\mathfrak{B}_1) + \tau_\Omega(\mathfrak{B}_2),$$

which together with (7) proves the lemma.

6.3.3. Proof of the Sufficiency of Condition (6.3/2)

1°. *Plan of the proof.* Starting from $\mathscr{N}_t = \{x: u(x) \geqslant t\}$ we construct the family of sets $\mathfrak{B}_t$ satisfying the conditions $\mathfrak{B}_t \cap \Omega = \mathscr{N}_t$, $P_{C\Omega}(\mathfrak{B}_t) = \tau_\Omega(\mathscr{N}_t)$, $\mathfrak{B}_t \subset \mathfrak{B}_\tau$ for $t > \tau$.

We first construct $\mathfrak{B}_t$ for a countable set $\{t_i\}$ which is everywhere dense on $(-\infty, \infty)$ (item 2°) and then for all other t (item 3°). Finally, in item 4° we introduce the function $\hat{u}(x) = \sup\{t: x \in \mathfrak{B}_t\}$ and prove that $\hat{u}(x)$ satisfies the conditions of Theorem 6.3.

2°. Since $u \in BV(\Omega)$ then for almost all t we have $P_\Omega(\mathscr{N}_t) < \infty$ by virtue of formula (6.1.6/1). Therefore, we can choose a countable set $\{t_i\}$, $t_i \neq t_j$ for $i \neq j$, which is everywhere dense on $(-\infty, \infty)$ and satisfies $P_\Omega(\mathscr{N}_{t_i}) < \infty$. From (6.3/2) it follows that $\tau_\Omega(\mathscr{N}_{t_i}) < \infty$.

We construct a sequence of sets $\mathfrak{B}_{t_i}$, $i = 1, 2, \ldots$, such that

$$1)\quad \mathfrak{B}_{t_i} \cap \Omega = \mathscr{N}_{t_i},$$

$$2)\quad P_{C\Omega}(\mathfrak{B}_{t_i}) = \tau_\Omega(\mathscr{N}_{t_i}),$$

$$3)\quad \mathfrak{B}_{t_i} \subset \mathfrak{B}_{t_j}, \qquad t_i > t_j.$$

According to Lemma 6.3.2/1 there exists a set $\mathfrak{B}_{t_1}$ satisfying the conditions 1) – 2). Suppose the sets $\mathfrak{B}_{t_1}, \ldots, \mathfrak{B}_{t_n}$ have already been constructed so that the conditions 1) – 3) are fulfilled for $i, j = 1, \ldots, n-1$. By Lemma 6.3.2/1 there exists a set $\mathfrak{B}^{(n)}$ satisfying 1) and 2). Let t_* be the largest of those numbers t_i, $i = 1, \ldots, n-1$, for which $t_i < t_n$, and let t^* be the smallest of those numbers t_i, $i = 1, \ldots, n-1$, for which $t_n < t_i$. We put

$$\mathfrak{B}_{t_n} = (\mathfrak{B}^{(n)} \cap \mathfrak{B}_{t_*}) \cup \mathfrak{B}_{t^*}.$$

It is clear that $\mathfrak{B}_{t_*} \supset \mathfrak{B}_{t_n} \supset \mathfrak{B}_{t^*}$. So $\mathfrak{B}_{t_n} \subset \mathfrak{B}_{t_i}$ for $t_n > t_i$ and $\mathfrak{B}_{t_n} \supset \mathfrak{B}_{t_i}$ for $t_n < t_i$, $i = 1, \ldots, n-1$. Since

$$\mathfrak{B}^{(n)} \cap \Omega = \mathscr{N}_{t_n}, \qquad \mathfrak{B}_{t_*} \cap \Omega = \mathscr{N}_{t_*} \supset \mathscr{N}_{t_n}, \qquad \mathfrak{B}_{t^*} \cap \Omega = \mathscr{N}_{t^*} \subset \mathscr{N}_{t_n}$$

then $\mathfrak{B}_{t_n} \cap \Omega = \mathscr{N}_{t_n}$. Applying Lemma 6.3.2/3 to the sets $\mathfrak{B}^{(n)}$, $\mathfrak{B}_{t_*}$ and then to the sets $\mathfrak{B}^{(n)} \cap \mathfrak{B}_{t_*}$, $\mathfrak{B}_{t^*}$ we obtain

$$P_{C\Omega}(\mathfrak{B}_{t_n}) = \tau_\Omega(\mathscr{N}_{t_n}).$$

Thus the collection of sets $\mathfrak{B}_{t_1}, \ldots, \mathfrak{B}_{t_n}$ satisfies the conditions 1) – 3) for $i, j = 1, \ldots, n$.

3°. Let $t \notin \{t_i\}$. From the set $\{t_i\}$ we select two monotone sequences $\{\alpha_i\}$, $\{\beta_i\}$ such that $\alpha_i < t < \beta_i$ and $\lim_{i\to\infty} \alpha_i = \lim_{i\to\infty} \beta_i = t$.

According to Lemma 6.3.2/1 there exists a set $\mathfrak{B}_t^{(0)}$ such that $\mathfrak{B}_t^{(0)} \cap \Omega = \mathcal{N}_t$ and $P_{C\Omega}(\mathfrak{B}_t^{(0)}) = \tau_\Omega(\mathcal{N}_t)$. Consider the sequence of sets $\mathfrak{B}_t^{(k)} = \mathfrak{B}_t^{(0)} \cap \mathfrak{B}_{\alpha_k}$, $k = 1, 2, \ldots$. It is clear that $\mathfrak{B}_t^{(k)} \cap \Omega = \mathcal{N}_t$, $\mathfrak{B}_t^{(k+1)} \subset \mathfrak{B}_t^{(k)}$. By virtue of Lemma 6.3.2/3 have $P_{C\Omega}(\mathfrak{B}_t^{(k)}) = \tau_\Omega(\mathcal{N}_t)$. We introduce the notation $\tilde{\mathfrak{B}}_t = \bigcap_{k=1}^{\infty} \mathfrak{B}_t^{(k)}$. Since $\mathfrak{B}_t^{(k)} \to \tilde{\mathfrak{B}}_t$ as $k \to \infty$ then

$$P_{C\Omega}(\tilde{\mathfrak{B}}_t) \leqslant \liminf_{k\to\infty} P_{C\Omega}(\mathfrak{B}_t^{(k)}) = \tau_\Omega(\mathcal{N}_t)\ .$$

On the other hand, $\tilde{\mathfrak{B}}_t \cap \Omega = \mathcal{N}_t$. Therefore $\tau_\Omega(\mathcal{N}_t) \leqslant P_{C\Omega}(\tilde{\mathfrak{B}}_t)$. Thus $P_{C\Omega}(\tilde{\mathfrak{B}}_t) = \tau_\Omega(\mathcal{N}_t)$.

Next consider the sequence of sets $\mathfrak{C}_t^{(k)} = \tilde{\mathfrak{B}}_t \cup \mathfrak{B}_{\beta_k}$, $k = 1, 2, \ldots$. In the same way as when we considered the sets $\mathfrak{B}_t^{(k)}$ we conclude that the set $\mathfrak{B}_t = \bigcup_{k=1}^{\infty} \mathfrak{C}_t^{(k)}$ is measurable and satisfies the conditions

$$1)\ \mathfrak{B}_t \cap \Omega = \mathcal{N}_t\,, \qquad 2)\ P_{C\Omega}(\mathfrak{B}_t) = \tau_\Omega(\mathcal{N}_t)\,, \qquad 3)\ \mathfrak{B}_{\beta_i} \subset \mathfrak{B}_t \subset \mathfrak{B}_{\alpha_i}\,,$$

$i = 1, 2, \ldots$.

Now let t, τ be arbitrary numbers, $t < \tau$. Then 3) implies that $\mathfrak{B}_t \supset \mathfrak{B}_\tau$.

4°. Consider the function $\hat{u}$ defined by $\hat{u}(x) = \sup\{t\colon x \in \mathfrak{B}_t\}$. We put

$$\mathfrak{A}_t = \{x\colon \hat{u}(x) \geqslant t\}\,, \qquad \mathfrak{C}_t = \{x\colon \hat{u}(x) > t\}\ .$$

Obviously, $\mathfrak{A}_t \supset \mathfrak{B}_t \supset \mathfrak{C}_t$. The sets $\mathfrak{A}_t \backslash \mathfrak{C}_t$ are mutually disjoint for different t and hence $m_n(\mathfrak{A}_t \backslash \mathfrak{C}_t) = 0$ for almost all t.

Thus the sets $\mathfrak{A}_t$, $\mathfrak{C}_t$ are measurable for almost all t. Moreover

$$P_{R^n}(\mathfrak{A}_t) = P_{R^n}(\mathfrak{B}_t) = P_{R^n}(\mathfrak{C}_t)\ .$$

We prove that $\hat{u}$ is locally summable. It is well known that the inequality

$$(1) \qquad (m_n(\mathscr{E}))^{(n-1)/n} \leqslant C(R,\varepsilon) P_{B_R}(\mathscr{E})$$

is valid for the subset $\mathscr{E}$ of the ball B_R such that $m_n(\mathscr{E}) < m_n(B_R - \varepsilon)$. (In particular, this follows from Lemma 3.2.1/1.) Let the closed ball B_δ be contained in Ω and let $B_R \supset B_\delta$. Then (1) implies

$$\begin{aligned} m_n(\mathscr{E}) &\leqslant C(R,\delta)[P_{B_R}(\mathscr{E}) + m_n(\mathscr{E} \cap B_\delta)] \\ &\leqslant C(R,\delta)[P_{R^n}(\mathscr{E}) + m_n(\mathscr{E} \cap B_\delta)] \end{aligned}$$

for any set $\mathscr{E} \subset B_R$. Putting $\mathscr{E} = \mathfrak{B}_t \cap B_R$ for $t \geqslant 0$ and $\mathscr{E} = B_R \backslash \mathfrak{B}_t$ for $t < 0$ in the latter inequality and using $P_{C\Omega}(\mathfrak{B}_t) = \tau_\Omega(\mathcal{N}_t)$ and estimate (6.3/2) we obtain

$$m_n(\mathfrak{B}_t \cap B_R) \leqslant C(R,\delta)[CP_\Omega(\mathcal{N}_t) + m_n(\mathcal{N}_t \cap B_\delta)]\,, \qquad t \geqslant 0\,,$$

$$m_n(B_R \backslash \mathfrak{B}_t) \leqslant C(R,\delta)[CP_\Omega(\mathcal{N}_t) + m_n((\Omega \backslash \mathcal{N}_t) \cap B_\delta)]\,, \quad t < 0\,.$$

Taking into account that $m_n(\mathfrak{B}_t) = m_n(\mathfrak{A}_t)$ for almost all t, from the latter two inequalities we obtain

$$\int_0^\infty m_n(\mathfrak{A}_t \cap B_R)\,dt + \int_{-\infty}^0 m_n(B_R \backslash \mathfrak{A}_t)\,dt$$

$$\leqslant C(R,\delta)\left[C\int_{-\infty}^\infty P_\Omega(\mathcal{N}_t)\,dt + \int_0^\infty m_n(\mathcal{N}_t \cap B_\delta)\,dt + \int_0^\infty m_n(B_\delta \backslash \mathcal{N}_t)\,dt\right],$$

which is equivalent to

$$\int_{B_R} |\hat{u}|\,dx \leqslant C(R,\delta)\left[C\|u\|_{BV(\Omega)} + \int_{B_\delta} |u|\,dx\right],$$

whence the local summability of $\hat{u}$ follows. Applying (6.1.6/1), (6.3/2) and recalling that $P_{R^n}(\mathfrak{C}_t) = P_{R^n}(\mathfrak{B}_t)$ for almost all t, we obtain

$$\|\hat{u}\|_{BV(R^n)} = \int_{-\infty}^\infty P_{R^n}(\mathfrak{C}_t)\,dt = \int_{-\infty}^\infty [P_\Omega(\mathfrak{B}_t) + P_{C\Omega}(\mathfrak{B}_t)]\,dt$$

$$= \int_{-\infty}^\infty [P_\Omega(\mathcal{N}_t) + \tau_\Omega(\mathcal{N}_t)]\,dt \leqslant C\int_{-\infty}^\infty P_\Omega(\mathcal{N}_t)\,dt = C\|u\|_{BV(\Omega)}\,,$$

i.e. $\hat{u} \in BV(R^n)$ and (6.3/1) is valid.

6.3.4. An Equivalent Statement of Theorem 6.3

Theorem 6.3 can be rephrased in terms of the extension operator $A_\Omega\colon u \to \hat{u}$ which associates with each $u \in BV(\Omega)$ its extension $\hat{u} \in BV(R^n)$.

First we put

$$\|A_\Omega\| = \sup\left\{\frac{\|\hat{u}\|_{BV(R^n)}}{\|u\|_{BV(\Omega)}} : u \in BV(\Omega)\right\}$$

and denote by $|\Omega|$ the infimum of those numbers k for which $\tau_\Omega(\mathscr{E}) \leqslant kP_\Omega(\mathscr{E})$ for all $\mathscr{E} \subset \Omega$.

Theorem. *The operator A_Ω exists and is bounded if and only if $|\Omega| < \infty$.*

Moreover, $\|A_\Omega\| \geqslant 1 + |\Omega|$ for any extension operator A_Ω and there exists an operator A_Ω with $\|A_\Omega\| = 1 + |\Omega|$.

6.3.5. One More Extension Theorem

Condition (6.3/2) in Theorem 6.3 is of a global nature. For example, nonconnected sets Ω do not satisfy it.

This impediment may be removed if we make the requirements on the extension operator less restrictive. Specifically, the following theorem is valid.

Theorem. *Let Ω be a bounded open set. In order for any function $u \in BV(\Omega)$ to have an extension $\hat{u} \in BV(R^n)$ with*

(1) $$\|\hat{u}\|_{BV(R^n)} \leqslant K(\|u\|_{BV(\Omega)} + \|u\|_{L(\Omega)}),$$

where K is independent of u, it is necessary and sufficient that there exists a $\delta > 0$ such that $\tau_\Omega(\mathscr{E}) \leqslant C P_\Omega(\mathscr{E})$ for any $\mathscr{E} \subset \Omega$ with diameter less than δ, the constant C being independent of $\mathscr{E}$.

Proof. Necessity. Let $\mathscr{E} \subset \Omega$ and let $\chi_\mathscr{E}$ be the characteristic function of $\mathscr{E}$ while $\hat{\chi}_\mathscr{E}$ is an extension of $\chi_\mathscr{E}$ satisfying (1). We have

$$K(P_\Omega(\mathscr{E}) + m_n(\mathscr{E})) \geqslant \|\hat{\chi}_\mathscr{E}\|_{BV(R^n)} \geqslant \int_0^1 P(\{x: \hat{\chi}_\mathscr{E} > t\})\,dt.$$

Since $\{x: \hat{\chi}_\mathscr{E} > t\} \cap \Omega = \mathscr{E}$ for $t \in (0,1)$, then

$$K(P_\Omega(\mathscr{E}) + m_n(\mathscr{E})) \geqslant \inf_{\mathfrak{B} \cap \Omega = \mathscr{E}} P(\mathfrak{B}).$$

By the inclusion $\mathscr{E} \subset \mathfrak{B}$ the latter estimate and the isoperimetric inequality (6.1.5/1) imply

(2) $$K(P_\Omega(\mathscr{E}) + m_n(\mathscr{E})) \geqslant n v_n^{1/n} (m_n(\mathscr{E}))^{(n-1)/n}.$$

We put $\delta = n/(2K)$. Then from (2) under the condition $\operatorname{diam} \mathscr{E} < \delta$ it follows that $m_n(\mathscr{E}) \leqslant P_\Omega(\mathscr{E})$. Therefore

$$2K P_\Omega(\mathscr{E}) \geqslant \inf_{\mathfrak{B} \cap \Omega = \mathscr{E}} P(\mathfrak{B}) \geqslant \tau_\Omega(\mathscr{E}).$$

Sufficiency. Consider the partition of unity $\alpha_i(x)$, $i = 1, \ldots, \nu$, such that $\bigcup_{i=1}^{\nu} \operatorname{supp} \alpha_i \supset \bar{\Omega}$, $\operatorname{diam} \operatorname{supp} \alpha_i < \delta$ and $|\operatorname{grad} \alpha_i| \leqslant d = \text{const}$. Let $u \in BV(\Omega)$. We put $\varphi_i = u\alpha_i$ and $\mathscr{N}_t = \{x: |\varphi_i| \geqslant t\}$. Since for all $t \neq 0$ we have $\operatorname{diam} \mathscr{N}_t < \delta$ then $\tau_\Omega(\mathscr{N}_t) \leqslant C P_\Omega(\mathscr{N}_t)$. Therefore, following the same argument as in the proof of sufficiency in Theorem 6.3 we obtain the function $\hat{\varphi}_i \in BV(R^n)$ such that $\hat{\varphi}_i = \varphi_i$ in Ω and

$$\|\hat{\varphi}_i\|_{BV(R^n)} \leqslant (C+1)\|\varphi_i\|_{BV(\Omega)} \leqslant (C+1)(\|u\|_{BV(\Omega)} + d\|u\|_{L(\Omega)}).$$

We put $\hat{u} = \sum \hat{\varphi}_i$. It is clear that $\hat{u} = u$ in Ω and

$$\|\hat{u}\|_{BV(R^n)} \leqslant v(C+1)(\|u\|_{BV(\Omega)} + d\|u\|_{L(\Omega)}) .$$

§ 6.4. Certain Exact Constants for Convex Domains

According to Theorem 6.3 the norm of the extension operator $BV(\Omega) \to BV(R^n)$ is expressed by the exact constant in the isoperimetric inequality (6.3/2). These constants can be found in some particular cases. For plane convex domains this constant has a simple geometrical interpretation (cf. Corollary 6.4.4/2). The constant is also easily calculated if Ω is an n-dimensional ball.

6.4.1. Lemmas on Approximation by Polyhedra

Lemma 1. *Let Ω be a bounded convex domain in R^n and let $\mathscr{E} \subset \Omega$, $P_{R^n}(\mathscr{E}) < \infty$. Then there exists a sequence of polyhedra Π_k such that $\Pi_k \to \mathscr{E}$ and*

(1) $$\lim_{k \to \infty} P_\Omega(\Pi_k) = P_\Omega(\mathscr{E}), \qquad \lim_{k \to \infty} P_{C\Omega}(\Pi_k) = P_{C\Omega}(\mathscr{E}) .$$

Proof. Let Ω_ε be the domain obtained from Ω by the similarity transformation with coefficient $1+\varepsilon$ and with center at a fixed point of Ω. We denote the image of $\mathscr{E}$ under the same transformation by $\mathscr{E}_\varepsilon$. It is clear that

$$P_{\Omega_\varepsilon}(\mathscr{E}_\varepsilon) = (1+\varepsilon)^{n-1} P_\Omega(\mathscr{E}), \qquad P_{C\Omega_\varepsilon}(\mathscr{E}_\varepsilon) = (1+\varepsilon)^{n-1} P_{C\Omega}(\mathscr{E}) .$$

Hence we can easily obtain that

(2) $$\lim_{\varepsilon \to 0} P_\Omega(\mathscr{E}_\varepsilon) = P_\Omega(\mathscr{E}), \qquad \lim_{\varepsilon \to 0} P_{C\Omega}(\mathscr{E}_\varepsilon) = P_{C\Omega}(\mathscr{E}) .$$

In fact, $(1+\varepsilon)^{n-1} P_\Omega(\mathscr{E}) \geqslant P_\Omega(\mathscr{E}_\varepsilon)$ and consequently

$$P_\Omega(\mathscr{E}) \geqslant \liminf_{\varepsilon \to 0} P_\Omega(\mathscr{E}_\varepsilon) \geqslant P_\Omega(\mathscr{E}) .$$

The latter inequality is a corollary of Lemma 6.1.3/1. Since

$$P_\Omega(\mathscr{E}) + P_{C\Omega}(\mathscr{E}) = P(\mathscr{E}), \qquad P_\Omega(\mathscr{E}_\varepsilon) + P_{C\Omega}(\mathscr{E}_\varepsilon) = P(\mathscr{E}_\varepsilon)$$

the first equality (2) implies the second. For almost all ε we have

(3) $$\operatorname{var} \nabla \chi_{\mathscr{E}_\varepsilon}(\partial \Omega) = 0 .$$

Let ε be subject to the latter condition. According to Theorem 6.1.3 there exists a sequence of polyhedra $\Pi_{k,\varepsilon}$ such that $\Pi_{k,\varepsilon} \to \mathscr{E}_\varepsilon$, $P(\Pi_{k,\varepsilon}) \to P(\mathscr{E}_\varepsilon)$ as $k \to \infty$. This and Lemma 6.1.2/3 yield $\operatorname{var} \nabla \chi_{\Pi_{k,\varepsilon}} \xrightarrow{\text{weakly}} \operatorname{var} \nabla \chi_{\mathscr{E}_\varepsilon}$. By virtue of (3) we have

$$\limsup_{k \to \infty} \operatorname{var} \nabla \chi_{\Pi_{k,\varepsilon}}(\partial \Omega) \leqslant \operatorname{var} \nabla \chi_{\mathscr{E}_\varepsilon}(\partial \Omega) = 0$$

and therefore

$$\lim_{k \to \infty} P_\Omega(\Pi_{k,\varepsilon}) = P_\Omega(\mathscr{E}_\varepsilon)\,, \qquad \lim_{k \to \infty} P_{C\Omega}(\Pi_{k,\varepsilon}) = P_{C\Omega}(\mathscr{E}_\varepsilon)\,. \tag{4}$$

We choose a sequence of numbers ε_i that satisfy (3) and such that $\varepsilon_i \to 0$ as $i \to \infty$. Then (2) and (4) imply

$$\lim_{i \to \infty} \lim_{k \to \infty} P_\Omega(\Pi_{k,\varepsilon_i}) = P_\Omega(\mathscr{E})\,,$$

$$\lim_{i \to \infty} \lim_{k \to \infty} P_{C\Omega}(\Pi_{k,\varepsilon_i}) = P_{C\Omega}(\mathscr{E})\,.$$

This concludes the proof.

Below we shall use the following elementary assertion.

Lemma 2. *Let Ω be a bounded convex domain in R^n and let Π be a finite polyhedron. Then $s(\partial \Pi \cap C\Omega) \geqslant s(\partial \Omega \cap \Pi)$.*

Lemma 3. *Let Ω be a bounded convex domain in R^n and let $\mathscr{E} \subset \Omega$, $P_\Omega(\mathscr{E}) < \infty$. Then there exists a sequence of polyhedra Π_k such that $\Pi_k \to \mathscr{E}$ and*

$$\lim_{k \to \infty} P_\Omega(\Pi_k \cap \Omega) = P_\Omega(\mathscr{E})\,, \qquad \lim_{k \to \infty} P_{C\Omega}(\Pi_k \cap \Omega) = P_{C\Omega}(\mathscr{E})\,.$$

Proof. By Lemma 1 there exists a sequence of polyhedra Π_k, $\Pi_k \to \mathscr{E}$, satisfying (1). It is clear that $P_\Omega(\Pi_k \cap \Omega) = P_\Omega(\Pi_k)$. According to Lemma 6.3.2/3 we have

$$P_{C\Omega}(\Pi_k \cap \Omega) \leqslant P_{C\Omega}(\Pi_k)\,.$$

Therefore

$$\lim_{k \to \infty} P_{C\Omega}(\Pi_k \cap \Omega) \leqslant \lim_{k \to \infty} P_{C\Omega}(\Pi_k) = P_{C\Omega}(\mathscr{E})\,, \tag{5}$$

$$\lim_{k \to \infty} P_\Omega(\Pi_k \cap \Omega) = \lim_{k \to \infty} P_\Omega(\Pi_k) = P_\Omega(\mathscr{E})\,. \tag{6}$$

Since $\Pi_k \cap \Omega \to \mathscr{E}$ then

$$P_{R^n}(\mathscr{E}) \leqslant \lim_{k \to \infty} P_{R^n}(\Pi_k \cap \Omega)\,. \tag{7}$$

From (6) and (7) we obtain $P_{C\Omega}(\mathscr{E}) \leqslant \lim_{k \to \infty} P_{C\Omega}(\Pi_k \cap \Omega)$ which together with (5) completes the proof.

6.4.2. On a Property of $P_{C\Omega}$

Lemma. *Let $P(\Omega)<\infty$ and suppose a normal to Ω exists s-almost everywhere on $\partial\Omega$. Then, for any set $\mathscr{E}\subset\Omega$*

$$P_{C\Omega}(\mathscr{E})+P_{C\Omega}(\Omega\backslash\mathscr{E})=s(\partial\Omega)\ .$$

Proof. By the equality $\chi_\Omega=\chi_{\mathscr{E}}+\chi_{\Omega\backslash\mathscr{E}}$ we have

$$\operatorname{var}\nabla\chi_\Omega(C\Omega)\leqslant\operatorname{var}\nabla\chi_{\mathscr{E}}(C\Omega)+\operatorname{var}\nabla\chi_{\Omega\backslash\mathscr{E}}(C\Omega)=P_{C\Omega}(\mathscr{E})+P_{C\Omega}(\Omega\backslash\mathscr{E}).$$

Since a normal to Ω exists s-almost everywhere on $\partial\Omega$, then by Theorem 6.2.2/1

$$\operatorname{var}\nabla\chi_\Omega(C\Omega)=P_{R^n}(\Omega)=s(\partial\Omega)\ .$$

Consequently,

$$s(\partial\Omega)\leqslant P_{C\Omega}(\mathscr{E})+P_{C\Omega}(\Omega\backslash\mathscr{E})\ .$$

We prove the reverse inequality. Let $\mathfrak{A}^*$, $\mathfrak{B}^*$ denote the reduced boundaries of the sets $\mathscr{E}$ and $\Omega\backslash\mathscr{E}$, respectively. The sets $\mathfrak{A}^*$ and $\mathfrak{B}^*$ are s-measurable (cf. Theorem 6.2.2/1). We note that the sets $\mathfrak{A}^*\cap\partial^*\Omega$ and $\mathfrak{B}^*\cap\partial^*\Omega$ are disjoint. In fact, suppose there exists a point $x\in\partial^*\Omega$ common to $\mathfrak{A}^*$ and $\mathfrak{B}^*$. Then the volume densities of $\mathscr{E}$ and $\Omega\backslash\mathscr{E}$ at the point x equal 1/2. But this is impossible because $x\in\partial^*\Omega$. Consequently,

$$s(\mathfrak{A}^*\cap\partial^*\Omega)+s(\mathfrak{B}^*\cap\partial^*\Omega)\leqslant s(\partial\Omega)\ .$$

It remains to use the equalities

$$s(\mathfrak{A}^*\cap\partial^*\Omega)=s(\mathfrak{A}^*\cap\partial\Omega)=P_{C\Omega}(\mathscr{E})\ ,$$

$$s(\mathfrak{B}^*\cap\partial^*\Omega)=s(\mathfrak{B}^*\cap\partial\Omega)=P_{C\Omega}(\Omega\backslash\mathscr{E})$$

(cf. Theorem 6.2.2/1). The lemma is proved.

6.4.3. An Expression for the Set Function $\tau_\Omega(\mathscr{E})$ for a Convex Domain Ω

Theorem. *If Ω is a bounded convex domain in R^n, then the equality*

$$\tau_\Omega(\mathscr{E})=\min[P_{C\Omega}(\mathscr{E}),\ P_{C\Omega}(\Omega\backslash\mathscr{E})] \tag{1}$$

is valid for any set $\mathscr{E}\subset\Omega$ with $P(\mathscr{E})<\infty$.

Proof. For the sake of definiteness, let

$$P_{C\Omega}(\mathscr{E})\leqslant P_{C\Omega}(\Omega\backslash\mathscr{E})\ ;$$

let the set $\mathfrak{B}$ be such that $\mathfrak{B} \cap \Omega = \mathscr{E}$, $P_{C\Omega}(\mathfrak{B}) = \tau_\Omega(\mathscr{E})$. Assume for the moment that $m_n(\mathfrak{B}) < \infty$.

According to Lemma 6.4.1/1 we can find a sequence of polyhedra Π_k, $\Pi_k \to \mathfrak{B}$ such that

$$\lim_{k\to\infty} P_\Omega(\Pi_k) = P_\Omega(\mathfrak{B}) , \qquad \lim_{k\to\infty} P_{C\Omega}(\Pi_k) = P_{C\Omega}(\mathfrak{B}) . \tag{2}$$

Since $m_n(\mathfrak{B}) < \infty$, the polyhedra Π_k are finite. By virtue of Lemma 6.4.1/2 we have $P_{C\Omega}(\Pi_k \cap \Omega) \leqslant P_{C\Omega}(\Pi_k)$. This and (2) yield

$$\limsup_{k\to\infty} P_{C\Omega}(\Pi_k \cap \Omega) \leqslant P_{C\Omega}(\mathfrak{B}) . \tag{3}$$

Using $\Pi_k \cap \Omega \to \mathfrak{B} \cap \Omega$ we obtain $P(\mathfrak{B} \cap \Omega) \leqslant \liminf_{k\to\infty} P(\Pi_k \cap \Omega)$ which together with (2) implies

$$P_{C\Omega}(\mathscr{E}) = P_{C\Omega}(\mathfrak{B} \cap \Omega) \leqslant \liminf_{k\to\infty} P_{C\Omega}(\Pi_k \cap \Omega) .$$

Hence from (6.4.3/3) it follows that $P_{C\Omega}(\mathscr{E}) \leqslant P_{C\Omega}(\mathfrak{B}) = \tau_\Omega(\mathscr{E})$. Thus $P_{C\Omega}(\mathscr{E}) = \tau_\Omega(\mathscr{E})$.

Now let $m_n(\mathfrak{B}) = \infty$. Since $P_{C\Omega}(\mathfrak{B}) < \infty$, then $m_n(C\mathfrak{B}) < \infty$ (cf. (6.1.7/1)). Further we note that

$$P_{C\Omega}(C\mathfrak{B}) = P_{C\Omega}(\mathfrak{B}) = \tau_\Omega(\mathscr{E}) = \tau_\Omega(\Omega \backslash \mathscr{E}) .$$

Hence, according to what we have proved above, $\tau_\Omega(\Omega\backslash\mathscr{E}) = P_{C\Omega}(\Omega\backslash\mathscr{E})$ and therefore, in view of (1),

$$\tau_\Omega(\mathscr{E}) = P_{C\Omega}(\Omega\backslash\mathscr{E}) \geqslant P_{C\Omega}(\mathscr{E}) .$$

Since, obviously, $\tau_\Omega(\mathscr{E}) \leqslant P_{C\Omega}(\mathscr{E})$, then $\tau_\Omega(\mathscr{E}) = P_{C\Omega}(\mathscr{E})$.

6.4.4. The Function $|\Omega|$ for a Convex Domain

Corollary 1. *Let Ω be a bounded convex domain. Then*

$$|\Omega| = \inf\{k\colon P_{C\Omega}(\mathscr{E}) \leqslant k P_\Omega(\mathscr{E})\} ,$$

where $\mathscr{E}$ is any subset of Ω with $P_{C\Omega}(\mathscr{E}) \leqslant \frac{1}{2} s(\partial\Omega)$.

The result follows immediately from Theorem 6.4.3 and Lemma 6.4.2.

Corollary 2. *Let Ω be a bounded convex domain in R^2. Then $|\Omega| = \dfrac{1}{2h} \cdot s(\partial\Omega)$ where h is the minimum length of those lines whose end points separate $\partial\Omega$ into arcs of equal length.*

Proof. We take an arbitrary $\varepsilon > 0$. Let $\mathscr{E}$ be a measurable subset of Ω such that $P_\Omega(\mathscr{E})>0$, $P_{C\Omega}(\mathscr{E})<\frac{1}{2}s(\partial\Omega)$ and

$$|\Omega|-\frac{P_{C\Omega}(\mathscr{E})}{P_\Omega(\mathscr{E})}<\varepsilon$$

(cf. Corollary 1). According to Lemma 6.4.1/3 we can find a polyhedron Π such that

$$|\Omega|-\frac{P_{C\Omega}(\Pi\cap\Omega)}{P_\Omega(\Pi)}<2\varepsilon\,.$$

Let A and B be the points of intersection of $\partial\Omega$ with some component of the boundary of Π. The points A and B can be chosen so that the segment of the component of $\partial\Pi$ being considered, bounded by the points A and B, lies entirely in Ω. The segment AB divides Ω into two sets Q and Q'. Let $P_{C\Omega}(Q)\leqslant P_{C\Omega}(Q')$. It is clear that

$$P_{C\Omega}(Q)/AB\geqslant P_{C\Omega}(\Pi\cap\Omega)/P_\Omega(\Pi)$$

and therefore

(1) $$|\Omega|-\frac{P_{C\Omega}(Q)}{AB}<2\varepsilon\,.$$

If $P_{C\Omega}(Q)=P_{C\Omega}(Q')$ then (1) implies the required assertion by virtue of the inequality $AB\geqslant h$ and the fact that ε is arbitrary.

Let $P_{C\Omega}(Q)<P_{C\Omega}(Q')$. We shift the segment AB parallel to itself to a new position $A'B'(A'\in\partial\Omega, B'\in\partial\Omega)$ so that $P_{C\Omega}(Q_1)=P_{C\Omega}(Q_1')$ where Q_1 and Q_1' are the domains into which the segment $A'B'$ divides Ω.

Elementary calculations show that

$$P_{C\Omega}(Q_1)/A'B'\geqslant P_{C\Omega}(Q)/AB$$

which together with (1) proves the corollary.

Lemma. *Let Ω be the unit ball in R^n. Then*

$$\inf\{P_{C\Omega}(\mathscr{E})\colon \mathscr{E}\subset\Omega,\ P_\Omega(\mathscr{E})=p=\text{const}\leqslant\omega_n\}$$

equals the area of the spherical part of the boundary of the spherical segment whose base has area p.

Proof. Let $\mathscr{E}\subset\Omega, P_\Omega(\mathscr{E})=p$. By virtue of Lemma 6.4.1/3 there exists a sequence of polyhedra Π_k, $\Pi_k\to\mathscr{E}$, such that

$$P_\Omega(\Pi_k)\to p\,,\qquad P_{C\Omega}(\Pi_k\cap\Omega)\to P_{C\Omega}(\mathscr{E})\,.$$

We perform the spherical symmetrization of $\Pi_k\cap\Omega$ relative to some ray l with origin at the center of Ω. We obtain the set Π_k', symmetric relative to l, with a piecewise smooth boundary and such that

$$P_\Omega(\Pi'_k) \leqslant P_\Omega(\Pi_k)\,, \qquad P_{C\Omega}(\Pi'_k) = P_{C\Omega}(\Pi_k \cap \Omega)\,.$$

We denote the spherical segment whose spherical part of the boundary is $\partial\Pi'_k \cap \partial\Omega$ by Q_k. It is clear that $P_\Omega(Q_k) \leqslant P_\Omega(\Pi'_k)$, $P_{C\Omega}(Q_k) = P_{C\Omega}(\Pi'_k)$. Hence the result follows.

The next assertions can be obtained from Lemma by simple calculations.

Corollary 3. 1) *If Ω is the unit ball in R^n then*

$$|\Omega| = \omega_n/2\pi v_{n-1}\,.$$

2) *If Ω is the unit ball in R^3 then, for any $\mathscr{E} \subset \Omega$,*

$$4\pi P_\Omega(\mathscr{E}) \geqslant P_{C\Omega}(\mathscr{E})(4\pi - P_{C\Omega}(\mathscr{E}))\,.$$

3) *If Ω is the unit disk then, for any $\mathscr{E} \subset \Omega$,*

$$P_\Omega(\mathscr{E}) \geqslant 2\sin(\tfrac{1}{2}P_{C\Omega}(\mathscr{E}))\,.$$

§ 6.5. The Rough Trace of Functions in $BV(\Omega)$ and Certain Integral Inequalities

6.5.1. The Definition of the Rough Trace and its Properties

On the reduced boundary of Ω we define *the rough trace u^* of a function $u \in BV(\Omega)$*. We put

$$u^*(x) = \sup\{t\colon P(\mathscr{N}_t) < \infty,\ x \in \partial^*\mathscr{N}_t\}\,,$$

where $x \in \partial^*\Omega$. (The supremum of the empty set is assumed to be $-\infty$.)

It is clear that if u has a limit value at a point $x \in \partial^*\Omega$ then $u^*(x) = \lim_{y\to x} u(y)$.

Lemma 1. *Let $s(\partial\Omega) < \infty$. Then $P_\Omega(\mathscr{E}) < \infty$ implies $P(\mathscr{E}) < \infty$ for any $\mathscr{E} \subset \Omega$.*

Proof. Since $s(\partial\Omega)$ is finite, we can construct a sequence of polyhedra Π_k, $\Pi_k \subset \Omega$, $\Pi_k \to \Omega$, such that $s(\partial\Pi_k) \leqslant K < \infty$. Because $P_\Omega(\mathscr{E}) < \infty$, we have $P_\Omega(\mathscr{E} \cap \Pi_k) \leqslant K_1 < \infty$. Moreover, $\mathscr{E} \cap \Pi_k \to \mathscr{E}$. Hence by Lemma 6.1.3/1 the result follows.

Corollary. *If $s(\partial\Omega) < \infty$ and $u \in BV(\Omega)$ then $P(\mathscr{N}_t) < \infty$ for almost all t.*

Lemma 2. *Let $s(\partial\Omega) < \infty$ and $u \in BV(\Omega)$. Then the rough trace u^* is s-measurable on $\partial^*\Omega$ and*

(1) $$s(\{x: x\in\partial^*\Omega, u^*(x)\geqslant t\}) = s(\partial^*\Omega\cap\partial^*\mathcal{N}_t)$$

for almost all t.

Proof. Let t be such that $P(\mathcal{N}_t)<\infty$. Consider the set

$$\mathcal{R}_t = \{x: x\in\partial^*\Omega, u^*(x)\geqslant t\}\,.$$

The definition of u^* implies $\mathcal{R}_t\supset\partial^*\mathcal{N}_t\cap\partial^*\Omega$. It is well known (Theorem 6.2.2/1) that the set $\partial^*\mathcal{N}_t\cap\partial^*\Omega$ is measurable relative to s. The sets $\mathcal{R}_t\backslash[\partial^*\mathcal{N}_t\cap\partial^*\Omega]$ are disjoint for different values of t; therefore $s(\mathcal{R}_t\backslash[\partial^*\mathcal{N}_t\cap\partial^*\Omega])=0$ for almost all t. Hence the set $\mathcal{R}_t$ is measurable for almost all t and consequently $u^*(x)$ is measurable.

6.5.2. On Summability of the Rough Trace

Theorem. *Suppose $P(\Omega)<\infty$ and that a normal to Ω exists s-almost everywhere on $\partial\Omega$. In order that for any $u\in BV(\Omega)$*

(1) $$\inf_c \int_{\partial\Omega} |u^*-c|\,s(dx)\leqslant k\,\|u\|_{BV(\Omega)}\,,$$

where k is independent of u, it is necessary and sufficient that the inequality

(2) $$\min\{P_{C\Omega}(\mathcal{E}),\, P_{C\Omega}(\Omega\backslash\mathcal{E})\}\leqslant kP_\Omega(\mathcal{E})$$

be valid for any $\mathcal{E}\subset\Omega$.

Proof. Necessity. Let $\mathcal{E}\subset\Omega$, $P_\Omega(\mathcal{E})<\infty$. By Lemma 6.5.1/1 we have $P(\mathcal{E})<\infty$. Let $\chi_{\mathcal{E}}$ be the characteristic function of the set $\mathcal{E}$. Then

$$\begin{aligned}\inf_c\int_{\partial\Omega}|\chi^*_{\mathcal{E}}(x)-c|\,s(dx) &= \min_c\{|1-c|\,s(\partial^*\mathcal{E}\cap\partial^*\Omega)+|c|\,s(\partial^*\Omega\backslash\partial^*\mathcal{E})\}\\ &= \min\{s(\partial^*\mathcal{E}\cap\partial^*\Omega),\, s(\partial^*\Omega\backslash\partial^*\mathcal{E})\}\\ &= \min\{P_{C\Omega}(\mathcal{E}), P_{C\Omega}(\Omega\backslash\mathcal{E})\}\,.\end{aligned}$$

(The preceding equality is valid since, by hypothesis, $s(\partial\Omega\backslash\partial^*\Omega)=0$.)

On the other hand, $\|\chi_{\mathcal{E}}\|_{BV(\Omega)}=P_\Omega(\mathcal{E})$. Applying (1) we arrive at (2).

Sufficiency. Let $u\in BV(\Omega)$. It is clear that $s(\partial\Omega\cap\partial^*\mathcal{N}_t)$ is a nonincreasing function of t. In fact, let $x\in\partial^*\Omega\cap\partial^*\mathcal{N}_t$ and let $\tau<t$. We have

$$\begin{aligned}1 &= \lim_{\varrho\to 0} 2v_n\varrho^{-n}m_n(\Omega\cap B_\varrho)\geqslant \lim_{\varrho\to 0}2v_n\varrho^{-n}m_n(\mathcal{N}_\tau\cap B_\varrho)\\ &\geqslant \lim_{\varrho\to 0}2v_n\varrho^{-n}m_n(\mathcal{N}_t\cap B_\varrho)=1\,,\end{aligned}$$

i.e. $x\in\partial^*\Omega\cap\partial^*\mathcal{N}_\tau$.

Similarly, $s(\partial\Omega\backslash\partial^*\mathcal{N}_t)$ is a nondecreasing function of t. From (6.1.6/1) we obtain

$$k\|u\|_{BV(\Omega)} = k\int_{-\infty}^{\infty} P_\Omega(\mathcal{N}_t)\,dt \geqslant \int_{-\infty}^{\infty} \min[s(\partial\Omega\cap\partial^*\mathcal{N}_t), s(\partial\Omega\backslash\partial^*\mathcal{N}_t)]\,dt\,.$$

Putting $t_0 = \sup\{t: P(\mathcal{N}_t) < \infty,\ s(\partial\Omega\cap\partial^*\mathcal{N}_t) \geqslant s(\partial\Omega\backslash\partial^*\mathcal{N}_t)\}$ we obtain

$$\begin{aligned} k\|u\|_{BV(\Omega)} &\geqslant \int_{t_0}^{\infty} s(\partial\Omega\cap\partial^*\mathcal{N}_t)\,dt + \int_{-\infty}^{t_0} s(\partial\Omega\backslash\partial^*\mathcal{N}_t)\,dt \\ &= \int_{t_0}^{\infty} s(\{x: u^*(x) \geqslant t\})\,dt + \int_{-\infty}^{t_0} s(\{x: u^*(x) \leqslant t\})\,dt \\ &= \int_{\partial\Omega} [u^*(x) - t_0]^+ s(dx) + \int_{\partial\Omega} [u^*(x) - t_0]^- s(dx) \\ &= \int_{\partial\Omega} |u^*(x) - t_0|\,s(dx)\,. \end{aligned}$$

Consequently,

$$k\|u\|_{BV(\Omega)} \geqslant \inf_c \int_{\partial\Omega} |u^* - c|\,s(dx)\,,$$

which completes the proof.

From Corollary 6.4.4/1 we obtain that the best constant in (1) is equal to $|\Omega|$ provided Ω is a convex domain. In particular, for a plane convex domain this constant coincides with the ratio of $\frac{1}{2}s(\partial\Omega)$ to the length of the smallest chord dividing $\partial\Omega$ into arcs of equal length (Corollary 6.4.4/2).

According to Corollary 6.4.4/3, the best constant in (1) equals $\omega_n/2v_{n-1}$ for the unit ball.

6.5.3. Exact Constants in Certain Integral Estimates for the Rough Trace

Definition 1. Let $\mathcal{A} \subset \bar{\Omega}$. Let $\tau_{\mathcal{A}}^{(\alpha)}$ denote the infimum of those k for which $[P_{C\Omega}(\mathcal{E})]^\alpha \leqslant k P_\Omega(\mathcal{E})$ is valid for all $\mathcal{E} \subset \Omega$ that satisfy

(1) $$m_n(\mathcal{E}\cap\mathcal{A}) + s(\mathcal{A}\cap\partial^*\mathcal{E}) = 0\,.$$

Theorem. *Let $P(\Omega) < \infty$ and suppose a normal to Ω exists s-almost everywhere on Ω. Then, for any function $u \in BV(\Omega)$ such that $u(\mathcal{A}\cap\Omega) = 0$, $u^*(\mathcal{A}\cap\partial^*\Omega) = 0$, the inequality*

(2) $$\int_{\partial\Omega} |u^*|\,s(dx) \leqslant \zeta_{\mathcal{A}}^{(1)} \|u\|_{BV(\Omega)}$$

is fulfilled. Moreover, the constant $\zeta_{\mathcal{A}}^{(1)}$ is exact.

Proof. We have

$$\int_{\partial\Omega} |u^*|\,s(dx) = \int_0^{\infty} s(\{x: u^* \geqslant t\})\,dt + \int_0^{\infty} s(\{x: -u^* \geqslant t\})\,dt\,.$$

By virtue of (6.1.6/1) the first integral on the right is equal to

$$\int_0^\infty s(\partial^* \mathcal{N}_t \cap \partial^* \Omega)\, dt = \int_0^\infty P_{C\Omega}(\mathcal{N}_t)\, dt .$$

Note that $m_n(\mathcal{A} \cap \mathcal{N}_t) + s(\mathcal{A} \cap \partial^* \mathcal{N}_t) = 0$ for almost all t. Consequently, by the definition of $\zeta_{\mathcal{A}}^{(1)}$,

$$\int_0^\infty s(\{x\colon u^* \geqslant t\})\, dt \leqslant \int_0^\infty P_{C\Omega}(\mathcal{N}_t)\, dt \leqslant \zeta_{\mathcal{A}}^{(1)} \int_0^\infty P_\Omega(\mathcal{N}_t)\, dt .$$

Similarly we have

$$\int_0^\infty s(\{x\colon -u^* \geqslant t\})\, dt \leqslant \int_{-\infty}^0 P_{C\Omega}(\Omega \setminus \mathcal{N}_t)\, dt \leqslant \zeta_{\mathcal{A}}^{(1)} \int_{-\infty}^0 P_\Omega(\mathcal{N}_t)\, dt .$$

Finally,

$$\int_{\partial\Omega} |u^*|\, s(dx) \leqslant \zeta_{\mathcal{A}}^{(1)} \|u\|_{BV(\Omega)} .$$

To prove the exactness of the constant $\zeta_{\mathcal{A}}^{(1)}$ it suffices to put $u = \chi_{\mathscr{E}}$ into (2), where $\mathscr{E}$ is a set satisfying (1).

Definition 2. We introduce the function

$$\zeta_\alpha(S) = \sup \left\{ \frac{[P_{C\Omega}(\mathscr{E})]^\alpha}{P_\Omega(\mathscr{E})} \colon \mathscr{E} \subset \Omega,\, P_\Omega(\mathscr{E}) > 0,\, P_{C\Omega}(\mathscr{E}) \leqslant S \right\} .$$

The preceding theorem implies the following obvious corollary.

Corollary. *Suppose that $P(\Omega) < \infty$ and a normal to Ω exists s-almost everywhere on $\partial\Omega$. Then for any $u \in BV(\Omega)$ with $s(\{x\colon u^*(x) \neq 0\}) \leqslant S$ the inequality*

$$\int_{\partial\Omega} |u^*|\, s(dx) \leqslant \zeta_1(S)\, \|u\|_{BV(\Omega)}$$

is valid. Moreover, the constant $\zeta_1(S)$ is exact.

From Lemma 6.4.4 it follows that for a ball the function $\zeta_1(S)$ coincides with the ratio of S to the area of the base of the spherical segment whose spherical part of the boundary has the area S.

In particular, $\zeta_1(S) = S/(2\sin(S/2))$ for $n = 2$ and $\zeta_1(S) = 4\pi/(4\pi - S)$ for $n = 3$.

Lemma. *Let Ω be a domain with $P(\Omega) < \infty$ and suppose a normal to Ω exists s-almost everywhere on $\partial\Omega$. Then*

$$\eta(S) \overset{\text{def}}{=} \inf\{P_\Omega(\mathscr{E})\colon \mathscr{E} \subset \Omega,\, P_{C\Omega}(\mathscr{E}) \geqslant S,\, P_{C\Omega}(\Omega \setminus \mathscr{E}) \geqslant S\} > 0 .$$

Proof. Let $\{\mathscr{E}_i\}$ be the minimizing sequence for $\eta(S)$. If

$$\liminf_{i\to\infty} \min\{m_n\mathscr{E}_i,\, m_n(\Omega\setminus\mathscr{E}_i)\}>0\ ,$$

then the result follows from Theorem 6.1.3 and Lemma 3.2.4. Let this lower limit be equal to zero and, for the sake of definiteness, let $m_n\mathscr{E}_i\to 0$. Then $m_n(\Omega\setminus\mathscr{E}_i)\to m_n(\Omega)$. By Lemma 6.1.3/1 we obtain

$$\liminf P(\Omega\setminus\mathscr{E}_i)\leqslant P(\Omega)=s(\partial\Omega)\ ,$$

and by Lemma 6.4.2

$$s(\partial\Omega)=P_{C\Omega}(\mathscr{E}_i)+P_{C\Omega}(\Omega\setminus\mathscr{E}_i)\ .$$

Moreover, we always have

$$P(\Omega\setminus\mathscr{E}_i)=P_\Omega(\Omega\setminus\mathscr{E}_i)+P_{C\Omega}(\Omega\setminus\mathscr{E}_i)\ .$$

Thus for any $\varepsilon>0$ and for large enough i we obtain

$$P_\Omega(\Omega\setminus\mathscr{E}_i)\geqslant P_{C\Omega}(\mathscr{E}_i)-\varepsilon\geqslant S-\varepsilon\ ,$$

i.e. $\inf P_\Omega(\Omega\setminus\mathscr{E})\geqslant S$. The lemma is proved.

We can easily see that the function η introduced in the preceding lemma is connected with ζ_α by the equality

$$\zeta_\alpha(S)=S^\alpha/\eta(S)\ .$$

The same lemma immediately implies that $\zeta_\alpha(S)$ is finite for all $S\in(0,s(\partial\Omega))$ provided Ω is a domain with $P(\Omega)=s(\partial\Omega)<\infty$ and $\zeta_\alpha(S)<\infty$ for some $S<s(\partial\Omega)$.

Hence from Theorem 6.5.2 we find that inequality (6.5.2/1) is valid if and only if $\zeta_1(S)<\infty$ for some $S\in(0,s(\partial\Omega))$.

6.5.4. More on Summability of the Rough Trace

Theorem. *Let $P(\Omega)<\infty$ and suppose a normal to Ω exists s-almost everywhere on $\partial\Omega$. In order for any function $u\in BV(\Omega)$ to satisfy the inequality*

$$\|u^*\|_{L(\partial\Omega)}\leqslant k(\|u\|_{BV(\Omega)}+\|u\|_{L(\Omega)})\ , \tag{1}$$

where the constant k is independent of u, it is necessary and sufficient that there exist a $\delta>0$ such that for each measurable set $\mathscr{E}\subset\Omega$ with diameter less than δ the inequality

(2) $$P_{C\Omega}(\mathscr{E}) \leqslant k_1 P_\Omega(\mathscr{E}),$$

where k_1 is a constant that is independent of $\mathscr{E}$, be valid.

The necessity of (2) easily follows by the insertion of $u = \chi_{\mathscr{E}}$ into (1) and then by application of the isoperimetric inequality. The sufficiency results from Theorem 6.5.3 if we make use of a partition of unity (cf. the proof of Theorem 6.2.2/2).

Remark. If each of the sets Ω_1, Ω_2 satisfies the hypothesis of the preceding theorem then their union has the same property.

The proof follows from formula (6.3.2/4).

6.5.5. Extension of a Function in $BV(\Omega)$ to $C\Omega$ by a Constant

In the present subsection we assume that $P(\Omega) < \infty$ and $s(\partial\Omega \backslash \partial^*\Omega) = 0$.

We introduce the notation $u_c(x) = u(x)$ for $x \in \Omega$, $u_c(x) = c$ for $x \in C\Omega$ where $c \in R^1$.

Lemma. *The equality*

(1) $$\|u_c\|_{BV(R^n)} = \|u\|_{BV(\Omega)} + \|u^* - c\|_{L(\partial\Omega)}$$

is valid.

Proof. We have

(2) $$\|u_c\|_{BV(R^n)} = \int_0^\infty P(\{x: |u_c - c| > t\})\,dt$$

$$= \int_0^\infty P_\Omega(\{x: |u-c| > t\})\,dt + \int_0^\infty P_{C\Omega}(\{x: |u-c| > t\})\,dt.$$

It is clear that

(3) $$\int_0^\infty P_\Omega(\{x: |u-c| > t\})\,dt = \|u\|_{BV(\Omega)}.$$

Further, since $s(\partial\Omega \backslash \partial^*\Omega) = 0$ then

$$\int_0^\infty P_{C\Omega}(\{x: |u-c| > t\})\,dt = \int_0^\infty s(\{x: (u-c)^* > t\})\,dt + \int_{-\infty}^0 s(\{x: (u-c)^* < t\})\,dt$$

$$= \int_{\partial\Omega} |(u-c)^*|\,s(dx) = \int_{\partial\Omega} |u^* - c|\,s(dx),$$

which together with (2) and (3) implies (1).

Let $B\mathring{V}(\Omega)$ denote the subset of $BV(\Omega)$ which contains functions with $\|u_0\|_{BV(R^n)} = \|u\|_{BV(\Omega)}$. Then from (1) it follows that $u \in B\mathring{V}(\Omega)$ if and only if $u^* = 0$ for the class of domains under consideration. Thus the elements of the factor-space $BV(\Omega)/B\mathring{V}(\Omega)$ are classes of functions which have the rough traces u^*.

Formula (1) and Theorem 6.5.2 imply the next assertion.

Corollary 1. *If for any* $\mathscr{E} \subset \Omega$

$$\min[P_{C\Omega}(\mathscr{E}), P_{C\Omega}(\Omega \setminus \mathscr{E})] \leqslant k P_\Omega(\mathscr{E}), \tag{4}$$

where k is a constant that is independent of $\mathscr{E}$, *then there exists a c such that*

$$\| u_c \|_{BV(R^n)} \leqslant (k+1) \| u \|_{BV(\Omega)} . \tag{5}$$

Conversely, if for each $u \in BV(\Omega)$ *there exists a c such that* (5) *is valid with k independent of u, then* (4) *holds for any* $\mathscr{E} \subset \Omega$.

Corollary 2. *In order for the inequality*

$$\| u_0 \|_{BV(R^n)} \leqslant k(\| u \|_{BV(\Omega)} + \| u \|_{L(\Omega)}) , \tag{6}$$

where k is independent of u, to hold for any $u \in BV(\Omega)$, *it is necessary and sufficient that there exists a* $\delta > 0$ *such that for any measurable set* $\mathscr{E} \subset \Omega$ *with* diam $\mathscr{E} < \delta$ *the inequality* $P_{C\Omega}(\mathscr{E}) \leqslant k_1 P_\Omega(\mathscr{E})$, *where* k_1 *is independent of* $\mathscr{E}$, *be valid.*

The necessity follows immediately from (1) and the isoperimetric inequality. The sufficiency results from (1) and Theorem 6.5.4.

Inequality (6.3.2/4) implies the following corollary.

Corollary 3. *If each of the sets* Ω_1, Ω_2 *satisfies the hypothesis of Corollary* 2, *then their union has the same property.*

In particular, this implies that any function in $BV(\Omega)$ can be extended by zero to the whole space so that (6) is valid for domains Ω which are finite unions of domains in $C^{0,1}$.

6.5.6. Multiplicative Estimates for the Rough Trace

Let $P(\Omega) < \infty$ and suppose a normal to Ω exists s-almost everywhere on $\partial\Omega$. Let $\mathscr{A}$ denote a subset of $\bar{\Omega}$; by $\zeta_{\mathscr{A}}^{(\alpha)}$, $\zeta_\alpha(S)$ we mean the functions introduced in Definitions 6.5.3/1 and 6.5.3/2.

The following assertion supplements Theorem 6.5.3.

Theorem. 1) *If* $\zeta_{\mathscr{A}}^{(1/q^*)} < \infty$, *where* $q^* \leqslant 1$, *then for any* $u \in BV(\Omega)$ *such that*

$$u(x) = 0 \quad \text{for } x \in \mathscr{A} \cap \Omega, \quad u^*(x) = 0 \quad \text{for } x \in \mathscr{A} \cap \partial^*\Omega , \tag{1}$$

the inequality

$$\| u^* \|_{L_q(\partial\Omega)} \leqslant C \| u \|_{BV(\Omega)}^{1-\varkappa} \| u^* \|_{L_t(\partial\Omega)}^{\varkappa} , \tag{2}$$

where $0<t<q<q^*$,

(3)
$$\varkappa=\frac{t(q^*-q)}{q(q^*-t)}$$

and $C^{q(q^*-t)/q^*(q-t)}\leqslant c\zeta_{\mathscr{A}}^{(1/q^*)}$, *is valid.*

2) *If for all* $u\in BV(\Omega)$ *satisfying* (1) *inequality* (2) *is valid with* $\varkappa$ *specified by* (3) *and with* $q^*>q$, $q^*>t$, *then*

$$\zeta_{\mathscr{A}}^{(1/q^*)}\leqslant C^{q(q^*-t)/q^*(q-t)}\,.$$

Proof. 1) Following the same line of reasoning as in the proof of Theorem 6.5.3, we obtain

(4)
$$\int_0^\infty [s(\Gamma_\tau)]^{1/q^*}d\tau\leqslant \zeta_{\mathscr{A}}^{(1/q^*)}\|u\|_{BV(\Omega)}\,,$$

where $\Gamma_\tau=\{x\in\partial\Omega: |u^*(x)|\geqslant\tau\}$.

In Lemma 1.3.3/2 we put $\xi=t^q$, $f(\xi)=s(\Gamma_\tau)$, $b=1/q^*$, $a\in(1,\infty)$, $\lambda=a(q-t)/q$, $\mu=(q^*-q)/q^*q$. Then

(5)
$$\int_0^\infty s(\Gamma_\tau)\tau^{q-1}d\tau\leqslant c\left(\int_0^\infty [s(\Gamma_\tau)]^a\tau^{at-1}d\tau\right)^{(q^*-q)/q(q^*-t)}\times\left(\int_0^\infty [s(\Gamma_\tau)]^{1/q^*}d\tau\right)^{q^*(q-t)/(q^*-t)}\,.$$

Since $a>1$ and the function $s(\Gamma_\tau)$ does not increase, Lemma 1.3.3/1 can be applied to the first factor. Then we have

(6)
$$\int_0^\infty [s(\Gamma_\tau)]^a\tau^{at-1}d\tau\leqslant c\left(\int_0^\infty s(\Gamma_\tau)\tau^{t-1}d\tau\right)^a=c\left(\int_{\partial\Omega}|u^*(x)|^t s(dx)\right)^a\,.$$

Combining (4) – (6) we arrive at item 1) of the theorem.

2) The lower bound for the constant C results by insertion of $\chi_{\mathscr{E}}$, where $\mathscr{E}$ satisfies (6.5.3/1), into (2).

Let us consider two domains for which we can obtain exact conditions for the boundedness of the function $\zeta_{\mathscr{A}}^{(\alpha)}$.

Example 1. Let $x=(x',x_n)$, $x'\in R^{n-1}$ and let

$$\Omega=\{x: 1<x_n<|x'|^{-\beta}, |x'|<1\}\,,\quad 0<\beta<n-2\,.$$

Further let $\mathscr{A}=\{x: x_n=1, |x'|<1\}$. We show that $\zeta_{\mathscr{A}}^{(\alpha)}<\infty$ for $\alpha=(n-1)/(n-2-\beta)$. (Using the sequence of sets $\mathscr{E}_m=\{x\in\Omega: x_n>m\}$, $m=1,2,\dots$ we can prove that this α is the best possible.)

Although Ω is not convex we can apply to it the proof of Lemma 6.3.2/3. Therefore it suffices to verify the estimate

$$[P_\Omega(\mathscr{E})]^{(n-1)/(n-2-\beta)} \leqslant c P_\Omega(\mathscr{E}) \tag{7}$$

for any set $\mathscr{E}$ which is the intersection of a polyhedron with Ω, $\mathscr{E} \cap \mathscr{A} = \varnothing$. Since (7) has already been obtained in Example 4.11.2/1, the result follows.

Example 2. Using the same argument and referring to Example 4.12/2, we can show that for

$$\Omega = \{x: |x'| < x_n^\beta, \ 0 < x_n < 1\}, \qquad \beta \geqslant 1$$

and for $\mathscr{A} = \{x: |x'| < 1, x_n = 1\}$ the value $\zeta_{\mathscr{A}}^{(\alpha)}$ is finite for $\alpha = \beta(n-1)/(\beta(n-2)+1)$ and that α is the best possible.

The theorem of the present subsection implies that the boundedness of the value $\zeta_{1/q^*}(S)$ is a necessary and sufficient condition for the validity of (2) for any function $u \in BV(\Omega)$ with $s(\{x: u^*(x) \neq 0\}) \leqslant S$ (cf. Corollary 6.5.3). Hence we easily conclude that the boundedness of $\zeta_{1/q^*}(S)$ for some $S < P(\Omega)$ is necessary and sufficient for the validity of the inequality

$$\|u^*\|_{L_q(\partial\Omega)} \leqslant (C_1 \|u\|_{BV(\Omega)} + C_2 \|u^*\|_{L_r(\partial\Omega)})^{1-\varkappa} \|u^*\|_{L_t(\partial\Omega)}^{\varkappa}, \tag{8}$$

where u is any function in $BV(\Omega)$, $r < q^*$ and $q^*, q, t, \varkappa$ are the same as in the theorem of the present subsection (cf. Theorem 4.3.3).

6.5.7. An Estimate for the Norm in $L_{n/(n-1)}(\Omega)$ of a Function in $BV(\Omega)$ with Summable Rough Trace

To conclude this section we prove an assertion similar to Corollary 3.6.3.

Theorem. *Suppose $P(\Omega) < \infty$ and that a normal to Ω exists s-almost everywhere on $\partial\Omega$. Then for any $u \in BV(\Omega)$ the inequality*

$$\|u\|_{L_{n/(n-1)}(\Omega)} \leqslant n v_n^{-1/n} (\|u\|_{BV(\Omega)} + \|u^*\|_{L(\partial\Omega)}) \tag{1}$$

is valid. Moreover, the constant $n v_n^{-1/n}$ is exact.

Proof. By (3.6.3/1) we have

$$\|u\|_{L_{n/(n-1)}(\Omega)} \leqslant \int_0^\infty [m_n \mathscr{N}_t]^{(n-1)/n} dt$$

$$= \int_0^\infty [m_n \mathscr{M}_t]^{(n-1)/n} dt + \int_{-\infty}^0 [m_n(\Omega \backslash \mathscr{M}_t)]^{(n-1)/n} dt,$$

where $\mathscr{M}_t = \{x: u(x) \geqslant t\}$. According to isoperimetric inequality (6.1.5/1) we obtain

$$[m_n \mathcal{M}_t]^{(n-1)/n} \leqslant n v_n^{-1/n} P(\mathcal{M}_t) = n v_n^{-1/n} [P_\Omega(\mathcal{M}_t) + s(\partial^* \mathcal{M}_t \cap \partial^* \Omega)] .$$

Since $s(\partial^* \mathcal{M}_t \cap \partial^* \Omega) = s(\{x: u^* \geqslant t\})$ for almost all t (Lemma 6.5.1/2) then

$$\int_0^\infty [m_n \mathcal{M}_t]^{(n-1)/n} dt \leqslant n v_n^{-1/n} \left[\int_0^\infty P_\Omega(\mathcal{M}_t)\, dt + \int_0^\infty s(\{x: u^* \geqslant t\})\, dt \right] .$$

Taking into account that $P_{C\Omega}(\mathcal{M}_t) + P_{C\Omega}(\Omega \setminus \mathcal{M}_t) = P(\Omega)$ by Lemma 6.4.2, we similarly obtain that

$$\int_{-\infty}^0 [m_n(\Omega \setminus \mathcal{M}_t)]^{(n-1)/n} dt \leqslant n v_n^{-1/n} \left[\int_{-\infty}^0 P_\Omega(\mathcal{M}_t)\, dt + \int_{-\infty}^0 s(\{x: u^* \leqslant t\})\, dt \right] .$$

Consequently,

$$\left[\int_\Omega |u|^{n/(n-1)} dx \right]^{(n-1)/n} \leqslant n v_n^{-1/n} \left\{ \int_{-\infty}^\infty P_\Omega(\mathcal{M}_t)\, dt + \int_0^\infty s(\{x: |u^*| \geqslant t\})\, dt \right\}$$

$$= n v_n^{-1/n} \left(\|u\|_{BV(\Omega)} + \int_{\partial\Omega} |u^*| s(dx) \right) .$$

The exactness of the constant in (1) is a corollary of the fact that (1) becomes an equality for $u = \chi_{B_\varrho}$ where B_ϱ is a ball in Ω.

Similarly to the preceding theorem we can generalize Theorem 3.6.3 to functions in $BV(\Omega)$.

§ 6.6. Traces of Functions in $BV(\Omega)$ on the Boundary and the Gauss-Green Formula

6.6.1 The Definition of the Trace

Let Ω be an open set in R^n and let the function u be summable in a neighborhood of a point $x \in \partial\Omega$. *The upper and the lower traces of the function u at the point x* are the numbers

$$\bar{u}(x) = \limsup_{\varrho \to 0} \frac{1}{m_n(B_\varrho(x) \cap \Omega)} \int_{B_\varrho(x) \cap \Omega} u(y)\, dy ,$$

$$\underline{u}(x) = \liminf_{\varrho \to 0} \frac{1}{m_n(B_\varrho(x) \cap \Omega)} \int_{B_\varrho(x) \cap \Omega} u(y)\, dy ,$$

respectively.

If $\bar{u}(x) = \underline{u}(x)$ then this common value is called *the trace* $\tilde{u}(x)$ *of the function u at the point* $x \in \partial\Omega$.

6.6.2. Coincidence of the Trace and the Rough Trace

Lemma. *Let $u \in BV(\Omega)$, $u \geqslant 0$ and let $\int_{\partial^* \Omega} u^*(x) s(dx) < \infty$. Then for any $x \in \partial^* \Omega$ the inequality*

$$u(x) \geqslant u^*(x) \tag{1}$$

is valid.

Proof. By virtue of Theorem 6.5.7, the function u is summable in Ω and hence the function $\underline{u}(x)$ is defined.

Inequality (1) is trivial provided $u^*(x) = 0$. Suppose $0 < u^*(x) < \infty$. We take an arbitrary $\varepsilon > 0$ and choose t to satisfy $0 < u^*(x) - t < \varepsilon$ and $P_\Omega(\mathcal{M}_t) < \infty$. Then $x \in \partial^* \mathcal{M}_t$ where $\mathcal{M}_t = \{y \colon u(y) \geqslant t\}$.

It is clear that the normal to $\mathcal{M}_t$ at the point x coincides with the normal to Ω. Consequently, we can find $r_0(x) > 0$ such that

$$1 - \varepsilon < \frac{m_n(\mathcal{M}_t \cap B_r(x))}{m_n(\Omega \cap B_r(x))} \leqslant 1 \tag{2}$$

for $0 < r < r_0(x)$. Since

$$\int_{B_r(x) \cap \Omega} u(y)\, dy = \int_0^\infty m_n(\mathcal{M}_\tau \cap B_r(x))\, d\tau ,$$

then (2) implies

$$\begin{aligned} \frac{1}{m_n(B_r \cap \Omega)} \int_{B_r \cap \Omega} u(y)\, dy &\geqslant \frac{1}{m_n(B_r \cap \Omega)} \int_0^t m_n(\mathcal{M}_\tau \cap B_r)\, d\tau \\ &\geqslant t \frac{m_n(\mathcal{M}_t \cap B_r)}{m_n(\Omega \cap B_r)} \geqslant (1 - \varepsilon) t , \end{aligned}$$

which proves (1) for $u^*(x) < \infty$.

In the case $u^*(x) = \infty$ the arguments are similar.

Theorem. *Let $P(\Omega) < \infty$ and suppose that a normal to Ω exists s-almost everywhere on $\partial \Omega$. If $u \in BV(\Omega)$ and $\int_{\partial \Omega} |u^*| s(dx) < \infty$ then the trace $\tilde{u}$ of the function u exists s-almost everywhere on $\partial \Omega$ and coincides with the rough trace u^*.*

Proof. According to Theorem 6.5.7, the function u is summable in Ω and, consequently, the upper and lower traces $\bar{u}$ and $\underline{u}$ are defined.

First consider the case of a nonnegative function u. Then by Lemma $\underline{u}(x) \geqslant u^*(x)$ for all $x \in \partial^* \Omega$.

Next we prove that the inequality $\bar{u}(x) \leqslant u^*(x)$ is valid for s-almost all $x \in \partial \Omega$, if $u \geqslant 0$. Suppose

$$s(\{x \in \partial^* \Omega \colon \bar{u}(x) > u^*(x)\}) > 0 .$$

Then there exists a $c > 0$ such that $s(Q) > 0$ where $Q = \{x \colon x \in \partial^* \Omega, \bar{u}(x) > u^*(x) + c\}$. Recalling the definition of $\bar{u}(x)$, for $x \in Q$ we have

$$c+u^*(x) \leqslant \limsup_{\varrho\to 0} \frac{1}{m_n(B_\varrho(x)\cap\Omega)} \int_0^\infty m_n(\mathscr{M}_t\cap B_\varrho(x))\,dt\,.$$

Since $x\in\partial^*\Omega$, then

(3)
$$\lim_{\varrho\to 0} \frac{2}{v_n\varrho^n} m_n(\Omega\cap B_\varrho(x)) = 1\,.$$

Therefore

(4)
$$c+u^*(x) \leqslant \frac{2}{v_n} \lim_{\varrho\to 0} \varrho^{-n} \int_0^\infty m_n(\mathscr{M}_t\cap B_\varrho(x))\,dt$$
$$\leqslant \left(\frac{2}{v_n}\right)^{(n-1)/n} \lim_{\varrho\to 0} \varrho^{1-n} \int_0^\infty [m_n(\mathscr{M}_t\cap B_\varrho(x))]^{(n-1)/n}\,dt\,.$$

Equality (3) implies

$$m_n(\mathscr{M}_t\cap B_\varrho(x)) \leqslant \alpha_\varrho \min\{m_n(\mathscr{M}_t\cap B_\varrho(x)),\, m_n(B_\varrho(x)\setminus\mathscr{M}_t)\}\,,$$

where α_ϱ does not depend on t and $\alpha_\varrho\to 1$ as $\varrho\to 0$. Applying the relative isoperimetric inequality (6.1.7/1), we obtain

(5)
$$[m_n(\mathscr{M}_t\cap B_\varrho(x))]^{(n-1)/n} \leqslant \alpha_\varrho^{(n-1)/n} \left(\frac{v_n}{2}\right)^{(n-1)/n} v_{n-1}^{-1} \operatorname{var}\nabla\chi_{\mathscr{M}_t}(B_\varrho(x))\,.$$

Noting that

$$\operatorname{var}\nabla\chi_{\mathscr{M}_t}(B_\varrho) = \operatorname{var}\nabla\chi_{\mathscr{M}_t}(B_\varrho\cap\Omega) + s(\partial^*\Omega\cap\partial^*\mathscr{M}_t)$$

and integrating (5) with respect to t, we obtain

(6)
$$\int_0^\infty [m_n(\mathscr{M}_t\cap B_\varrho(x))]^{(n-1)/n}\,dt$$
$$\leqslant \alpha_n^{(n-1)/n} \left(\frac{v_n}{2}\right)^{(n-1)/n} v_{n-1}^{-1} \left\{\int_0^\infty \operatorname{var}\nabla\chi_{\mathscr{M}_t}(B_\varrho(x)\cap\Omega)\,dt + \int_0^\infty s(\partial^*\Omega\cap\partial^*\mathscr{M}_t)\,dt\right\}$$
$$= \alpha_\varrho^{(n-1)/n} \left(\frac{v_n}{2}\right)^{(n-1)/n} v_{n-1}^{-1} \left\{\operatorname{var}\nabla u(B_\varrho(x)) + \int_{\partial^*\Omega\cap B_\varrho(x)} u^*(y)\,s(dy)\right\}.$$

Comparing (4) and (6) and taking into account that $\alpha_\varrho\to 1$ as $\varrho\to 0$ we obtain

(7)
$$c+u^*(x) \leqslant v_{n-1}^{-1} \left\{\limsup_{\varrho\to 0} \varrho^{1-n} \operatorname{var}\nabla u(B_\varrho(x)) + \limsup_{\varrho\to 0} \varrho^{1-n} \int_{\partial^*\Omega\cap B_\varrho(x)} u^*(y)\,s(dy)\right\}.$$

According to formula (6.2.4/7),

$$\lim_{\varrho\to 0} \varrho^{1-n} \operatorname{var} \nabla \chi_\Omega(B_\varrho(x)) = v_{n-1}$$

for s-almost all $x \in \partial^*\Omega$. On the other hand, $\operatorname{var} \nabla \chi_\Omega(B_\varrho) = s(\partial^*\Omega \cap B_\varrho)$. Therefore, for s-almost all $x \in Q$ inequality (7) can be rewritten in the form

$$c + u^*(x) \leqslant v_{n-1}^{-1} \limsup_{\varrho\to 0} \varrho^{1-n} \operatorname{var} \nabla u(B_\varrho(x)) + \limsup_{\varrho\to 0} \frac{1}{s(\partial^*\Omega \cap B_\varrho(x))} \int_{\partial^*\Omega \cap B_\varrho(x)} u^*(y)s(dy) . \tag{8}$$

The integral $I(\mathscr{E}) = \int_{\mathscr{E}} u^*(y)s(dy)$ is absolutely continuous relative to the measure $s(\mathscr{E})$. So the derivative

$$\frac{dI}{ds}(x) = \lim_{\varrho\to 0} \frac{1}{s(\partial^*\Omega \cap B_\varrho(x))} \int_{\partial^*\Omega \cap B_\varrho(x)} u^*(y)s(dy) = u^*(x)$$

exists for s-almost all $x \in \partial^*\Omega$ (see, for instance, Hahn and Rosenthal [86], p. 290). Therefore, for s-almost all $x \in Q$ inequality (8) can be rewritten as

$$c v_{n-1} \leqslant \limsup_{\varrho\to 0} \varrho^{1-n} \operatorname{var} \nabla u(B_\varrho(x)) . \tag{9}$$

Since $\operatorname{var} \nabla u(R^n) < \infty$, $\operatorname{var} \nabla u(Q) = 0$ then Lemma 6.2.5/1 and (9) imply $s(Q) = 0$. The assertion is proved.

Now let u be an arbitrary function in $BV(\Omega)$. Then the functions $u^+ = \frac{1}{2}(u + |u|)$, $u^- = \frac{1}{2}(|u| - u)$ are also in $BV(\Omega)$. By virtue of what we proved above, the equalities

$$\tilde{u}^+(x) = (u^+(x))^* , \quad \tilde{u}^-(x) = (u^-(x))^* \tag{10}$$

are valid s-almost everywhere on $\partial^*\Omega$. Consequently, the trace $\tilde{u}$ of the function u exists s-almost everywhere on $\partial^*\Omega$. Moreover,

$$\tilde{u}(x) = \tilde{u}^+(x) - \tilde{u}^-(x) . \tag{11}$$

On the other hand, it is clear that

$$(u^+(x))^* = \begin{cases} u^*(x) & \text{if } u^*(x) < 0 , \\ 0 & \text{if } u^*(x) \geqslant 0 , \end{cases}$$

$$(u^-(x))^* = \begin{cases} -u^*(x) & \text{if } u^*(x) < 0 , \\ 0 & \text{if } u^*(x) \geqslant 0 \end{cases}$$

and, thus, we always have

(12) $$u^*(x) = (u^+(x))^* - (u^-(x))^* .$$

By comparing equalities (10) – (12) we conclude that $\tilde{u}(x) = u^*(x)$.

6.6.3. The Trace of the Characteristic Function

The hypothesis of Theorem 6.6.2 may be weakened for the characteristic function. Namely, the following lemma holds.

Lemma. *Let $P(\Omega) < \infty$, $\mathscr{E} \subset \Omega$, $P_\Omega(\mathscr{E}) < \infty$. Then the trace $\tilde{\chi}_\mathscr{E}$ of the function $\chi_\mathscr{E}$ exists for s-almost all $x \in \partial^* \Omega$.*

Proof. We put

$$C_k = \left\{x \colon x \in \partial^* \Omega,\ \chi_\mathscr{E}(x) < 1,\ \bar{\chi}_\mathscr{E} > \frac{1}{k}\right\}, \qquad k = 2, 3, \ldots .$$

Since $\chi_\mathscr{E}^*(x) = 1$ for $x \in \partial^* \Omega \cap \partial^* \mathscr{E}$ and $\chi_\mathscr{E}^*(x) = 0$ for $x \in \partial^* \Omega \backslash \partial^* \mathscr{E}$ then the functions $\tilde{\chi}_\mathscr{E}$ and $\chi_\mathscr{E}^*$ coincide on the set $\partial^* \Omega \backslash \bigcup_{k=2}^{\infty} C_k$.

It remains to prove that $s(C_k) = 0$, $k = 2, 3, \ldots$. Using the inclusion $C_k \subset \partial^* \Omega$, for $x \in C_k$ we obtain

(1) $$\bar{\chi}_\mathscr{E}(x) = \limsup_{\varrho \to 0} \frac{m_n(\mathscr{E} \cap B_\varrho(x))}{m_n(\Omega \cap B_\varrho(x))} = \frac{2}{v_n} \limsup_{\varrho \to 0} m_n(\mathscr{E} \cap B_\varrho(x)) \geqslant k^{-1} .$$

By Lemma 6.5.1/2 we have $P(\mathscr{E}) < \infty$. Therefore (6.1.7/1) implies

$$m_n(\mathscr{E} \cap B_\varrho(x)) \leqslant C[\operatorname{var} \nabla_{R^n} \chi_\mathscr{E}(B_\varrho(x))]^{n/(n-1)} .$$

Comparing this with (1), we obtain

(2) $$\limsup_{\varrho \to 0} \varrho^{1-n} \operatorname{var} \nabla \chi_\mathscr{E}(B_\varrho(x)) \geqslant \left(\frac{v_n}{2kC}\right)^{(n-1)/n} .$$

Since $C_k \cap \partial^* \mathscr{E} = \varnothing$ then $\operatorname{var} \nabla \chi_\mathscr{E}(C_k) = 0$. So (2) along with Lemma 6.2.5/1 yields $s(C_k) = 0$ and the result follows.

6.6.4. On Summability of the Trace of a Function in $BV(\Omega)$

Theorem. *Let $P(\Omega) < \infty$ and suppose that a normal to Ω exists s-almost everywhere on $\partial \Omega$. Then:*

1) *if for any measurable set $\mathscr{E}$ the inequality*

(1) $$\min\{P_{C\Omega}(\mathscr{E}), P_{C\Omega}(\Omega\setminus\mathscr{E})\} \leqslant k P_\Omega(\mathscr{E}),$$

where k is independent of $\mathscr{E}$, *is valid, then the trace* $\tilde{u}$ *exists for any* $u \in BV(\Omega)$. *Moreover,*

$$\inf_c \int_{\partial\Omega} |\tilde{u} - c|\, s(dx) \leqslant k \|u\|_{BV(\Omega)};$$

2) *if inequality* (2), *with a constant k that is independent of u, is valid for any* $u \in BV(\Omega)$ *having a trace* $\tilde{u}$ *on* $\partial\Omega$ *then for any measurable set* $\mathscr{E} \subset \Omega$ *the estimate* (1) *is true.*

Proof. 1) By Theorem 6.5.2 the rough trace of u is summable on $\partial\Omega$. Consequently, by Theorem 6.6.2 s-almost everywhere on $\partial\Omega$ there exists the trace $\tilde{u}$ which coincides with u^*. Therefore inequality (6.5.2/1) implies (2).

2) Let $\mathscr{E}$ be a measurable subset of Ω with $P_\Omega(\mathscr{E}) < \infty$. By virtue of Lemma 6.6.3 the trace $\tilde{\chi}_{\mathscr{E}}$ of the function $\chi_{\mathscr{E}}$ exists s-almost everywhere and equals $\chi^*_{\mathscr{E}}$. So, by inserting $u = \chi_{\mathscr{E}}$ into (2), we obtain

$$\inf \int_{\partial\Omega} |\chi^*_{\mathscr{E}} - c|\, s(dx) \leqslant k P_\Omega(\mathscr{E}),$$

which is equivalent to (1) (compare with the proof of necessity in Theorem 6.5.2). The theorem is proved.

6.6.5. The Gauss-Green Formula for Functions in $BV(\Omega)$

Lemma. *For any function* $u \in BV(\Omega)$ *and any measurable set* $\mathfrak{B} \subset \Omega$ *the equality*

(1) $$\nabla u(\mathfrak{B}) = \int_{-\infty}^{\infty} \nabla \chi_{\mathscr{M}_t}(\mathfrak{B})\, dt,$$

where $\mathscr{M}_t = \{x\colon u(x) \geqslant t\}$, *is valid.*

Proof. It suffices to prove (1) for $u \geqslant 0$. Let φ be an infinitely differentiable function with compact support in Ω. Then

$$-\int_\Omega \varphi \nabla u(dx) = \int_\Omega u \nabla \varphi(dx) = \int_\Omega \int_0^\infty \chi_{\mathscr{M}_t}(x)\, dt\, \nabla \varphi(dx).$$

By the Fubini theorem the double integral equals

$$\int_0^\infty dt \int_\Omega \chi_{\mathscr{M}_t}(x)\, \nabla \varphi(dx).$$

Moreover, we note that

(2) $$\int_\Omega \varphi \nabla u(dx) = \int_0^\infty dt \int_\Omega \varphi \nabla \chi_{\mathscr{M}_t}(dx) = \int_\Omega \varphi\, dx \int_0^\infty \nabla \chi_{\mathscr{M}_t}\, dt$$

for almost all t. Here we may reverse the order of integration since equality (6.1.6/1) implies the finiteness of the integral

$$\int_0^\infty dt \int_\Omega |\varphi| \operatorname{var} \nabla \chi_{\mathscr{M}_t}(dx) .$$

So equality (1) immediately results from (2).

Theorem (The Gauss-Green Formula). *Let $P(\Omega) < \infty$ and suppose that a normal to Ω exists s-almost everywhere on $\partial\Omega$. Then for any function $u \in BV(\Omega)$ whose rough trace is summable on the boundary of Ω, the equality*

$$\nabla v(\Omega) = \int_{\partial\Omega} u^*(x)\, v(x)\, s(dx) ,$$

where $v(x)$ is the normal to Ω at the point x, is valid.

Proof. Since $\nabla \chi_{\mathscr{E}}(R^n) = 0$ for any set $\mathscr{E}$ with $P(\mathscr{E}) < \infty$, then by Lemma

$$\nabla u(\Omega) = \int_{-\infty}^{\infty} \nabla \chi_{\mathscr{M}_t}(\Omega)\, dt = \int_{-\infty}^{\infty} \nabla \chi_{\mathscr{M}_t}(\partial\Omega \cap \partial^* \mathscr{M}_t)\, dt .$$

Using $s(\partial\Omega \backslash \partial^*\Omega) = 0$ and the coincidence of the normal to $\mathscr{M}_t$ with that to Ω on $\partial^*\Omega \cap \partial^*\mathscr{M}_t$, we obtain

$$\nabla \chi_{\mathscr{M}_t}(\partial\Omega \cap \partial^*\mathscr{M}_t) = \int_{\partial^*\Omega \cap \partial^*\mathscr{M}_t} v(x)\, s(dx) = \nabla \chi_\Omega(\partial^*\mathscr{M}_t) .$$

Thus

$$\begin{aligned}
\nabla u(\Omega) &= \int_0^\infty \nabla \chi_\Omega(\partial^*\mathscr{M}_t)\, dt + \int_{-\infty}^0 \nabla \chi_\Omega(\partial^*\mathscr{M}_t)\, dt \\
&= \int_0^\infty \nabla \chi_\Omega(\partial^*\mathscr{M}_t)\, dt - \int_{-\infty}^0 \nabla \chi_\Omega(\partial^*\Omega \backslash \partial^*\mathscr{M}_t)\, dt \\
&= \int_0^\infty \nabla \chi_\Omega(\{x : u^* \geqslant t\})\, dt - \int_{-\infty}^0 \nabla \chi_\Omega(\{x : u^* \leqslant t\})\, dt \\
&= \int_{\partial\Omega} u^* \nabla \chi_\Omega(dx) \\
&= \int_{\partial\Omega} u^*(x)\, v(x)\, s(dx) .
\end{aligned}$$

The theorem is proved.

The example of the disk with a slit

$$\{z = \varrho e^{i\theta} : 0 < \varrho < 1,\ 0 < \theta < 2\pi\}$$

and of the function $u(z) = \theta$ shows that the condition $s(\partial\Omega \backslash \partial^*\Omega) = 0$ cannot be omitted under our definition of the trace.

Theorems 6.6.2 and 6.6.5 immediately imply the following corollary.

Corollary. *Let* $P(\Omega) < \infty$, $s(\partial\Omega \backslash \partial^* \Omega) = 0$. *If for any* $\mathscr{E} \subset \Omega$

$$\min\{P_{C\Omega}(\mathscr{E}), P_{C\Omega}(\Omega \backslash \mathscr{E})\} \leqslant k P_\Omega(\mathscr{E}) ,$$

where k is independent of $\mathscr{E}$, *then the trace* $\tilde{u}(x)$ *exists for any* $u \in BV(\Omega)$ *and the Gauss-Green formula*

$$\nabla u(\Omega) = \int_{\partial\Omega} \tilde{u}(x)\, \nu(x)\, s(dx)$$

is valid.

§ 6.7. Comments to Chapter 6

The first two sections contain well-known facts from the theory of sets with finite perimeter and from the theory of functions in BV. The foundation of this theory was laid by Caccioppoli [39, 40] and De Giorgi [49, 50]. Its further development is due to Krickeberg [118], Fleming [64], Fleming and Rishel [65], and others. The results in subsections 6.1.6, 6.1.3 – 6.1.5 are due (up to the presentation) to De Giorgi [49, 50]. Theorem 6.1.2 is a modification of a result by Krickeberg [118]. Formula (6.1.6/1) in 6.1.6 was obtained by Fleming and Rishel [65].

The results of § 6.2 were established by De Giorgi [50] and supplemented by Federer [58].

At the present time the theory of sets with finite perimeter can be considered as a part of the theory of integral currents (cf. Federer [61], part 4.5).

§§ 6.3 – 6.6 contain an expanded presentation of the paper by Burago and Maz'ja [36].

Bokowski and Sperner [33] obtained the estimates for the functions $\eta(S)$ and λ_M for convex domains by the radii of inscribed and circumscribed balls.

For various facts concerning isoperimetric inequalities see the book by Burago and Zalgaller [35] and the review paper by Osserman [206].

Souček [235] studied the properties of functions whose derivatives of order l are charges.

In connection with the contents of the present chapter see also the paper by Vol'pert [252].

Chapter 7. Certain Function Spaces, Capacities and Potentials

The present chapter is of an auxiliary nature. Here we collect (mostly without proofs) the results of function theory which are applied later or are related to the facts used in the sequel. First we discuss the theorems on spaces of functions having derivatives of arbitrary positive order (§ 7.1). The theory of these spaces is essentially presented in monographs (cf. Stein [237], Peetre [210], Nikol'skiĭ [202], Besov, Il'in and Nikol'skiĭ [27], Triebel [244, 245]) though in some cases the reader interested in the proofs will have to refer to the original papers. Section 7.2 deals with the properties of capacities and nonlinear potentials. Unfortunately, this material is dispersed throughout the journals. However, an attempt at its systematic exposition would lead to an inadmissible enlargement of the volume. In any case, the presented statements are sufficient for our further considerations.

§ 7.1. The Spaces of Functions Differentiable of Arbitrary Positive Order

7.1.1. The Spaces w_p^l, W_p^l, b_p^l, B_p^l for $l>0$

For $p \geqslant 1$ and integer $l>0$, let w_p^l denote the completion of the space $\mathscr{D}$ with respect to the norm $\| \nabla_l u \|_{L_p}$.

For $p \geqslant 1$ and fractional l we define w_p^l as the completion of $\mathscr{D}$ with respect to the norm

(1) $$\left(\int \| \Delta_y u \|^p_{w_p^{[l]}} |y|^{-n-p\{l\}} dy\right)^{1/p} .$$

Here $\Delta_y u(x) = u(x+y) - u(x)$, $[l]$ and $\{l\}$ are the integer and fractional parts of l, respectively.

Replacing the norm (1) by the norm

(2) $$\|u\|_{b_p^l} = \left(\int \|\Delta_y^2 u\|^p_{L_p} |y|^{-n-pl} dy\right)^{1/p}, \quad 0<l\leqslant 1 ,$$

in the latter definition, we obtain the space b_p^l (here $\Delta_y^2 u(x) = u(x+y) - 2u(x) + u(x-y)$). For $l>1$ we put $\|u\|_{b_p^l} = \|\nabla u\|_{b_p^{l-1}}$.

Further let W_p^l and B_p^l be the completions of $\mathscr{D}$ with respect to the norms $\|u\|_{w_p^l} + \|u\|_{L_p}$ and $\|u\|_{b_p^l} + \|u\|_{L_p}$.

For fractional l the norms in w_p^l and b_p^l, as well as the norms in W_p^l and B_p^l, are equivalent. In fact, the identity

$$2(u(x+h)-u(x)) = -[u(x+2h)-2u(x+h)+u(x)] + [u(x+2h)-u(x)]$$

implies the estimates

$$(2-2^l)\mathscr{H}_l u \leqslant \mathscr{G}_l u \leqslant (2+2^l)\mathscr{H}_l u\,, \quad 0<l<1\,,$$

where

$$(\mathscr{H}_l u)(x) = \left(\int |(\Delta_y u)(x)|^p |y|^{-n-pl} dy\right)^{1/p},$$

$$(\mathscr{G}_l u)(x) = \left(\int |(\Delta_y^2 u)(x)|^p |y|^{-n-pl} dy\right)^{1/p}.$$

The utility of the defined spaces is mostly due to the following theorem.

Theorem 1. *For* $p\in[1,\infty)$, $l>0$, $m=1,2,\ldots$ *we have*

(3) $$\|u\|_{b_p^l(R^n)} \sim \inf_{\{U\}} \||y|^{m-\{l\}-p^{-1}} \nabla_{m+[l]} U\|_{L_p(R^{n+1})}\,,$$

where $U\in\mathscr{D}(R^{n+1})$ *is an arbitrary extension of* $u\in\mathscr{D}(R^n)$ *to the space* $R^{n+1}=\{(x,y)\colon x\in R^n,\ y\in R^1\}$.

Proof. We restrict ourselves to the derivation of (3) for $0<l\leqslant 1$, $m=2$. Let $U\in\mathscr{D}(R^{n+1})$, $u=U|_{R^n}$. We put $\bar\Delta_t^{(2)}u(x,t)=u(x,2t)-2u(x,t)+u(x,0)$. It can be easily seen that

(4) $$\bar\Delta_t^{(2)}u(x,t) = \int_0^t (t-\tau)\frac{d^2}{d\tau^2}[u(x,t+\tau)+u(x,t-\tau)]\,d\tau\,.$$

We can also readily check that

(5) $$\bar\Delta_t^{(2)}u(x,0) = -2\bar\Delta_{|h|}^{(2)}u(x,|h|)+2\Delta_h^{(2)}u(x,|h|)-\Delta_h^{(2)}u(x,2|h|) + \bar\Delta_{|h|}^{(2)}u(x+h,|h|)+\bar\Delta_{|h|}^{(2)}u(x-h,|h|)\,.$$

We consider only the first and the second summands since the others can be estimated in a similar way. By (4) we obtain

$$\|\bar\Delta_{|h|}^{(2)}u(\cdot,|h|)\|_{L_p(R^n)} \leqslant 2\int_0^{2|h|} y \left\|\frac{d^2}{dy^2}U(x,y)\right\|_{L_p(R^n)} dy\,.$$

Therefore (for $l\in(0,1]$, $p\geqslant 1$),

(6) $$\int_{R^n} \|\bar\Delta_{|h|}^{(2)}u(\cdot,|h|)\|_{L_p(R^n)}^p \frac{dh}{|h|^{n+pl}}$$

$$\leqslant c\int_0^\infty\left(\int_0^{2\varrho} y\left\|\frac{d^2U}{dy^2}(\cdot,y)\right\|_{L_p(R^n)}dy\right)^p\frac{d\varrho}{\varrho^{1+pl}}$$

$$\leqslant c\int_0^\infty y^{(2-l)p-1}\left\|\frac{d^2U}{dy^2}(\cdot,y)\right\|^p_{L_p(R^n)}dy\,.$$

Next we proceed to the second item in (5). We have

$$\Delta_h^{(2)}u(x,|h|)=\int_0^1(1-\lambda)\frac{d^2}{d\lambda^2}[u(x+\lambda h,|h|)+u(x-\lambda h,|h|)]\,d\lambda\,.$$

By the Minkowski inequality

$$\|\Delta_h^{(2)}u(\cdot,|h|)\|_{L_p(R^n)}\leqslant c|h|^2\|\nabla_{2,x}u(\cdot,|h|)\|_{L_p(R^n)}\,.$$

Hence

$$\int_{R^n}\|\Delta_h^{(2)}u(\cdot,|h|)\|^p_{L_p(R^n)}\frac{dh}{|h|^{n+pl}}\leqslant c\int_0^\infty y^{(2-l)p-1}\|\nabla_{2,x}U(\cdot,y)\|^p_{L_p(R^n)}dy\,,$$

which together with (6) yields the upper bound for the norm $\|u\|_{b_p^l}$. We proceed to the lower estimate.

Let $u\in\mathscr{D}(R^n)$ and let Π be the extension operator to the space $R^{n+1}=\{X=(x,y)\colon x\in R^n,\ y\in R^1\}$ defined by

$$(\Pi u)(X)=y^{-n}\int_{R^n}\pi\left(\frac{\xi-x}{y}\right)u(\xi)\,d\xi\,, \tag{7}$$

where

$$\pi\in C_0^\infty(B_1)\,,\qquad \int_{R^n}\pi(x)\,dx=1\,,\qquad \pi(x)=\pi(-x)\,.$$

Using the evenness of the function π, for $|\alpha|=2$ we obtain

$$(D_x^\alpha\Pi u)(X)=y^{-n-2}\int_{R^n}(D^\alpha\pi)\left(\frac{\xi-x}{y}\right)u(\xi)\,d\xi$$

$$=y^{-n-2}\int_{R^n}(D^\alpha\pi)(h/y)\,\Delta_h^{(2)}u(x)\,dh$$

where, as before, $\Delta_h^{(2)}u(x)=u(x+h)-2u(x)+u(x-h)$. Therefore for $|\alpha|=2$ we have

$$|(D_x^\alpha\Pi u)(X)|\leqslant cy^{-n-2}\int_{B_y}|\Delta_h^{(2)}u(x)|\,dh\,.$$

Since

$$(\Pi u)(X)=y^{-n}\int\pi(h/y)\,\Delta_y^{(2)}u(x)\,dh+2u(x)\,,$$

then

$$\left|\left(\frac{\partial^2}{\partial y^2}\Pi u\right)(X)\right| \leqslant c y^{-n-2} \int_{B_y} |\Delta_h^{(2)} u(x)|\,dh\,.$$

We can easily check that the same estimate is also true for $|\partial^2 \Pi/\partial x_i \partial y|$. So the second derivatives of u are bounded and

$$\int_0^\infty y^{-1+p(2-l)} \|(\nabla_2 \Pi u)(\cdot, y)\|_{L_p(R^n)}^p dy \leqslant \int_0^\infty y^{-1+p(l+n)} \left\| \int_{B_y} |\Delta_y^{(2)} u(\cdot)|\,dh \right\|_{L_p(R^n)}^p dy\,.$$

By virtue of the Minkowski inequality the right-hand side does not exceed

$$c \int_0^\infty y^{-1-pl-n} \left(\int_{B_y} \|\Delta_h^{(2)} u(\cdot)\|_{L_p(R^n)} dh \right)^p dy$$

$$\leqslant c \int_{R^n} \|\Delta_h^{(2)} u(\cdot)\|_{L_p(R^n)}^p \int_{|h|}^\infty y^{-1-pl-n} dy\,dh$$

$$= c \int_{R^n} \|\Delta_h^{(2)} u(\cdot)\|_{L_p(R^n)}^p |h|^{-n-pl} dh$$

and the required lower estimate for the norm $\|u\|_{b_p^l}$ follows.

Next we show that the function Πu can be approximated by the sequence of extensions $U_k \in \mathscr{D}(R^{n+1})$ of the function u in the metric $\| |y|^{2-l-p^{-1}} \nabla_2 U \|_{L_p(R^{n+1})}$. Let $\eta_k(X) = \eta(X/k)$ where $\eta \in \mathscr{D}(R^{n+1})$, $\eta = 1$ for $|X| < k$ and $k = 1, 2, \dots$. Since $(D^\alpha \Pi u)(X) = O((|X|+1)^{-n-|\alpha|})$ for $0 < |\alpha| \leqslant 2$ then $\nabla_2(\Pi u - \eta_k \Pi u) = O((|X|+1)^{-n-2})$. Furthermore,

$$\operatorname{supp}(\Pi u - \eta_k \Pi u) \subset \{X \in R^{n+1} : |X| > k\}\,.$$

Consequently,

$$\| |y|^{2-l-p^{-1}} \nabla_2 (\Pi u - \eta_k \Pi u) \|_{L_p(R^{n+1})} = O(k^{-l-n+n/p}) = o(1)$$

as $k \to \infty$. It remains to approximate each of the functions $\eta_k \Pi u$ by a sequence of mollifications.

Similarly we can show the following analogous assertion for the space $B_p^l(R^n)$.

Theorem 2. *For* $p \in [1, \infty)$, $l > 0$, $m = 1, 2, \dots$ *we have*

$$\|u\|_{B_p^l(R^n)} \sim \inf_{\{U\}} \left(\| |y|^{m-\{l\}-p^{-1}} \nabla_{m+[l]} U \|_{L_p(R^{n+1})} + \|U\|_{L_p(R^{n+1})} \right).$$

Theorems 1 and 2 have a long history. For $p = 2$, $\{l\} = m - \frac{1}{2}$ they were established by Aronszajn [17], Babič and Slobodeckiĭ [21], Freud and Králik [67]. The particular case $n = p = 2$, $m = l = 1$ is actually contained in the papers of Douglas [53], 1931, and Beurling [28], 1940. The generalization for $p \neq 2$

is due to Gagliardo [69] for $l = 1 - 1/p$. Theorems 1 and 2 were proved, in a form similar to that above, by Uspenskiĭ [248] (cf. also Lizorkin [135]).

The present state of the theory of spaces with "weighted" norms is discussed in the books by Triebel [245], Kufner [119] and in the survey [26].

In conclusion we state the following trace theorem for functions in $w_1^1(R^{n+1})$, $W_1^1(R^{n+1})$ on a hyperplane.

Theorem 3. *We have*

$$\|u\|_{L_1(R^n)} \sim \inf_{\{U\}} \|\nabla U\|_{L_1(R^{n+1})} \sim \inf_{\{U\}} \|U\|_{W_1^1(R^{n+1})},$$

where $u \in \mathcal{D}(R^n)$ *and* $\{U\}$ *is the collection of all extensions of* u *to* R^{n+1}, $U \in \mathcal{D}(R^{n+1})$.

This assertion is proved in the paper by Gagliardo [69] (cf. also the book by Besov, Il'in and Nikol'skiĭ [27]).

7.1.2. The Riesz and Bessel Potential Spaces

With each function $u \in \mathcal{D} = \mathcal{D}(R^n)$ we associate its Fourier transform

$$\hat{u}(\xi) = Fu(\xi) = (2\pi)^{-n/2} \int e^{ix\xi} u(x)\, dx .$$

The same notation will be retained for the Fourier transform of the distribution u contained in the space $\mathcal{D}'$ dual of $\mathcal{D}$. We denote the convolution of distributions by a star, $*$.

The scales of "fractional" spaces different from the spaces introduced in 7.1.1 are defined by means of the operators

$$(-\Delta)^{l/2} = F^{-1} |\xi|^l F, \quad (-\Delta + 1)^{l/2} = F^{-1}(1 + |\xi|^2)^{l/2} F,$$

where Δ is the Laplace operator.

Namely, let h_p^l and H_p^l $(1 < p < \infty, l > 0)$ denote the completion of the space $\mathcal{D}$ with respect to the norms

$$\|u\|_{h_p^l} = \|(-\Delta)^{l/2} u\|_{L_p}, \quad \|u\|_{H_p^l} = \|(-\Delta + 1)^{l/2} u\|_{L_p}.$$

The following assertion is the Mihlin theorem on Fourier integral multipliers [187].

Theorem 1. *Let the function* Φ *defined on* $R^n \backslash \{0\}$ *have the derivatives* $\partial^k \Phi(\lambda)/\partial\lambda_{j_1} \ldots \partial\lambda_{j_k}$, *where* $0 \leqslant k \leqslant n$ *and* $1 \leqslant j_1 < j_2 < \cdots < j_k \leqslant n$. *Further let*

$$|\lambda|^k \left| \frac{\partial^k \Phi(\lambda)}{\partial\lambda_{j_1} \ldots \partial\lambda_{j_k}} \right| \leqslant M = \text{const} .$$

Then for all $u \in L_p$

$$\|F^{-1}\Phi Fu\|_{L_p} \leqslant cM\|u\|_{L_p}, \quad 1 < p < \infty,$$

where c is a constant that depends only on n and p.

Corollary 1. *Let $l = 1, 2, \ldots$, then there exist positive numbers c and C that depend only on n, p, l such that*

$$c\|(-\varDelta)^{l/2}u\|_{L_p} \leqslant \|\nabla_l u\|_{L_p} \leqslant C\|(-\varDelta)^{l/2}u\|_{L_p} \tag{1}$$

for all $u \in \mathscr{D}$.

Proof. Let α be a multi-index with $|\alpha| = l$. Then

$$F^{-1}\xi^\alpha Fu = F^{-1}\xi^\alpha|\xi|^{-l}|\xi|^l Fu.$$

The function $\xi^\alpha|\xi|^{-l}$ satisfies the hypothesis of Theorem 1 which leads to the rightmost estimate in (1). On the other hand,

$$|\xi|^l = |\xi|^{2l}|\xi|^{-l} = \left(\sum_{|\alpha|=l} c_\alpha \xi^\alpha \xi^\alpha\right)|\xi|^{-l},$$

where $c_\alpha = l!/\alpha!$, so

$$F^{-1}|\xi|^l Fu = \sum_{|\alpha|=l} c_\alpha F^{-1}\frac{\xi^\alpha}{|\xi|^l}\xi^\alpha Fu.$$

Again, by applying Theorem 1, we obtain the leftmost estimate in (1).

The following corollary has a similar proof.

Corollary 2. *Let $l = 1, 2, \ldots$. There exist positive numbers c and C that depend only on n, p, l such that*

$$c\|u\|_{W_p^l} \leqslant \|(-\varDelta+1)^{l/2}u\|_{L_p} \leqslant C\|u\|_{W_p^l}$$

for all $u \in \mathscr{D}$.

Thus, $w_p^l = h_p^l$ and $W_p^l = H_p^l$ provided $p > 1$ and l is an integer.

For the proof of the following theorem see the paper by Havin and the author [171].

Theorem 2. *Let $pl < n$, $p > 1$. Then $u \in h_p^l$ if and only if $u = (-\varDelta)^{-l/2}f \equiv c|x|^{l-n} * f$, where $f \in L_p$.*

A similar well-known assertion for the space H_p^l is contained in the following theorem.

Theorem 3. *The function u is contained in H_p^l, $p > 1$, if and only if*

$$u = (-\varDelta+1)^{-l/2}f \equiv G_l * f,$$

where $f \in L_p$, $G_l(x) = c\,|x|^{(l-n)/2} K_{(n-l)/2}(|x|)$, K_ν *is the modified Bessel function of the third kind.*

For $|x| \leqslant 1$ the estimates

$$G_l(x) \leqslant \begin{cases} c|x|^{l-n}, & 0<l<n\,, \\ c\log(2/|x|)\,, & l=n\,, \\ c, & l>n \end{cases}$$

are valid. If $|x| \geqslant 1$, then

$$G_l(x) \leqslant c\,|x|^{(l-n-1)/2} e^{-|x|}\,.$$

The integral operators

$$f \xrightarrow{I_l} |x|^{l-n} * f\,, \quad f \xrightarrow{J_l} G_l * f$$

are called the Riesz potential and the Bessel potential, respectively. Thus Theorems 2 and 3 state that each element of the space $h_p^l (pl<n)$ (H_p^l) is the Riesz (Bessel) potential with density in L_p.

Next we formulate the theorem due to Strichartz [238] on equivalent norms in the spaces h_p^l and H_p^l.

Theorem 4. *Let* $\{l\} > 0$ *and let*

$$(2) \qquad (\mathscr{D}_{\{l\}} v)(x) = \left(\int_0^\infty \left[\int_{|\theta|<1} |v(x+\theta y) - v(x)|\,d\theta \right]^2 y^{-1-2\{l\}} dy \right)^{1/2}.$$

Then

$$(3) \qquad \|u\|_{h_p^l} \sim \|\mathscr{D}_{\{l\}} \nabla_{[l]} u\|_{L_p}\,,$$

$$(4) \qquad \|u\|_{H_p^l} \sim \|\mathscr{D}_{\{l\}} \nabla_{[l]} u\|_{L_p} + \|u\|_{L_p}\,.$$

The next theorem by Šapošnikova [222], similar to Theorems 1.7.1/1 and 1.7.1/2, contains the characterization of $h_p^l(R^n)$ in terms of extensions to R^{n+k}. The two-sided estimates for the L_p-norm of a function u on R^1 by its harmonic extension to $R^1 \times (0,\infty)$ are due to Littlewood, Paley, Zigmund and Marcinkiewicz. Let the Littlewood-Paley function $g(u)$ be defined by

$$[g(u)](x) = \left(\int_0^\infty |\nabla U(x,y)|^2 y\,dy \right)^{1/2},$$

where $U(x,y)$ is the Poisson integral of u. The basic result here is the equivalence of the norms $\|u\|_{L_p(R^1)}$ and $\|g(u)\|_{L_p(R^1)}$, $1<p<\infty$. In the book by Stein [237] this equivalence is proved for R^n.

Theorem 5. *The norm of* $u \in \mathscr{D}(R^n)$ *in* $h_p^l(R^n)$, $0<l<1$, *is equivalent to*

$$\inf_{\{U\}} \left\{ \int_{R^n} \left(\int_{R^k} |y|^{2-2l-k} |\nabla U|^2 dy \right)^{p/2} dx \right\}^{1/p},$$

where the infimum is taken over all extensions $U \in \mathscr{D}(R^{n+k})$ *of* u *to* $R^{n+k} = \{(x,y): x \in R^n, y \in R^k\}$.

Similarly,

$$\|u\|_{H_p^l} \sim \inf_{\{U\}} \left\{ \int_{R^n} \left(\int_{R^k} |y|^{2-2l-k} (|\nabla U|^2 + |U|^2) dy \right)^{p/2} dx \right\}^{1/p}.$$

7.1.3. Some Other Properties of the Introduced Function Spaces

The following two theorems, whose proofs can be found in the books by Stein [237], Peetre [210], Nikol'skiĭ [202], and Triebel [245], are the classical facts of the theory of the spaces b_p^l, B_p^l, h_p^l, H_p^l.

Theorem 1. *If* $2 \leqslant p < \infty$ *then* $h_p^l \subset b_p^l$, $H_p^l \subset B_p^l$. *If* $1<p<2$ *then* $b_p^l \subset h_p^l$, $B_p^l \subset H_p^l$.

Theorem 2. (i) *If* $p \in (1, \infty)$, $l>0$, *then*

$$\|u\|_{b_p^l(R^n)} \sim \inf_{\{U\}} \|U\|_{h_p^{l+1/p}(R^{n+1})}.$$

Here and in (ii) *the notation* $\{U\}$ *has the same meaning as in Theorem* 1.7.1/1.

(ii) *If* $p \in [1, \infty)$, $l>0$ *then*

$$\|u\|_{b_p^l(R^n)} \sim \inf_{\{U\}} \|U\|_{b_p^{l+1/p}(R^{n+1})}.$$

In items (i) *and* (ii) *one can replace b and h by B and H, respectively.*

A far-reaching generalization of relations (i), (ii) is given in the paper by Jonsson and Wallin [108] where functions in B_p^l on the so called d-sets F are extended to R^n. The latter sets are defined by the relation

$$H_d(F \cap B(x, \varrho)) \sim \varrho^d$$

which is valid for all $x \in F$ and $\varrho < \delta$, where H_d is d-dimensional Hausdorff measure (cf. 1.2.4).

Henceforth we denote by $\mu\mathscr{B}$ the ball with radius μr, concentric with the ball $\mathscr{B}$ of radius r. Similarly, with the cube $\mathscr{Q}$ with edge length d we associate the concentric cube $\mu\mathscr{Q}$ with sides parallel to those of $\mathscr{Q}$ and with edge length μd.

Next we state the theorem which is easily derived from (7.1.2/4) (cf. Strichartz [238]) for the spaces H_p^l, $\{l\}>0$. For W_p^l and B_p^l it is a simple corollary of the definitions of these spaces.

Theorem 3. *Let* $\{\mathscr{B}^{(j)}\}_{j\geqslant 0}$ *be a covering of* R^n *by unit balls which has a finite multiplicity depending only on n. Further, let* $O^{(j)}$ *be the center of the ball* $\mathscr{B}^{(j)}$, $O^{(0)}=O$ *and let* $\eta_j(x)=\eta(x-O^{(j)})$ *where* $\eta\in C_0^\infty(2\mathscr{B}^{(0)})$, $\eta=1$ *on* $\mathscr{B}^{(0)}$. *Then*

(1) $$\|u\|_{S_p^l}\sim\Big(\sum_{j\geqslant 0}\|u\eta_j\|^p_{S_p^l}\Big)^{1/p},$$

where $S_p^l=H_p^l$, W_p^l *or* B_p^l *and* $s_p^l=h_p^l$, w_p^l *or* b_p^l, *respectively.*

We can easily check that for any $v\in C_0^\infty(B_1)$ "the generalized Friedrichs inequality"

(2) $$\|v\|_{L_p}\leqslant c\|v\|_{s_p^l}$$

is valid. Therefore the norm $\|u\eta_j\|_{s_p^l}$ in (1) can be replaced by the equivalent norm $\|u\eta_j\|_{S_p^l}$.

When dealing with an imbedding of a Banach space $\mathscr{X}$ into another Banach space $\mathscr{Y}$ (notation: $\mathscr{X}\subset\mathscr{Y}$) we always mean a continuous imbedding.

Theorem 4. (1) *If* $l=1,2,\ldots$, *then* $b_1^l\subset w_1^l$.

(2) *If* $p>1$, $l>\lambda\geqslant 0$, $n>(l-\lambda)p$ *and* $l-n/p=\lambda-n/\pi$ *then* $h_p^l\subset h_\pi^\lambda$.

(3) *If* $p\geqslant 1$, $l>\lambda>0$, $n>(l-\lambda)p$ *and* $l-n/p=\lambda-n/\pi$ *then* $b_p^l\subset b_\pi^\lambda$.

(4) *If* $p\geqslant 1$, $l>0$, $n>lp$ *and* $1/\pi=1/p-l/n$ *then* $b_p^l\subset L_\pi$.

(5) *If* $l=1,2,\ldots$, $n\geqslant l-\lambda$ *and* $l-n=\lambda-n/\pi$ *then* $w_1^l\subset b_\pi^\lambda$.

Replacing the letters b, h, w by B, H, W in (1)–(5) *we also obtain true assertions.*

(6) *If* $p>1$, $l>\lambda\geqslant 0$, $n=(l-\lambda)p$, *then* $H_p^l\subset H_\pi^\lambda$ *for any* $\pi\in(1,\infty)$. *If* $p>1$, $lp>n$, *then* $H_p^l\subset L_\infty\cap C$.

(7) *If* $p>1$, $l>\lambda>0$, $n=(l-\lambda)p$, *then* $B_p^l\subset B_\pi^\lambda$ *for any* $\pi\in(1,\infty)$.

(8) *If* $p>1$, $l>0$, $n=lp$, *then* $B_p^l\subset L_\pi$ *for any* $\pi\in(1,\infty)$.

(9) *If* $p>1$, $lp>n$, *then* $B_p^l\subset L_\infty\cap C$.

Various proofs of assertions (1)–(4), (6)–(9) can be found in the monographs mentioned at the beginning of the present subsection. The proof of (5) is due to Solonnikov [234]. The imbedding (2) is an immediate corollary of the continuity of the operator $(-\Delta)^{(\lambda-l)/2}$: $L_p\to L_\pi$ established by Sobolev [230]. Item (1) follows from the inequalities

$$\|\nabla_l u\|_{L_1(R^n)}\leqslant c_1\|\nabla_{l+1}U\|_{L_1(R^{n+1})}\leqslant c_2\|y\nabla_{l+2}U\|_{L_1(R^{n+1})}$$

and from Theorem 7.1.1/1. (Here $U\in\mathscr{D}(R^{n+1})$ is an arbitrary extension of the function $u\in\mathscr{D}(R^n)$.) The same theorem together with the inequality

$$\||y|^{1-\{\lambda\}-1/\pi}\nabla_{[\lambda]+1}U\|_{L_\pi(R^{n+1})}\leqslant c\||y|^{-\{l\}}\nabla_{[l]+1}U\|_{L_1(R^{n+1})}$$

which results from Corollary 2.1.6/4, leads to (3) for $p=1$. The same result for $p>1$ follows from the imbedding

$$h_p^{l+1/p}(R^{n+1}) \subset h_\pi^{\lambda+1/\pi}(R^{n+1})$$

(cf. item (2) above and part (i) of Theorem 2).

The corresponding assertions for the spaces H_p^l and B_p^l can be obtained in a similar way. The imbedding in (6) easily follows from the definition of the Bessel potential. The properties (7) and (9) result from (6) applied to the space $H_p^{l+1/p}(R^{n+1})$, and (8) is a corollary of (7).

Besides the above-mentioned literature in which imbedding, trace and extension theorems are established for various fractional-order and more general spaces, we also cite (with no intention of claiming completeness) the papers by Besov [25], Burenkov [37, 38], Volevič and Panejah [251], Golovkin [79, 80], Golovkin and Solonnikov [81], Il'in [105, 106], Kudrjavcev [121], Solonnikov [233], Aronszajn, Mulla and Szeptycki [18], Taibleson [239, 240], the first chapter of the book by Hörmander [99], the book by Gel'man and the author [73].

§ 7.2. Some Facts from Potential Theory

7.2.1. The Capacity cap(e, S_p^l) and Its Properties

With each function space $S_p^l = H_p^l$, W_p^l, B_p^l, h_p^l, w_p^l, b_p^l introduced in § 7.1, we associate a set function called *the capacity*. Namely, for any compactum $e \subset R^n$ we put

$$\operatorname{cap}(e, S_p^l) = \inf\{\|u\|_{S_p^l}^p : u \in C_0^\infty,\ u \geqslant 1 \text{ on } e\}.$$

If E is an arbitrary subset of R^n, then we call the numbers

$$\underline{\operatorname{cap}}(E, S_p^l) = \sup\{\operatorname{cap}(e, S_p^l) : e \subset E,\ e \text{ is a compactum}\},$$

$$\overline{\operatorname{cap}}(E, S_p^l) = \inf\{\underline{\operatorname{cap}}(G, S_p^l) : G \supset E,\ G \text{ is an open set}\}$$

the *inner* and *outer capacities* of E, respectively.

Theorem 7.1.3/3 implies the relation

(1) $$\operatorname{cap}(e, S_p^l) \sim \sum_{i \geqslant 0} \operatorname{cap}(e \cap \mathscr{B}^{(i)}, S_p^l),$$

where $\{\mathscr{B}^{(i)}\}$ is the sequence of balls introduced in Theorem 7.1.3/3.

We state certain well-known properties of the capacity cap$(\cdot, S_p^l)$, where $S_p^l = H_p^l$ or h_p^l, $p > 1$ (cf. Rešetnjak [216], Meyers [182], Maz'ja and Havin [171]).

1) *If the set $e \subset R^n$ is compact then for each $\varepsilon > 0$ there exists an open set $G \subset R^n$ such that $G \supset e$ and*

$$\operatorname{cap}(e', S_p^l) < \operatorname{cap}(e, S_p^l) + \varepsilon\,,$$

where e' is an arbitrary compact subset of G.

2) *If the set $e \subset R^n$ is compact, then*

$$\overline{\operatorname{cap}}(e, S_p^l) = \operatorname{cap}(e, S_p^l)\,.$$

3) *If $E_1 \subset E_2 \subset R^n$ then*

$$\underline{\operatorname{cap}}(E_1, S_p^l) \leqslant \underline{\operatorname{cap}}(E_2, S_p^l)\,, \qquad \overline{\operatorname{cap}}(E_1, S_p^l) \leqslant \overline{\operatorname{cap}}(E_2, S_p^l)\,.$$

4) *If $\{E_k\}_{k=1}^{\infty}$ is a sequence of sets in R^n and $E = \bigcup_k E_k$, then*

$$\overline{\operatorname{cap}}(E, S_p^l) \leqslant \sum_{k=1}^{\infty} \overline{\operatorname{cap}}(E_k, S_p^l)\,.$$

It is well known that *any analytic (in particular, any Borel) set $E \subset R^n$ is measurable with respect to the capacity* $\operatorname{cap}(\cdot, S_p^l)$ (i.e. $\overline{\operatorname{cap}}(E, S_p^l) = \underline{\operatorname{cap}}(E, S_p^l)$) (cf. Meyers [182], Maz'ja and Havin [171]).

We introduce one more capacity:

$$c_{k,p}(E) = \inf\{\|f\|_{L_p}^p : f \in L_p, f \geqslant 0 \text{ and } \int k(x-y) f(y)\, dy \geqslant 1 \text{ for all } x \in E\}\,,$$

where k is a positive decreasing continuous function on the halfaxis $(0, +\infty)$ (cf. Meyers [182]).

We list some connections between the two capacities.

(i) *If $S_p^l = H_p^l$ or h_p^l and k is the Bessel or Riesz kernel, then*

$$c_{k,p}(E) = c \operatorname{cap}(E, S_p^l)\,.$$

(ii) *If* $\operatorname{diam} E \leqslant 1$ *and $pl < n$, then*

$$\operatorname{cap}(E, H_p^l) \sim \operatorname{cap}(E, h_p^l) \tag{2}$$

(cf. Adams and Meyers [9]). Relations similar to (2) are also valid for other pairs of spaces, e.g., B_p^l, b_p^l and W_p^l, w_p^l.

(iii) *If $2 \leqslant p < \infty$, then*

$$\operatorname{cap}(E, H_p^l) \sim \operatorname{cap}(E, B_p^l)$$

(cf. Sjödin [225]). *Moreover, the equalities* $\operatorname{cap}(E, H_p^l) = 0$ *and* $\operatorname{cap}(E, B_p^l) = 0$ *hold simultaneously provided $2 - l/n < p < 2$* (Adams [4]). *For arbitrary $p \in (1, \infty)$, $l > 0$ the inequality*

$$\operatorname{cap}(E, H_p^l) \leqslant c \operatorname{cap}(E, B_p^l)\,,$$

where c is a constant that depends only on n, p, l, is valid (cf. Sjödin [225] and Adams [4]).

(iv) *If* $E \subset R^n$, $l>0$, $1<p<\infty$ *then*

$$\operatorname{cap}(E, B_p^l(R^n)) \sim \operatorname{cap}(E, H_p^{l+1/p}(R^{n+1})) \sim \operatorname{cap}(E, B_p^{l+1/p}(R^{n+1}))$$

(cf. Sjödin [225]).

(v) *Let* $m, l>0$, $1<p, q<\infty$. *For* $E \subset R^n$ *the inequality*

$$[\operatorname{cap}(E, h_q^m)]^{n-lp} \leqslant c[\operatorname{cap}(E, h_p^l)]^{n-mq}, \qquad mq<lp<n,$$

is valid.

If, in addition, $E \subset B_1$, *then*

$$[\operatorname{cap}(E, H_q^m)]^{n-lp} \leqslant c[\operatorname{cap}(E, H_p^l)]^{n-mq}, \qquad mq<lp<n,$$

$$\left[\log \frac{c_0}{\operatorname{cap}(E, H_q^m)}\right]^{1-p} \leqslant c \operatorname{cap}(E, H_p^l), \qquad mq<lp=n,$$

$$[\operatorname{cap}(E, H_q^m)]^{p-1} \leqslant c[\operatorname{cap}(E, H_p^l)]^{q-1}, \qquad mq=lp=n,\ p\leqslant q.$$

Putting $E=B_r$ we conclude that all power exponents here are exact. Items (iv) and (v) are due to Adams and Hedberg [8].

7.2.2. Nonlinear Potentials

Nonlinear potential theory has turned out to be a useful tool in the study of the capacities introduced in 7.2.1. It was developed in the papers by Havin and Maz'ja [171], Adams and Meyers [10], Hedberg and Wolff [96], and others. Here we collect some facts from this theory.

Let $p \in (1, \infty)$, $n>pl$. Each nonnegative measure μ given on the Borel σ-algebra of the space R^n generates the function $U_{p,l}\mu$ defined on R^n by

$$(U_{p,l}\mu)(x) = \int_{R^n} |x-y|^{l-n} \left(\int_{R^n} |z-y|^{l-n} d\mu(z) \right)^{1/(p-1)} dy \tag{1}$$

or, equivalently,

$$U_{p,l}\mu = I_l(I_l\mu)^{p'-1}, \qquad p+p'=pp'.$$

For $p=2$, by changing the order of integration in (1) and taking into account the composition formula

$$\int |y-z|^{l-n} |y-x|^{l-n} dy = \text{const}\, |z-x|^{2l-n}$$

(cf. Landkof [125]) we obtain

$$(U_{2,l}\mu)(x) = c\int \frac{d\mu(z)}{|z-x|^{n-2l}} \,.$$

The function $U_{2,l}\mu$ is the Riesz potential of order $2l$ (for $l=1$ it is the Newton potential). Similarly, $U_{p,l}\mu$ is called the nonlinear Riesz potential ((p,l)-potential).

The nonlinear Bessel potential is defined as

$$V_{p,l}\mu = J_l(J_l\mu)^{p'-1} \,.$$

The potentials $U_{p,l}\mu$ and $V_{p,l}\mu$ satisfy the rough maximum principle.

Proposition 1. *Let $P\mu$ be either one of the potentials $U_{p,l}\mu$ or $V_{p,l}\mu$. Then there exists a constant $\mathfrak{M}$ that depends only on n, p, l such that*

$$(P\mu)(x) \leqslant \mathfrak{M} \sup\{(P\mu)(x) \colon x \in \operatorname{supp}\mu\} \,.$$

This assertion was proved in the papers by Havin and Maz'ja [171], Adams and Meyers [9]. It is well known that we can take $\mathfrak{M}=1$ for $p=2$, $l\leqslant 1$ (cf. Landkof [125]). In general this is impossible even for $p=2$ (cf. Landkof [125]).

The next assertion contains the basic properties of the so-called (p,l)-capacitary measure (cf. Meyers [182], Maz'ja and Havin [171]).

Proposition 2. *Let E be a subset of R^n. If $\overline{\operatorname{cap}}(E, h_p^l) < \infty$ then there exists a unique measure μ_E with the following properties:*

1) $\|I_l\mu_E\|_{L_{p/(p-1)}}^{p/(p-1)} = \overline{\operatorname{cap}}(E, h_p^l)$;

2) $(U_{p,l}\mu_E)(x) \geqslant 1$ *for (p,l)-quasi all $x \in E$*

(the notion "(p,l)-quasi everywhere" means everywhere except a set of zero outer capacity $\overline{\operatorname{cap}}(\cdot, h_p^l)$);

3) $\operatorname{supp}\mu_E \subset \bar{E}$;

4) $\mu_E(\bar{E}) = \overline{\operatorname{cap}}(E, h_p^l)$;

5) $(U_{p,l}\mu_E)(x) \leqslant 1$ *for all $x \in \operatorname{supp}\mu_E$.*

The measure μ_E is called *the capacitary measure of E* and $U_{p,l}\mu_E$ is called *the capacitary potential of E.*

The latter proposition remains valid after the replacement of h_p^l by H_p^l, of $U_{p,l}\mu$ by $V_{p,l}\mu$ and of I_l by J_l.

Besides, we note that the capacity $\operatorname{cap}(e, S_p^l)$ (for $S_p^l = h_p^l$ or H_p^l) can be defined as

(2) $$\operatorname{cap}(e, S_p^l) = \sup\{\mu(e) \colon \operatorname{supp}\mu \subset e,\ (P\mu)(x) \leqslant 1\} \,,$$

where $P = U_{p,l}$ or $V_{p,l}$ (cf. Maz'ja and Havin [171]).

Next we present some pointwise estimates for (p, l)-potentials which are obvious in the linear case and nontrivial in the nonlinear case.

Proposition 3 (Maz'ja and Havin [171] and Adams [3]).

(i) *If* $2 - l/n < p < n/l$, *then*

$$(V_{p,l}\mu)(x) \leqslant c \int_0^\infty \left(\frac{\mu(B(x, \varrho))}{\varrho^{n-lp}} \right)^{1/(p-1)} e^{-c\varrho} \frac{d\varrho}{\varrho}. \tag{3}$$

(ii) *If* $p > 1$ *and* $\varphi(\varrho) = \sup_x \mu(B(x, \varrho))$, *then*

$$(V_{p,l}\mu)(x) \leqslant c \int_0^\infty \left(\frac{\varphi(\varrho)}{\varrho^{n-lp}} \right)^{1/(p-1)} e^{-c\varrho} \frac{d\varrho}{\varrho}. \tag{4}$$

The same estimates, without the factor $e^{-c\varrho}$, *are valid for the potential* $U_{p,l}\mu$.

It is almost obvious that the following estimate, opposite to (3),

$$(V_{p,l}\mu)(x) \geqslant c \int_0^\infty \left(\frac{\mu(B(x, \varrho))}{\varrho^{n-lp}} \right)^{1/(p-1)} e^{-c\varrho} \frac{d\varrho}{\varrho} \tag{5}$$

is valid for all $p \in (1, \infty)$, $l > 0$, whereas (3) is not true for $p \leqslant 2 - l/n$. The latter result is obtained by replacing μ by a point charge.

Recently Wolff showed (cf. Hedberg and Wolff [96]) that for $pl < n$ the inequality

$$\| I_l \mu \|_{L_{p/(p-1)}}^{p/(p-1)} \leqslant c \int_0^\infty W_{p,l} \mu \, d\mu, \tag{6}$$

where

$$(W_{p,l}\mu)(x) = \int_0^\infty \left(\frac{\mu(B(x, \varrho))}{\varrho^{n-lp}} \right)^{1/(p-1)} \frac{d\varrho}{\varrho},$$

is valid. The analogous inequality for Bessel potentials is

$$\| J_l \mu \|_{L_{p/(p-1)}}^{p/(p-1)} \leqslant c \int_0^\infty S_{p,l} \mu \, d\mu, \tag{7}$$

where $pl \leqslant n$ and

$$(S_{p,l}\mu)(x) = \int_0^\infty \left(\frac{\mu(B(x, \varrho))}{\varrho^{n-lp}} \right)^{1/(p-1)} e^{-c\varrho} \frac{d\varrho}{\varrho}. \tag{8}$$

The estimates reverse to (6) and (7) follow immediately from (5).

Remark. The absence of the inequality (3) for $p \leqslant 2 - l/n$ caused serious difficulties in attempts at a satisfactory generalization of basic facts of the classical potential theory to the nonlinear case.

Using inequalities (6) and (7) Hedberg (cf. the above-mentioned paper by Hedberg and Wolff) managed to surmount this difficulty by virtue of an analog of the nonlinear potential theory in which the roles of $U_{p,l}\mu$ and $V_{p,l}\mu$ are played by the functions $\mathscr{W}_{p,l}\mu$ and $\mathscr{S}_{p,l}\mu$ which are equivalent to $W_{p,l}\mu$ and $S_{p,l}\mu$.

Upper pointwise estimates similar to (3) are obtained for the case $1 < p \leqslant 2 - l/n$ under the additional assumption that the potential is bounded. Namely, the following proposition is true.

Proposition (Adams and Meyers [9]).

(i) *If* $1 < p < 2 - l/n$ *and* $(U_{p,l}\mu)(x) \leqslant K$ *for all* $x \in R^n$ *then*

$$(U_{p,l}\mu)(x) \leqslant cK^{\gamma} \int_0^{\infty} \left(\frac{\mu(B(x,\varrho))}{\varrho^{n-lp}} \right)^{(n-l)/(n-lp)} \frac{d\varrho}{\varrho}, \tag{9}$$

where $\gamma = ((2-p)n - l)/(n-lp)$.

(ii) *If* $p = 2 - l/n$ *and* $(U_{p,l}\mu)(x) \leqslant K$ *for all* $x \in R^n$ *then*

$$(U_{p,l}\mu)(x) \leqslant c \int_0^{\infty} \left(\frac{\mu(B(x,\varrho))}{\varrho^{n-lp}} \log \left(cK^{p-1} \frac{\varrho^{n-lp}}{\mu(B(x,\varrho))} \right) \right)^{p'-1} \frac{d\varrho}{\varrho}. \tag{10}$$

(The condition $(U_{p,l}\mu)(x) \leqslant K$ *for all* $x \in R^n$ *implies the estimate*

$$\mu(B(x,\varrho)) \leqslant e^{-1} a K^{p-1} \varrho^{n-lp}.)$$

7.2.3. Metric Properties of the Capacity

The following relations are useful (cf. Meyers [182]).

If $pl < n$ and $0 < \varrho < 1$, then

$$\operatorname{cap}(B_\varrho, H_p^l) \sim \varrho^{n-pl}. \tag{1}$$

If $pl < n$ and $0 < \varrho < \infty$, then

$$\operatorname{cap}(B_\varrho, h_p^l) = c\varrho^{n-pl}. \tag{2}$$

For $pl = n$, $0 < \varrho \leqslant 1$ we have

$$\operatorname{cap}(B_\varrho, H_p^l) \sim (\log 2/\varrho)^{1-p}. \tag{3}$$

If $pl > n$, then $\operatorname{cap}(\{x\}, H_p^l) > 0$. Thus, only the empty set has zero capacity.

The following equivalence relations for the capacity of a parallelepiped were obtained by D.R. Adams [6].

Proposition 1. *Let* $0 < a_1 \leqslant a_2 \leqslant \cdots \leqslant a_n$, $a = (a_1, a_2, \ldots, a_n)$ *and let* $Q(a) = \{x \in R^n: |x_j| \leqslant a_j, j = 1, \ldots, n\}$.

(i) *If* $k-1 < lp < k$, $k = 1, \ldots, n$, *then*

$$\operatorname{cap}(Q(a), h_p^l) \sim a_k^{k-lp} \prod_{j=k+1}^{n} a_j .$$

(Here the product equals unity provided $k = n$.*)*

(ii) *If* $lp = k$, $k = 1, 2, \ldots, n-1$, *then*

$$\operatorname{cap}(Q(a), h_p^l) \sim \min\left\{\left(\log \frac{a_{k+1}}{a_k}\right)^{1-p}, 1\right\} \prod_{j=k+1}^{n} a_j .$$

Similar two-sided estimates are valid for $\operatorname{cap}(Q(a), H_p^l)$.

If T is a quasi-isometric mapping of R^n onto itself, then $\operatorname{cap}(TE, S_p^l) \sim \operatorname{cap}(E, S_p^l)$, where $S_p^l = H_p^l$ or h_p^l. This is a simple corollary of (7.2.2/2).

Meyers [183] showed that $\operatorname{cap}(PE, S_p^l) \leqslant \operatorname{cap}(E, S_p^l)$ provided P is a projector $R^n \to R^k$, $k < n$ and $S_p^l = H_p^l$ or h_p^l.

For any set $E \subset R^n$ and for any nondecreasing positive function φ on $[0, \infty)$ we define *the Hausdorff* φ*-measure*

$$H(E, \varphi) = \lim_{\varepsilon \to +0} \inf_{\{\mathscr{B}^{(i)}\}} \sum_i \varphi(r_i) ,$$

where $\{\mathscr{B}^{(i)}\}$ is any covering of the set E by open balls $\mathscr{B}^{(i)}$ with radii $r_i < \varepsilon$. If $\varphi(t) = t^d$, then d is called the dimension of the Hausdorff measure. The d-dimensional Hausdorff measure $H_d(E)$ is equal to $v_d H(E, t^d)$ (cf. 1.2.4). For $d = n$ the measure H_n coincides with the n-dimensional Lebesgue measure m_n.

The following propositions contain noncoinciding but in a certain sense, exact necessary and sufficient conditions for positiveness of the capacity formulated in terms of Hausdorff measures.

Proposition 2. *Let* $1 < p \leqslant n/l$ *and let* φ *be a nonnegative nondecreasing function on* $[0, \infty)$ *with* $\varphi(0) = 0$ *and*

$$\int_0^\infty \left(\frac{\varphi(t)}{t^{n-pl}}\right)^{1/(p-1)} \frac{dt}{t} < \infty . \tag{4}$$

Then for any Borel set E in R^n *with positive Hausdorff* φ*-measure we have*

$$\operatorname{cap}(E, H_p^l) > 0 .$$

(The latter is a corollary of (7.2.2/4); cf. Maz'ja and Havin [171].)

Proposition 3. *Let E be a Borel set in R^n.*

1) *If $n>pl$ and $H_{n-pl}(E)<\infty$, then* $\operatorname{cap}(E, S_p^l)=0$, *where $S_p^l=h_p^l$ or H_p^l.*

2) *If $n=pl$ and $H(E,\varphi)<\infty$, where $\varphi(r)=|\log r|^{1-p}$, then* $\operatorname{cap}(E, H_p^l)=0$ (cf. Meyers [182], Maz'ja and Havin [171]).

Next we present one more sufficient condition for the vanishing of $\operatorname{cap}(E, H_p^l)$ (Maz'ja and Havin [171]).

Proposition 4. *Let $\mathcal{N}$ be a measurable nonnegative function on* $[0,\infty)$. *Suppose, for any positive r, the set E can be covered by at most $\mathcal{N}(r)$ closed balls whose radii do not exceed r.*

If

$$\int_0 [\mathcal{N}(r)]^{1/(1-p)} r^{(n-pl)/(1-p)-1} dr=\infty,$$

then $\operatorname{cap}(E, H_p^l)=0$.

Using Propositions 2 and 4, we can give a complete description of the n-dimensional Cantor sets E with positive $\operatorname{cap}(E, H_p^l)$.

Let $\mathcal{L}=\{l_j\}_{j=1}^{\infty}$ be a decreasing sequence of positive numbers such that $2l_{j+1}<l_j$ $(j=1,2,\dots)$ and let Δ_1 be a closed interval with length l_1. Let e_1 denote a set contained in Δ_1, which equals the union of two closed intervals Δ_2 and Δ_3 with length l_2 and which contains both ends of the interval Δ_1. We put $E_1=\underbrace{e_1\times e_1\dots\times e_1}_{n\text{-times}}$. Next we repeat the procedure with the intervals Δ_2 and Δ_3 (here the role of l_2 passes to l_3) and thus obtain four closed intervals with length l_3. Let their union be denoted by e_2; $E_2=\underbrace{e_2\times e_2\times\dots\times e_2}_{n\text{-times}}$ and so on. We put

$$E(\mathcal{L})=\bigcap_{j=1}^{\infty} E_j\,.$$

Propostion 5 (Maz'ja and Havin [171]). *The following properties are equivalent:*

(i) $\operatorname{cap}(E(\mathcal{L}), H_p^l)>0$;

(ii) $\sum_{j\geqslant 1} 2^{jn/(1-p)} l_j^{(n-pl)/(1-p)}<\infty$ *for $n>pl$,*

$\sum_{j\geqslant 1} 2^{jn/(1-p)} \log\frac{l_j}{l_{j+1}}<\infty$ *for $n=pl$.*

7.2.4. Refined Functions

The function φ in H_p^l is called *refined or (p,l)-refined* if there exists a sequence of functions $\{\varphi_m\}_{m\geqslant 1}$ in $\mathcal{D}$ which converges to φ in H_p^l and such that for each $\varepsilon>0$ there exists an open set ω with $\operatorname{cap}(\omega, H_p^l)<\varepsilon$ and $\varphi_m\to\varphi$ uniformly on $R^n\backslash\omega$.

Another (equivalent) definition is: the function $\varphi\in H_p^l$ is called refined if for each $\varepsilon>0$ there exists an open set ω such that $\operatorname{cap}(\omega, H_p^l)<\varepsilon$ and the restriction of φ to $R^n\backslash\omega$ is continuous.

We list the basic properties of refined functions.

1) *If* $\varphi \in H_p^l$ *then there exists a refined function* $\tilde{\varphi}$ *which coincides with* φ *almost everywhere (with respect to n-dimensional Lebesgue measure) in* R^n.

2) *If* φ_1 *and* φ_2 *are refined functions which coincide almost everywhere (with respect to n-dimensional Lebesgue measure), then* φ_1 *and* φ_2 *coincide quasi-everywhere.*

3) *Each sequence of refined functions in* H_p^l *that converges to a refined function* φ *in* H_p^l *contains a subsequence that converges to* φ *quasi-everywhere.*

For the proofs of these assertions see the paper by Havin and the author [171], where references to the earlier literature are given.

For $pl > n$ these properties become trivial since $H_p^l \subset C$.

The following result due to Bagby and Ziemer [23] shows that a function in H_p^l coincides with a function in $C^m (m \leqslant l)$ outside some set which is small with respect to the corresponding capacity.

Proposition. *Let* $u \in H_p^l$, $1 < p < \infty$, *and let m be an integer,* $0 \leqslant m \leqslant l$. *Then for each* $\varepsilon > 0$ *there exists a function* $u_\varepsilon \in C^m$ *and an open set* ω *such that* $\operatorname{cap}(\omega, H_p^{l-m}) < \varepsilon$ *and* $u(x) = u_\varepsilon(x)$ *for all* $x \in R^n \setminus \omega$.

In conclusion we add to the above-mentioned literature on nonlinear potentials the lectures by D. R. Adams [7] which also contain a survey of some other problems that we do not touch upon here.

Chapter 8. On Summability with Respect to an Arbitrary Measure of Functions with Fractional Derivatives

§ 8.1. Description of Results

According to Corollary 2.3.3, for $q \geqslant p$ the inequality

$$\| u \|_{L_q(\mu, R^n)} \leqslant A \| \nabla u \|_{L_p(R^n)}, \qquad u \in C_0^\infty, \tag{1}$$

follows from the "isoperimetric" inequality

$$(\mu(E))^{p/q} \leqslant p^{-p}(p-1)^{p-1} A^p \operatorname{cap}(E, w_p^1).$$

Here and henceforth E is an arbitrary Borel set in R^n and w_p^1 is the completion of C_0^∞ with respect to the norm $\| \nabla u \|_{L_p}$.

On the other hand, if (1) is valid for any $u \in C_0^\infty$, then

$$(\mu(E))^{p/q} \leqslant A^p \operatorname{cap}(E, w_p^1)$$

for all $E \subset R^n$.

The present chapter contains similar results in which the role of w_p^1 is played by the spaces H_p^l, h_p^l, W_p^l, w_p^l, B_p^l, b_p^l.

Namely, let S_p^l be any one of these spaces. Then the best constant in

$$\| u \|_{L_q(\mu)} \leqslant A \| u \|_{S_p^l}, \qquad u \in C_0^\infty, \tag{2}$$

where $q \geqslant p$, is equivalent to the best constant in the "isoperimetric" inequality

$$(\mu(E))^{p/q} \leqslant B \operatorname{cap}(E, S_p^l). \tag{3}$$

The estimate $A \geqslant B$ immediately follows from the definition of capacity. The reverse estimate is a deeper fact, its proof being based on the inequality

$$\int_0^\infty \operatorname{cap}(\mathcal{N}_t, S_p^l)\, t^{p-1} dt \leqslant C \| u \|_{S_p^l}^p, \tag{4}$$

where $u \in S_p^l$, $\mathcal{N}_t = \{x: |u(x)| \geqslant t\}$ and C is a constant that is independent of u. In § 8.2 we present three proofs of inequality (4) with different fields of application.

We might ask if there exists a necessary and sufficient condition for (4) that is formulated without the capacity and with arbitrary sets E. From the D.R. Adams Theorem 1.4.1 it follows that this is so for the Riesz potential space $S_p^l = h_p^l$, $pl < n$. The condition given by Adams is

$$\mu(B(x, \varrho)) \leqslant C\varrho^s , \tag{5}$$

where $s = q(n/p - l)$ and $B(x, \varrho)$ is any ball with center x and radius ϱ.

Thus, inequality (5) with $q > p$ implies the isoperimetric inequality (3) for any set E.

In § 8.5 we give a direct proof of more general assertions of this kind. Namely, for any ball $B(x, r)$, let

$$\mu(B(x, r)) \leqslant \Phi(\operatorname{cap}(B_r, h_p^l)) , \tag{6}$$

where $B_r = B(0, r)$, Φ is an increasing function subject to some additional requirements and μ is a measure in R^n. Then for all Borel sets $E \subset R^n$

$$\mu(E) \leqslant c\,\Phi(c \operatorname{cap}(E, h_p^l)) . \tag{7}$$

By this theorem along with the equivalence of (2) and (3), we show in § 8.6 that inequalities similar to (6) are necessary and sufficient for the validity of estimates for traces of Riesz and Bessel potentials in Orlicz spaces $L_M(\mu)$ and, in particular, in $L_q(\mu)$. Besides, this gives a new proof of the aforementioned D.R. Adams theorem where no interpolation is used. Another corollary, possibly of interest in its own right, claims that the inequality

$$\| u \|_{L_q(\mu)} \leqslant c \| u \|_{H_p^l} ,$$

where $q > p > 1$, $lp = n$ is fulfilled if and only if

$$\mu(B(x, r)) \leqslant c \,|\log r\,|^{-q/p'}$$

for all balls $B(x, r)$ with radii $r \in (0, \frac{1}{2})$.

Next we state some other results relating the conditions for (2).

(a) If $S_p^l = H_p^l$, $pl < n$, then (2) is valid simultaneously with (5), where $0 < \varrho < 1$ (see § 8.6).

(b) In the case $pl > n$ a necessary and sufficient condition for (2) with $S_p^l = H_p^l$ is

$$\sup\{\mu(B(x, 1)\colon x \in R^n\} < \infty$$

(see § 8.6).

(c) For $q=p$, condition (5) is not sufficient for (2) (cf. Remark 8.6/2). So in this case, which is probably the most important for applications, we have to deal with a less explicit condition than (3).

(d) In § 8.4 we give the following necessary and sufficient condition for the validity of (2) provided $p>q>0$.

Let $\{g_j\}_{j=-\infty}^{+\infty}$ be any sequence of open sets such that $\bar{g}_{j+1} \subset g_j$ and $\mu_j = \mu(g_j)$, $\gamma_j = \operatorname{cap}(g_j, S_p^l)$, where $S_p^l = h_p^l$ or $S_p^l = H_p^l$, $p>1$. The inequality (2) with $q<p$ holds if and only if

$$\sum_{j=-\infty}^{+\infty} \left(\frac{(\mu_j - \mu_{j+1})^{1/q}}{\gamma_j^{1/p}} \right)^{pq/(p-q)} \leqslant \text{const} .$$

This implies the simpler sufficient condition

$$\int_0^\infty \left(\frac{t}{\varkappa(t)} \right)^{q/(p-q)} dt < \infty ,$$

where $\varkappa(t) = \inf\{\operatorname{cap}(E, S_p^l) \colon \mu(E) \geqslant t\}$ (cf. 8.4.3).

(e) In case $pl>n$, $p>q$ a necessary and sufficient condition for (2) can be written in the essentially simpler form

$$\sum_i (\mu(\mathcal{Q}^{(i)}))^{p/(p-q)} < \infty ,$$

where $\{\mathcal{Q}^{(i)}\}$ is the sequence of closed cubes, edge length 1, which forms the coordinate grid in R^n (cf. 8.4.4).

(f) We note also that in case $q=1$, $p>1$, the inequality (2) with $S_p^l = h_p^l$ or $S_p^l = H_p^l$ is equivalent to the inclusion $I_l \mu \in L_{p'}$ or $J_l \mu \in L_{p'}$, respectively (here I_l and J_l are the Riesz and the Bessel potentials) (cf. 8.4.4).

(g) In § 8.7 we consider the case $p=1$. For $S_1^l = b_1^l$ in addition to Theorem 1.4.3 it is shown that (2) holds simultaneously with (5), where $p=1$, $q \geqslant 1$. If $S_1^l = B_1^l$, we have to add the condition $\varrho \in (0,1)$ in (5). We recall that according to Theorem 1.4.3 the same pertains to the cases $s_1^l = w_1^l$, $S_1^l = W_1^l$.

(h) Using the interpretation of b_p^l and B_p^l, $p>1$ as the trace spaces of the corresponding potential spaces, we obtain theorems on b_p^l and B_p^l from the theorems concerning h_p^l and H_p^l (cf. Remark 8.6/3).

Section 8.8 contains some applications of results obtained in §§ 8.2–8.7. There we present necessary and sufficient conditions for the compactness of the imbedding operator of H_p^l into $L_q(\mu)$, etc. In § 8.8 we also state some corollaries to previous theorems. They concern the negative spectrum of the operator $(-\Delta)^l - p(x)$, $p(x) \geqslant 0$, $x \in R^n$.

§ 8.2. An Estimate for the Integral of the Capacity of a Set Bounded by a Level Surface

8.2.1. The Case of Second Order Derivatives

In 2.3.1 we obtained inequality (8.1/4) for $S_p^l = \mathring{L}_p^1(\Omega)$. In trying to generalize the proof for functions with derivatives of order $l > 1$, we encounter some difficulties. These difficulties arise because the truncation of a function in S_p^l along its levels does not belong to S_p^l. Here we show how this obstacle can be surmounted for the case $l = 2$, $p > 1$.

Let e be a compact subset of Ω and

$$\operatorname{cap}^+(e, \mathring{L}_p^2(\Omega)) = \inf\left\{ \int_\Omega |\nabla_2 u|^p dx \colon u \in \mathscr{D}(\Omega),\ u \geqslant 0 \text{ in } \Omega,\right.$$
$$\left. u = 1 \text{ in a neighborhood of } e \right\}.$$

Theorem. *For any nonnegative function in* $\mathscr{D}(\Omega)$ *the inequality*

$$\int_0^\infty \operatorname{cap}^+(\mathscr{N}_t, \mathring{L}_p^2(\Omega))\, t^{p-1} dt \leqslant c \int_\Omega |\nabla_2 u|^p dx\,, \tag{1}$$

where $p \in (1, \infty)$, *is valid.*

For the proof of this theorem we need the following lemma.

Lemma. *If* $u \in \mathscr{D}(R^1)$, $u \geqslant 0$, *then*

$$\int_{R^1} \frac{|u'|^{2p}}{u^p} dt \leqslant \left(\frac{2p-1}{p-1}\right)^p \int_{R^1} |u''|^p dt\,, \tag{2}$$

where the integration is taken over the support of u.

Proof. Obviously, for $\varepsilon > 0$,

$$\int_{R^1} \frac{|u'|^{2p}}{(u+\varepsilon)^p} dt = \frac{1}{1-p} \int_{R^1} |u'|^{2p-2} u' ((u+\varepsilon)^{1-p})' dt\,.$$

Integrating by parts, we obtain

$$\int_{R^1} \frac{|u'|^{2p}}{(u+\varepsilon)^p} dt = \frac{2p-1}{p-1} \int_{R^1} \frac{|u'|^{2(p-1)}}{(u+\varepsilon)^{p-1}} u'' dt$$
$$\leqslant \frac{2p-1}{p-1} \left(\int_{R^1} |u''|^p dt \right)^{1/p} \left(\int_{R^1} \frac{|u'|^{2p}}{(u+\varepsilon)^p} dt \right)^{(p-1)/p}.$$

Therefore,

$$\int_{R^1} \frac{|u'|^{2p}}{(u+\varepsilon)^p}\, dt \leqslant \left(\frac{2p-1}{p-1}\right) \int_{R^1} |u''|^p dt\,.$$

It remains to pass to the limit as $\varepsilon \to +0$. The lemma is proved.

Proof of the Theorem. It is clear that

$$\int_0^\infty \operatorname{cap}^+(\mathcal{N}_t, \mathring{L}_p^2(\Omega))\, d(t^p) \leqslant c \sum_{j=-\infty}^{+\infty} 2^{-pj} \operatorname{cap}^+(g_j, \mathring{L}_p^2(\Omega))\,,$$

where $g_j = \{x\colon u(x) \geqslant 2^{-j}\}$. Using the monotonicity of $\operatorname{cap}^+(\cdot, \mathring{L}_p^2(\Omega))$ we obtain

$$\int_0^\infty \operatorname{cap}^+(\mathcal{N}_t, \mathring{L}_p^2(\Omega))\, d(t^p) \leqslant c \sum_{j=-\infty}^{+\infty} 2^{-pj} \gamma_j\,,$$

where $\gamma_j = \operatorname{cap}^+(g_j, \mathring{L}_p^2(g_{j+1}))$.

It remains to prove the inequality

$$\sum_{j=-\infty}^{+\infty} 2^{-pj} \gamma_j \leqslant c \int_\Omega |\nabla_2 u|^p dx\,. \tag{3}$$

For this purpose we shall use the "smooth truncation" procedure. We introduce a nondecreasing function $\alpha \in C^\infty[0,1]$ which is equal to zero in a neighborhood of $t=0$ and to unity in a neighborhood of $t=1$. Further, we consider the function $f \in C^\infty(0,\infty)$, defined on $[t_{j+1}, t_j]$ by

$$f(u) = t_{j+1} + \alpha\left(\frac{u - t_{j+1}}{t_j - t_{j+1}}\right)(t_j - t_{j+1})\,,$$

where $t_j = 2^{-j}$. Since the restriction of the function

$$(f(u) - t_{j+1})(t_j - t_{j+1})^{-1}$$

to the set $g_{j+1} \backslash g_j$, extended by unity on g_j and by zero outside g_{j+1}, is a nonnegative function in $\mathscr{D}(g_{j+1})$, then

$$2^{-pj} \operatorname{cap}^+(g_j, \mathring{L}_p^2(g_{j+1})) \leqslant c \int_{g_{j+1}\backslash g_j} |\nabla_2 f(u(x))|^p dx\,.$$

This implies

$$\sum_{j=-\infty}^{+\infty} 2^{-pj} \gamma_j \leqslant c \int_\Omega |\nabla_2 f(u(x))|^p dx\,. \tag{4}$$

Since $|f'(v)| \leqslant c$, $|f''(v)| \leqslant c v^{-1}$, then

$$\sum_{j=-\infty}^{+\infty} 2^{-pj}\gamma_j \leqslant c\left(\int_\Omega |\nabla_2 u|^p dx + \int_\Omega \frac{|\nabla u|^{2p}}{u^p} dx\right).$$

Estimating the second integral on the right by Lemma, we arrive at (3). The theorem is proved.

If Ω coincides with the whole space R^n and $n > 2p$, $p > 1$, then the restriction $u \geqslant 0$ in the latter theorem can be removed. Namely, the following corollary is valid.

Corollary. *If* $n > 2p$, $p > 1$ *then for any* $u \in \mathscr{D}(R^n)$

$$\int_0^\infty \operatorname{cap}^+(\mathscr{N}_t, \mathring{L}_p^2)\, d(t^p) \leqslant c \int_{R^n} |\nabla_2 u|^p dx.$$

Proof. Let $u \in \mathscr{D}(R^n)$ and let $\eta_m(x) = \eta(x/m)$ where $\eta \in \mathscr{D}(B_2)$, $\eta = 1$ on B_1 and m is a large enough number. We put $v = |x|^{2-n} * |\Delta u|$. Mollifying the function $(1+m^{-1})\eta_m v$, we obtain the sequence of functions w_m in $\mathscr{D}$ with the properties: $|u| \leqslant w_m$,

(5) $$\lim_{m\to\infty} \|\nabla_2 w_m\|_{L_p} \leqslant c \|\nabla_2 u\|_{L_p}.$$

Clearly,

$$\int_0^\infty \operatorname{cap}^+(\mathscr{N}_t, \mathring{L}_p^2)\, d(t^p) \leqslant \int_0^\infty \operatorname{cap}(\{x: w_m(x) > t\}, \mathring{L}_p^2)\, d(t^p)$$

and by Theorem we obtain

$$\int_0^\infty \operatorname{cap}^+(\mathscr{N}_t, \mathring{L}_p^2)\, d(t^p) \leqslant c \|\nabla w_m\|^p_{L_p(R^n)}.$$

Passing to the limit and making use of (5), we complete the proof.

A direct generalization of this proof for derivatives of higher than second order is impossible since there is no similar lemma for higher derivatives. In fact, the example of a function $R^1 \ni t \to u \in \mathscr{D}(R^1)$, $u \geqslant 0$, coinciding with t^2 for $|t| < 1$, shows that the finiteness of the norm $\|u^{(l)}\|_{L_p(R^1)}$ does not imply the finiteness of the integral

$$\int_{R^1} |u^{(j)}(t)|^{pl/j} u(t)^{p(j-l)/j} dt$$

for $l > 2$.

Nevertheless, in the next subsection it is shown that "the smooth truncation" is adequate for $\Omega = R^n$ and any integer $l > 0$ being applied not to an arbitrary nonnegative function but to a potential with nonnegative density.

8.2.2. A Proof Based on the Smooth Truncation of a Potential Near its Level Surfaces

We introduce the Hardy-Littlewood maximal operator T defined by

$$(1) \qquad (Tg)(x) = \sup_{r>0} \frac{1}{m_n B_r} \int_{B_r(x)} |g(\xi)|\, d\xi\,.$$

Lemma (Hedberg [93]). *Let $0<\theta<1$, $0<r<n$ and let $I_r f$ be the Riesz potential of order r with nonnegative density f, i.e. $I_r f = |x|^{r-n} * f$. Then*

$$(2) \qquad (I_{r\theta} f)(x) \leqslant c[(I_r f)(x)]^{\theta}[(Tf)(x)]^{1-\theta}\,.$$

Proof. For any $\delta>0$ we have

$$\int_{|y-x|\geqslant\delta} f(y)\,|x-y|^{r\theta-n} dy \leqslant \delta^{r(\theta-1)} \int_{|y-x|\geqslant\delta} f(y)\,|x-y|^{-n+r} dy \leqslant \delta^{r(\theta-1)}(I_r f)(x)\,.$$

On the other hand,

$$(3) \qquad \int_{|y-x|\leqslant\delta} f(y)\,|x-y|^{r\theta-n} dy = \sum_{k=0}^{\infty} \int_{\delta 2^{-k-1}<|y-x|<\delta 2^{-k}} f(y)\,|x-y|^{r\theta-n} dy$$

$$\leqslant c \sum_{k=0}^{\infty} (\delta 2^{-k})^{r\theta} (\delta 2^{-k})^{-n} \int_{|y-x|\leqslant \delta 2^{-k}} f(y)\,dy$$

$$\leqslant c\delta^{r\theta}(Tf)(x) \sum_{k=0}^{\infty} 2^{-kr\theta}\,.$$

Consequently,

$$(I_{r\theta} f)(x) \leqslant c(\delta^{r\theta}(Tf)(x) + \delta^{r(\theta-1)}(I_r f)(x))\,.$$

Putting $\delta^r = (I_r f)(x)/(Tf)(x)$, we arrive at (2).

Corollary. *Let l be an integer, $0<l<n$, $I_l f = |x|^{l-n} * f$, where $f \geqslant 0$ and let F be a function in $C^l(0,\infty)$ such that*

$$t^{k-1}|F^{(k)}(t)| \leqslant Q\,, \quad k=0,\dots,l\,.$$

Then

$$|\nabla_l F(I_l f)| \leqslant cQ(Tf + |\nabla_l I_l f|)$$

almost everywhere in R^n.

Proof. We have

$$|\nabla_l F(u)| \leqslant c \sum_{k=1}^{l} |F^{(k)}(u)| \sum_{j_1+\dots+j_k=l} |\nabla_{j_1} u| \cdots |\nabla_{j_k} u|$$

$$\leqslant cQ \sum_{k=1}^{l} \sum_{j_1+\dots+j_k=l} \frac{|\nabla_{j_1} u|}{u^{1-j_1/l}} \cdots \frac{|\nabla_{j_k} u|}{u^{1-j_k/l}}\,.$$

Since $|\nabla_s u| \leqslant I_{l-s} f$, then

$$|\nabla_l F(u)| \leqslant c Q\left(|\nabla_l I_l f| + \sum_{k=1}^{l} \sum_{j_1+\dots+j_k=l}' \frac{I_{l-j_1} f \dots I_{l-j_k} f}{(I_l f)^{1-j_1/l} \dots (I_l f)^{1-j_k/l}}\right),$$

where the sum Σ' is taken over all collections of numbers $j_1, \dots, j_k$ less than l. The result follows by an application of Lemma.

Let w be a nonnegative function in R^n satisfying the Muckenhoupt condition

(4) $$\sup_{\mathscr{Q}} \left(\frac{1}{m_n \mathscr{Q}} \int_{\mathscr{Q}} w^p dx\right)\left(\frac{1}{m_n \mathscr{Q}} \int_{\mathscr{Q}} w^{-p'} dx\right)^{p-1} < \infty,$$

where the supremum is taken over all cubes $\mathscr{Q}$. This condition ensures the continuity of the operators T and $\nabla_l I_l$ in the space of functions φ with the finite norm $\|w\varphi\|_{L_p}$ (cf. Muckenhoupt [195], Coifman and Fefferman [46]).

Theorem. *Let $p>1$, $l=1,2,\dots, lp<n$. Inequality* (8.1/4), *where S_p^l is the completion of C_0^∞ with respect to the norm $\|w\nabla_l u\|_{L_p}$, is valid.*

Proof. Let $u \in C_0^\infty(R^n)$, $u = I_l f$, $v = I_l |f|$. We can easily see that $v \in C^l(R^n)$ and $v(x) = O(|x|^{l-n})$ as $|x| \to \infty$. Since $v(x) \geqslant |u(x)|$, then putting $t_j = 2^{-j}$ $(j=0, \pm 1, \dots)$, we obtain

(5) $$\int_0^\infty \operatorname{cap}(\mathscr{N}_t, S_p^l)\, d(t^p) \leqslant c \sum_{j=-\infty}^{\infty} 2^{-pj} \gamma_j,$$

where $\gamma_j = \operatorname{cap}(\{x: v(x) \geqslant t_j\}, S_p^l)$. Using the same argument as in the proof of (8.2.1/4), we obtain

$$\sum_{j=-\infty}^{+\infty} 2^{-pj} \gamma_j \leqslant c \|f(v)\|_{S_p^l}^p,$$

where f is the function introduced in the proof of Theorem 8.2.1. By Corollary 1 the preceding norm is majorized by

(6) $$c(\|wT|f|\|_{L_p} + \|w \nabla_l I_l |f|\|_{L_p}).$$

Since the weight function w satisfies (4), the sum (6) does not exceed

$$c_1 \|wf\|_{L_p} = c_1 \|w(-\Delta)^l I_l u\|_{L_p} \leqslant c \|w \nabla_l u\|_{L_p}.$$

The theorem is proved.

Corollary. *Inequality* (8.1/4), *where $S_p^l = b_p^l$, $p>1$, $l>0$, is valid.*

Proof. Let U be an arbitrary extension of $u \in C_0^\infty(R^n)$ to the space $R^{n+1} = \{\mathscr{X} = (x, x_{n+1}): x \in R^n, x_{n+1} \in R^1\}$. According to Theorem 7.1.1/1,

$$\|u\|_{b_p^l(R^n)} \sim \inf_{\{U\}} \|U\|_{\mathring{L}_p^{[l]+1}(R^{n+1}, x_{n+1}^{1-\{l\}-1/p})},$$

where $\mathring{L}_p^k(R^{n+1}, w)$ is the completion of $C_0^\infty(R^{n+1})$ with respect to the norm $\|w \nabla_k u\|_{L_p(R^{n+1})}$. Consequently,

$$\operatorname{cap}(e, b_p^l(R^n)) \sim \operatorname{cap}(e, L_p^{[l]+1}(R^{n+1}, x_{n+1}^{1-\{l\}-1/p})) .$$

We can easily check that the function $\mathscr{X} \to w(\mathscr{X}) = x_{n+1}^{1-\{l\}-1/p}$ satisfies (4). Therefore the last theorem yields

$$\int_0^\infty \operatorname{cap}(\mathscr{N}_t, b_p^l(R^n))\, d(t^p) \leqslant c \|U\|^p_{\mathring{L}_p^{[l]+1}(R^{n+1}, x_{n+1}^{1-\{l\}-1/p})} .$$

We complete the proof by minimizing the right-hand side over all extensions of u to R^{n+1}.

8.2.3. A Proof Based on the Maximum Principle for Nonlinear Potentials

Let $K\mu$ be the linear Bessel or Riesz potential of order l with density μ and let $K(K\mu)^{p'-1}$ be the nonlinear potential generated by K. Further, let $\mathfrak{M}$ denote the constant in the rough maximum principle for the potential $K(K\mu)^{p'-1}$ (cf. Proposition 7.2.2/1).

Theorem. *Inequality* (8.1/4), *where S_p^l is either H_p^l or $h_p^l (pl < n)$, is valid. The best constant C in* (8.1/4) *satisfies*

$$C \leqslant (p')^{p-1} \mathfrak{M} \qquad \text{if } p \geqslant 2 ,$$
$$C \leqslant (p')^p p^{-1} \mathfrak{M}^{p-1} \qquad \text{if } p < 2 .$$

Proof. For the sake of brevity, let $c(t) = \operatorname{cap}(\mathscr{N}_t, S_p^l)$. It suffices to assume $u = Kf, f \geqslant 0, f \in L_p$. Let μ_t denote the capacitary measure of $\mathscr{N}_t$ (cf. Proposition 7.2.2/2).

The left-hand side in (8.1/4) does not exceed

$$\int_0^\infty \int Kf\, d\mu_t t^{p-2} dt = \int f\, dx \int_0^\infty K\mu_t t^{p-2} dt ,$$

which is majorized by

$$\|f\|_{L_p} \left\| \int_0^\infty t^{p-2} K\mu_t dt \right\|_{L_{p'}} .$$

Thus, to get the result it suffices to obtain the estimate

$$\int \left(\int_0^\infty t^{p-2} K\mu_t dt \right)^{p'} dx \leqslant C^{p'-1} \int_0^\infty c(t) t^{p-1} dt . \tag{1}$$

First we note that by the maximum principle

$$\int (K\mu_\tau)^{p'-1} K\mu_t dx \leqslant \mathfrak{M} c(t) . \tag{2}$$

Next, we consider separately the cases $p \geqslant 2$ and $p < 2$. Let $p \geqslant 2$. The left-hand side in (1) can be written as

$$p' \int \int_0^\infty K\mu_\tau \left(\int_\tau^\infty K\mu_t t^{p-2} dt \right)^{p'-1} \tau^{p-2} d\tau dx .$$

By virtue of the Hölder inequality this expression is majorized by

$$p' \left(\int \int_0^\infty \tau^{p-1} (K\mu_\tau)^{p'} d\tau dx \right)^{2-p'} \left(\int \int_0^\infty (K\mu_\tau)^{p'-1} \int_\tau^\infty K\mu_t t^{p-2} dt\, d\tau dx \right)^{p'-1} ,$$

which by (2) does not exceed

$$p' \mathfrak{M}^{p'-1} \left(\int_0^\infty \| K\mu_t \|_{L_{p'}}^{p'} t^{p-1} dt \right)^{2-p'} \left(\int_0^\infty c(t)\, t^{p-1} dt \right)^{p'-1} .$$

Thus (8.1/4) follows for $p \geqslant 2$.

Let $p < 2$. The left-hand side in (1) is equal to

$$p' \int \int_0^\infty K\mu_t t^{p-2} dt \left(\int_0^t K\mu_\tau \tau^{p-2} d\tau \right)^{p'-1} dx .$$

So, by Minkowski's inequality it is majorized by

$$p' \int_0^\infty \left(\int_0^t \left(\int (K\mu_\tau)^{p'-1} K\mu_t dx\right)^{p-1} \tau^{p-2} d\tau \right)^{p'-1} t^{p-2} dt .$$

Estimating this value via (2), we obtain that it is majorized by

$$p' \mathfrak{M} \int_0^\infty c(t) \left(\int_0^t \tau^{p-2} d\tau \right)^{p'-1} t^{p-2} dt$$

and (8.1/4) follows for $p < 2$.

§ 8.3. Conditions for the Validity of Imbedding Theorems in Terms of Isoperimetric Inequalities

We state the generalization of Theorem 2.3.2 to the case of Bessel and Riesz potential spaces in R^n. We omit the proof since it duplicates that of Theorem 2.3.2.

Theorem. *The best constant in the inequality*

$$\| |u|^p \|_{L_M(\mu)} \leqslant A \| u \|^p_{S_p^l}, \tag{1}$$

where $S_p^l = h_p^l$ *for* $pl < n$ *or* $S_p^l = H_p^l$ *for* $pl \leqslant n$, $p \in (1, \infty)$, *is equivalent to*

$$B = \sup \left\{ \frac{\mu(E) N^{-1}(1/\mu(E))}{\operatorname{cap}(E, S_p^l)} : E \subset R^n, \operatorname{cap}(E, S_p^l) > 0 \right\}.$$

Namely, $B \leqslant A \leqslant pBC$, *where* C *is the constant in* (8.1/4) (cf. Theorem 8.2.3).

This assertion immediately implies the following corollary.

Corollary. *The best constant* $C_{p,q}$ *in*

$$\| u \|_{L_q(\mu)} \leqslant C_{p,q} \| u \|_{S_p^l}, \tag{2}$$

where $q \geqslant p > 1$ *and* S_p^l *is one of the spaces in the preceding theorem, satisfies*

$$B_{p,q} \leqslant C_{p,q} \leqslant B_{p,q} (pC)^{1/p}.$$

Here

$$B_{p,q} = \sup \left\{ \frac{\mu(E)^{p/q}}{\operatorname{cap}(E, S_p^l)} : E \subset R^n, \operatorname{cap}(E, S_p^l) > 0 \right\}$$

and C *is the constant in* (8.1/4).

A theorem due to D. R. Adams [5] states that inequality (2) with $q = p > 1$, $lp < n$ and $S_p^l = h_p^l$ holds if and only if, for all compact sets $e \subset R^n$,

$$\| I_l \mu_e \|^{p'}_{L_{p'}} \leqslant \operatorname{const} \mu(e),$$

where μ_e is the restriction of the measure μ to e.

This result follows from the preceding corollary and the next proposition.

Proposition 1. *Let* $p \in (1, \infty)$, $lp < n$. *Then we have the relation* $Q \sim R$, *where*

$$Q = \sup_e \frac{\mu(e)}{\operatorname{cap}(e, h_p^l)}, \qquad R = \sup_e \frac{\| I_l \mu_e \|^{p'}_{L_{p'}}}{[\mu(e)]^{p-1}},$$

and the suprema are taken over all compacta e *in* R^n.

Proof. For any $u \in C_0^\infty$, $u \geqslant 1$ on e, we obtain

$$\mu(e) \leqslant \int u(x)\, d\mu_e(x) \leqslant \|(-\Delta)^{-l/2}\mu_e\|_{L_{p'}} \|(-\Delta)^{l/2} u\|_{L_p},$$

which can be rewritten as

$$\mu(e) \leqslant c \| I_l \mu_e \|_{L_{p'}} \| u \|_{h_p^l}.$$

Taking the minimum of the right-hand side over all functions u, we obtain

$$\mu(e) \leqslant c R^{1/p} \mu(e)^{1/p'} [\operatorname{cap}(e, h_p^l)]^{1/p}.$$

On the other hand, by virtue of Corollary,

$$\int |u|^p d\mu \leqslant c Q \| u \|_{h_p^l}^p.$$

Therefore,

$$|\int u\, d\mu_e|^p \leqslant c Q \mu(e)^{p-1} \|(-\Delta)^{l/2} u\|_{L_{p'}}^p,$$

which yields

$$\| I_l \mu_e \|_{L_{p'}} \leqslant c Q^{1/p} \mu(e)^{1/p'}.$$

Thus $h \leqslant cQ$. The proof is complete.

In the same way, we can obtain the relation

$$\sup_e \frac{\mu(e)}{\operatorname{cap}(e, H_p^l)} \sim \sup_e \frac{\| J_l \mu_e \|_{L_{p'}}^p}{[\mu(e)]^{p-1}},$$

where e is either an arbitrary compactum in R^n or a compactum with diameter not exceeding unity.

To conclude the present section, we note that with the same arguments as in the proof of Proposition 1 together with Theorem 8.2.2 we arrive at the following proposition.

Proposition 2. *Let $p > 1$, $l = 1, 2, \ldots$, $lp < n$ and let w be a nonnegative function that satisfies the Muckenhoupt condition* (8.2.2/4). *Then the best constant C_p in*

$$\| u \|_{L_p(\mu)} \leqslant C_p \| w \nabla_l u \|_{L_p}, \qquad u \in C_0^\infty,$$

satisfies the relation

$$C_p \sim \sup_e \frac{\left\| \frac{1}{w} I_l \mu_e \right\|_{L_{p'}}^p}{[\mu(e)]^{p-1}},$$

where e is an arbitrary compactum in R^n.

§ 8.4. The Imbedding into $L_q(\mu)$ for $p>q>0$

In the present section we find a necessary and sufficient condition for the validity of (8.3/2) for $p>q>0$, $p>1$. For the proof we need the lemma in the next subsection.

8.4.1. An Auxiliary Estimate

We shall use the notation $K\mu$, $K(K\mu)^{p'-1}$ and $\mathfrak{M}$ introduced at the beginning of 8.2.3. Let $\{g_j\}_{j=-\infty}^{+\infty}$ denote a sequence of open sets in R^n and $\{t_j\}_{j=-\infty}^{+\infty}$ an increasing sequence of positive numbers. Further let $\gamma_j = \operatorname{cap}(g_j, S_p^l)$, where $S_p^l = H_p^l (pl \leqslant n)$ or $S_p^l = h_p^l (pl < n)$, and let v_j be the capacitary measure of g_j.

Lemma. *The inequality*

$$\left\| \sum_j (t_{j+1}-t_j)(Kv_j)^{p'-1} \right\|_{L_p}^p \leqslant B_p \sum_j t_{j+1}^{p-1}(t_{j+1}-t_j)\gamma_j, \tag{1}$$

where $B_p \leqslant p\mathfrak{M}^{p-1}$ for $p \leqslant 2$ and $B_p \leqslant p(p-1)^{p-1}\mathfrak{M}$ for $p \geqslant 2$, is valid.

Proof. The case $p \leqslant 2$. Since $x^\alpha - y^\alpha \leqslant \alpha x^{\alpha-1}(x-y)$ for $\alpha \geqslant 1$, $x>y\geqslant 0$, then for any positive sequence $\{\alpha_j\}_{j=-\infty}^{+\infty}$ we have

$$\left(\sum_j \alpha_j\right)^p = \sum_j \left[\left(\sum_{i\geqslant j}\alpha_i\right)^p - \left(\sum_{i\geqslant j+1}\alpha_i\right)^p\right] \leqslant p\sum_j \alpha_j\left(\sum_{i\geqslant j}\alpha_i\right)^{p-1}.$$

Hence the left-hand side in (1) does not exceed

$$\int p \sum_j (t_{j+1}-t_j)(Kv_j)^{p'-1}\left(\sum_{j\geqslant i}(t_{i+1}-t_i)(Kv_i)^{p'-1}\right)^{p-1} dx = \int p \sum_j (t_{j+1}-t_j)$$
$$\times (t_{j+1}^{p-1}(Kv_j)^{p'})^{2-p}(t_{j+1}^{p-2}Kv_j)^{p-1}\left(\sum_{j\geqslant i}(t_{i+1}-t_i)(Kv_i)^{p'-1}\right)^{p-1} dx.$$

By the Hölder inequality and the maximum principle for nonlinear potentials the preceding integral is majorized by

$$p\left(\sum_j (t_{j+1}-t_j)\, t_{j+1}^{p-1}\int (Kv_j)^{p'} dx\right)^{2-p}$$
$$\times\left(\sum_j (t_{j+1}-t_j)\, t_{j+1}^{p-2}\sum_{j\geqslant i}(t_{i+1}-t_i)\int Kv_j (Kv_i)^{p'-1} dx\right)^{p-1}$$
$$\leqslant p\mathfrak{M}^{p-1}\left(\sum_j (t_{j+1}-t_j)\, t_{j+1}^{p-1}\gamma_j\right)^{2-p}\left(\sum_j (t_{j+1}-t_j)\, t_{j+1}^{p-2}\gamma_j \sum_{j\geqslant i}(t_{i+1}-t_i)\right)^{p-1}$$

and (1) follows for $p \leqslant 2$.

The case $p>2$. It sufficies to use only a finite collection of $\{t_j\}$ and $\{\gamma_j\}$. Following the same line of reasoning as at the beginning of the proof we find that the left-hand side in (1) is majorized by

$$p\int \sum_j (t_{j+1}-t_j)(K\nu_j)^{p'-1}\left(\sum_{j\leqslant i}(t_{i+1}-t_i)(K\nu_i)^{p'-1}\right)^{p-1} dx\,,$$

which by Minkowski's inequality does not exceed

$$p\sum_j (t_{j+1}-t_j)\left(\sum_{j\leqslant i}(t_{i+1}-t_i)\left(\int (K\nu_j)^{p'-1}K\nu_i\,dx\right)^{1/(p-1)}\right)^{p-1}.$$

According to the maximum principle, the latter is majorized by

$$p\mathfrak{M}\sum_j (t_{j+1}-t_j)\,\sigma_j^{p-1}$$

where

$$\sigma_j=\sum_{j\leqslant i}(t_{i+1}-t_i)\,\gamma_i^{p'-1}\,.$$

Further we note that

$$\begin{aligned}\sum_j (t_{j+1}-t_j)\,\sigma_j^{p-1} &= \sum_j t_{j+1}(\sigma_j^{p-1}-\sigma_{j+1}^{p-1})\\ &\leqslant (p-1)\sum_j t_{j+1}(\sigma_j-\sigma_{j+1})\,\sigma_j^{p-2}\\ &= (p-1)\sum_j t_{j+1}(t_{j+1}-t_j)\,\gamma_j^{p'-1}\sigma_j^{p-2}\\ &\leqslant (p-1)\left(\sum_j \sigma_j^{p-1}(t_{j+1}-t_j)\right)^{(p-2)/(p-1)}\\ &\quad\times\left(\sum_j \gamma_j t_{j+1}^{p-1}(t_{j+1}-t_j)\right)^{1/(p-1)}.\end{aligned}$$

Consequently,

$$\sum_j (t_{j+1}-t_j)\,\sigma_j^{p-1}\leqslant (p-1)^{p-1}\sum_j t_{j+1}^{p-1}(t_{j+1}-t_j)\,\gamma_j\,.$$

8.4.2. The Main Theorem

Let $\mathfrak{S}$ be any sequence of open sets $\{g_j\}_{j=-\infty}^{+\infty}$ such that $\bar{g}_{j+1}\subset g_j$. We put $\mu_j=\mu(g_j)$, $\gamma_j=\operatorname{cap}(g_j,S_p^l)$ and

$$D_{p,q}=\sup_{\{\mathfrak{S}\}}\left(\sum_{j=-\infty}^{+\infty}\left(\frac{(\mu_j-\mu_{j+1})^{1/q}}{\gamma_j^{1/p}}\right)^{pq/(p-q)}\right)^{(p-q)/pq}.$$

Theorem. *The best constant in* (8.3/2), *where* $p>q>0$, *is equivalent to* $D_{p,q}$.

Proof. a) We show that

(1) $$C_{p,q} \leqslant (4pC)^{1/p} D_{p,q},$$

where C is the constant in (8.1/4).

Let $f \in C_0^\infty$, $f \geqslant 0$, $u = Kf$, $g_j = \{x: (Kf)(x) > \alpha^j\}$, where $\alpha > 1$. Obviously,

$$\|u\|_{L_q(\mu)}^q \leqslant \sum_j \alpha^{q(j+1)}[\mu(g_j) - \mu(g_{j+1})] = \sum_j \alpha^{q(j+1)} \frac{\mu_j - \mu_{j+1}}{\gamma_j^{q/p}} \gamma_j^{q/p}.$$

By Hölder's inequality the last sum does not exceed

$$D_{p,q}^q \left(\sum_j \alpha^{p(j+1)} \gamma_j \right)^{q/p}.$$

Next we note that

$$\sum_j \alpha^{p(j+1)} \gamma_j \leqslant \frac{p\alpha^{2p}}{\alpha^p - 1} \sum_j \int_{\alpha^{j-1}}^{\alpha^j} \operatorname{cap}(\mathscr{N}_t, S_p^l)\, t^{p-1}\, dt.$$

Putting $\alpha^p = 2$ in this inequality, we obtain

$$\sum_j \alpha^{p(j+1)} \gamma_j \leqslant 4p \int_0^\infty \operatorname{cap}(\mathscr{N}_t, S_p^l)\, t^{p-1}\, dt.$$

Consequently,

(2) $$\|u\|_{L_q(\mu)} \leqslant (4pC)^{1/p} D_{p,q} \|u\|_{S_p^l}$$

and (1) follows.

b) We prove that

(3) $$C_{p,q} \geqslant B_p^{-1/p} D_{p,q},$$

where B_p is the constant in Lemma 8.4.1.

Let $t_0, t_{\pm 1}, \ldots, t_{\pm N}$ be positive numbers which will be specified later, $t_{j+1} > t_j$, $t_{-N} = 0$. We put

$$u = \sum_{|j| < N} (t_{j+1} - t_j) K(K\mu_j)^{p'-1},$$

where μ_j is the capacitary measure of the set g_j contained in an arbitrary sequence $\mathfrak{S}$. By Lemma 8.4.1 we have

(4) $$\|u\|_{S_p^l} \leqslant B_p^{1/p} \left(\sum_{|j| < N} t_{j+1}^p \gamma_j \right)^{1/p}.$$

Since $K(K\mu_j)^{p'-1} \geqslant 1$ quasi-everywhere on g_j and since (8.3/1) implies $\mu(E)^{p/q} \leqslant C_p \operatorname{cap}(E, S_p^l)$ for any set E, then μ-almost-everywhere on g_j the inequality $K(K\mu_j)^{p'-1} \geqslant 1$ is valid. Therefore

$$\|u\|_{L_q(\mu)} \geqslant \Big\| \sum_{|j|<N} (t_{j+1}-t_j)\,\chi_j \Big\|_{L_q(\mu)} ,$$

where χ_j is the characteristic function of g_j. Hence

$$\|u\|^q_{L_q(\mu)} \geqslant \Big\| \sum_{|j|<N} t_{j+1}(\chi_j-\chi_{j+1}) \Big\|^q_{L_q(\mu)} = \sum_{|j|<N} t^q_{j+1}(\mu_j-\mu_{j+1}) . \tag{5}$$

We put

$$t_{j+1} = \left(\frac{\mu_j-\mu_{j+1}}{\gamma_j} \right)^{1/(p-q)} .$$

Then from (4) and (5) we obtain

$$\left(\sum_{|j|<N} \frac{(\mu_j-\mu_{j+1})^{p/(p-q)}}{\gamma_j^{q/(p-q)}} \right)^{(p-q)/pq} \leqslant C_{p,q} B_p^{1/p} .$$

Passing to the limit as $N\to\infty$ we complete the proof of (3) and hence that of the theorem.

8.4.3. A Sufficient Condition ($p>q>0$)

We introduce the function

$$(0,\infty) \ni t \to \varkappa(t) = \inf_E \operatorname{cap}(E, S^l_p) ,$$

where the infimum is taken over all $E\subset R^n$ such that $\mu(E)\geqslant t$.

We can give the following sufficient condition for the validity of (8.3/2) for $p>q>0$ in terms of the function $\varkappa$:

$$\int_0^\infty \left(\frac{t}{\varkappa(t)} \right)^{q/(p-q)} dt < \infty . \tag{1}$$

Corollary. *The inequality*

$$\|u\|_{L_q(\mu)} \leqslant \left(\frac{p}{p-q} \right)^{(p-q)/pq} (4pC)^{1/p} \left(\int_0^\infty \left(\frac{t}{\varkappa(t)} \right)^{q/(p-q)} dt \right)^{(p-q)/pq} \|u\|_{S^l_p} , \tag{2}$$

where $0<q<p$, $p>1$, *is fulfilled.*

Proof. Inequality (2) follows immediately from (8.4.2/2) and the estimates

$$\sum_j \left(\frac{(\mu_j-\mu_{j+1})^{p/q}}{\gamma_j} \right)^{q/(p-q)} \leqslant \sum_j \frac{\mu_j^{p/(p-q)}-\mu_{j+1}^{p/(p-q)}}{\gamma_j^{q/(p-q)}} \leqslant \int_0^\infty \frac{d(t^{p/(p-q)})}{(\varkappa(t))^{q/(p-q)}} .$$

8.4.4. Two Simple Cases

For $pl > n$ the necessary and sufficient condition for the validity of (8.3/2), where $S_p^l = H_p^l$, W_p^l or B_p^l, can be written in essentially simpler form than in Theorem 8.4.2. Namely, the following assertion holds.

Theorem 1. *If $pl > n$, $p > q$ and $C_{p,q}$ is the best constant in* (8.3/2), *then*

$$C_{p,q} \sim \left(\sum_{i \geqslant 0} \mu(\mathcal{Q}^{(i)})^{p/(p-q)} \right)^{(p-q)/pq}, \tag{1}$$

where $\{\mathcal{Q}^{(i)}\}$ is the sequence of closed cubes with edge length 1 *forming the coordinate grid in R^n.*

Proof. Let $O^{(i)}$ be the center of $\mathcal{Q}^{(i)}$, $O^{(0)} = O$ and let $2\mathcal{Q}^{(i)}$ be the concentric cube of $\mathcal{Q}^{(i)}$ with edges parallel to those of $\mathcal{Q}^{(0)}$ and having edge length 2. We put $\eta_i(x) = \eta(x - O^{(i)})$, where $\eta \in C_0^\infty(2\mathcal{Q}^{(0)})$, $\eta = 1$ on $\mathcal{Q}^{(0)}$. We have

$$\begin{aligned} \|u\|^q_{L_q(\mu)} &\leqslant \sum_{i \geqslant 0} \|u\|^q_{C(\overline{\mathcal{Q}^{(i)}})} \mu(\mathcal{Q}^{(i)}) \\ &\leqslant \left(\sum_{i \geqslant 0} \mu(\mathcal{Q}^{(i)})^{p/(p-q)} \right)^{1-q/p} \left(\sum_{i \geqslant 0} \|u\|^p_{C(\overline{\mathcal{Q}^{(i)}})} \right)^{q/p}. \end{aligned} \tag{2}$$

Next we note that for $pl > n$

$$\|u\|_{C(\overline{\mathcal{Q}^{(i)}})} \leqslant \|u\eta_i\|_{S_p^l}, \tag{3}$$

where $S_p^l = h_p^l$, w_p^l or b_p^l (cf. (7.1.3/2) and items (6), (9) of Theorem 7.1.3/4). Now (7.1.3/2), (2) and (3) imply the upper bound for $C_{p,q}$.

To obtain the lower bound for $C_{p,q}$ it suffices to insert the function

$$u_N(x) = \sum_{i=0}^{N} \mu(\mathcal{Q}^{(i)}) \eta_i(x), \quad N = 1, 2, \ldots$$

into (8.3/2). This concludes the proof.

The constant $C_{p,q}$ can be easily calculated for $q = 1$.

Theorem 2. *Let S_p^l be either H_p^l or h_p^l. Then*

$$C_{p,1} = \|K\mu\|_{L_{p'}},$$

where $K\mu$ is either the Riesz or the Bessel potential.

Proof. Let $|u| \leqslant Kf$, $f \geqslant 0$ and $\|f\|_{L_p} = \|u\|_{S_p^l}$. We have

$$\int |u| \, d\mu \leqslant \int f K\mu \, dx \leqslant \|f\|_{L_p} \|K\mu\|_{L_{p'}},$$

which gives $C_{p,1} \leqslant \|K\mu\|_{L_{p'}}$. The reverse inequality follows by the substitution of $u = K(K\mu)^{1/(p-1)}$ into (8.3/2) with $q = 1$.

§ 8.5. A Cartan Type Theorem and Estimates for Capacities

In this section we establish the equivalence of inequalities of the type (8.1.6) and (8.1.7). This follows from a theorem giving an estimate for the size of the set where the functions $W_{p,l}\mu$ and $S_{p,l}\mu$, introduced in 7.2.2, majorize a given value. Such estimates were first obtained for harmonic functions by Cartan [44] (cf. also Nevanlinna [198]). For linear Riesz potentials they are given in Landkof [125].

The same scheme is used here for the nonlinear case.

Lemma. *Let $1<p\leqslant n/l$ and let μ be a finite measure in R^n. Let φ denote an increasing function on $[0,+\infty)$ with $\varphi(0)=0$, $\varphi(r)=\varphi(r_0)=\mu(R^n)$ for $r>r_0$. Further let D be the set $\{x\in R^n\colon (P\mu)(x)>Y[\varphi]\}$, where $P\mu=W_{p,l}\mu$ for $pl<n$, $P\mu=S_{p,l}\mu$ for $pl=n$ and*

$$Y[\varphi]=\begin{cases}\displaystyle\int_0^\infty\left(\frac{\varphi(r)}{r^{n-lp}}\right)^{p-1}\frac{dr}{r} & \text{for } 1<p<n/l\,,\\[2ex] \displaystyle\int_0^\infty(\varphi(r))^{p'-1}e^{-br}r^{-1}dr & \text{for } p=n/l\end{cases}\quad.$$

Then D can be covered by a sequence of balls of radii $r_k\leqslant r_0$ such that

$$\sum_k\varphi(r_k)\leqslant c\mu(R^n)\,. \tag{1}$$

Proof. First, consider the case $1<p<n/l$. Let $x\in D$. Suppose $\mu(B(x,r))\leqslant\varphi(r)$ for all $r>0$. Then

$$(W_{p,l}\mu)(x)=\int_0^\infty\left(\frac{\mu(B(x,r))}{r^{n-lp}}\right)^{p'-1}\frac{dr}{r}\leqslant\int_0^\infty\left(\frac{\varphi(r)}{r^{n-lp}}\right)^{p'-1}\frac{dr}{r}\,.$$

But the latter means that $x\notin D$. This contradiction shows that given any $x\in D$ there exists an $r=r(x)\in(0,r_0)$ such that $\varphi(r)<\mu(B(x,r))\leqslant\mu(R^n)$. Applying Theorem 1.2.1 we select a covering $\{B(x_k,r_k)\}$, $k=1,2,\ldots$, of D with finite multiplicity $c=c(n)$ in the union of balls $\{B(x,r(x))\}$, $x\in D$. It is clear that

$$\sum_k\varphi(r_k)<\sum_k\mu(B(x_k,r_k))\leqslant c\mu(R^n)\,,$$

and the result follows for $1<p<n/l$. For $p=n/l$ the proof is the same.

In the next theorem we denote by Φ a nonnegative increasing function on $[0,+\infty)$ such that $t\Phi(t^{-1})$ decreases and tends to zero as $t\to\infty$. Further, for all $u>0$, let

$$\int_u^{+\infty}\Psi(t)t^{-1}dt\leqslant c\Psi(u)\,, \tag{2}$$

where

$$\Psi(v)=\begin{cases}(v\,\Phi(v^{-1}))^{p'-1} & \text{for } 1<p<n/l\,,\\ v(\Phi(v^{1-p}))^{p'-1} & \text{for } p=n/l\,.\end{cases}$$

Theorem. *Let $p\in(1,n/l]$ and let μ be a finite measure in R^n. Further let m be a positive number such that*

$$m^{p-1}>\mu(R^n) \quad \textit{for } p=n/l\,.$$

Then the set $G=\{x\in R^n\colon (P\mu)(x)>m\}$ can be covered by a sequence of balls $\{B(x_k,r_k)\}$ with

$$\sum_k \Phi(\operatorname{cap}(B_{r_k},S_p^l))<c\,\Phi(c\,m^{1-p}\mu(R^n))\,. \tag{3}$$

Here $S_p^l=h_p^l$ for $lp<n$ and $S_p^l=H_p^l$ for $lp=n$.

Proof. Let $\varkappa=\operatorname{cap}(B_1,h_p^l)$ for $n>lp$. For $n=lp$ we define $\varkappa$ as

$$\varkappa=\min\{t\colon \operatorname{cap}(B_r,H_p^l)\leqslant t\,|\log r|^{1-p},\ r<e^{-1}\}\,.$$

Further let $Q=\mu(R^n)$. In Lemma we put $\varphi(r)=Q$ for $r>r_0$ and

$$\varphi(r)=\begin{cases}Q\,\Phi(\varkappa r^{n-lp})/\Phi(\varkappa r_0^{n-lp}) & \text{if } pl<n,\ r\leqslant r_0\,,\\ Q\,\Phi(\varkappa|\log r|^{1-p})/\Phi(\varkappa|\log r_0|^{1-p}) & \text{if } pl=n,\ r\leqslant r_0\,.\end{cases}$$

Here and henceforth r_0 is a number which will be specified later to satisfy the inequality $m>Y[\varphi]$ (the number $Y[\varphi]$ was defined in Lemma).

1. Let $1<p<n/l$. We have

$$Y[\varphi]=\int_0^{r_0}\left(\frac{\varphi(r)}{r^{n-lp}}\right)^{p'-1}\frac{dr}{r}+Q^{p'-1}\frac{p-1}{n-lp}\,r_0^{(n-lp)/(1-p)}\,.$$

We show that the integral on the right does not exceed

$$c\,Q^{p'-1}r_0^{(n-lp)/(1-p)}\,.$$

This is equivalent to the inequality

$$(\Phi(\varkappa r_0^{n-lp}))^{1-p'}\int_0^{r_0}\left(\frac{\Phi(\varkappa r^{n-lp})}{r^{n-lp}}\right)^{p'-1}\frac{dr}{r}\leqslant c\,r_0^{(n-lp)/(1-p)}\,.$$

Putting $\varkappa r^{pl-n}=t$, $\varkappa r_0^{pl-n}=t_0$, we rewrite the latter as

$$\int_{t_0}^{\infty}(t\,\Phi(t^{-1}))^{p'-1}t^{-1}dt\leqslant c(t_0\Phi(t_0^{-1}))^{p'-1}\,,$$

which is fulfilled by virtue of (8.5/2). Thus

$$Y[\varphi] < cQ^{p'-1} r_0^{(n-lp)/(1-p)}$$

and the inequality $Y[\varphi] < m$ is satisfied provided we put

$$r_0^{n-lp} = (cm^{-1})^{p-1} Q .$$

We introduce the set $D = \{x \in R^n : (P\mu)(x) > Y[\varphi]\}$ which is open by the lower semicontinuity of $P\mu$. Since $m > cY[\varphi]$ then $G \subset D$. Let $\{B(x_k, r_k)\}$ be the sequence of balls constructed in Lemma for the set D by the function φ specified here. Inequality (1) can be rewritten as

$$\sum_k \Phi(\varkappa r_k^{n-lp}) \leqslant c\Phi(cm^{1-p} Q) .$$

Thus we obtain the covering of G by balls $\{B(x_k, r_k)\}$ satisfying (3).

2. Let $p = n/l$ and let $r_0 < 1/e$. We have

(4) $$Y[\varphi] = \int_0^{r_0} (\varphi(r))^{p'-1} e^{-cr} r^{-1} dr + Q^{p'-1} \int_{r_0}^{\infty} e^{-cr} r^{-1} dr .$$

The second integral is majorized by

$$\int_{r_0}^{\infty} e^{-br} r^{-1} dr < \int_{r_0}^{1} r^{-1} dr + \int_1^{\infty} e^{-cr} dr \leqslant (1 + c^{-1} e^{-c}) |\log r_0| .$$

We show that the first integral on the right in (4) does not exceed $cQ^{p'-1} \times |\log r_0|$. In other words we prove that

$$(\Phi(\varkappa |\log r_0|^{1-p}))^{1-p'} \int_0^{r_0} (\Phi(\varkappa |\log r|^{1-p}))^{p'-1} \frac{dr}{r} < c |\log r_0| .$$

Putting $\varkappa |\log r| = t$, $\varkappa |\log r_0| = t_0$, we rewrite the preceding inequality as

$$\int_{t_0}^{\infty} (\Phi(t^{1-p}))^{p'-1} dt \leqslant c t_0 (\Phi(t_0^{1-p}))^{p'-1} ,$$

which is fulfilled by virtue of (2). Therefore there exists a constant $c \in (1, \infty)$ such that

$$Y[\varphi] < cQ^{p'-1} |\log r_0| .$$

Thus the inequality $Y[\varphi] < m$ is satisfied provided we set

$$|\log r_0|^{1-p} = (cm^{-1})^{p-1} Q .$$

The completion of the proof follows the same line of reasoning as for $p \in (1, n/l)$.

Remark 1. The proof of the theorem shows that in the case $pl = n$ we can take the radii of the balls, covering G, to be less than $1/e$.

Corollary 1. *Let* $1 < p \leqslant n/l$ *and let* Φ *be the function defined just before the last theorem. Further let* K *be a compactum in* R^n *with* $\operatorname{cap}(K, S_p^l) > 0$ *where* $S_p^l = h_p^l$ *for* $pl < n$ *and* $S_p^l = H_p^l$ *for* $pl = n$. *Then there exists a covering of* K *by balls* $B(x_k, r_k)$ *such that*

$$\sum_k \Phi(\operatorname{cap}(B_{r_k}, S_p^l)) < c\,\Phi(c \operatorname{cap}(K, S_p^l)) , \tag{5}$$

where c *is a constant that depends on* n, p, l *and on the function* Φ. *In the case* $pl = n$ *we may assume that* $r_k \leqslant e^{-1}$.

Proof. We limit consideration to the case $pl < n$. For $pl = n$ the argument is the same.

We put

$$C(K) = \inf\{\textstyle\int W_{p,l}\mu \, d\mu \colon W_{p,l}\mu \geqslant 1 \ (p, l)\text{-quasi everywhere on } K\} .$$

By (7.2.2/6) the capacities $C(K)$ and $\operatorname{cap}(K, h_p^l)$ are equivalent. In the paper by Hedberg and Wolff [96] it is shown that the extremal measure μ_K for the above variational problem exists and that $C(K) = \mu_K(K)$. We introduce the set $G_\varepsilon = \{x \in R^n \colon W_{p,l}\mu_K(x) \geqslant 1 - \varepsilon\}$, where $\varepsilon > 0$. Since $W_{p,l}\mu_K(x) \geqslant 1$ for (p, l)-quasi-every $x \in K$, then $E \subset G_\varepsilon \cup E_0$ where $\operatorname{cap}(E_0, h_p^l) = 0$.

By Theorem there exists a covering of G_ε by balls $B(x_j, r_j)$ for which (3) is valid with $m = 1 - \varepsilon$ and $\mu(R^n) = \operatorname{cap}(K, h_p^l)$. Since $\Psi(t)/t$ is summable on $[1, +\infty)$, the function $\varphi(r) = \Phi(\operatorname{cap}(B_r, h_p^l))$ satisfies (7.2.3/4). This and Proposition 7.2.3/2 imply that the set E_0 has zero Hausdorff φ-measure. Therefore E_0 can be covered by balls $B(y_i, \varrho_i)$ so that

$$\sum_i \Phi(\operatorname{cap}(B_{\varrho_i}, h_p^l)) < \varepsilon .$$

The balls $B(x_j, r_j)$ and $B(y_i, \varrho_i)$ form the required covering.

Corollary 2. *Let* $p \in (1, n/l]$ *and let* $S_p^l = h_p^l$ *for* $lp < n$, $S_p^l = H_p^l$ *for* $lp = n$. *Further, let* Φ *be the function defined just before Theorem. If measure* μ *is such that*

$$\mu(B(x, \varrho)) \leqslant \Phi(c \operatorname{cap}(B_\varrho, S_p^l)) , \tag{6}$$

then, for any Borel set E *with the finite capacity* $\operatorname{cap}(E, S_p^l)$, *the inequality*

$$\mu(E) \leqslant c\,\Phi(c \operatorname{cap}(E, S_p^l)) , \tag{7}$$

where c *is a constant that depends on* n, p, l *and* Φ, *is valid.*

Proof. It suffices to derive (7) for a compactum E. According to Corollary 1 there exists a covering of E by balls $B(x_k, r_k)$ satisfying (5). Using the additivity of μ as well as estimate (6), we obtain

$$\mu(E) \leqslant \mu\left(\bigcup_k B(x_k, r_k)\right) \leqslant \sum_k \mu(B(x_k, r_k))$$

$$\leqslant \sum_k \Phi(c\,\mathrm{cap}(B_{r_k}, S_p^l)) < c\,\Phi(c\,\mathrm{cap}(E, S_p^l)) .$$

The result follows.

Remark 2. According to (7.2.1/2) we have $\mathrm{cap}(E, H_p^l) \sim \mathrm{cap}(E, h_p^l)$ if $\mathrm{diam}\,E \leqslant 1$. Therefore under the additional requirement $\mathrm{diam}\,E \leqslant 1$ we may also put $S_p^l = H_p^l$ in Corollary 2 for $pl < n$.

To prove this assertion we need to verify that the measure $R^n \supset A \to \mu_1(A) = \mu(A \cap E)$ satisfies (6).

Let $\mathrm{diam}\,E \leqslant 1$ and, for all $r \in (0, 1)$, let

$$\mu(B(x, r)) \leqslant \Phi(\mathrm{cap}(B_r, H_p^l)) . \tag{8}$$

For $r < 1$ we have

$$\mu_1(B(x, r)) = \mu(B(x, r) \cap E) \leqslant \mu(B(x, r))$$

$$\leqslant \Phi(\mathrm{cap}(B_r, H_p^l)) \leqslant \Phi(c\,\mathrm{cap}(B_r, h_p^l)) .$$

In the case $r \geqslant 1$

$$\mu_1(B(x, r)) \leqslant \mu(B(y, 1))$$

for any $y \in E$. Hence, using (8) and the monotonicity of the capacity, we obtain

$$\mu_1(B(x, r)) \leqslant \Phi(\mathrm{cap}(B_1, H_p^l)) \leqslant \Phi(c\,\mathrm{cap}(B_r, h_p^l)) .$$

Thus the measure μ_1 satisfies (6).

§ 8.6. Imbedding Theorems (Conditions in Terms of Balls)

Theorem. *Let M be a convex function and let N be the complementary function of M. Further let Φ be the inverse function of $t \to tN^{-1}(1/t)$ subject to condition* (8.5/2). *Then*

(α) *The best constant A in* (8.3/1) *with $S_p^l = h_p^l$, $lp < n$, is equivalent to*

$$C_1 = \sup\{\varrho^{lp-n}\mu(B(x, \varrho))N^{-1}(1/\mu(B(x, \varrho))): x \in R^n,\ \varrho > 0\} .$$

(β) *The best constant A in* (8.3/1) *with $S_p^l = H_p^l$ is equivalent to*

$$C_2 = \sup\{\varrho^{lp-n}\mu(B(x, \varrho))N^{-1}(1/\mu(B(x, \varrho))): x \in R^n,\ 0 < \varrho < 1\}$$

if $pl < n$ and to

$$C_3 = \sup\{|\log \varrho|^{p-1}\mu(B(x,\varrho))N^{-1}(1/\mu(B(x,\varrho))): x\in R^n, 0<\varrho<\tfrac{1}{2}\}$$

if $pl = n$.

The proof immediately follows from Theorem 8.3 and the equivalence $B \sim C_j, j = 1, 2, 3$, obtained in Corollary 8.5/2 and Remark 8.5/2.

Remark 1. We can easily see that in the case $pl > n$ the constant A in (8.3/1) with $S_p^l = H_p^l$ is equivalent to

$$C_4 = \sup\{\mu(B(x,1)N^{-1}(1/\mu(B(x,1))): x\in R^n\}.$$

Indeed, let $\{\eta^{(j)}\}$ be a partition of unity subordinate to a covering of R^n by unit balls $\{\mathscr{B}^{(j)}\}$ with finite multiplicity. From the definition of the norm in $L_M(\mu)$ and the Sobolev theorem on imbedding H_p^l into L_∞ we obtain

$$\begin{aligned} \||u|^p\|_{L_M(\mu)} &\leqslant c\sum_j \||u\eta^{(j)}|^p\|_{L_M(\mu)} \\ &\leqslant c_1 \sum_j \|\chi(\cdot, \mathscr{B}^{(j)})\|_{L_M(\mu)} \|u\eta^{(j)}\|_{H_p^l}^p \\ &\leqslant c_1 C_4 \sum_j \|u\eta^{(j)}\|_{H_p^l}^p . \end{aligned}$$

The last sum does not exceed $c\|u\|_{H_p^l}^p$ (cf. Theorem 7.1.3/3); hence $A \leqslant c_2 C_4$. The opposite estimate follows from (8.3/1) by substitution of the function $\eta \in C_0^\infty(B(x,2))$, $\eta = 1$ on $B(x,1)$.

Now the D.R. Adams Theorem 1.4.1 follows from (α) of the previous theorem where $M(t) = t^{q/p}$, $q > p$.

Remark 2. We show that the condition (8.1/5) with $s = n - pl$ is not sufficient for (8.1/2) to hold in case $q = p$. Let $q = p$, $n > pl$. We choose a Borel set E with finite positive $(n-pl)$-dimensional Hausdorff measure. We can take E to be closed and bounded (since any Borel set of positive Hausdorff measure contains a bounded subset having the same property). By the Frostman theorem (see Carleson [43], Theorem 1, Ch. 2) there exists a measure $\mu \neq 0$ with support in E such that

$$\mu(B(x,\varrho)) \leqslant c\varrho^{n-pl}, \tag{1}$$

where c is a constant that is independent of x and ϱ. By Proposition 7.2.3/3, $\operatorname{cap}(E, H_p^l) = 0$. On the other hand, from (8.1/2) it follows that $\mu(E) \leqslant A \operatorname{cap}(E, H_p^l)$ and hence $\mu(E) = 0$. This contradiction shows that (8.1/2) fails although (1) holds.

Setting $M(t) = t^{q/p}$ in the previous theorem we obtain the following result for the case $lp = n$.

Corollary 1. *If* $lp = n$, $q > p > 1$ *then the exact constant* A *in*

$$\|u\|_{L_q(\mu)} \leqslant A\|u\|_{H_p^l} \tag{2}$$

is equivalent to

$$C_5 = \sup\{|\log \varrho|^{p-1}[\mu(B(x,\varrho))]^{p/q}: x \in R^n, 0<\varrho<\tfrac{1}{2}\}.$$

From the theorem of the present section we easily obtain the following assertion relating the case $pl = n$ and measures of positive dimension.

Corollary 2. *Let* $pl = n$ *and* $M(t) = \exp(t^{p'-1}) - 1$. *The inequality* (8.3/1) *holds if and only if for some* $\beta > 0$

$$\sup\{\varrho^{-\beta}\mu(B(x,\varrho)): x \in R^n, 0<\varrho<1\} < \infty .$$

Proof. Since $N'(t) = (\log t)^{p-1}(1+o(1))$ as $t \to \infty$ then $\Phi^{-1}(t) = tN^{-1}(1/t) = (\log t)^{1-p}(1+o(1))$. Hence, $\log \Phi(t) = -t^{p'-1}(1+o(1))$. Obviously, Φ satisfies the condition (8.5/2). Now it remains to use $\operatorname{cap}(B_\varrho, H_p^l) \sim |\log \varrho|^{1-p}$ with $\varrho \in (0, \frac{1}{2})$ and to apply Theorem. The proof is complete.

Remark 3. Since $B_p^l(R^n)$ is the space of traces on R^n of functions in $H_p^{l+1/p}(R^{n+1})$, Theorem and Corollary 1 still hold if the space $H_p^l(R^n)$ is replaced by $B_p^l(R^n)$.

Remark 4. We can obtain assertions similar to Theorem and Corollaries 1, 2 by replacing u by $\nabla_k u$ in the left-hand sides of inequalities (8.3/1) and (2). For example, the generalization of Corollary 1 runs as follows.

If $(l-k)p = n$, $q > p > 1$ then the best constant in

$$\|\nabla_k u\|_{L_q(\mu)} \leqslant A\,\|u\|_{H_p^l} \tag{3}$$

is equivalent to C_5.

The estimate $A \leqslant cC_5$ needs no additional arguments. To prove the reverse inequality we place the origin at an arbitrary point of the space and put

$$u(x) = x_1^k \zeta\left(\frac{\log|x|}{\log \varrho}\right),$$

where $\varrho \in (0, \frac{1}{2})$ and $\zeta \in C^\infty(R^1)$, $\zeta(t) = 1$ for $t > 1$, $\zeta(t) = 0$ for $t < \frac{1}{2}$ into (3). It is clear that $\operatorname{supp} u \subset B_{\varrho^{1/2}}$. Using standard but rather cumbersome estimates we can show that, for $|x| < \frac{1}{2}$,

$$(D_l u)(x) \leqslant c\,|x|^{-n/p}\,|\log|x||^{-1},$$

where $D_l u$ is the Strichartz function (7.1.2/2) for $\{l\} > 0$ and $D_l u = |\nabla_l u|$ for $\{l\} = 0$. Hence from Theorem 7.1.2/4 we have

$$\|u\|_{H_p^l}^p \leqslant c\,|\log \varrho|^{1-p} .$$

On the other hand,

$$\| \nabla_k u \|^q_{L_q(\mu)} \geqslant k!\ \mu(B_\varrho)\,.$$

Consequently, $A \geqslant cC_5$.

§ 8.7. Imbedding Theorems for $p=1$

The aim of the present section is to prove the following theorem which complements Theorem 1.4.3.

Theorem 1. *Let k be a nonnegative integer, $0<l-k\leqslant n$, $1\leqslant q<\infty$. Then the best constant A in*

$$\| \nabla_k u \|_{L_q(\mu)} \leqslant A \, \| u \|_{b_1^l} \tag{1}$$

is equivalent to

$$K = \sup_{x,\,\varrho>0} \varrho^{l-k-n} \mu(B(x,\varrho))^{1/q}\,.$$

Proof. α) We show that $A \geqslant cK$. We put $u(\xi) = (x_1-\xi_1)^k \varphi(\varrho^{-1}(x-\xi))$, where $\varphi \in C_0^\infty(B_2)$, $\varphi=1$ on B_1, into (8.7/1). Since

$$\| \nabla_k u \|^q_{L_q(\mu)} \geqslant k!\ \mu(B(x,\varrho))\,,$$

$$\| u \|_{S_1^l} = c\varrho^{n-l+k}\,,$$

then $A \geqslant cK$.

β) We prove that $A \leqslant cK$. Let $q>1$. By virtue of Theorem 8.6 and Remark 8.6/2 we have

$$\| \nabla_k u \|_{L_q(\mu)} \leqslant c \sup_{x,\,\varrho} \frac{\mu(B(x,\varrho))^{1/q}}{\varrho^{k-(l-n+n/t)+n/t}} \, \| u \|_{b_t^{l-n-n/t}}\,,$$

where t is a number sufficiently close to unity, $t>1$. It remains to apply items (iii) and (iv) of Theorem 7.1.3/4.

Next we show that $A \leqslant cK$ for $q=1$. It suffices to consider the case $k=0$. Let $l \in (0,1)$. According to Corollary 2.1.5,

$$\| u \|_{L(\mu,R^n)} \leqslant cK \int_{R^{n+1}} |y|^{-l} |\nabla_z U| \, dz\,,$$

where $U \in C_0^\infty(R^{n+1})$ is an arbitrary extension of a function u to R^{n+1}. Taking into account the relation

$$\| u \|_{b_1^l} \sim \inf_U \int_{R^{n+1}} |y|^{-l} |\nabla_z U| \, dz\,,$$

contained in Theorem 7.1.1/1, we arrive at $A \leqslant cK$.

If $l=1$, then by Theorem 1.4.3

$$\|u\|_{L(\mu,R^n)} \leqslant cK \|\nabla_{2,z} U\|_{L(R^{n+1})}.$$

Minimizing the right-hand side over all U we conclude that $A \leqslant cK$ for the space b_1^1.

Suppose the estimate $A \leqslant cK$ is established for $l \in (N-2, N-1)$, where N is an integer, $N \geqslant 2$. We prove it for $l \in (N-1, N]$. We have

$$\int |u|\, d\mu(x) = c \int \left| \int \frac{(\xi - x)\nabla_\xi u(\xi)}{|\xi - x|^n} d\xi \right| d\mu(x) \leqslant c \int |\nabla u| I_1 \mu\, dx,$$

where $I_1 \mu = |x|^{1-n} * \mu$. By the induction hypothesis the latter integral does not exceed

$$c \sup_{x,r} \left(r^{l-1-n} \int_{B(x,r)} I_1 \mu(\xi)\, d\xi \right) \|\nabla u\|_{b_1^{l-1}}.$$

By Lemma 1.4.3 with $q=1$ the last supremum is majorized by cK. The theorem is proved.

Remark 1. We substitute the function u defined by $u(x) = \eta(x/\varrho)$ where $\eta \in C_0^\infty(R^n)$, $\varrho > 0$, into (1). Let $\varrho \to \infty$. Then (1) is not fulfilled for $l-k>n$ provided $\mu \neq 0$.

For $l-k=n$, $q<\infty$ inequality (1) holds if and only if $\mu(R^n)<\infty$.

Theorem 2. *Let* $0<k<l$, $l-k \leqslant n$, $1 \leqslant q < \infty$. *The best constant* C_0 *in*

$$\|\nabla_k u\|_{L_q(\mu,R^n)} \leqslant C_0 \|u\|_{b_1^l} \tag{2}$$

is equivalent to

$$K_0 = \sup_{x;\, \varrho \in (0,1)} \varrho^{l-k-n} \mu(B(x,\varrho))^{1/q}.$$

Proof. The estimate $C_0 \geqslant cK_0$ follows in the same way as $C \geqslant cK$ in Theorem 1. To prove the reverse inequality we use the partition of unity $\{\varphi_j\}_{j \geqslant 1}$ subordinate to the covering of R^n by open balls with centers at the nodes of a sufficiently fine coordinate grid and apply Theorem 1 to the norm $\|\nabla_k(\varphi_j u)\|_{L_q(\mu_j)}$ where μ_j is the restriction of μ to the support of φ_j. Then

$$\int |\nabla_k u|^q d\mu \leqslant c \sum_j \int |\nabla_k(\varphi_j u)|^q d\mu_j \leqslant cK_0^q \sum_j \|\varphi_j u\|_{s_1^l}^q \leqslant cK_0^q \left(\sum_j \|\varphi_j u\|_{s_1^l} \right)^q,$$

where $s_1^l = w_1^l$ or b_1^l. (Here we made use of the inequality $\sum a_i^q \leqslant (\sum a_i)^q$, where $a_i \geqslant 0$, $q \geqslant 1$.) Now reference to Theorem 7.1.3/3 completes the proof.

Remark. For $l-k \geqslant n$ the best constant in (2) is equivalent to one of the following values:

$$\sup_{x\in R^n} [\mu(B(x,1))]^{1/q} \qquad \text{if } q \geqslant 1\,,$$

$$\Big(\sum_{i\geqslant 0} \mu(\mathcal{Q}^{(i)})^{(1-q)^{-1}}\Big)^{(1-q)q^{-1}} \qquad \text{if } 0<q<1\,,$$

where $\{\mathcal{Q}^{(i)}\}$ is the same sequence as in Theorem 8.4.4/1. The proof is contained in Remark 8.6/1 and Theorem 8.4.4/1.

§ 8.8. Applications

8.8.1. Criteria for Compactness

The theorems proved in the previous sections of the present chapter imply necessary and sufficient conditions for compactness of imbedding operators of the spaces H_p^l, h_p^l, W_p^l, w_p^l, B_p^l and b_p^l into $L_q(\mu)$. The proof of these results follows the standard arguments (compare with Theorems 2.4.2/1 and 2.4.2/2), so we restrict ourselves to the next four statements. The first two theorems are based on Corollary 8.3.

Theorem 1. *Let $p>1$, $pl<n$ and let s_p^l be any one of the spaces h_p^l, w_p^l, b_p^l. Any set of functions in $\mathcal{D}$, bounded in s_p^l, is relatively compact in $L_q(\mu)$ if and only if*

$$\lim_{\delta\to 0} \sup\left\{\frac{\mu(e)}{\operatorname{cap}(e, s_p^l)} : e\subset R^n,\ \operatorname{diam} e \leqslant \delta\right\} = 0\,, \tag{1}$$

$$\lim_{\varrho\to\infty} \sup\left\{\frac{\mu(e)}{\operatorname{cap}(e, s_p^l)} : e\subset R^n\backslash B_\varrho\right\} = 0\,, \tag{2}$$

where $B_\varrho = \{x\colon |x|<\varrho\}$.

Theorem 2. *Let $p>1$, $pl\leqslant n$ and let S_p^l be any of the spaces H_p^l, W_p^l, B_p^l. A set of functions in $\mathcal{D}$, bounded in S_p^l, is relatively compact in $L_q(\mu)$ if and only if condition* (1) *and*

$$\lim_{\varrho\to\infty} \sup\left\{\frac{\mu(e)}{\operatorname{cap}(e, S_p^l)} : e\subset R^n\backslash B_\varrho,\ \operatorname{diam} e \leqslant 1\right\} = 0 \tag{3}$$

are valid.

Theorems 3 and 4 below follow from Theorem 8.6 and Corollary 8.6/1, respectively.

Theorem 3. *Let $p\geqslant 1$, $l>0$, $pl<n$. Further let $1\leqslant q<\infty$ if $p=1$ and $p<q<\infty$ if $p>1$. Then the set $\{u\in\mathcal{D}\colon \|u\|_{W_p^l}\leqslant 1\}$ is relatively compact in $L_q(\mu)$ if and only if*

$$\text{(i)} \quad \lim_{\delta \to +0} \sup_{x;\, \varrho \in (0,\delta)} \varrho^{l-n/p} [\mu(B(x,\varrho))]^{1/q} = 0 \,,$$

$$\text{(ii)} \quad \lim_{|x| \to \infty} \sup_{\varrho \in (0,1)} \varrho^{l-n/p} [\mu(B(x,\varrho))]^{1/q} = 0 \,.$$

Theorem 4. *Let $p>1$, $l>0$, $pl=n$ and $q>p$. Then the set $\{u \in \mathscr{D}: \|u\|_{W_p^l} \leqslant 1\}$ is relatively compact in $L_q(\mu)$ if and only if*

$$\text{(i)} \quad \lim_{\delta \to 0} \sup_{x;\, \varrho \in (0,\delta)} |\log \varrho|^{1-1/p} [\mu(B(x,\varrho))]^{1/q} = 0 \,,$$

$$\text{(ii)} \quad \lim_{|x| \to \infty} \sup_{2\varrho < 1} |\log \varrho|^{1-1/p} [\mu(B(x,\varrho))]^{1/q} = 0 \,.$$

8.8.2. Applications to the Theory of Elliptic Operators

Corollary 8.3 has immediate applications to the spectral theory of elliptic operators. Let

$$S_h = h(-\Delta)^l - p(x) \,, \qquad x \in R^n \,,$$

where $p \geqslant 0$ and h is a positive number. The results in § 2.5 concerning the Schrödinger operator $-h\Delta - p(x)$ have natural analogs for the operators S_h. Duplicating with minor modifications the proofs of Theorems 2.5.3–2.5.6 and other assertions in § 2.5, we can derive conditions for the semiboundedness of the operator S_h as well as conditions for the discreteness, finiteness or infiniteness of the negative part of its spectrum. Here we present the statements of two typical theorems of this kind.

Theorem 1. *Let $n > 2l$ and let $\mathfrak{M}$ denote the constant in the maximum principle for the Riesz potential of order $2l$.*

1) *If*

$$\limsup_{\delta \to 0} \left\{ \frac{\int_e p(x)\,dx}{\operatorname{cap}(e, h_2^l)} : \operatorname{diam} e \leqslant \delta \right\} < (4\mathfrak{M})^{-1} \,,$$

then the operator S_1 is semibounded.

2) *If the operator S_1 is semibounded, then*

$$\limsup_{\delta \to 0} \left\{ \frac{\int_e p(x)\,dx}{\operatorname{cap}(e, h_2^l)} : \operatorname{diam} e \leqslant \delta \right\} \leqslant 1 \,.$$

Theorem 2. *Let $n > 2l$. The conditions*

$$\limsup_{\delta \to 0} \left\{ \frac{\int_e p(x)\,dx}{\operatorname{cap}(e, h_2^l)} : \operatorname{diam} e \leqslant \delta \right\} = 0 \,,$$

$$\limsup_{\varrho\to\infty}\left\{\frac{\int_e p(x)\,dx}{\operatorname{cap}(e,h_2^l)} : e\subset R^n\backslash B_\varrho,\ \operatorname{diam} e\leqslant 1\right\}=0$$

are necessary and sufficient for the semiboundedness of the operator S_h and for the discreteness of its negative spectrum for all $h>0$.

§ 8.9. Comments to Chapter 8

§ 8.2. Inequalities similar to (8.1/4) were proved in the author's paper [152], where (8.1.4) (and even a stronger estimate in which the role of the capacity of the set Q_t is played by the capacity of the condenser $Q_t\backslash Q_{2t}$) were derived for $l=1$ and $l=2$. In the more difficult case $l=2$ the proof was based on the procedure of "smooth truncation" of the potential near equipotential surfaces (cf. 8.2.1). By combining this procedure with the Hedberg inequality (8.2.2/2). D. R. Adams [5] established (8.1/4) for the Sobolev space W_p^l for any integer l. The proof of D. R. Adams is presented in 8.2.2. The same tools together with Theorem 7.1.1/1 on traces of functions in the weighted Sobolev space were used by the author to derive (8.1/4) for functions in W_p^l for all $p>1$, $l>0$. This implies the validity of (8.1/4) for the Bessel potential space H_p^l for all fractional $l>2$ but only for $p\geqslant 2$. The latter restriction was removed by Dahlberg [48] whose proof is also based on "smooth truncation" and on subtle estimates for potentials with nonnegative density. Finally, recently Hansson [87, 88] found a new proof of (8.1/4) for spaces of potentials which uses no truncation. Hansson's approach is suitable for a wide class of potentials with general kernels. In 8.2.3 we presented the author's proof (cf. [168]) of inequality (8.1/4) based on Hansson's idea [87] but, apparently, simpler.

§ 8.3. The equivalence of imbedding theorems and isoperimetric inequalities, connecting measures and capacities, was discovered by the author in 1962 (cf. Maz'ja [144, 146]). Results of this kind were later obtained in the papers by Maz'ja [152, 160], D. R. Adams [5], Maz'ja and Preobraženskiĭ [176], and others.

§ 8.4. The results are due to the author [168].

§§ 8.5 – 8.6. Here the presentation mostly follows the paper by the author and Preobraženskiĭ [176]. In comparison with this paper the requirements on the function Φ are made less restrictive for $1<p<2-l/n$ by virtue of results due to Hedberg and Wolff [96] which appeared later. Remark 8.6/2 was proved by D. R. Adams [5], and Corollary 8.6/2 was established earlier by D. R. Adams [1] by a different method.

§ 8.7. The results are due to the author [163].

Theorems of the present chapter were applied to the problem of the description of classes of multipliers in various spaces of differentiable functions (cf. Maz'ja [162, 168], Maz'ja and Šapošnikova [177], [179], [181]). Let the class of multipliers acting from one function space S_1 into another function space S_2 be denoted by $M(S_1 \to S_2)$. In other words, $M(S_1 \to S_2) = \{\gamma\colon \gamma u \in S_2$ for all $u \in S_1\}$. The norm of the element γ in $M(S_1 \to S_2)$ is equal to the norm of the operator of multiplication by γ. The following equivalent norms for the spaces $M(W_p^m \to W_q^l)$ (m and l are integers, $m \geqslant l$) are presented in the papers by the author and Šapošnikova [177] and by the author [168]. The norm of γ in $M(W_p^m \to W_q^l)$ is denoted by $\|\gamma\|_{(p,m)\to(q,l)}$.

α) If $1 < p \leqslant n/m$, then

$$(1) \quad \|\gamma\|_{(p,m)\to(p,l)} \sim \sup_{e,\,\mathrm{diam}\,e \leqslant 1} \left(\frac{\|\nabla_l \gamma\|_{L_p(e)}}{[\mathrm{cap}(e, W_p^m)]^{1/p}} + \frac{\|\gamma\|_{L_p(e)}}{[\mathrm{cap}(e, W_p^{m-l})]^{1/p}} \right).$$

β) If $1 < p < q$ or $1 = p \leqslant q$, then

$$\|\gamma\|_{(p,m)\to(q,l)} \sim \begin{cases} \sup\limits_{x \in R^n,\, \varrho \in (0,1)} \varrho^{m-n/p} (\|\nabla_l \gamma\|_{L_q(B_\varrho(x))} + \varrho^{-l} \|\gamma\|_{L_q(B_\varrho(x))}) \\ \quad \text{for } mp < n; \\ \sup\limits_{x \in R^n,\, \varrho \in (0,1)} ((\log 2/\varrho)^{1/p'} \|\nabla_l \gamma\|_{L_q(B_\varrho(x))} + \varrho^{-l} \|\gamma\|_{L_q(B_\varrho(x))}) \\ \quad \text{for } mp = n,\ p > 1; \\ \sup\limits_{x \in R^n} \|\gamma\|_{W_q^l(B_1(x))} \quad \text{for } mp > n \text{ and for } p = 1,\ m = n. \end{cases}$$

γ) If $1 < q < p$, then

$$\|\gamma\|_{(p,m)\to(q,l)}$$

$$\sim \sup_{\{\mathfrak{S}\}} \left(\sum_{j=-\infty}^{+\infty} \left(\frac{\|\nabla_l \gamma\|_{L_q(g_j \setminus g_{j-1})}}{[\mathrm{cap}(g_j, W_p^m)]^{1/p}} + \frac{\|\gamma\|_{L_q(g_j \setminus g_{j-1})}}{[\mathrm{cap}(g_j, W_p^{m-l})]^{1/p}} \right)^{pq/(p-q)} \right)^{(p-q)/pq}.$$

Besides, for $1 \leqslant q < p$, $pm > n$

$$\|\gamma\|_{(p,m)\to(q,l)} \sim \left(\sum_i \|\gamma\|_{W_p^l(\mathscr{Q}^{(i)})}^{pq/(p-q)} \right)^{(p-q)/pq}.$$

(The notation is the same as in 3.4.2, 8.4.4.)

Added in Proof. Recently Kerman and Sawyer proved that e in the definition of R on p. 370 can be replaced by any ball (see E. Sawyer "Multipliers of Besov and power-weighted L^2 spaces". Indiana Univ. Math. J., 1984, v. 33, N3, 353–366).

According to a theorem by Verbitskiĭ, the denominator in the second summand in (1) can be omitted (see the book by Maz'ja & Šapošnikova "Theory of Multipliers in Spaces of Differentiable Functions", Pitman, 1985).

Both these results enable one to reformulate α).

Chapter 9. A Variant of Capacity

§ 9.1. The Capacity Cap

9.1.1. Simple Properties of the Capacity $\mathrm{Cap}(e, \mathring{L}_p^l(\Omega))$

In 7.2.1 we introduced the capacity $\mathrm{cap}(e, S_p^l)$ of a compactum $e \subset R^n$ for any one of the spaces $S_p^l = H_p^l$, h_p^l, B_p^l, etc. In other words, we considered the set function $\inf\{\|u\|_{S_p^l}^p : u \in \mathfrak{N}(e)\}$, where $\mathfrak{N}(e) = \{u \in \mathscr{D}: u \geqslant 1 \text{ on } e\}$.

Replacing $\mathfrak{N}(e)$ by $\mathfrak{M}(e, \Omega) = \{u \in C_0^\infty(\Omega): u = 1 \text{ in a neighborhood of } e\}$ we obtain another set function which appears to be useful in various applications. This new set function will also be called the capacity. Here it will be denoted by $\mathrm{Cap}(e, S_p^l(\Omega))$.

Having in mind further applications we restrict ourselves to capacities Cap generated by the spaces $\mathring{L}_p^l(\Omega)$ and W_p^l, $l = 1, 2, \ldots$.

The inner and outer capacities of an arbitrary subset of the set Ω are defined by

$$\underline{\mathrm{Cap}}(E, \mathring{L}_p^l(\Omega)) = \sup_{e \subset E} \mathrm{Cap}(e, \mathring{L}_p^l(\Omega)) ,$$

$$\overline{\mathrm{Cap}}(E, \mathring{L}_p^l(\Omega)) = \inf_{G \supset E} \underline{\mathrm{Cap}}(G, \mathring{L}_p^l(\Omega)) ,$$

respectively. Here e is an arbitrary compact subset of E and G is an arbitrary open subset of Ω containing E. If the inner and outer capacities coincide, their common value is called the capacity of the set E and is denoted by $\mathrm{Cap}(E, \mathring{L}_p^l(\Omega))$.

Henceforth when speaking of the (p, l)-capacity we shall mean this set function.

The definition of the capacity $\mathrm{Cap}(e, \mathring{L}_p^l(\Omega))$ immediately implies the following two properties.

Monotonicity. If $e_1 \subset e_2$ and $\Omega_1 \supset \Omega_2$, then

$$\mathrm{Cap}(e_1, \mathring{L}_p^l(\Omega_1)) \leqslant \mathrm{Cap}(e_2, \mathring{L}_p^l(\Omega_2)) .$$

Right continuity. For each $\varepsilon > 0$ there exists a neighborhood ω of the compactum e with $\bar{\omega} \subset \Omega$ such that for an arbitrary compactum e' with $e \subset e' \subset \omega$ we have

$$\mathrm{Cap}(e', \mathring{L}_p^l(\Omega)) \leqslant \mathrm{Cap}(e, \mathring{L}_p^l(\Omega)) + \varepsilon .$$

The following three propositions establish the simplest connections between the capacities $\mathrm{Cap}(\cdot, S_1)$ and $\mathrm{Cap}(\cdot, S_2)$.

Proposition 1. *Let ω and Ω be open sets in R^n with $D = \operatorname{diam}\Omega < \infty$ and $\bar{\omega} \subset \Omega$. Then for any compactum $e \subset \omega$, located at the distance Δ_e from $\partial\omega$, the inequality*

$$\mathrm{Cap}(e, \mathring{L}_p^l(\omega)) \leqslant c \left(\frac{D}{\Delta_e}\right)^{lp} \mathrm{Cap}(e, \mathring{L}_p^l(\Omega))$$

is valid.

Proof. Let $u \in \mathfrak{M}(e, \Omega)$ and let $\alpha \in C_0^\infty(\omega)$, $\alpha = 1$ in a neighborhood of e and $|\nabla_i \alpha(x)| \leqslant c\Delta_e^{-i}$, $i = 1, 2, \ldots$ (cf. Stein [237], § 2, Ch. 6). Then

$$\mathrm{Cap}(e, \mathring{L}_p^l(\omega)) \leqslant \|\nabla_l(\alpha u)\|_{L_p(\omega)}^p \leqslant c \sum_{i=0}^{l} \Delta_e^{(j-l)p} \|\nabla_j u\|_{L_p(\Omega)}^p .$$

It remains to make use of the Friedrichs inequality

$$\|\nabla_i u\|_{L_p(\Omega)} \leqslant c D^{l-i} \|\nabla_l u\|_{L_p(\Omega)} .$$

The proof is complete.

The following proposition can be proved in a similar way.

Proposition 2. *Let $e \subset \Omega$, $D = \operatorname{diam}\Omega$, $\Delta_e = \operatorname{dist}\{e, \partial\Omega\}$. Then*

$$c_1 \min\{1, \Delta_e^{lp}\} \leqslant \frac{\mathrm{Cap}(e, W_p^l)}{\mathrm{Cap}(e, \mathring{L}_p^l(\Omega))} \leqslant c_2 \max\{1, D^{lp}\} .$$

An immediate corollary of the imbedding $\mathring{L}_p^l(R^n) \subset \mathring{L}_q^m(R^n)$ for appropriate values of p, l, q, m is the following.

Proposition 3. *Let $n > lp$, $p > 1$ or $n \geqslant l$, $p = 1$. If $e \subset B_r$, then*

$$\mathrm{Cap}(e, \mathring{L}_p^l(B_{2r})) \leqslant c\,\mathrm{Cap}(e, \mathring{L}_p^l) , \tag{1}$$

where $c = c(n, p, l)$.

Proof. Let $u \in \mathfrak{M}(e)$, $\alpha \in \mathfrak{M}(\bar{B}_r, B_{2r})$. We have

$$\|\nabla_l(\alpha u)\|_{L_p(B_{2r})} \leqslant c \sum_{j=0}^{l} \|\nabla_j u\|_{L_p(B_{2r})} \leqslant c_1 \sum_{j=0}^{l} \|\nabla_j u\|_{L_{q_j}} \leqslant c_2 \|\nabla_l u\|_{L_p} ,$$

where $q_j = pn(n-(l-j)p)^{-1}$.

Next we present two lower bounds for $\mathrm{Cap}(e, \mathring{L}_p^l(\Omega))$.

Proposition 4. *Let $e \subset \Omega \cap R^s$, $s \leqslant n$. Then*

$$\mathrm{Cap}(e, \mathring{L}_p^l(\Omega)) \geqslant c(m_s e)^{p/q} ,$$

where $q = ps/(n-lp)$ *for* $p>1$, $s>n-lp>0$, *or* $s \geqslant n-l \geqslant 0$ *for* $p=1$. *The constant* c *depends only on* n, p, l, q.

For the proof it suffices to apply the inequality

$$\| u \|_{L_q(R^s)} \leqslant c \| \nabla_l u \|_{L_p(R^n)}$$

to an arbitrary $u \in \mathfrak{M}(e, \Omega)$.

Proposition 5. *If* Ω *is open set,* e *is a compactum in* Ω *and* $d_e = \operatorname{dist}(e, \partial\Omega)$, *then*

$$\operatorname{Cap}(e, \mathring{L}_p^l(\Omega)) \geqslant c d_e^{n-pl}, \tag{2}$$

where $pl>n$, $p>1$ *or* $l \geqslant n$, $p=1$.

Proof. For any $u \in \mathfrak{M}(e, \Omega)$ we have

$$1 = |u(x)|^p \leqslant c d_e^{pl-n} \int_{|y-x|<d_e} |\nabla_l u|^p dy, \qquad x \in e.$$

Therefore $1 \leqslant c d_e^{l-n/p} \| \nabla_l u \|_{L_p(\Omega)}$. The result follows.

Corollary. *Let* $pl>n$, $p>1$ *or* $l \geqslant n$, $p=1$ *and let* x_0 *be a point in* B_ϱ. *Then*

$$\operatorname{Cap}(x_0, \mathring{L}_p^l(B_{2\varrho})) \sim \varrho^{n-lp}. \tag{3}$$

Proof. The lower estimate for the capacity follows from Proposition 5 and the upper estimate results from substituting the function $u(x) = \eta((x-x_0)\varrho^{-1})$, where $\eta \in C_0^\infty(B_1)$, into the norm $\| \nabla_l u \|_{L_p(B_{2\varrho})}$.

9.1.2. The Capacity of a Continuum

Proposition 1. *Let* $n>lp>n-1$, $p \geqslant 1$ *and let* e *be a continuum with diameter* d. *Then*

$$\operatorname{Cap}(e, \mathring{L}_p^l) \sim d^{n-lp}. \tag{1}$$

Proof. We include e in the ball $\bar{B}_d$ with radius d and we denote the concentric ball with radius $2d$ by B_{2d}. Using the monotonicity of the capacity, we obtain

$$\operatorname{Cap}(e, \mathring{L}_p^l) \leqslant \operatorname{Cap}(\bar{B}_d, \mathring{L}_p^l) = c d^{n-lp}.$$

Let O and P be points in e with $|O-P| = d$. Let the axis Ox_n be directed from O to P. We introduce the notation

$$x = (x', x_n), \quad x' = (x_1, \ldots, x_{n-1}), \quad e(t) = e \cap \{x \colon x_n = t\},$$
$$B_{2d}^{(n-1)}(t) = B_{2d} \cap \{x \colon x_n = t\}, \quad \nabla_l' = \{\partial^l / \partial x_1^{\alpha_1} \ldots \partial x_{n-1}^{\alpha_{n-1}}\},$$

$$\alpha_1+\dots+\alpha_{n-1}=l\,.$$

For any $u\in\mathfrak{M}(e,B_{2d})$ we have

$$\int_{B_{2d}}|\nabla_l u|^p dx\geqslant\int_0^d dt\int_{B_{2d}^{(n-1)}(t)}|\nabla_l' u|^p dx'\geqslant\int_0^d \operatorname{Cap}[e(t),\mathring{L}_p^l(B_{2d}^{(n-1)}(t))]\,dt\,.$$

Since $e(t)\neq\varnothing$, $e(t)\subset\bar{B}_d$ and $pl>n-1$, then

$$\operatorname{Cap}(e(t),\mathring{L}_p^l(B_{2d}^{(n-1)}(t)))\geqslant c d^{n-1-lp}\,.$$

Minimizing $\|\nabla_l u\|^p_{L_p(B_{2d})}$ over the set $\mathfrak{M}(e,B_{2d})$, we obtain

$$\operatorname{Cap}(e,\mathring{L}_p^l(B_{2d}))\geqslant c d^{n-lp}\,.$$

To complete the proof it remains to use estimate (8.1.1/1).

Proposition 2. *If $n=lp$, $p>1$, then for any continuum e with diameter d, $2d<D$, the equivalence*

$$\operatorname{Cap}(e,\mathring{L}_p^l(B_D))\sim\left(\log\frac{D}{d}\right)^{1-p} \tag{2}$$

holds. Here B_D is the open ball with radius D and with center $O\in e$.

Proof. First we derive the upper bound for the capacity. Let the function v be defined on $B_D\backslash B_d$ as follows

$$v(x)=\left[\log\frac{D}{d}\right]^{-1}\log\frac{D}{|x|}\,.$$

Let α denote a function in $C^\infty[0,1]$ equal to zero near $t=0$, to unity near $t=1$ and such that $0\leqslant\alpha(t)\leqslant 1$. Further let $u(x)=\alpha[v(x)]$ for $x\in B_D\backslash B_d$, $u(x)=1$ in B_d and $u(x)=0$ outside B_D. It is clear that $u\in\mathfrak{M}(B_d,B_D)$. Besides, we can easily see that

$$|\nabla_l u(x)|\leqslant c\left[\log\frac{D}{d}\right]^{-1}|x|^{-l}$$

on $B_D\backslash B_d$. This implies

$$\operatorname{Cap}(\bar{B}_d,\mathring{L}_p^l(B_D))\leqslant\int_{B_D}|\nabla_l u(x)|^p dx$$

$$\leqslant c\left[\log\frac{D}{d}\right]^{-p}\int_{B_D\backslash B_d}|x|^{-lp}dx=c\left[\log\frac{D}{d}\right]^{1-p}.$$

We proceed to the lower bound for the capacity. Let P and Q be points in e with $|P-Q|=d$. By (r,ω) we denote the spherical coordinates of a point in the coordinate system with origin Q, $r>0$, $\omega\in\partial B_1(Q)$. Let u be a function in $\mathfrak{M}(e, B_{2D}(Q))$ such that

$$\int_{B_{2D}(Q)} |\nabla_l u|^p dx \leqslant \gamma-\varepsilon\,,$$

where $\gamma=\operatorname{Cap}(e, \mathring{L}_p^l(B_{2D}(Q))\leqslant \operatorname{Cap}(e, \mathring{L}_p^l(B_D))$ and ε is a small positive number. We introduce the function

$$U(r)=\|u(r,\cdot)\|_{L_p(\partial B_1(Q))}\,.$$

Since $u=1$ at least one point of the sphere $\{x: |x-Q|=r\}$, where $r<d$ and $pl>n-1$, then

$$|1-U(r)|\leqslant c\,\|u(r,\cdot)-U(r)\|_{W_p^l(\partial B_1(Q))}\,.$$

Hence

$$\left|1-2d^{-1}\int_{d/2}^{d} U(r)\,dr\right| \leqslant c\sum_{j=1}^{l} d^{j-l}\|\nabla_j u\|_{L_p(B_d(Q)\setminus B_{d/2}(Q))}\,. \tag{3}$$

Using $(l-1)p<n$ we obtain

$$\int_{B_{2D}(Q)} r^{(j-l)p}|\nabla_j u|^p dx \leqslant c\int_{B_{2D}(Q)} |\nabla_l u|^p dx\,,\qquad 1\leqslant j<l\,. \tag{4}$$

Therefore the right-hand side in (3) does not exceed

$$c\,\|\nabla_l u\|_{L_p(B_{2D}(Q))}\leqslant c_0(\gamma-\varepsilon)\,.$$

If $\gamma\geqslant(2c_0)^{-1}$, then the required estimate follows. Let $\gamma<(2c_0)^{-1}$. Then

$$\int_{d/2}^{d} U(r)\,dr > d/4$$

and $U(r_0)>\frac{1}{2}$ for some $r_0\in(d/2, d)$. Using (4) once more we conclude that

$$\gamma-\varepsilon\geqslant c\int_{\partial B_1(Q)} d\omega\int_{d}^{2D} |r\nabla u|^p\frac{dr}{r}-\varepsilon\,.$$

By virtue of the Hölder inequality we have

$$\gamma-\varepsilon\geqslant c\int_{r_0}^{2D}|rU'(r)|^p\frac{dr}{r}-\varepsilon\geqslant c\left(\log\frac{2D}{d}\right)^{1-p}\left|\int_{r_0}^{2D}U'(r)\,dr\right|^p$$

$$=c\left(\log\frac{2D}{d}\right)^{1-p}U(r_0)^p\geqslant 2^{-p}c\left(\log\frac{D}{d}\right)^{1-p}.$$

The result follows.

9.1.3. The Capacity of a Cylinder

Proposition 1. *Let $C_{\delta,d}$ be the cylinder*

$$\{x: (x', x_n): |x'| \leqslant \delta, |x_n| \leqslant d/2\}$$

where $0 < 2\delta < d$ and $Q_{2d} = \{x: |x_i| < d\}$. Then

$$\operatorname{Cap}(C_{\delta,d}, \mathring{L}_p^l(Q_{2d})) \sim \begin{cases} d\delta^{n-pl-1} & \text{for } n-1 > pl \\ d\left(\log \dfrac{d}{\delta}\right)^{1-p} & \text{for } n-1 = pl. \end{cases}$$

Proof. Let $u \in \mathfrak{M}(C_{\delta,d}, Q_{2d})$. Obviously,

$$\int_{Q_{2d}} |\nabla_l u|^p dx \geqslant \int_{-d/2}^{d/2} dx_n \int_{Q_{2d}^{(n-1)}} |\nabla_l' u|^p dx', \tag{1}$$

where $\nabla_l' = \{\partial^l/\partial x_1^{\alpha_1} \ldots \partial x_{n-1}^{\alpha_{n-1}}\}$, $\alpha_1 + \cdots + \alpha_{n-1} = l$, $Q_{2d}^{(n-1)} = \{x': |x_i| < d$, $i = 1, \ldots, n-1\}$.The inner integral on the right in (1) exceeds

$$\operatorname{Cap}(B_\delta^{(n-1)}, \mathring{L}_p^l(B_\varrho^{(n-1)})),$$

where $B_\varrho^{(n-1)}$ is the $(n-1)$-dimensional ball $\{x: |x'| < \varrho\}$ and $\varrho = 2(n-1)^{1/2} d$. Hence from Propositions 9.1.2/1 and 9.1.2/2 it follows that the integral under consideration majorizes $c\delta^{n-pl-1}$ for $n-1 > pl$ and $c(\log d/\delta)^{1-p}$ for $n-1 = pl$. Minimizing the left-hand side of (1) over the set $\mathfrak{M}(C_{\delta,d}, Q_{2d})$, we obtain the required lower estimate for the capacity.

We proceed to the upper bound. Let $x' \to u(x')$ be a smooth function with support in the ball $B_d^{(n-1)}$ that is equal to unity in a neighborhood of the ball $B_\delta^{(n-1)}$. Further, we introduce the function $\eta_d(x) = \eta(x/d)$, where $\eta \in \mathfrak{M}(\bar{Q}_1, Q_2)$. Since the function $x \to \eta_d(x) u(x')$ is in the class $\mathfrak{M}(C_{\delta,d}, Q_{2d})$ then

$$\begin{aligned} \operatorname{Cap}(C_{\delta,d}, \mathring{L}_p^l(Q_{2d})) &\leqslant \int_{Q_{2d}} |\nabla_l(u\eta_d)|^p dx \\ &\leqslant cd \sum_{k=0}^{l} d^{-pk} \int_{B_d^{(n-1)}} |\nabla_{l-k} u|^p dx' \leqslant c_1 d \int_{B_d^{(n-1)}} |\nabla_l u|^p dx'. \end{aligned}$$

Minimizing the latter integral and using Propositions 9.1.2/1, 9.1.2/2, we arrive at the required estimate.

9.1.4. The Sets of Zero Capacity $\operatorname{Cap}(\cdot, W_p^l)$

The definition of the capacity $\operatorname{Cap}(\cdot, \mathring{L}_p^l(\Omega))$ and Proposition 9.1.1/2 imply that $\operatorname{Cap}(e, W_p^l) = 0$ if and only if there exists a bounded open set Ω containing e such that $\mathrm{Cap}(e, \mathring{L}_p^l(\Omega)) = 0$. The choice of Ω is not essential by Proposition 9.1.1/2.

From Corollary 9.1.1, for $lp > n$, $p > 1$ and for $l \geqslant n$, $p = 1$, we obtain that the equality $\mathrm{Cap}(e, W_p^l) = 0$ is valid only if $e = \varnothing$.

Proposition 9.1.1/3 shows that in any one of the cases $n > lp$, $p > 1$ or $n \geqslant l$, $p = 1$ the equalities $\mathrm{Cap}(e, W_p^l) = 0$ and $\mathrm{Cap}(e, \mathring{L}_p^l) = 0$ are equivalent. Corollary 9.1.1 and Propositions 9.1.2/1 and 9.1.2/2 imply that no similar property is true for $n \leqslant lp$, $p > 1$. To be precise, $\mathrm{Cap}(e, \mathring{L}_p^l) = 0$ for any compactum e provided $n \leqslant lp$, $p > 1$.

§ 9.2. On (p, l)-polar Sets

Let $W_{p'}^{-l}$ denote the space of linear continuous functionals T: $u \to (u, T)$ on W_p^l.

The set $E \subset R^n$ is called a (p, l)-polar set if zero is the only element in $W_{p'}^{-l}$ with support in E.

Theorem 1. *The space $\mathscr{D}(\Omega)$ is dense in W_p^l if and only if $C\Omega$ is a (p, l)-polar set.*

Proof. 1) Suppose $\mathscr{D}(\Omega)$ is not dense in W_p^l. Then there exists a nonzero functional $T \in W_{p'}^{-l}$, equal to zero on $\mathscr{D}(\Omega)$, i.e. with support in $C\Omega$. (Here we make use of the following corollary of the Hahn-Banach theorem. Let M be a linear set in the Banach space B and let x_0 be an element of B situated at a positive distance from M. Then there exists a nonzero functional $T \in B^*$ such that $(x, T) = 0$ for all $x \in M$.) Consequently, $C\Omega$ is not a (p, l)-polar set.

2) Suppose $\mathscr{D}(\Omega)$ is dense in W_p^l. For any functional $T \in W_{p'}^{-l}$ with support in $C\Omega$ we have

$$(u, T) = 0$$

for all $u \in \mathscr{D}(\Omega)$. Therefore, the latter is valid for all $u \in W_p^l$ and so $T = 0$. Thus, $C\Omega$ is a (p, l)-polar set.

Theorem 2. *The set E is (p, l)-polar if and only if $\underline{\mathrm{Cap}}(E, W_p^l) = 0$.*

Proof. 1) Let $\underline{\mathrm{Cap}}(E, W_p^l) = 0$ and $T \in W_{p'}^{-l}$, $\mathrm{supp}\, T \subset E$. Without loss of generality we may assume that $\mathrm{supp}\, T$ is a compactum (otherwise we could take αT with $\alpha \in \mathscr{D}$ instead of T). We take an arbitrary $\varphi \in \mathscr{D}$ and a sequence $\{u_m\}_{m \geqslant 1}$ of functions in $\mathscr{D}$ which equal unity in a neighborhood of $\mathrm{supp}\, T$ and tend to zero in W_p^l. Since $\varphi(1 - u_m) = 0$ in a neighborhood of T then $(\varphi, T) = (\varphi u_m, T)$. The right-hand side converges to zero as $m \to \infty$; hence $(\varphi, T) = 0$ for all $\varphi \in \mathscr{D}$. Since $\mathscr{D}$ is dense in W_p^l then $T = 0$.

2) Let E be a (p, l)-polar set. Then any compactum K in E is also a (p, l)-polar set, and $\mathscr{D}(R^n \backslash K)$ is dense in W_p^l. Let $v \in \mathfrak{M}(K)$. By virtue of the density of $\mathscr{D}(R^n \backslash K)$ in W_p^l there exists a sequence $v_m \in \mathscr{D}(R^n \backslash K)$ that converges to v

in W_p^l. Every function $v_m - v$ equals unity near K, has compact support and $\| v_m - v \|_{W_p^l} \to 0$ as $m \to \infty$. Therefore $\mathrm{Cap}(K, W_p^l) = 0$. The proof is complete.

Taking into account the assertion just proved we can give an equivalent formulation of Theorem 1.

Theorem 3. *The space $\mathscr{D}(\Omega)$ is dense in W_p^l if and only if $\underline{\mathrm{Cap}}(C\Omega, W_p^l) = 0$.*

§ 9.3. The Equivalence of Two Capacities

We compare the capacities $\mathrm{Cap}(e, \mathring{L}_p^1)$ and $\mathrm{cap}(e, \mathring{L}_p^1)$, $p \geqslant 1$. Obviously, the first capacity majorizes the second. In fact, for the function $v_\varepsilon = \min\{(1-\varepsilon)^{-1} u, 1\}$ there exists a sequence in $\mathfrak{M}(e)$ that converges to v_ε in $\mathring{L}_p^1$ for arbitrary number $\varepsilon \in (0,1)$ and a function $u \in \mathfrak{N}(e)$. Therefore

$$\mathrm{Cap}(e, \mathring{L}_p^1) \leqslant \int |\nabla v_\varepsilon|^p dx \leqslant (1-\varepsilon)^{-p} \int |\nabla u|^p dx$$

and so $\mathrm{Cap}(e, \mathring{L}_p^1) \leqslant \mathrm{cap}(e, \mathring{L}_p^1)$. Thus the capacities $\mathrm{Cap}(e, \mathring{L}_p^1)$ and $\mathrm{cap}(e, \mathring{L}_p^1)$ coincide.

Since the truncation along the level surfaces does not keep functions in the spaces $\mathring{L}_p^l$ and W_p^l for $l > 1$, the above argument is not applicable to the proof of equivalence of the capacities Cap and cap, generated by these spaces. Nevertheless, in the present section we show that the equivalence occurs for $p > 1$.

9.3.1. An Auxiliary Multiplicative Inequality

The following assertion is applied in 9.3.2. It is a particular case of the Gagliardo-Nirenberg theorem (cf. 1.4.8).

Lemma 1. *If $u \in \mathring{L}_p^l \cap L_\infty$, $p > 1$ and $m = 1, 2, \ldots, l-1$, then*

$$\| \nabla_m u \|_{L_{pl/m}} \leqslant c \| u \|_{L_\infty}^{1-m/l} \| \nabla_l u \|_{L_p}^{m/l}. \tag{1}$$

First we derive a simple inequality for functions on R^1.

Lemma 2. *Let m be a positive integer, $q > m+1$ and let v be any function on R^1 with the finite norm*

$$\| v'' \|_{L_{q/(m+1)}(R^1)} + \| v \|_{L_{q/(m-1)}(R^1)}.$$

Then

$$\| v' \|_{L_{q/m}(R^1)} \leqslant c \| v'' \|_{L_{q/(m+1)}(R^1)}^{1/2} \| v \|_{L_{q/(m-1)}(R^1)}^{1/2},$$

where

$$c=\begin{cases}\left(\dfrac{m-1}{q-m-1}\right)^{1/2} & \textit{for } q<2m\,,\\[2ex] \left(\dfrac{q-m}{m}\right)^{1/2} & \textit{for } q\geqslant 2m\,.\end{cases}$$

Proof. We introduce the notation

$$b_j=\int |v^{(j)}|^{q/(m+j-1)}dx\,.$$

(The integral is taken over R^1.) First consider the case $q<2m$. Let $\delta=q(2m-q)/2m(m-1)$. By Hölder's inequality we have

$$b_1=\int |v|^{\delta}\frac{|v'|^{q/m}}{|v|^{\delta}}dx\leqslant\left(\int |v|^{q/(m-1)}dx\right)^{1-q/2m}\left(\int\frac{|v'|^2}{|v|^{(2m-q)/(m-1)}}dx\right)^{q/2m}.$$

Integrating by parts in the last integral, which is justified by the inequality $(2m-q)(m-1)^{-1}<1$, we obtain that it does not exceed

$$\frac{m-1}{q-m-1}\int |v|^{(q-m-1)/(m-1)}|v''|\,dx\leqslant\frac{m-1}{q-m-1}\,b_0^{1-(m+1)/q}b_2^{(m+1)/q}\,.$$

Let $q\geqslant 2m$. Integration by parts in b_1 yields

$$b_1\leqslant\left(\frac{q}{m}-1\right)\int |vv''|\,|v'|^{q/m-2}dx\,.$$

Applying the Hölder inequality with exponents $p_1=q/(q-m)$, $p_2=q/(m-1)$, $p_3=m$ to the preceding integral we conclude that

$$b_1\leqslant\frac{q-m}{m}\,b_1^{1-2m/q}b_0^{(m-1)/q}b_2^{(m+1)/q}\,.$$

Thus

$$b_1\leqslant c\,b_0^{(m-1)/2m}b_2^{(m+1)/2m}\,,$$

where $c=\left(\dfrac{m-1}{q-m-1}\right)^{q/2m}$ for $q<2m$ and $c=\left(\dfrac{q-m}{m}\right)^{q/2m}$ for $q\geqslant 2m$.

Proof of Lemma 1. Let $q>m+1$ and let

$$a_m=\|\nabla_m u\|_{L_{q/m}}\,,\qquad m=0,1,\ldots,l\,.$$

By Lemma 2 we have $a_m\leqslant c_1a_{m+1}^{1/2}a_{m-1}^{1/2}$. Hence, using induction, we obtain $a_m\leqslant c_2a_0^{(l-m)/m}a_l^{m/l}$ for $q=pl$. The result follows.

Corollary. *If* $u, v \in \mathring{L}_p^l \cap L_\infty$, *then*

(2) $$\| \nabla_l(uv) \|_{L_p} \leqslant c(\|u\|_{L_\infty} \| \nabla_l v \|_{L_p} + \|v\|_{L_\infty} \| \nabla_l u \|_{L_p}) .$$

Proof. By virtue of Lemma 1 we have

$$\| \nabla_l(uv) \|_{L_p} \leqslant c \sum_{k=0}^{l} \| |\nabla_k u| |\nabla_{l-k} v| \|_{L_p}$$
$$\leqslant c \sum_{k=0}^{l} \| \nabla_k u \|_{L_{pl/k}} \| \nabla_{l-k} v \|_{L_{pl/(l-k)}}$$
$$\leqslant c \sum_{k=0}^{l} \|u\|_{L_\infty}^{1-k/l} \| \nabla_l u \|_{L_p}^{k/l} \|v\|_{L_\infty}^{k/l} \| \nabla_l v \|_{L_p}^{1-k/l} .$$

The result follows.

9.3.2. The Relation Cap ~ cap for $p > 1$

Theorem 1. *Let* $p > 1$, $n > pl$, $l = 1, 2, \ldots$. *Then*

(1) $$\operatorname{cap}(e, \mathring{L}_p^l) \leqslant \operatorname{Cap}(e, \mathring{L}_p^l) \leqslant c \operatorname{cap}(e, \mathring{L}_p^l)$$

for any compactum e.

Proof. The left inequality results from the inclusion $\mathfrak{M}(e) \subset \mathfrak{N}(e)$. We proceed to the upper bound for Cap. Let G denote a bounded open set such that $G \supset e$ and

$$\operatorname{cap}(\bar{G}, L_p^l) \leqslant \operatorname{cap}(e, \mathring{L}_p^l) + \varepsilon .$$

Let U be the (p, l)-capacitary potential of the set $\bar{G}$ (cf. 7.2.2). By Proposition 7.2.2/2 the inequality $U \geqslant 1$ is valid (p, l)-quasi-everywhere in $\bar{G}$ and, therefore, quasi-everywhere in some neighborhood of the compactum e. We apply the mollification with radius m^{-1}, $m = 1, 2, \ldots$ to U and multiply the result by the truncating function η_m, $\eta_m(x) = \eta(x/m)$, where $\eta \in C_0^\infty$, $\eta(0) = 1$. So we obtain a sequence of functions $\{U_m\}_{m \geqslant 1}$ in C_0^∞ such that $0 \leqslant U_m \leqslant c$ in R^n, $U_m \geqslant 1$ in a neighborhood of e and

(2) $$\lim_{m \to \infty} \| \nabla_l U_m \|_{L_p}^p \leqslant \operatorname{cap}(e, \mathring{L}_p^l) + \varepsilon .$$

(The inequality $U_m \leqslant c$ follows from Proposition 7.2.2/1.)

We introduce the function

$$w = 1 - [(1 - U_m)_+]^{l+1} ,$$

which obviously has compact support and is in C^l. Besides,

$$\| \nabla_l w \|_{L_p} \leqslant \| \nabla_l [(1 - U_m)^{l+1}] \|_{L_p} .$$

Applying Corollary 9.3.1, we obtain

$$\| \nabla_l w \|_{L_p} \leqslant c \| \nabla_l U_m \|_{L_p} .$$

It remains to make use of inequality (2).

The following theorem has a similar proof.

Theorem 2. *Let $p>1$, $l=1,2,\ldots$. Then*

$$\operatorname{cap}(e, W_p^l) \leqslant \operatorname{Cap}(e, W_p^l) \leqslant c \operatorname{cap}(e, W_p^l) \tag{3}$$

for any compactum e.

Corollary 1. *Let $p>1$, $l=1,2,\ldots$, and let e be a closed subset of the cube $\bar{Q}_d = \{x\colon 2|x_i| \leqslant d\}$. Then*

$$\operatorname{cap}(e, \mathring{L}_p^l(Q_{2d})) \leqslant \operatorname{Cap}(e, \mathring{L}_p^l(Q_{2d})) \leqslant c \operatorname{cap}(e, \mathring{L}_p^l(Q_{2d})) . \tag{4}$$

Proof. It suffices to derive (4) for $d=1$. The left inequality is trivial; the right inequality follows from Proposition 9.1.1/2 and Theorem 2.

It is probably not known whether estimates (1) and (3) are true for $p=1$, $1<l<n$.

Remark. The proofs of Theorems 1 and 2 and of Corollary 1 do not change provided we replace the class $\mathfrak{M}(e, \Omega)$ in the definition of the capacity Cap by the narrower one:

$$\{u \in C_0^\infty(\Omega)\colon u=1 \text{ in a neighborhood of } e,\ 0 \leqslant u \leqslant 1\} .$$

Corollary 2. *Let $p>1$, $l=1,2,\ldots$ and let e_1, e_2 be compacta in $\bar{Q}_d$. Then*

$$\operatorname{Cap}(e_1 \cup e_2, \mathring{L}_p^l(Q_{2d})) \leqslant c_* \sum_{i=1}^{2} \operatorname{Cap}(e_i, \mathring{L}_p^l(Q_{2d})) , \tag{5}$$

where c_* is a constant that depends only on n, p, l.

Proof. Let $u_i \in \mathfrak{M}(e_i, Q_{2d})$, $0 \leqslant u_i \leqslant 1$, $i=1,2$, and let

$$\| \nabla_l u_i \|_{L_p}^p \leqslant c \operatorname{cap}(e_i, \mathring{L}_p^l(Q_{2d})) + \varepsilon \tag{6}$$

(cf. preceding Remark). The function $u=u_1+u_2$ is contained in $C_0^\infty(Q_{2d})$ and satisfies the inequality $u \geqslant 1$ on $e_1 \cup e_2$. Hence from Corollary we obtain

$$\operatorname{Cap}(e_1 \cup e_2, \mathring{L}_p^l(Q_{2d})) \leqslant c \operatorname{cap}(e_1 \cup e_2, \mathring{L}_p^l(Q_{2d}))$$
$$\leqslant c \| \nabla_l u \|_{L_p}^p \leqslant 2^{p-1} c \sum_{i=1}^{2} \| \nabla_l u_i \|_{L_p}^p ,$$

which together with (6) leads to (5).

§ 9.4. Comments to Chapter 9

§ 9.1. The capacity $\mathrm{Cap}(e, \mathring{L}_2^l(\Omega))$ was introduced by the author [145]. The content of this section follows, to a large extent, the author's paper [156].

§ 9.2. The definition of a $(2, l)$-polar set is borrowed from the paper by Hörmander and Lions [100]. The results of this section are due to Littman [134]. Concerning Theorem 9.1.4/2 see the earlier paper by Grušin [82].

§ 9.3. The equivalence of the capacities $\mathrm{Cap}(e, \mathring{L}_p^l)$ and $\mathrm{cap}(e, \mathring{L}_p^l)$ was established by the author [151, 153] for integer l. For fractional l the equivalence of the corresponding capacities is proved by D. R. Adams and Polking [11]. The proof of Lemma 9.3.1/1 follows the author's paper [153]. Another proof of Theorem 9.3.2/1, based on "smooth truncation" and on the Hedberg inequality (8.2.2/2), is contained in the paper by D. R. Adams [5].

Chapter 10. An Integral Inequality for Functions on a Cube

Let Q_d be an open n-dimensional cube with edge length d and with sides parallel to coordinate axes. Let $p \geqslant 1$, and k, l be integers, $0 \leqslant k \leqslant l$. We denote a function in $W_p^l(Q_d)$, $p \geqslant 1$, by u.

The inequality

$$\| u \|_{L_q(Q_d)} \leqslant C \sum_{j=k+1}^{l} d^{j-l} \| \nabla_j u \|_{L_p(Q_d)} \tag{1}$$

with q in the same interval as in the Sobolev imbedding theorem often turns out to be useful. This inequality occurs repeatedly in the following chapters. Obviously, (1) is not valid for all $u \in W_p^l(Q_d)$, but it holds provided u is subject to additional requirements.

In the present chapter we establish two-sided estimates for the best constant C in (1). In §§ 10.1, 10.2 we mainly consider the case of u vanishing near a compactum $e \subset \bar{Q}_d$ and $k = 0$. The existence of C is equivalent to the positiveness of the (p, l)-capacity of e. For a (p, l)-unessential set e, upper and lower bounds for C are stated in terms of this capacity. If $q \geqslant p$ and e is (p, l)-essential, i.e. its capacity is comparable with the capacity of the cube, then C is estimated by the so-called (p, l)-inner diameter.

In 10.3 the function u is *a priori* contained in an arbitrary linear subset $\mathfrak{C}$ of the space $W_p^l(Q_d)$. There we present the generalization of the basic theorem in 10.1 and give applications for concrete classes $\mathfrak{C}$. In this connection we have to introduce some functions of the class $\mathfrak{C}$ which play a role similar to that of the (p, l)-capacity.

In conclusion we note that the statements as well as the proofs of results in the present chapter remain valid after replacing the cube Q_d by an arbitrary bounded Lipschitz domain with diameter d.

§ 10.1. The Connection Between the Best Constant and the Capacity (The Case $k = 1$)

10.1.1. Definition of a (p, l)-Unessential Set

Definition. Let e be a compact subset of the cube $\bar{Q}_d$. In either one of the cases $n \geqslant pl$, $p > 1$ or $n > l$, $p = 1$ we say that e is *a (p, l)-unessential subset of Q_d* if

(1) $$\operatorname{Cap}(e, \mathring{L}_p^l(Q_{2d})) \leqslant \gamma d^{n-pl},$$

where γ is a sufficiently small constant that depends only on n, p, l. For the purposes of the present chapter we can take γ to be an arbitrary positive number satisfying the inequality

(2) $$\gamma \leqslant 4^{-pn}.$$

If (1) fails, then, by definition, e is a (p, l)-essential subset of $\bar{Q}_d$.

For $n<pl$, $p>1$ or for $n \leqslant l$, $p=1$ only the empty set is called (p, l)-unessential.

The collection of all (p, l)-unessential subsets of the cube $\bar{Q}_d$ will be denoted by $\mathcal{N}(Q_d)$.

10.1.2. The Main Theorem

Let $\bar{u}_{Q_d}$ denote the mean value of u on the cube Q_d, i.e.

$$\bar{u}_{Q_d} = [m_n(Q_d)]^{-1} \int_{Q_d} u\, dx .$$

We introduce the seminorm

$$\mathbf{|} u \mathbf{|}_{p,l,Q_d} = \sum_{j=1}^{l} d^{j-l} \| \nabla_j u \|_{L_p(Q_d)} .$$

Theorem. *Let e be a closed subset of the cube $\bar{Q}_d$.*

1) *For all $u \in C^\infty(\bar{Q}_d)$ with* $\operatorname{dist}(\operatorname{supp} u, e) > 0$ *the inequality*

(1) $$\| u \|_{L_q(Q_d)} \leqslant C \mathbf{|} u \mathbf{|}_{p,l,Q_d},$$

where $q \in [1, pn(n-pl)^{-1}]$ for $n>pl$, $p \geqslant 1$ and $q \in [1, \infty)$ for $n=pl$, $p>1$, is valid. Moreover, the constant C admits the estimate

(2) $$C^{-p} \geqslant c_1 d^{-np/q} \operatorname{Cap}(e, \mathring{L}_p^l(Q_{2d})) .$$

2) *For functions $u \in C^\infty(\bar{Q}_d)$ with* $\operatorname{dist}(\operatorname{supp} u, e) > 0$, *let*

(3) $$\| u \|_{L_q(Q_{d/2})} \leqslant C \mathbf{|} u \mathbf{|}_{p,l,Q_d},$$

where $e \in \mathcal{N}(Q_d)$ and q satisfies the same conditions as in 1). *Then*

(4) $$C^{-p} \leqslant c_2 d^{-np/q} \operatorname{Cap}(e, \mathring{L}_p^l(Q_{2d})) .$$

For the proof of this theorem we need the following lemma.

Lemma. *Let e be a compactum in $\bar{Q}_1$. There exists a constant c such that*

(5) $$c^{-1}\operatorname{Cap}(e, \mathring{L}_p^l(Q_2)) \leqslant \inf\{\|1-u\|^p_{V_p^l(Q_1)}: u \in C^\infty(\bar{Q}_1), \operatorname{dist}(\operatorname{supp} u, e) > 0\}$$
$$\leqslant c \operatorname{Cap}(e, \mathring{L}_p^l(Q_2)) .$$

Proof. To obtain the left estimate we need the following well-known assertion (cf. Theorem 1.1.16).

There exists a linear continuous mapping A: $C^{k-1,1}(\bar{Q}_d) \to C^{k-1,1}(\bar{Q}_{2d})$, $k = 1, 2, \ldots$, such that (i) $Av = v$ on $\bar{Q}_d$, (ii) if $\operatorname{dist}(\operatorname{supp} v, e) > 0$, then $\operatorname{dist}(\operatorname{supp} A v, e) > 0$, and (iii)

(6) $$\|\nabla_i(Av)\|_{L_p(Q_{2d})} \leqslant c \|\nabla_i v\|_{L_p(Q_d)}, \quad i = 0, 1, \ldots, l, \quad 1 \leqslant p \leqslant \infty .$$

Let $v = A(1-u)$. Let η denote a function in $\mathscr{D}(Q_2)$ which is equal to unity in a neighborhood of the cube Q_1. Then

(7) $$\operatorname{Cap}(e, Q_2) \leqslant c \int_{Q_2} |\nabla_l(\eta v)|^p dx \leqslant c \|v\|^p_{V_p^l(Q_2)} .$$

Now the left estimate in (5) follows from (6) and (7).

Next we derive the rightmost estimate in (5). Let $w \in \mathfrak{M}(e, Q_2)$. Then

$$\|w\|^p_{V_p^l(Q_1)} \leqslant c \sum_{k=0}^{l} \|\nabla_k w\|^p_{L_p(Q_2)} \leqslant c \|\nabla_l w\|^p_{L_p(Q_2)} .$$

Minimizing the last norm over the set $\mathfrak{M}(e, Q_2)$ we obtain

$$\|w\|^p_{V_p^l(Q_1)} \leqslant c \operatorname{Cap}(e, \mathring{L}_p^l(Q_2)) .$$

We complete the proof by minimizing the left-hand side.

Proof of the theorem. If suffices to consider only the case $d = 1$ and then use a similarity transformation.

1) Let $N = \|u\|_{L_p(Q_1)}$. Since $\operatorname{dist}(\operatorname{supp} u, e) > 0$, then by Lemma we have

$$\operatorname{Cap}(e, \mathring{L}_p^l(Q_2)) \leqslant c \|1 - N^{-1}u\|^p_{V_p^l(Q_1)} = cN^{-p} |u|^p_{p,l,Q_1} + c\|1 - N^{-1}u\|^p_{L_p(Q_1)},$$

i.e.

(8) $$N^p \operatorname{Cap}(e, \mathring{L}_p^l(Q_2)) \leqslant c |u|^p_{p,l,Q_1} + c \|N-u\|^p_{L_p(Q_1)} .$$

Without loss of generality, we may assume that $\bar{u}_{Q_1} \geqslant 0$. Then

$$|N - \bar{u}_{Q_1}| = \|u\|_{L_p(Q_1)} - \|\bar{u}_{Q_1}\|_{L_p(Q_1)} \leqslant \|u - \bar{u}_{Q_1}\|_{L_p(Q_1)} .$$

Consequently,

(9) $$\|N-u\|_{L_p(Q_1)} \leqslant \|N - \bar{u}_{Q_1}\|_{L_p(Q_1)} + \|u - \bar{u}_{Q_1}\|_{L_p(Q_1)} \leqslant 2\|u - \bar{u}_{Q_1}\|_{L_p(Q_1)} .$$

By (8), (9) and the Poincaré inequality

$$\|u - \bar{u}_{Q_1}\|_{L_p(Q_1)} \leqslant c \|\nabla u\|_{L_p(Q_1)}$$

we obtain

$$\operatorname{Cap}(e, \mathring{L}_p^l(Q_2))\, \|u\|^p_{L_p(Q_1)} \leqslant c\, \mathbf{|} u \mathbf{|}^p_{p,l,Q_1}\,.$$

From the Sobolev imbedding theorem and the preceding inequality we conclude that

$$\|u\|^p_{L_q(Q_1)} \leqslant c(\mathbf{|} u \mathbf{|}^p_{p,l,Q_1} + \|u\|^p_{L_p(Q_1)}) \leqslant c\{1 + [\operatorname{Cap}(e, \mathring{L}_p^l(Q_2))]^{-1}\}\mathbf{|} u \mathbf{|}^p_{p,l,Q_1}\,.$$

So the first item of the theorem follows.

2) For $pl > n$, $p > 1$ or for $l \geqslant n$, $p = 1$ the assertion is trivial. Consider the other values of v and l. Let $\psi \in \mathfrak{M}(e, Q_2)$ be such that

$$\| \nabla_l \psi \|^p_{L_p(Q_2)} \leqslant \operatorname{Cap}(e, \mathring{L}_p^l(Q_2)) + \varepsilon \tag{10}$$

and let $u = 1 - \psi$. Applying the inequality

$$\| \nabla_j \psi \|_{L_p(Q_2)} \leqslant c\, \| \nabla_l \psi \|_{L_p(Q_2)}\,, \qquad j = 1, \ldots, l-1\,,$$

we obtain

$$\mathbf{|} u \mathbf{|}_{p,l,Q_1} = \mathbf{|} \psi \mathbf{|}_{p,l,Q_1} \leqslant c\, \| \nabla_l \psi \|_{L_p(Q_2)}\,.$$

Hence from (10) it follows that

$$\|u\|_{L_p(Q_{1/2})} \leqslant cC[\operatorname{Cap}(e, \mathring{L}_p^l(Q_2)) + \varepsilon]^{1/p}\,.$$

By Hölder's inequality we have

$$1 - \bar{\psi}_{Q_{1/2}} = \bar{u}_{Q_{1/2}} \leqslant cC[\operatorname{Cap}(e, \mathring{L}_p^l(Q_2))]^{1/p}\,. \tag{11}$$

It remains to show that the mean value of ψ on $Q_{1/2}$ is small. Noting that

$$\int_{-1}^{1} |w|\,dt \leqslant \int_{-1}^{1} |t|\,|w'|\,dt \leqslant \int_{-1}^{1} |w'|\,dt$$

for any function $w \in C^1[-1,1]$ satisfying $w(-1) = w(1) = 0$ we obtain

$$\begin{aligned} \int_{Q_{1/2}} \psi\,dx &\leqslant \int_{Q_2} |\psi|\,dx \leqslant \int_{Q_2} \left|\frac{\partial \psi}{\partial x_1}\right| dx \leqslant \int_{Q_2} \left|\frac{\partial^2 \psi}{\partial x_1^2}\right| dx \\ &\leqslant \cdots \leqslant \int_{Q_2} \left|\frac{\partial^l \psi}{\partial x_1^l}\right| dx \leqslant 2^{(p-1)n/p} \| \nabla_l \psi \|_{L_p(Q_2)}\,. \end{aligned} \tag{12}$$

Therefore,

$$\bar{\psi}_{Q_{1/2}} \leqslant 2^{(2p-1)n/p}[\operatorname{Cap}(e, Q_2) + \varepsilon]^{1/p}\,.$$

This and (10.1.1/1), (10.1.1/2) imply

$$\bar{\psi}_{Q_{1/2}} \leqslant 2^{-n/p}\,,$$

which together with (11) completes the proof of the second part of the theorem.

10.1.3. A Variant of Theorem 10.1.2 and its Corollaries

In the following theorem, which will be used in Chapter 12, we prove an assertion similar to the first part of Theorem 10.1.2 and relating to a wider class of functions.

Theorem. *Let e be a closed subset of $\bar{Q}_d$ and let δ be a number in the interval* $(0,1)$. *Then for all functions in the set*

$$\{u\in C^\infty(\bar{Q}_d):\ \bar{u}_{Q_d}\geqslant 0,\ u(x)\leqslant \delta d^{-n/p}\|u\|_{L_p(Q_d)} \text{ for all } x\in e\}$$

inequality (10.1.2/1) *is valid and*

$$C^{-p}\geqslant c(1-\delta)^p d^{-np/q}\operatorname{cap}(e,\mathring{L}_p^l(Q_{2d}))\,.$$

Proof. Duplicating the proof of Lemma 10.1.2/1, we obtain

$$\begin{aligned} c^{-1}\operatorname{cap}(e,\mathring{L}_p^l(Q_2)) &\leqslant \inf\{\|1-u\|^p_{V_p^l(Q_1)}:\ u\in C^\infty(\bar{Q}_1),\ u\leqslant 0 \text{ on } e\}\\ &\leqslant c\operatorname{cap}(e,\mathring{L}_p^l(Q_2))\,. \end{aligned}$$

Further, we note that the inequality $1-N^{-1}u\geqslant 1-\delta$ on e implies

$$(1-\delta)^p\operatorname{cap}(e,\mathring{L}_p^l(Q_2))\leqslant c\,\|1-N^{-1}u\|^p_{V_p^l(Q_1)}$$

and follow the argument of the proof of the first part of Theorem 10.1.2.

Corollary 1. *Let e be a closed subset of $\bar{Q}_d$. Then the inequality*

$$\|u\|^p_{L_q(Q_d)}\leqslant c\left(d^{p-n+np/q}\|\nabla u\|^p_{L_p(Q_d)}+\frac{d^{np/q}}{\operatorname{cap}(e,\mathring{L}_p^l(Q_{2d}))}\|\nabla_l u\|^p_{L_p(Q_d)}\right) \tag{1}$$

is valid for all functions $u\in C^\infty(\bar{Q}_d)$ that vanish on e.

Proof. It suffices to put $d=1$. Let

$$P(u)=\sum_{0\leqslant|\beta|<l}x^\beta\int_{Q_1}\varphi_\beta(y)u(y)\,dy$$

be the polynomial in the generalized Poincaré inequality for the cube Q_1 (see Lemma 1.1.11). Further let $S(u)=P(u)-\int_{Q_1}\varphi_0(y)u(y)\,dy$. Since all functions φ_β are orthogonal to unity for $|\beta|>0$, then

$$|S(u)|\leqslant c\|\nabla u\|_{L_p(Q_1)}\,. \tag{2}$$

It suffices to obtain (1) under the assumption

$$\|\nabla u\|_{L_p(Q_1)} \leqslant \delta \|u\|_{L_p(Q_1)},$$

where $\delta = \delta(n,p,l)$ is a small constant. Then the function $v = u - S(u)$ satisfies the inequality

$$|v(x)| \leqslant c\delta \|v\|_{L_p(Q_1)}$$

on e. To be precise, let $\bar{v}_{Q_1} \geqslant 0$. Applying the theorem in the present section to the function v, we obtain

$$\|v\|^p_{L_q(Q_1)} \leqslant \frac{c}{\operatorname{cap}(e, \mathring{L}^l_p(Q_2))} \sum_{j=1}^{l} \|\nabla_j v\|^p_{L_p(Q_1)}.$$

Hence from Lemma 1.1.11 we obtain

$$\|u - S(u)\|^p_{L_q(Q_1)} \leqslant \frac{c}{\operatorname{cap}(e, \mathring{L}^l_p(Q_2))} \sum_{j=1}^{l} \|\nabla_j (u - P(u))\|^p_{L_p(Q_1)}$$

$$\leqslant \frac{c}{\operatorname{cap}(e, \mathring{L}^l_p(Q_2))} \|\nabla_l u\|^p_{L_p(Q_1)}.$$

Now reference to (2) completes the proof.

Corollary 1 implies the following assertion.

Corollary 2. *Let e be a closed subset of $\bar{Q}_d$. The inequality*

(3)
$$\|u\|^p_{L_q(Q_d)} \leqslant c\left(d^{pk-n+np/q}\|\nabla_k u\|^p_{L_p(Q_d)} + \frac{d^{np/q}}{\operatorname{cap}(e, \mathring{L}^{l-k+1}_p(Q_{2d}))}\|\nabla_l u\|^p_{L_p(Q_d)}\right)$$

is valid for all functions $u \in C^\infty(\bar{Q}_d)$ that vanish on e along with all derivatives up to the order k, $k < l$.

Proof. It suffices to derive (3) for $q = p$ and $d = 1$. According to Corollary 1,

$$\|\nabla_j u\|^p_{L_p(Q_1)} \leqslant c\left(\|\nabla_{j+1} u\|^p_{L_p(Q_1)} + \frac{1}{\operatorname{cap}(e, \mathring{L}^{l-j}_p(Q_1))}\|\nabla_l u\|^p_{L_p(Q_1)}\right)$$

for $j = 0, 1, \ldots, k-1$. Therefore

$$\|u\|^p_{L_p(Q_1)} \leqslant c\left(\|\nabla_k u\|^p_{L_p(Q_1)} + \sum_{j=0}^{k-1} \frac{1}{\operatorname{cap}(e, L^{l-j}_p(Q_1))}\|\nabla_l u\|^p_{L_p(Q_1)}\right).$$

Since

$$\operatorname{cap}(e, L^{l-j}_p(Q_1)) \geqslant \operatorname{cap}(e, L^{l-k+1}_p(Q_1))$$

for $j = 0, \ldots, k-1$, the result follows.

Remark 1. According to Corollary 9.3.2/1, for $p>1$ we can replace cap by Cap in the statements of Theorem and Corollaries 1, 2.

Remark 2. From Proposition 9.1.1/3 it follows that we can replace $\operatorname{cap}(e, \mathring{L}_p^l(Q_{2d}))$ by $\operatorname{cap}(e, \mathring{L}_p^l(R^n))$ in the statements of Theorem and Corollary 1 for $n>lp$. A similar remark applies to Corollary 2 in case $n>p(l-k+1)$.

Remark 3. Proposition 7.2.2/2 and the properties of (p, l)-refined functions (see 7.2.4) imply that in the definition of the capacity $\operatorname{cap}(E, h_p^l)$ of a Borel set we can minimize the norm $\|u\|_{h_p^l}$ over all (p, l)-refined functions in h_p^l satisfying the inequality $u(x) \geqslant 1$ for (p, l)-quasi-every $x \in E$. Therefore in the theorem of the present subsection we could deal with (p, l)-refined functions in $V_p^l(Q_d)$ for which the inequality

$$u(x) \leqslant \delta d^{-n/p} \|u\|_{L_p(Q_d)}$$

is valid (p, l)-quasi everywhere on the Borel set $E \subset \bar{Q}_d$. Similarly, in Corollary 1 we could consider a Borel set $E \subset \bar{Q}_d$ and (p, l)-refined functions in $V_p^l(Q_d)$ equal to zero quasi-everywhere on E. The class of functions in Corollary 2 can also be enlarged if we consider the class $\mathfrak{C}^k(E)$ of refined functions $u \in V_p^l(Q_d)$ such that $D^\alpha u(x) = 0$ for $(p, l-|\alpha|)$-quasi all $x \in E$ and for all multi-indices of order $|\alpha| \leqslant k$.

§ 10.2. A Connection Between Best Constant and the (p, l)-inner Diameter (The Case $k=1$)

10.2.1. The Set Function $\lambda_{p,q}^l(G)$

Definition. With any open set $G \subset Q_d$ we associate the number

$$\lambda_{p,q}^l(G) = \inf \frac{\| u \|_{p,l,Q_d}^p}{\|u\|_{L_q(Q_d)}^p},$$

where $p \geqslant 1$ and the infimum is taken over all functions $u \in C^\infty(\bar{Q}_d)$ that vanish in a neighborhood of $\overline{Q_d \backslash G}$.

By Theorem 10.1.2, if $\overline{Q_d \backslash G}$ is a (p, l)-unessential subset of $\bar{Q}_d$, then

$$\lambda_{p,q}^l(G) \sim d^{-np/q} \operatorname{Cap}(\overline{Q_d \backslash G}, \mathring{L}_p^l(Q_{2d})) .$$

This relation fails without the condition of smallness on the (p, l)-capacity of $Q_d \backslash G$. If G is "small" then the value $\lambda_{p,q}^l(G)$ becomes large (for instance, we can easily check that $\lambda_{p,q}^l(G) \sim \varepsilon^{n-pl-np/q}$ provided G is a cube with small edge length ε) whereas

$$\operatorname{cap}(\overline{Q_d \backslash G}, \mathring{L}_p^l(Q_{2d})) \leqslant c d^{n-pl}.$$

In the present section we give the description of the set function $\lambda_{p,q}^l(G)$ for $q \geqslant p \geqslant 1$ in certain new terms connected with the (p,l)-capacity under the condition that $\overline{Q_d \backslash G} \notin \mathcal{N}(Q_d)$.

10.2.2. Definition of the (p, l)-inner Diameter

We fix the cube Q_d and we denote by $\mathfrak{Q}_\delta$ an arbitrary cube in Q_d with edge length δ and with sides parallel to those of Q_d.

Definition. Let G be an open subset of Q_d. The supremum of δ for which the set $\{\mathfrak{Q}_\delta \colon \overline{\mathfrak{Q}_\delta \backslash G} \in \mathcal{N}(\mathfrak{Q}_\delta)\}$ is not empty will be called the *(p, l)-inner (cubic) diameter of G relative to Q_d* and denoted by $D_{p,l}(G, Q_d)$.

In the case $Q_d = R^n$ we shall use the notation $D_{p,l}(G)$ and call it the *(p,l)-inner (cubic) diameter of G.*

Obviously, $D_{p,l}(G, Q_d) = d$ provided $\overline{Q_d \backslash G}$ is a (p, l)-unessential subset of $\bar{Q}_d$.

Let $n < pl$, $p > 1$ or $n = l$, $p = 1$. By definition, for such p and l, all the sets except the empty set are (p, l)-essential. Therefore, for any open set $G \subset Q_d$, the (p,l)-inner (cubic) diameter $D_{p,l}(G, Q_d)$ coincides with the inner (cubic) diameter $D(G)$, i.e. with the supremum of edge lengths of cubes $\mathfrak{Q}_\delta$ inscribed in G.

10.2.3. Estimates for the Best Constant by the (p, l)-inner Diameter

The following theorem contains two-sided estimates for $\lambda_{p,q}^l(G)$ for $q \geqslant p \geqslant 1$.

Theorem 1. *Let G be an open subset of Q_d such that $\overline{Q_d \backslash G}$ is a (p, l)-essential subset of $\bar{Q}_d$.*

1) *For all functions $u \in C^\infty(\bar{Q}_d)$ that vanish in a neighborhood of $\overline{Q_d \backslash G}$ inequality* (10.1.2/1) *is valid with $q \geqslant p \geqslant 1$ and*

$$C \leqslant c_1 [D_{p,l}(G, Q_d)]^{l-n(p^{-1}-q^{-1})}. \tag{1}$$

2) *If for all functions $u \in C^\infty(\bar{Q}_d)$ that vanish in a neighborhood of the set $\overline{Q_d \backslash G}$ inequality* (10.1.2/1) *is valid, then*

$$C \geqslant c_2 [D_{p,l}(G, Q_d)]^{l-n(p^{-1}-q^{-1})}. \tag{2}$$

Proof. 1) Assume for the moment that $D_{p,l}(G, Q_d) < d$. We denote an arbitrary number in $(D_{p,l}(G, Q_d), d]$ by δ. The definition of the (p,l)-inner diameter implies that, for any cube $\bar{\mathfrak{Q}}_\delta$, the set $e = \overline{\mathfrak{Q}_\delta \backslash G}$ is a (p, l)-essential subset, i.e.

$$\operatorname{cap}(\mathfrak{Q}_\delta \cap e, \mathring{L}_p^l(\mathfrak{Q}_{2\delta})) > \gamma \delta^{n-pl}. \tag{3}$$

(Here and in what follows $\mathfrak{Q}_{c\delta}$ is the open cube with edge length $c\delta$ whose center coincides with that of $\mathfrak{Q}_\delta$ and whose sides are parallel to the sides of

$\mathfrak{Q}_\delta$.) In case $D_{p,l}(G, Q_d) = d$ we put $\delta = d$. Then (3) is also valid since, by hypothesis, e is a (p,l)-essential subset of the cube $\bar{\mathfrak{Q}}_\delta = \bar{Q}_d$.

According to the first part of Theorem 10.1.2 and inequality (3), we have

$$(4)\qquad \|u\|^p_{L_q(\mathfrak{Q}_\delta)} \leqslant \frac{c\delta^{np/q}}{\operatorname{cap}(\mathfrak{Q}_\delta \cap e, \mathring{L}^l_p(\mathfrak{Q}_{2\delta}))} \mathbf{|} u \mathbf{|}^p_{p,l,\mathfrak{Q}_\delta} \leqslant c\delta^{lp-n(1-p/q)} \mathbf{|} u \mathbf{|}^p_{p,l,\mathfrak{Q}_\delta}.$$

We construct a covering of Q_d by cubes $\mathfrak{Q}_\delta$ whose multiplicity does not exceed some number which depends only on n. Next we sum (4) over all cubes of the covering. Then

$$(5)\qquad \|u\|^p_{L_p(Q_d)} \leqslant c\delta^{lp} \sum_{j=1}^{l} \delta^{p(j-l)} \|\nabla_j u\|^p_{L_p(Q_d)}.$$

Using a well-known multiplicative inequality, we obtain

$$(6)\qquad \|\nabla_j v\|_{L_p(Q_d)} \leqslant c \|v\|^{1-j/l}_{L_p(Q_d)} \left(\sum_{i=0}^{l} d^{i-l} \|\nabla_i v\|_{L_p(Q_d)} \right)^{j/l}$$

(cf. Lemma 1.4.7). Putting $v = u - \bar{u}_{Q_d}$ in (6) and applying the Poincaré inequality

$$\|u - \bar{u}_{Q_d}\|_{L_p(Q_d)} \leqslant cd \|\nabla u\|_{L_p(Q_d)},$$

we obtain

$$\|\nabla_j u\|_{L_p(Q_d)} \leqslant c \|u\|^{1-j/l}_{L_p(Q_d)} \mathbf{|} u \mathbf{|}^{j/l}_{p,l,Q_d}.$$

Hence from (5) with $q = p$ we obtain

$$1 \leqslant c \sum_{j=1}^{l} \left(\delta^l \frac{\mathbf{|} u \mathbf{|}_{p,l,Q_d}}{\|u\|_{L_p(Q_d)}} \right)^{pj/l}.$$

Therefore

$$(7)\qquad \|u\|_{L_p(Q_d)} \leqslant c\delta^l \mathbf{|} u \mathbf{|}_{p,l,Q_d}$$

and the first part of the theorem follows for $q = p$. Let $q > p$. Summing the inequality

$$\|u\|^p_{L_p(\mathfrak{Q}_\delta)} \leqslant c\delta^{lp-n(1-p/q)} (\|\nabla_l u\|^p_{L_p(\mathfrak{Q}_\delta)} + \delta^{-pl} \|u\|^p_{L_p(\mathfrak{Q}_\delta)})$$

over all cubes of the covering $\{\mathfrak{Q}_\delta\}$ and making use of the inequality $(\sum a_i)^\varepsilon \leqslant \sum a_i^\varepsilon$, where $a_i > 0$, $0 < \varepsilon < 1$, we conclude that

$$\|u\|^p_{L_p(Q_d)} \leqslant c\delta^{lp-n(1-p/q)} (\|\nabla_l u\|^p_{L_p(Q_d)} + \delta^{-l} \|u\|^p_{L_p(Q_d)}).$$

It remains to apply inequality (7).

2) Let $0 < \delta < D_{p,l}(G, Q_d)$ and let $\bar{\mathfrak{Q}}_\delta$ be a cube having a (p,l)-unessential intersection with $\overline{Q_d \backslash G}$. Let η denote a function in $C^\infty(\mathfrak{Q}_\delta)$ that vanishes

near $\partial\mathfrak{Q}_\delta$, is equal to unity on the cube $\mathfrak{Q}_{\delta/2}$ and satisfies $|\nabla_j\eta|\leqslant c\delta^{-j}$, $j=1,2,\ldots$. If v is an arbitrary function in $C^\infty(\bar{\mathfrak{Q}}_\delta)$ that vanishes near $Q_d\backslash G$ then the function $u=\eta v$ extended by zero in the exterior of $\mathfrak{Q}_\delta$ satisfies (10.1.2/3) by the hypothesis of the theorem. Therefore

$$\|v\|_{L_p(\mathfrak{Q}_{\delta/2})}\leqslant C\sum_{j=1}^{l}\|\nabla_j(\eta v)\|_{L_p(\mathfrak{Q}_\delta)}\leqslant cC\sum_{j=1}^{l}\sum_{k=0}^{j}\delta^{k-j}\|\nabla_k v\|_{L_p(\mathfrak{Q}_\delta)}$$

$$\leqslant cC(\mathbf{|}v\mathbf{|}_{p,l,\mathfrak{Q}_\delta}+\delta^{-l}\|v\|_{L_p(\mathfrak{Q}_\delta)}).$$

This and the estimate

$$\|v\|_{L_p(\mathfrak{Q}_\delta)}\leqslant c(\delta\|\nabla v\|_{L_p(\mathfrak{Q}_\delta)}+c\delta^{n(p^{-1}-q^{-1})}\|v\|_{L_q(\mathfrak{Q}_{\delta/2})})$$

yield

(8) $$\|v\|_{L_p(\mathfrak{Q}_{\delta/2})}\leqslant c'C(\mathbf{|}v\mathbf{|}_{p,l,\mathfrak{Q}_\delta}+\delta^{-l+n(p^{-1}-q^{-1})}\|v\|_{L_q(\mathfrak{Q}_{\delta/2})}).$$

We may assume that $2c'C\delta^{-l+n(p^{-1}-q^{-1})}<1$ since the reverse inequality is the required inequality (3). Then by (8)

$$\|v\|_{L_q(\mathfrak{Q}_{\delta/2})}\leqslant 2c'C\mathbf{|}v\mathbf{|}_{p,l,\mathfrak{Q}_\delta}$$

and (2) follows from the second part of Theorem 10.1.2 applied to the cube $\mathfrak{Q}_\delta$. The proof is complete.

In each of the cases $pl<n$, $p>1$ and $l=n$, $p=1$, Theorem 1 can be stated in terms of the inner diameter $D(G)$.

Theorem 2. *Let G be an arbitrary open subset of Q_d, $G\neq Q_d$ and let the numbers n,p,l satisfy either of the conditions $pl>n$, $p>1$ or $l=n$, $p=1$. Further, let C be the best constant in* (10.1.2/1) *with $q\in[p,\infty)$. Then*

(9) $$C\sim D(G)^{l-n(p^{-1}-q^{-1})}.$$

§ 10.3. Estimates for the Best Constant in the General Case

Let $\mathfrak{C}$ denote a linear subset of the space $W_p^l(Q_d)$. Our goal is the study of the inequality

(1) $$\|u\|_{L_q(Q_d)}\leqslant C\sum_{j=k+1}^{l}d^{j-l}\|\nabla u\|_{L_p(Q_d)},$$

where $u\in\mathfrak{C}$ and q is the same as in Theorem 10.1.2. The norm on the right in (1) can be replaced by an equivalent one retaining only the summands corresponding to $j=l$ and $j=k+1$.

10.3.1. A Necessary and Sufficient Condition for the Validity of the Basic Inequality

Let $\bar{\mathfrak{C}}$ be the closure of $\mathfrak{C}$ in the metric of the space $V_p^l(Q_d)$ and let $\mathbb{P}_k$ be the set of polynomials Π of degree $k \leqslant l-1$, normalized by

$$d^{-n} \int_{Q_d} |\Pi|^p dx = 1 . \tag{1}$$

Theorem. *Inequality* (10.3/1) *is valid if and only if* $\mathbb{P}_k \cap \bar{\mathfrak{C}} = \varnothing$.

Proof. The necessity of this condition is obvious. We will prove the sufficiency.

If $\mathbb{P}_k \cap \bar{\mathfrak{C}} = \varnothing$ then in $\bar{\mathfrak{C}}$ we can introduce the norm

$$\| u \|_{\mathfrak{C}} = \sum_{j=k+1}^{l} d^{j-l} \| \nabla_j u \|_{L_p(Q_d)} ,$$

which makes it a Banach space. Let I be the identity mapping from $\bar{\mathfrak{C}}$ into $L_p(Q_d)$. Since $\bar{\mathfrak{C}} \subset V_p^l(Q_d) \subset L_q(Q_d)$ then I is defined on $\bar{\mathfrak{C}}$. We will show that it is closed. Let $\| u_m \|_{\mathfrak{C}} \to 0$ and $\| u_m - u \|_{L_q(Q_d)} \to 0$ as $m \to \infty$. Then there exists a sequence of polynomials $\{\Pi_m\}_{m \geqslant 1}$ of degree not higher than k such that $u_m - \Pi_m \to 0$ in $L_q(Q_d)$. Consequently, $u = \lim \Pi_m$ in the space $V_p^l(Q_d)$ and since $\mathbb{P}_k \cap \bar{\mathfrak{C}} = \varnothing$ then $u = 0$. Thus I is closed. Now from the Banach theorem it follows that E is continuous, that is, (10.3/1) is valid. The theorem is proved.

As an example consider the class $\mathfrak{C}^r(E)$ ($r = 0, \ldots, l-1$, E is a Borel subset of $\bar{Q}_d$) of $(p, l-j)$-refined functions $u \in V_p^l(Q_d)$, $p > 1$ such that $\nabla_j u = 0$ $(p, l-j)$-quasi-everywhere on E, $j = 0, \ldots, r$.

Since any sequence of (p, l)-refined functions that converges in $V_p^l(Q_d)$ contains a subsequence that converges (p, l)-quasi-everywhere (cf. 7.2.4), then $\mathfrak{C}^r(E)$ is a closed subset of $V_p^l(Q_d)$.

Thus, according to Theorem 1, inequality (10.3/1) is valid for all $u \in \mathfrak{C}^r(E)$ if and only if $\mathbb{P}_k$ does not contain a polynomial Π such that $\nabla_j \Pi = 0$ $(p, l-j)$-quasi-everywhere on E, $j = 0, \ldots, r$.

10.3.2. Capacities of Function Classes

Let Π be a polynomial in $\mathbb{P}_k$ and let

$$\operatorname{cap}(\mathfrak{C}, \Pi, \mathring{L}_p^l(Q_{2d})) = \inf \int_{Q_{2d}} | \nabla_l u |^p dx ,$$

where the infimum is taken over all functions $u \in \mathring{L}_p^l(Q_{2d})$ such that the restriction of $u - \Pi$ to $\bar{Q}_d$ is contained in a linear subset $\mathfrak{C}$ of the space $V_p^l(Q_d)$.

With $\mathfrak{C}$ we associate l capacities

$$\operatorname{CAP}_k(\mathfrak{C}, \mathring{L}_p^l(Q_{2d})) = \inf_{\{\Pi: \Pi \in \mathbb{P}_k\}} \operatorname{cap}(\mathfrak{C}, \Pi, \mathring{L}_p^l(Q_{2d})) .$$

In other words,

$$\mathrm{CAP}_k(\mathfrak{C}, \mathring{L}_p^l(Q_{2d})) = \inf_{\{\Pi, u\}} \int_{Q_{2d}} |\nabla_l u|^p dx \tag{1}$$

where the infimum is taken over all pairs $\{\Pi, u\}$, $\Pi \in \mathbb{P}_k$, $u|_{\bar{Q}_d} \in \mathfrak{C}$, $\Pi - u \in \mathring{L}_p^l(Q_{2d})$.

It is clear that $\mathrm{CAP}_k(\mathfrak{C}, \mathring{L}_p^l(Q_{2d}))$ does not increase as k increases. The following inequality is valid:

$$\mathrm{CAP}_k(\mathfrak{C}, \mathring{L}_p^l(Q_{2d})) \leqslant c d^{n-pl}. \tag{2}$$

In fact, let $\eta \in \mathfrak{M}(\bar{Q}_1, Q_2)$ and let $\eta_d(x) = \eta(x/d)$. Since $1 \in \mathbb{P}_k$ and the restriction of the function $1 - \eta_d$ to Q_d equals zero, the pair $\{1, \eta_d\}$ is admissible for the problem (1). This implies (2).

We introduce the norm

$$|||u|||_{V_p^l(Q_d)} = \sum_{j=0}^{l} d^{j-l} \| \nabla_j u \|_{L_p(Q_d)}.$$

The next assertion is similar to Lemma 10.1.2/1.

Lemma. *The capacity* $\mathrm{CAP}_k(\mathfrak{C}, \mathring{L}_p^l(Q_d))$ *is equivalent to the following capacity of the class* $\mathfrak{C}$:

$$\inf |||\Pi - u|||^p_{V_p^l(Q_d)}, \tag{3}$$

where the infimum is taken over all pairs $\{\Pi, u\}$, $\Pi \in \mathbb{P}_k$, $\Pi - u \in V_p^l(Q_d)$, $u \in \mathfrak{C}$.

Proof. We have

$$\mathrm{CAP}_k(\mathfrak{C}, \mathring{L}_p^l(Q_{2d})) \leqslant \int_{Q_{2d}} |\nabla_l(\eta_d(\Pi - Au))|^p dx,$$

where A is the extension operator in Lemma 10.1.2/1. Obviously, the right-hand side does not exceed $c|||\Pi - Au|||^p_{V_p^l(Q_d)}$. From (10.1.2/6) it follows that $A\Pi = \Pi$. Therefore, using (10.1.2/6) once more we obtain

$$\mathrm{CAP}_k(\mathfrak{C}, \mathring{L}_p^l(Q_{2d})) \leqslant c\, |||\Pi - u|||^p_{V_p^l(Q_d)}.$$

Minimizing the right-hand side, we arrive at the required upper bound for CAP_k.

We now prove the lower estimate. Since $(\Pi - u)|_{Q_d}$ can be extended to a function in $\mathring{L}_p^l(Q_{2d})$, the classes of admissible functions in the definitions of both capacities under consideration are simultaneously empty or nonempty. Let $\Pi \in \mathbb{P}_k$, $v \in \mathring{L}_p^l(Q_{2d})$, $(\Pi - v)|_{\bar{Q}_d} \in \mathfrak{C}$. Then capacity (3) does not exceed

$$|||v|||_{V_p^l(Q_d)} \leqslant c\,\| \nabla_l v \|_{L_p(Q_{2d})} .$$

The lemma is proved.

10.3.3. Estimates for the Best Constant in the Basic Inequality

From Theorem 10.3.1 it follows that (10.3/1) is valid if and only if

$$\mathrm{CAP}_k(\mathfrak{C}, \mathring{L}_p^l(Q_{2d})) > 0 .$$

The next theorem yields two-sided estimates for the best constant C in (10.3/1) expressed in terms of the capacity $\mathrm{CAP}_k(\mathfrak{C}, \mathring{L}_p^l(Q_{2d}))$.

Theorem. 1) *If* $\mathrm{CAP}_k(\mathfrak{C}, \mathring{L}_p^l(Q_{2d})) > 0$ *then, for all* $u \in \mathfrak{C}$ *inequality* (10.3/1) *is valid with*

(1) $$C \leqslant c d^{n/q} [\mathrm{CAP}_k(\mathfrak{C}, \mathring{L}_p^l(Q_{2d}))]^{-1/p} .$$

2) *If* (10.3/1) *is valid for all* $u \in \mathfrak{C}$ *and if*

$$\mathrm{CAP}_k(\mathfrak{C}, \mathring{L}_p^l(Q_{2d})) \leqslant c_0 d^{n-pl} ,$$

where c_0 *is a small enough constant that depends only on* n, p, l, k, *then*

(2) $$C \geqslant c d^{n/q} [\mathrm{CAP}_k(\mathfrak{C}, \mathring{L}_p^l(Q_{2d}))]^{-1/p} .$$

Proof. 1) Let $u \in \mathfrak{C}$ be normalized by

(3) $$\| u \|_{L_p(Q_d)} = d^{n/p}$$

and let Π be any polynomial in $\mathbb{P}_k$. According to Lemma 10.3.2 we have

(4) $$[\mathrm{CAP}_k(\mathfrak{C}, \mathring{L}_p^l(Q_{2d}))]^{1/p} \leqslant c \sum_{i=0}^{k} d^{i-l} \| \nabla_i (\Pi - u) \|_{L_p(Q_d)} + c \sum_{i=k+1}^{l} d^{i-l} \| \nabla_i u \|_{L_p(Q_d)} .$$

Hence from the inequality

$$\| \nabla_i v \|_{L_p(Q_d)} \leqslant c d^{l-i} \| \nabla_l v \|_{L_p(Q_d)} + c d^{-i} \| v \|_{L_p(Q_d)}$$

we obtain that the first sum in (4) does not exceed

$$c d^{-l} \| \Pi - u \|_{L_p(Q_d)} + c \| \nabla_l u \|_{L_p(Q_d)} .$$

Therefore

(5) $$[\mathrm{CAP}_k(\mathfrak{C}, \mathring{L}_p^l(Q_{2d}))]^{1/p} \leqslant c d^{-l} \| \Pi - u \|_{L_p(Q_d)} + c \sum_{i=k+1}^{l} d^{i-l} \| \nabla_i u \|_{L_p(Q_d)} .$$

For each $u \in V_p^l(Q_d)$ there exists a polynomial π of degree less than $k+1$ such that

(6) $$\|\pi - u\|_{L_p(Q_d)} \leqslant c' d^{k+1} \|\nabla_{k+1} u\|_{L_p(Q_d)}.$$

First suppose that

$$\|\nabla_{k+1} u\|_{L_p(Q_d)} > (2c')^{-1} d^{n/p-k-1}.$$

Then by virtue of (10.3.2/2) we have

(7) $$[\mathrm{CAP}_k(\mathfrak{C}, \mathring{L}_p^l(Q_{2d}))]^{1/p} \leqslant c d^{k-l+1} \|\nabla_{k+1} u\|_{L_p(Q_d)}.$$

Now let

$$\|\nabla_{k+1} u\|_{L_p(Q_d)} \leqslant (2c')^{-1} d^{n/p-k-1}.$$

From (6) we obtain

$$\|\pi - u\|_{L_p(Q_d)} \leqslant 2^{-1} d^{n/p} = 2^{-1} \|u\|_{L_p(Q_d)}$$

and consequently

(8) $$2^{-1} d^{n/p} \leqslant \|\pi\|_{L_p(Q_d)} \leqslant 3 \cdot 2^{-1} d^{n/p}.$$

We put $\Pi = d^{n/p} \|\pi\|_{L_p(Q_d)}^{-1} \pi$. Then (8) implies

$$\|\Pi - u\|_{L_p(Q_d)} \leqslant 2 \left\| \pi - d^{-n/p} \|\pi\|_{L_p(Q_d)} u \right\|_{L_p(Q_d)}.$$

Obviously, the right-hand side does not exceed

$$2\|\pi - u\|_{L_p(Q_d)} + 2\|u\|_{L_p(Q_d)} \left| d^{-n/p} \|\pi\|_{L_p(Q_d)} - 1 \right|$$

$$= 2\|\pi - u\|_{L_p(Q_d)} + 2 \left| \|\pi\|_{L_p(Q_d)} - \|u\|_{L_p(Q_d)} \right| \leqslant 4 \|\pi - u\|_{L_p(Q_d)}.$$

Using (6), we obtain

$$\|\Pi - u\|_{L_p(Q_d)} \leqslant 4 c' d^{k+1} \|\nabla_{k+1} u\|_{L_p(Q_d)},$$

which together with (5) and (7) yields the estimate

(9) $$[\mathrm{CAP}_k(\mathfrak{C}, \mathring{L}_p^l(Q_{2d}))]^{1/p} \leqslant c \sum_{i=k+1}^{l} d^{i-l} \|\nabla_i u\|_{L_p(Q_d)}$$

for all $u \in \mathfrak{C}$, normalized by equality (3).

From the Sobolev imbedding theorem and (10.3.2/2) we obtain

$$\|u\|_{L_p(Q_d)} \leqslant c d^{k+1+n(p^{-1}-q^{-1})} \|\nabla_{k+1} u\|_{L_p(Q_d)} + c d^{n(q^{-1}-p^{-1})} \|u\|_{L_p(Q_d)}$$

$$\leqslant c d^{k-l+nq^{-1}+1} [\mathrm{CAP}_k(\mathfrak{C}, \mathring{L}_p^l(Q_{2d}))]^{-1/p} \|\nabla_{k+1} u\|_{L_p(Q_d)}$$

$$+ c d^{n(q^{-1}-p^{-1})} \|u\|_{L_p(Q_d)},$$

which together with (9) yields (10.3/1) with the constant C satisfying (10.3.3/1).

2) Let ε be an arbitrary positive number, $\Pi \in \mathbb{P}_k$, $\psi \in \mathring{L}_p^l(Q_{2d})$, $(\Pi - \psi)|_{Q_d} \in \mathfrak{C}$ and let

$$\int_{Q_{2d}} |\nabla_l \psi|^p dx \leqslant \mathrm{CAP}_k(\mathfrak{C}, \mathring{L}_p^l(Q_{2d})) + \varepsilon d^{n-lp}.$$

Since the restriction of $\psi - \Pi$ to $\bar{Q}_d$ is contained in $\mathfrak{C}$ then by the hypothesis of the theorem

$$\| \psi - \Pi \|_{L_q(Q_d)} \leqslant C \sum_{j=k+1}^{l} d^{j-l} \| \nabla_j \psi \|_{L_p(Q_d)}. \tag{10}$$

The right-hand side does not exceed

$$cC \| \nabla_l \psi \|_{L_p(Q_d)} \leqslant cC(\mathrm{CAP}_k(\mathfrak{C}, \mathring{L}_p^l(Q_{2d})) + \varepsilon d^{n-lp})^{1/p}$$

because $\psi \in \mathring{L}_p^l(Q_{2d})$. Similarly,

$$\| \psi \|_{L_q(Q_d)} \leqslant c d^{l+n(q^{-1}-p^{-1})} \| \nabla_l \psi \|_{L_p(Q_{2d})} \leqslant c(c_0 + \varepsilon)^{1/p} d^{n/q}.$$

Thus

$$\| \psi - \Pi \|_{L_q(Q_d)} \geqslant \| \Pi \|_{L_q(Q_d)} - c(c_0 + \varepsilon)^{1/p} d^{n/q}$$

and by (10)

$$\| \psi \|_{L_q(Q_d)} \leqslant c(c_0 + \varepsilon)^{1/p} d^{n/q} + cC(\mathrm{CAP}_k(\mathfrak{C}, \mathring{L}_p^l(Q_{2d})) + \varepsilon d^{n-lp})^{1/p}. \tag{11}$$

Now we note that

$$\| \Pi \|_{L_p(Q_d)} \leqslant c d^{n(p^{-1}-q^{-1})} \| \Pi \|_{L_q(Q_d)}.$$

The preceding estimate follows from the Hölder inequality for $p \leqslant q$. In case $p > q$ it results as follows:

$$\begin{aligned} \|\Pi\|_{L_p(Q_d)} &\leqslant c(d^{k+1} \| \nabla_{k+1} \Pi \|_{L_p(Q_d)} + d^{n(p^{-1}-q^{-1})} \|\Pi\|_{L_q(Q_d)}) \\ &= c d^{n(p^{-1}-q^{-1})} \|\Pi\|_{L_q(Q_d)}. \end{aligned}$$

Since $\Pi \in \mathbb{P}_k$, then $\|\Pi\|_{L_p(Q_d)} = d^{n/p}$. Therefore $\|\Pi\|_{L_q(Q_d)} \geqslant c d^{n/q}$. Using the smallness of the constant c_0, we arrive at (10.3.3/2). The theorem is proved.

10.3.4. The Class $\mathfrak{C}_0(e)$ and the Capacity $\mathrm{Cap}_k(e, \mathring{L}_p^l(Q_{2d}))$

The rest of the section deals with the class

$$\mathfrak{C}_0(e) = \{u \in C^\infty(\bar{Q}_d) \colon \mathrm{dist}(\operatorname{supp} u, e) > 0\}, \tag{1}$$

where e is a compact subset of the cube $\bar{Q}_d$.

We introduce the following set function:

$$\mathrm{Cap}_k(e, \mathring{L}_p^l(Q_{2d})) = \inf_{\Pi \in \mathbb{P}_k} \inf_{\{f\}} \int_{Q_{2d}} |\nabla_l f|^p dx, \tag{2}$$

where $p \geqslant 1$ and $\{f\}$ is a collection of functions in $\mathring{L}_p^l(Q_{2d})$ such that $f = \Pi$ in a neighborhood of e where $\Pi \in \mathbb{P}_k$.

Since $\mathbb{P}_0 = \{\pm 1\}$ then

$$\operatorname{Cap}_0(e, \mathring{L}_p^l(Q_{2d})) = \operatorname{Cap}(e, \mathring{L}_p^l(Q_{2d}))\ .$$

We show that the capacities $\operatorname{Cap}_k(e, \mathring{L}_p^l(Q_{2d}))$ and $\operatorname{CAP}_k(\mathfrak{C}_0(e), \mathring{L}_p^l(Q_{2d}))$ are equivalent.

Lemma. *The following inequalities are valid:*

$$\operatorname{CAP}_k(\mathfrak{C}_0(e), \mathring{L}_p^l(Q_{2d})) \leqslant \operatorname{Cap}_k(e, \mathring{L}_p^l(Q_{2d}))$$
$$\leqslant c\,\operatorname{CAP}_k(\mathfrak{C}_0(e), \mathring{L}_p^l(Q_{2d}))\ .$$

Proof. The upper inequality is an obvious corollary of the definitions of the two capacities.

We shall prove the lower inequality. Let $\Pi \in \mathbb{P}_k$, $u \in \mathfrak{C}_0(e)$, let A be the extension operator in Lemma 10.1.2/2 and let η_d be the function used in the proof of inequality (10.3.2/2). From property (ii) of the operator A it follows that $\eta_d(\Pi - Au)$ is contained in the class $\{f\}$ introduced in the definition of $\operatorname{Cap}_k(e, \mathring{L}_p^l(Q_{2d}))$. Therefore

$$\operatorname{Cap}_k(e, \mathring{L}_p^l(Q_{2d})) \leqslant \|\eta_d(\Pi - Au)\|^p_{\mathring{L}_p^l(Q_{2d})} \leqslant c\,\|\Pi - Au\|^p_{V_p^l(Q_{2d})}\ .$$

Taking into account the equality $A\Pi = \Pi$ and estimate (10.1.2/6) for the function $v = \Pi - u$ we complete the proof by reference to Lemma 10.3.2.

From Theorem 10.3.1, applied to the class $\mathfrak{C}_0(e)$, and from the preceding lemma there immediately follows an assertion which coincides with Theorem 10.1.2 for $k = 0$.

Corollary. 1) *If* $\operatorname{Cap}_k(e, \mathring{L}_p^l(Q_{2d})) > 0$ *then for all* $u \in \mathfrak{C}_0(e)$ *inequality* (10.3/1) *is valid and*

$$C \leqslant c\, d^{n/q}\,[\operatorname{Cap}_k(e, \mathring{L}_p^l(Q_{2d}))]^{-1/p}\ .$$

2) *If* (10.3/1) *is valid for all* $u \in \mathfrak{C}_0(e)$ *and if*

$$\operatorname{Cap}_k(e, \mathring{L}_p^l(Q_{2d})) \leqslant c_0 d^{n-pl}\ ,$$

where c_0 *is a small enough constant that depends only on n*

$$C \geqslant c\, d^{n/q}\,[\operatorname{Cap}_k(e, \mathring{L}_p^l(Q_{2d}))]^{-}$$

10.3.5. A Lower Bound for Cap_k

We derive a lower bound for $\mathrm{Cap}_k(e, \mathring{L}_p^l(Q_{2d}))$ by the capacity $\mathrm{Cap}(e, \mathring{L}_p^{l-k}(Q_{2d}))$.

Proposition. *The following inequality is valid:*

$$\mathrm{Cap}_k(e, \mathring{L}_p^l(Q_{2d})) \geqslant c d^{-kp}\, \mathrm{Cap}(e, \mathring{L}_p^{l-k}(Q_{2d})) \,. \tag{1}$$

Proof. It suffices to consider the case $d=1$. From the inequality

$$\| \nabla_l v \|_{L_p(Q_2)} \geqslant c \| \nabla_{l-k} v \|_{L_p(Q_2)} , \qquad v \in \mathring{L}_p^l(Q_2) ,$$

we obtain

$$\mathrm{Cap}(e, \mathring{L}_p^l(Q_2)) \geqslant c\, \mathrm{Cap}(e, \mathring{L}_p^{l-k}(Q_2)) \,. \tag{2}$$

Let $\Pi \in \mathbb{P}_k$ and let f be a function in $\mathring{L}_p^l(Q_{2d})$ such that $f = \Pi$ in a neighborhood of e. Obviously, the difference $\partial \Pi / \partial x_i - \partial f / \partial x_i$ is contained in $\mathfrak{C}_0(e)$ for all $i = 1, \ldots, n$. For some i, let

$$\| \partial \Pi / \partial x_i \|_{L_p(Q_2)} \geqslant \varepsilon , \tag{3}$$

where ε is a positive number (that depends only on k, l, n) which will be specified later. Then

$$\| \nabla_l f \|^p_{L_p(Q_2)} \geqslant \left\| \nabla_{l-1} \frac{\partial f}{\partial x_i} \right\|^p_{L_p(Q_2)} \geqslant \varepsilon^p\, \mathrm{Cap}_{k-1}(e, \mathring{L}_p^{l-1}(Q_2)) \,. \tag{4}$$

If for all $i = 1, \ldots, n$ inequality (3) fails, then the condition $\|\Pi\|_{L_p(Q_1)} = 1$ implies

$$|\, |\Pi(x)| - 1 \,| \leqslant c \varepsilon , \qquad x \in Q_2 \,.$$

We can take $\varepsilon = (2c)^{-1}$. Since $\Pi = f$ on e, then $|f(x)| \geqslant \frac{1}{2}$, $x \in e$, and hence

$$\| \nabla_l f \|^p_{L_p(Q_2)} \geqslant 2^{-p}\, \mathrm{Cap}(e, \mathring{L}_p^l(Q_2)) \,.$$

The preceding result and (4) yield

$$\mathrm{Cap}_k(e, \mathring{L}_p^l(Q_2)) \geqslant c \min\{\mathrm{Cap}_{k-1}(e, \mathring{L}_p^{l-1}(Q_2)), \mathrm{Cap}(e, \mathring{L}_p^l(Q_2))\} \,.$$

Applying (2) we complete the proof.

We present an example of a set for which

$$\mathrm{Cap}_1(e, \mathring{L}_2^2(Q_2)) = 0 \quad \text{and} \quad \mathrm{Cap}(e, \mathring{L}_2^2(Q_2)) > 0 \,.$$

Example. Let $n=3$, $p=2$, $l=2$ and let e be the center of the cube $: |x_i| < \frac{1}{2}\}$. Since by the Sobolev imbedding theorem

$$|u(e)|^2 \leqslant c \int_{Q_2} |\nabla_2 u|^2 dx$$

for all $u \in \mathscr{D}(Q_2)$ then $\operatorname{Cap}(e, \mathring{L}_2^2(Q_2)) \geqslant c^{-1} > 0$.

We show that $\operatorname{Cap}_1(e, \mathring{L}_2^2(Q_2)) = 0$. Let $\Pi = 2\sqrt{3}x$. Obviously, $\Pi \in \mathbb{P}_k$. Let η_ε denote a function in $\mathfrak{M}(\bar{Q}_\varepsilon, Q_{2\varepsilon})$ such that $|\nabla_j \eta_\varepsilon| \leqslant c\varepsilon^{-j}$. The function $\Pi\eta_\varepsilon$ coincides with Π in a neighborhood of e; hence

$$\operatorname{Cap}_1(e, \mathring{L}_2^2(Q_2)) \leqslant \int_{Q_2} |\nabla_2(\Pi\eta_\varepsilon)|^2 dx .$$

On the other hand, the last integral is $O(\varepsilon)$. Thus $\operatorname{Cap}_1(e, \mathring{L}_2^2(Q_2)) = 0$.

Remark. In connection with the above example consider the quadratic forms

$$S_1(u,u) = \int_{Q_1} \left[\sum_{i,j=1}^{3} \left(\frac{\partial^2 u}{\partial x_i \partial x_j} \right)^2 + \sum_{i,j=1}^{3} \left(\frac{\partial u}{\partial x_i} \right)^2 \right] dx ,$$

$$S_2(u,u) = \int_{Q_1} \sum_{i,j=1}^{3} \left(\frac{\partial^2 u}{\partial x_i \partial x_j} \right)^2 dx ,$$

defined on functions $u \in C^\infty(\bar{Q}_1)$ which vanish near the center of the cube Q_1. The forms generate the operators $\Delta^2 - \Delta$ and Δ^2 with the Neumann boundary data on ∂Q_1 and with the complementary condition $u = 0$ at the point e. Corollary 10.3.4 and the above example imply that the first operator is positive definite and that the second is not.

In general, for $p = 2$, the basic results of the present section can be reformulated as necessary and sufficient conditions for positive definiteness and as two-sided estimates for the first eigenvalue of the elliptic operator generated by the quadratic form $S(u,u)$. This form is given on a linear subset $\mathfrak{C}$ of the space $V_2^l(Q_1)$ and satisfies the "coerciveness" condition

$$c_1 \sum_{j=k+1}^{l} \|\nabla_j u\|^2_{L_2(Q_1)} \leqslant S(u,u) \leqslant c_2 \sum_{j=k+1}^{l} \|\nabla_j u\|^2_{L_2(Q_1)}$$

for all $u \in \mathfrak{C}$.

10.3.6. Estimates for the Best Constant in the Case of Small (p, l)-inner Diameter

Here we show that the best constant in (10.3/1) (for $q \geqslant p \geqslant 1$ and $\mathfrak{C} = \mathfrak{C}_0(\cdot$ is equivalent to some power of the (p, l)-inner diameter of $\bar{Q}_d \backslash e$ provid diameter is small.

Lemma. *Let G be an open subset of the cube Q_d such t*

(1) $$D_{p,l}(G, Q_d) \leqslant c_0 d ,$$

where c_0 is a small enough constant that depends only on n, p, l. Then for all functions $u \in C^\infty(\bar{Q}_d)$ that vanish in a neighborhood of $\bar{Q}_d \backslash G$ the inequality

$$\| \nabla_j u \|_{L_p(Q_d)} \leqslant c\,[D_{p,l}(G, Q_d)]^{l-j} \| \nabla_l u \|_{L_p(Q_d)}, \tag{2}$$

where $j = 0, 1, \ldots, l-1$, is valid.

Proof. If suffices to assume that $d = 1$ and $l > 1$. We put $D = D_{p,l}(G, Q_1)$. Since $\delta < 1$, then $\overline{Q_d \backslash G} \notin \mathcal{N}(Q_1)$. Therefore, according to Theorems 10.2.3/1 and 10.2.3/2, we have

$$\| u \|_{L_p(Q_1)} \leqslant c D^l \sum_{j=1}^{l} \| \nabla_j u \|_{L_p(Q_1)} .$$

Hence from the inequality

$$\| \nabla_j u \|_{L_p(Q_1)} \leqslant c(\| \nabla_l u \|_{L_p(Q_1)} + \| u \|_{L_p(Q_1)})$$

we obtain that

$$\| u \|_{L_p(Q_1)} \leqslant c D^l (\| \nabla_l u \|_{L_p(Q_1)} + \| u \|_{L_p(Q_1)}) .$$

Thus, (2) follows for $j = 0$.

To obtain the estimate for $\| \nabla_j u \|_{L_p(Q_1)}$ with $j \geqslant 1$ we can use the inequality

$$\| \nabla_j u \|_{L_p(Q_1)} \leqslant c(\| \nabla_l u \|_{L_p(Q_1)} + \| u \|_{L_p(Q_1)})^{j/l} \| u \|_{L_p(Q_1)}^{(l-j)/l} .$$

The lemma is proved.

Theorem. *Let q be the same number as in Theorem* 10.1.2 *and let condition* (1) *be valid. Then for all functions $u \in C^\infty(\bar{Q}_d)$ that vanish in a neighborhood of $\bar{Q}_d \backslash G$ the inequality*

$$\| u \|_{L_q(Q_d)} \leqslant C \sum_{j=k+1}^{l} d^{j-l} \| \nabla_j u \|_{L_p(Q_d)}, \tag{3}$$

where $k = 0, 1, \ldots, l-1$, is fulfilled. The best constant in (3) *satisfies the inequalities*

$$c_1 [D_{p,l}(G, Q_d)]^{l-n(p^{-1}-q^{-1})} \leqslant C \leqslant c_2 [D_{p,l}(G, Q_d)]^{l-n(p^{-1}-q^{-1})} . \tag{4}$$

(In the case $n < pl$, $p > 1$ or $n = l$, $p = 1$ the value $D_{p,l}(G, Q_d)$ can be replaced by the inner diameter $D(G, Q_d)$ in (3) *and* (4).*)*

Proof. The rightmost estimate in (4) follows from (10.2.3/1) and the above lemma, and the leftmost estimate is contained in the second part of Theorem 10.2.3/1 and in Theorem 10.2.3/2.

Remark. The smallness of the (p, l)-inner diameter is essential for the validity of Theorem. In fact, let G be the cube $Q_1 \subset R^3$ with center excluded. Then $d = 1$, $D(G) = \frac{1}{2}$, whereas, according to Remark 10.3.5, the inequality

$$\| u \|_{L_2(Q_1)} \leqslant C \| \nabla_2 u \|_{L_2(Q_1)}$$

is not true. (This can be seen directly by insertion of the function $u(x) = x_1\zeta(x/\varepsilon)$, where $\varepsilon > 0$, $\zeta = 0$ on $B_1(0)$, $\zeta = 1$ outside $B_2(0)$, into (5).)

10.3.7. Application to the Boundary Uniqueness Theorem for Analytic Functions in the Class $L_p^1(U)$

From inequality (10.1.2/1) we can deduce an estimate for the integral of the logarithm of the modulus of a function in L_p^1 which characterizes the smallness of the set of zeros of this function that suffices for this integral to be finite (see Maz'ja and Havin [173].

Let E be a Borel set in $R^{n-1} = \{x = (x', x_n) \in R^n : x_n = 0\}$ and let $\{\mathscr{B}\}$ be a collection of n-dimensional open balls with centers in R^{n-1}. We denote a concentric ball with double the radius by $2\mathscr{B}$. Let $s(\mathscr{B}) = m_{n-1}(R^{n-1} \cap \mathscr{B})$, $c(E \cap \mathscr{B}) = \operatorname{cap}(E \cap \mathscr{B}, \mathring{W}_2^1(2\mathscr{B}))$, $S = \sum_{\{\mathscr{B}\}} s(\mathscr{B})$. We designate the number of different balls $\mathscr{B}$ which contain a point x by χ.

Lemma. *Let φ be a $(p, 1)$-refined function of the class $L_p^1(\bigcup \mathscr{B})$ that vanishes on $E \cap G$. Then*

$$\frac{1}{S} \int_{\cup(\mathscr{B} \cap R^{n-1})} \log|\varphi(x')|\chi(x')\,dx' \tag{1}$$

$$\leqslant \frac{1}{pS} \sum_{\{\mathscr{B}\}} s(\mathscr{B}) \log \frac{s(\mathscr{B})}{c(E \cap \mathscr{B})} + \frac{1}{p} \log\left[\frac{c}{S} \int_{\cup\mathscr{B}} |\nabla\varphi|^p \chi\,dx\right],$$

where $c = c(n, p)$, $p \geqslant 1$.

Proof. If $(\mathscr{X}, \Sigma, \mu)$ is a measure space with finite μ and f is a nonnegative function defined on $\mathscr{X}$ and measurable with respect to the σ-algebra Σ, then for any $p > 0$

$$\exp\left(\frac{1}{\mu(\mathscr{X})} \int_{\mathscr{X}} \log f\,d\mu\right) \leqslant \left(\frac{1}{\mu(\mathscr{X})} \int_{\mathscr{X}} f^p\,d\mu\right)^{1/p}. \tag{2}$$

Therefore

$$\frac{1}{S(\mathscr{B})} \int_{\mathscr{B} \cap R^{n-1}} \log|\varphi|\,dx' \leqslant \frac{1}{p} \log\left(\frac{1}{s(\mathscr{B})} \int_{\mathscr{B} \cap R^{n-1}} |\varphi|^p\,dx'\right),$$

where the ball $\mathscr{B}$ is arbitrary. Now we note that, for $p \geqslant 1$,

$$\frac{1}{s(\mathscr{B})} \int_{\mathscr{B} \cap R^{n-1}} |\varphi|^p\,dx'$$

$$\leqslant c\left(\frac{1}{m_n(\mathscr{B})} \int_{\mathscr{B}} |\varphi|^p\,dx + \frac{1}{\operatorname{cap}(\mathscr{B}, \mathring{W}_p^1(2\mathscr{B}))} \int_{\mathscr{B}} |\nabla\varphi|^p\,dx\right)$$

and make use of inequality (10.1.2/1) and Remark 10.1.3/3. We have

$$\frac{1}{m_n(\mathscr{B})} \int_{\mathscr{B}} |\varphi|^p\,dx \leqslant \frac{c}{c(E \cap \mathscr{B})} \int_{\mathscr{B}} |\nabla\varphi|^p\,dx.$$

Then

$$\frac{1}{s(\mathscr{B})} \int_{\mathscr{B} \cap R^{n-1}} |\varphi|^p dx' \leqslant \frac{c}{c(E \cap \mathscr{B})} \int_{\mathscr{B}} |\nabla \varphi|^p dx$$

and consequently

$$\int_{\cup(\mathscr{B} \cap R^{n-1})} \log|\varphi|\chi dx' = \sum_{\{\mathscr{B}\}} \int_{\mathscr{B} \cap R^{n-1}} \log|\varphi| dx' \leqslant \frac{1}{p} \sum_{\{\mathscr{B}\}} \left[S(\mathscr{B}) \log \frac{S(\mathscr{B})}{c(E \cap \mathscr{B})} \right]$$

$$+ \frac{1}{p} \sum_{\{\mathscr{B}\}} \left[S(\mathscr{B}) \log \left(\frac{c}{s(\mathscr{B})} \int_{\mathscr{B}} |\nabla \varphi|^p dx \right) \right].$$

Applying (2) to the last sum we arrive at the required estimate.

By virtue of (1) we can prove the uniqueness theorem for analytic functions of the class L_p^1 in the unit disk U (see the paper by Havin and the author [173], where this problem is considered in detail and where a bibliography is given).

Let $\mathfrak{A}$ be the set of all functions analytic in the disk U and let $\mathscr{X} \in \mathfrak{A}$. We say that a set E, contained in the interval $(0, 2\pi)$, is the uniqueness set for $\mathscr{X}$ if each function $f \in \mathscr{X}$ with $\lim_{r \to 1-0} f(re^{i\theta}) = 0$ for any $\theta \in E$ vanishes identically on U.

Let E be a Borel set in the interval $(0, 2\pi)$ and let $\{\delta\}$ be a set of pairwise disjoint open intervals $\delta \subset (0, 2\pi)$. Denote the length of δ by $l(\delta)$, the disk with diameter δ by $\mathscr{B}$, and the concentric disk with double the radius by $2\mathscr{B}$. We also use the notation $c(E \cap \delta) = \operatorname{cap}(E \cap \delta, \mathring{W}_p^1(2\mathscr{B}))$.

Let E satisfy the condition

$$\sum l(\delta) \log \frac{l(\delta)}{c(E \cap \delta)} = -\infty \tag{3}$$

and let an analytic function $f \in L_p^1(U)$ satisfy $\lim_{r \to 1-0} f(re^{i\theta}) = 0$ for any $\theta \in E$. From (1) it follows that

$$\int_0^{\infty} \log \left(\lim_{r \to 1-0} |f(re^{i\theta})| \right) d\theta = -\infty$$

(see Havin and Maz'ja [173]) which together with the well-known uniqueness theorem for analytic functions of the Hardy class H^1 shows that $f(z) = 0$ for all $z \in U$. Thus E is the uniqueness set for $L_p^1(U)$.

Since $c(E \cap \delta) \sim 1$ for $p > 2$, then in this case we can omit $c(E \cap \delta)$ in (3). For $p < 2$ we can replace $\operatorname{cap}(E \cap \delta, W_p^1(R^2))$ by $\operatorname{cap}(E \cap \delta)$.

§ 10.4. Comments to Chapter 10

§ 10.1. The notion of an "unessential set" applied to sets of small Wiener capacity was introduced by Molčanov [189] who proved Theorem 10.1.2 for $p = 2$, $l = 1$ (in an implicit form). A new approach was proposed by the author

[145] (see also Maz'ja [156]) for the case $l>1$. These results were rediscovered by Donoghue [53], R.A. Adams [12] and Polking [212].

Inequality (10.1.3/3) and the particular case (10.1.3/1) of it, which refines the first part of Theorem 10.1.2, were established by Hedberg [95] for $p>1$ who used a different method for which the restriction $p \neq 1$ is important. In 10.1.3 these results follow from Theorem 10.1.3 which was implicitly proved in the author's paper [156]. We note that our proof is also valid for the case $p=1$.

Inequality (10.1.3/3) plays an important role in the aforementioned paper by Hedberg where the well-known problem of spectral synthesis in Sobolev spaces is solved. The basic result of Hedberg runs as follows.

Let $u \in W_p^l(R^n)$, $p>1$ and let m be a positive integer. Let K be a closed subset of R^n and $D^\alpha u|_K = 0$ for all α with $0 \leqslant |\alpha| \leqslant l-1$. Then $u \in \mathring{W}_p^l(R^n \backslash K)$, i.e. there exist functions $u_m \in C_0^\infty(R^n \backslash K)$ such that $\lim_{m\to\infty} \|u-u_m\|_{W_p^l(R^n)} = 0$.

An obvious corollary to this theorem is the following uniqueness theorem for the Dirichlet problem (see Hedberg [95]).

Let $\Omega \subset R^n$ be an open bounded set in R^n and let u be a solution of $\Delta^l u = 0$ in Ω in the space $W_2^m(R^n)$ satisfying $D^\alpha u|_{\partial\Omega} = 0$, $0 \leqslant |\alpha| \leqslant l-1$. Then $u=0$ in Ω.

§ 10.2. A set function similar to $\lambda_{2,2}^l$ was introduced and applied to the investigation of the uniqueness conditions for the solution of the first boundary value problem by Kondrat'ev [115, 116]. In these papers it is called the capacity $C_{l,d}^n$. The connection of $\lambda_{p,q}^l$ with the (p,l)-inner diameter was studied by the author [158].

§ 10.3. The results of this section (except Proposition 10.3.5 and those of subsection 10.3.6) are borrowed from the author's paper [156].

Proposition 10.3.5 was published in the author's book [166]. This proposition together with Corollary 10.3.4 shows that the constant C in Corollary 10.3.4 satisfies the inequality

$$C \leqslant c d^{k+n/q} [\mathrm{Cap}(e, \mathring{L}_p^{l-k}(Q_{2d}))]^{-1/p}$$

which was obtained earlier by a direct method in the paper of Hedberg [94] (compare with the stronger inequality (10.1.3/3) which was discussed in the comments to § 10.1).

In connection with the content of the present chapter we mention the paper by Meyers [184] in which the inequality

$$\|u - Lu\|_{W_p^k(\Omega)} \leqslant C \|\nabla_{k+1} u\|_{W_p^{l-k-1}(\Omega)}, \qquad u \in W_p^l(\Omega),$$

where L is a projection mapping $W_p^l(\Omega) \to \mathscr{P}_k$ and Ω is a Lipschitz domain, is studied.

A certain family of "polynomial (p,l)-capacities" similar to $\mathrm{cap}(\mathfrak{C}_0(e), \Pi, \mathring{L}_p^l(Q_{2d}))$ was used by Bagby [22] in the study of approximation in L_p by solutions of elliptic equations.

Chapter 11. Imbedding of the Space $\overset{\circ}{L}{}_p^l(\Omega)$ into Other Function Spaces

§ 11.1. Preliminaries

If $n > pl$, $p > 1$ or $n \geqslant l$, $p = 1$ then for all $u \in \mathscr{D}(\Omega)$ the Sobolev inequality

$$\|u\|_{L_q(\Omega)} \leqslant C \|\nabla_l u\|_{L_p(\Omega)}, \tag{1}$$

where $q = pn/(n - pl)$, is valid. By virtue of (1) the mapping $\mathscr{D}(\Omega) \ni u \to u \in L_q(\Omega)$ is continuous. Since $\mathscr{D}(\Omega)$ is dense in $\overset{\circ}{L}{}_p^l(\Omega)$, this mapping can be uniquely extended to $\overset{\circ}{L}{}_p^l(\Omega)$ so that the extended operator is continuous. We can easily show that this operator is one to one. In fact, let zero be the image of $u \in \overset{\circ}{L}{}_p^l(\Omega)$ in $L_q(\Omega)$ and let a sequence $\{u_m\}_{m \geqslant 1}$ of functions in $\mathscr{D}(\Omega)$ converge to u in $L_p^l(\Omega)$. Then for all multi-indices α with $|\alpha| = l$ and for all $\varphi \in \mathscr{D}(\Omega)$

$$\lim_{m \to \infty} \int_\Omega \varphi D^\alpha u_m dx = \lim_{m \to \infty} (-1)^l \int_\Omega u_m D^\alpha \varphi dx = 0 .$$

Since the sequence $D^\alpha u_m$ converges in $L_p(\Omega)$, it tends to zero.

The above considerations show that each element of $\overset{\circ}{L}{}_p^l(\Omega)$ (for $n > pl$, $p > 1$ or $n \geqslant l$, $p = 1$) can be identified with a function in $L_q(\Omega)$ and the identity mapping

$$\overset{\circ}{L}{}_p^l(\Omega) \ni u \to u \in L_q(\Omega)$$

is one to one, linear and continuous (i.e. it is a topological imbedding).

If $n \leqslant lp$, $p > 1$ or $n < l$, $p = 1$ and if (1) is valid for some $q > 0$ with a constant C that is independent of $u \in \mathscr{D}(\Omega)$, then we arrive at the same conclusion. However, for these values of n, l, p inequality (1) does not hold and, moreover, in general $\overset{\circ}{L}{}_p^l(\Omega)$ is not imbedded into the space of distributions $\mathscr{D}'(\Omega)$.

The theorems of the present chapter contain necessary and sufficient conditions for the topological imbedding of $\overset{\circ}{L}{}_p^l(\Omega)$ into $\mathscr{D}'(\Omega)$, $L_q(\Omega, \text{loc})$, $L_q(\Omega)$ (§§ 11.1 – 11.4). In § 11.5 we obtain the conditions for the compactness of the imbedding $\overset{\circ}{L}{}_p^l(\Omega) \subset L_q(\Omega)$. In § 11.6 the results of previous sections are applied to the study of the first boundary value problem for elliptic equations of order $2l$.

§ 11.2. The Imbedding $\mathring{L}_p^l(\Omega) \subset \mathscr{D}'(\Omega)$

The object of the present section is to prove the following assertion.

Theorem. *The space* $\mathring{L}_p^l(\Omega)$ $(1 \leqslant p < \infty)$ *is topologically imbedded into* $\mathscr{D}'(\Omega)$ *if and only if any one of the following conditions holds:*

1) $n > pl, p > 1$ *or* $n \geqslant l, p = 1$;
2) $C\Omega$ *is not* $(p, n/p)$*-polar if* $n = pl, p > 1$;
3) $C\Omega$ *is not empty if* $n < pl$ *and* n/p *is not integer*;
4) $C\Omega$ *is not* $(p, n/p)$*-polar or it is not contained in an* $(n-1)$*-dimensional hyperplane if* $n < pl$ *and* n/p *is integer.*

Taking into account Theorem 9.2/2 we may read *"the set of zero inner* $(p, n/p)$*-capacity"* for *"*$(p, n/p)$*-polar set"* in the last theorem.

11.2.1. Auxiliary Assertions

Lemma 1. *The space* $\mathring{L}_p^l(\Omega)$ *is topologically imbedded into* $\mathscr{D}'(\Omega)$ *if and only if, for any* $\psi \in \mathscr{D}(\Omega)$, *the functional*

$$\mathscr{D}(\Omega) \ni u \to \int_\Omega u\,\psi\,dx \equiv (u, \psi) \in \mathscr{D}'(\Omega) \tag{1}$$

is continuous with respect to the norm $\|\nabla_l u\|_{L_p(\Omega)}$.

Proof. 1) *If* $\mathring{L}_p^l \subset \mathscr{D}'(\Omega)$, then any sequence $u_m \in \mathscr{D}'(\Omega)$ which is a Cauchy sequence in the norm $\|\nabla_l u\|_{L_p(\Omega)}$, converges in $\mathscr{D}'(\Omega)$. Consequently, the functional (u, ψ) is continuous.

2) Let the functional (u, ψ) be continuous in the norm $\|\nabla_l u\|_{L_p(\Omega)}$. Then the mapping (1) can be continuously extended to $\mathring{L}_p^l(\Omega)$. It remains to show that the resulting mapping is one to one. Let u_m be a Cauchy sequence in $\mathring{L}_p^l(\Omega)$ that converges to zero in $\mathscr{D}'(\Omega)$. Obviously, for all $\varphi \in \mathscr{D}(\Omega)$ and all multi-indices α with $|\alpha| = l$ we have

$$\int_\Omega \varphi D^\alpha u_m dx = (-1)^l \int_\Omega u_m D^\alpha \varphi dx \to 0\,.$$

Since the sequence $D^\alpha u_m$ converges in $L_p(\Omega)$, it tends to zero.

Corollary. *The space* $\mathring{L}_p^l(\Omega)$ *is imbedded into* $\mathscr{D}'(\Omega)$ *if and only if*

$$|(u, \psi)| \leqslant K \|\nabla_l u\|_{L_p(R^n)} \tag{2}$$

for any $\psi \in \mathscr{D}(\Omega)$ *and for all* $u \in \mathscr{D}(\Omega)$.

Lemma 2. *The space* $\mathring{L}_p^l(\Omega)$ *is imbedded into* $\mathscr{D}'(\Omega)$ *if and only if for any* $\psi \in \mathscr{D}(\Omega)$ *there exists a distribution* $T \in \mathscr{D}'(\Omega)$ *with support in* $C\Omega$ *such that*

$$|(u, \psi - T)| \leqslant K \|\nabla_l u\|_{L_p(R^n)}\,, \qquad u \in \mathscr{D}(R^n)\,. \tag{3}$$

Proof. Necessity. Let $\mathring{L}_p^l(\Omega) \subset \mathscr{D}'(\Omega)$. Then by the above corollary inequality (2) is valid for all $u \in \mathscr{D}(\Omega)$. The space $\mathscr{D}(\Omega)$ can be identified with the subspace $\mathscr{D}(R^n)$ by zero extension to $C\Omega$. By the Hahn-Banach theorem, functional (1) can be extended to a functional $u \to (u, s)$ on $\mathscr{D}(R^n)$ which is continuous with respect to the norm $\|\nabla_l u\|_{L_p(R^n)}$, i.e. to a functional satisfying

$$|(u,s)| \leqslant K \|\nabla_l u\|_{L_p(R^n)}, \tag{4}$$

where K does not depend on u. Since $s = \psi$ on Ω, the support of the distribution $T = \psi - s$ is contained in $C\Omega$. The estimates (3) and (4) are equivalent.

Sufficiency. Suppose (3) is valid. Then the functional $\mathscr{D}(R^n) \ni u \to (u, s)$ with $s = \psi - T$ is continuous with respect to the norm $\|\nabla_l u\|_{L_p(R^n)}$ on $\mathscr{D}(R^n)$ and hence on $\mathscr{D}(\Omega)$ where it coincides with (1). It remains to refer to Corollary.

Lemma 3. *Let $n \leqslant pl$ for $p > 1$ or $n < l$ for $p = 1$. If for any $\psi \in \mathscr{D}(\Omega)$ there exists a distribution $T \in W_{p'}^{-l}(R^n)$ with compact support in $C\Omega$ such that*

$$(x^\beta, \psi - T) = 0 \tag{5}$$

for all multi-indices β with $|\beta| \leqslant k = [l - n/p]$ then the space $\mathring{L}_p^l(\Omega)$ is imbedded into $\mathscr{D}'(\Omega)$.

Proof. Let B_ϱ be the ball $\{x: |x| < \varrho\}$ containing the supports of ψ and T. We show that (3) is valid for all $u \in \mathscr{D}(R^n)$. Indeed, for any polynomial P of degree not higher than k we have

$$|(u, \psi - T)| = |(u - P, \psi - T)| = |((u - P)\eta, \psi - T)|,$$

where $\eta \in \mathscr{D}(B_{2\varrho})$, $\eta = 1$ in B_ϱ. Let $K = \|\psi - T\|_{W_{p'}^{-l}(R^n)}$. Then

$$|(u, \psi - T)| \leqslant K \|(u - P)\eta\|_{W_p^l(R^n)} \leqslant C(\|\nabla_l u\|_{L_p(R^n)} + \|u - P\|_{L_p(B_{2\varrho})}) .$$

Applying the inequality

$$\inf_{\mathscr{P}_k} \|u - P\|_{L_p(B_{2\varrho})} \leqslant C \|\nabla_{k+1} u\|_{L_p(B_{2\varrho})},$$

where $\mathscr{P}_k$ is the set of all polynomials of degree not higher than k, as well as the inequalities

$$\|\nabla_{k+1} u\|_{L_p(B_{2\varrho})} \leqslant C \|\nabla_{k+1} u\|_{L_q(B_{2\varrho})} \leqslant c \|\nabla_l u\|_{L_p(R^n)},$$

where $q = pn[n - p(l - k - 1)]^{-1}$, we arrive at (3). The lemma is proved.

11.2.2. The Case $\Omega = R^n$

Lemma. *Let $n \leqslant lp$ for $p>1$ or $n<l$ for $p=1$ and let α be a multi-index of order $|\alpha| \leqslant l-n/p$. Then there exists a sequence of functions $u_\nu \in \mathscr{D}(R^n)$ such that $u_\nu \to x^\alpha$ in $\mathscr{D}'(R^n)$ and $u_\nu \to 0$ in $\mathring{L}_p^l(R^n)$.*

Proof. Let η be an infinitely differentiable function on $(0, \infty)$ which is equal to unity in a neighborhood of $[0,1]$ and to zero in a neighborhood of $[2, \infty)$, and let $|\alpha|<l-n/p$. Clearly, the sequence

$$u_\nu(x) = x^\alpha \eta(\nu^{-1}|x|)$$

converges to x^α in $\mathscr{D}'(\Omega)$. On the other hand,

$$\|\nabla_l u_\nu\|_{L_p(R^n)} \leqslant \text{const}\, \nu^{n/p+|\alpha|-l} \xrightarrow[\nu\to\infty]{} 0\,.$$

Let $|\alpha| = l-n/p$. We put

$$v_\nu(x) = \frac{1}{\log \nu} \log \frac{\nu^2}{|x|}$$

for $x \in B_{\nu^2} \backslash B_\nu = \{x\colon \nu^2 > |x| \geqslant \nu\}$ $(\nu>2)$. By $\varphi(t)$ we denote a function in $C^\infty[0,1]$ equal to zero near $t=0$ and to unity near $t=1$. Further, let $w_\nu(x) = \varphi[v_\nu(x)]$ for $x \in B_{\nu^2} \backslash B_\nu$, $w_\nu(x) = 1$ in B_ν and $w_\nu(x) = 0$ outside B_{ν^2}. It is clear that $u_\nu(x) = x^\alpha w_\nu(x)$ converges to x^α in $\mathscr{D}'(R^n)$. On the other hand, since

$$|\nabla_j w_\nu(x)| \leqslant \text{const}\,(\log \nu)^{-1} |x|^{-j}$$

for $j>0$, then

$$\|\nabla_l u_\nu\|_{L_p(R^n)} \leqslant \text{const}\,(\log \nu)^{-1} \Big(\int\limits_{B_{\nu^2}\backslash B_\nu} |x|^{(|\alpha|-l)p} dx \Big)^{1/p}$$

$$= \text{const}\,(\log \nu)^{1/p-1} \xrightarrow[\nu\to\infty]{} 0\,.$$

Theorem. *The space $\mathring{L}_p^l(R^n)$ is imbedded into $\mathscr{D}'(R^n)$ if and only if $n>lp$, $p>1$, or $n \geqslant l$, $p=1$.*

The necessity follows immediately from Lemma and the sufficiency from the estimate

$$\|u\|_{L_{pn/(n-lp)}(\Omega)} \leqslant c(n,l,p)\, \|\nabla_l u\|_{L_p(\Omega)}$$

and the proof of the one-to-one correspondence presented in § 11.1.

Corollary. *The space $\mathring{L}_p^l(\Omega)$ is imbedded into $\mathscr{D}'(\Omega)$ for any open set Ω if and only if $n>lp$, $p>1$ or $n \geqslant l$, $p=1$.*

The necessity was proved in the preceding theorem. Extending any $u \in \mathscr{D}(\Omega)$ by zero to $C\Omega$ we obtain the imbedding $\mathscr{D}(\Omega) \subset \mathscr{D}(R^n)$ and hence the imbedding $\mathscr{D}'(R^n) \subset \mathscr{D}'(\Omega)$. Therefore

$$\overset{\circ}{L}{}_p^l(\Omega) \subset \overset{\circ}{L}{}_p^l(R^n) \subset \mathscr{D}'(R^n) \subset \mathscr{D}'(\Omega) .$$

Here and henceforth $\subset$ means a topological imbedding.

11.2.3. The Case $n = pl$, $p > 1$

Lemma. *If a closed set E is not a (p, l)-polar set, then there exists a distribution $T \in W_{p'}^{-l}(R^n)$ with compact support in E such that* $(1, T) = 1$.

Proof. Since E is not (p, l)-polar, there exists a distribution $S \in W_{p'}^{-l}(R^n)$, $S \neq 0$ with support in E. Let the function $T = \varphi S$ satisfy $(\varphi, S) = 1$. Obviously, the distribution $T = \varphi S$ satisfies the requirements of the lemma.

Theorem. *Let $n = lp$, $p > 1$. In order that $\overset{\circ}{L}{}_p^l(\Omega) \subset \mathscr{D}'(\Omega)$ it is necessary and sufficient that $C\Omega$ is not a $(p, n/p)$-polar set.*

Proof. Necessity. From Lemma 11.2.2 it follows that, if the function $\psi \in \mathscr{D}(\Omega)$ with $(1, \psi) \neq 0$ is arbitrary, then the inequality

$$|(u, \psi)| \leqslant C \| \nabla_l u \|_{L_p(R^n)}$$

can not be valid for all $u \in \mathscr{D}(R^n)$. Since $\overset{\circ}{L}{}_p^l(\Omega) \subset \mathscr{D}'(\Omega)$, there exists a distribution $T \in \mathscr{D}'(R^n)$ such that $\operatorname{supp} T \subset C\Omega$ and

$$|(u, \psi - T)| \leqslant c \| \nabla_l u \|_{L_p(R^n)}$$

for all $u \in \mathscr{D}(R^n)$ (see Lemma 11.2.1/2). Obviously, $T \neq 0$. Moreover,

$$|(u, T)| \leqslant c \| \nabla_l u \|_{L_p(R^n)} + |(u, \psi)| \leqslant c \| u \|_{W_p^l(R^n)} ,$$

i.e. $T \in W_{p'}^{-l}(R^n)$. Thus $C\Omega$ is not a $(p, n/p)$-polar set.

Sufficiency. Since $C\Omega$ is not a $(p, n/p)$-polar set, there exists a distribution $T_0 \in W_{p'}^{-l}(R^n)$ with compact support in $C\Omega$ such that $(1, T_0) = 1$. Let $\psi \in \mathscr{D}(\Omega)$. We put $T = (\psi, 1)\, T_0$. Since $(1, \psi - T) = 0$, then, according to Lemma 11.2.1/3 (where $k = 0$), $\overset{\circ}{L}{}_p^l(\Omega) \subset \mathscr{D}'(\Omega)$. The theorem is proved.

11.2.4. The Case $n < pl$ and Fractional n/p

Theorem. *If $n < pl$ and if n/p is fractional then the condition $C\Omega \neq \varnothing$ is necessary and sufficient for the imbedding $\overset{\circ}{L}{}_p^l(\Omega) \subset \mathscr{D}'(\Omega)$.*

Proof. Necessity. If $C\Omega = \varnothing$, then by Theorem 11.2.2 the space $\overset{\circ}{L}{}_p^l(\Omega)$ is not imbedded into $\mathscr{D}'(\Omega)$.

Sufficiency. Let $C\Omega \neq \varnothing$. We may assume $0 \in C\Omega$. We put

$$T = \sum_{|\alpha| \leqslant k} (-1)^{\alpha} \frac{(\psi, x^{\alpha})}{\alpha!} D^{\alpha} \delta(x) ,$$

where δ is the Dirac delta-function, D is usual differentiation, $k=[l-n/p]$ and $\psi \in \mathscr{D}(\Omega)$. Since $k<l-n/p$ then $D^{\alpha}\delta \in W_{p'}^{-l}(R^n)$ for $|\alpha| \leqslant k$ and $T \in W_{p'}^{-l}(R^n)$. Besides, obviously, $(x^{\beta}, \psi - T) = 0$ for $|\beta| \leqslant k$. It remains to make use of Lemma 11.2.1/3. The theorem is proved.

11.2.5. The Case $n<pl$, $1<p<\infty$ and Integer n/p

Theorem. *Let n/p be an integer, $n<pl$, $1<p<\infty$. The space $\mathring{L}_p^l(\Omega)$ is imbedded into $\mathscr{D}'(\Omega)$ if and only if $C\Omega$ is not a $(p, n/p)$-polar set and is not contained in an $(n-1)$-dimensional hyperplane.*

Proof. We put $k=l-n/p$.

Sufficiency. a) Suppose the set $C\Omega$ is not a $(p, n/p)$-polar set. Then by Lemma 11.2.3 there exists a distribution $T_0 \in W_{p'}^{k-l}(R^n)$ with compact support in $C\Omega$ such that $(1, T_0) = 1$. We put

$$T = \sum_{|\alpha| \leqslant k} a_{\alpha}(-1)^{|\alpha|} D^{\alpha} T_0 .$$

Obviously, T is a distribution in $W_{p'}^{-l}(R^n)$ with compact support in $C\Omega$.

It remains to show that given any $\psi \in \mathscr{D}(\Omega)$ we can find numbers a_{α} so that (11.2.1/5) holds for all multi-indices β with $|\beta| \leqslant k$. In other words the linear algebraic system

$$\sum_{|\alpha| \leqslant k} a_{\alpha}(D^{\alpha} T_0, x^{\beta}) = (\psi, x^{\beta}), \quad |\beta| \leqslant k,$$

must be solvable. Since $(D^{\gamma} T_0, 1) = 0$ for $|\gamma| > 0$, this system can be rewritten in the form

(1)
$$\sum_{\alpha \leqslant \beta} a_{\alpha} \frac{\beta!}{(\beta-\alpha)!} (T_0, x^{\beta-\alpha}) = (\psi, x^{\beta}) .$$

The matrix of system (1) is triangular with nonzero elements on the main diagonal (it consists of the numbers $\beta!\,(T_0, 1) = \beta!$). Thus (1) is solvable.

b) Suppose $C\Omega$ is not in an $(n-1)$-dimensional hyperplane. Suppose the points $0, a_1, \ldots, a_n$ are situated in $C\Omega$ and are affinely independent. Further, let $\psi \in \mathscr{D}(\Omega)$. We introduce the distribution

$$T = P_0(-i\nabla)\delta(x) + \sum_{j=1}^{n} P_j(-i\nabla)\delta(x-a_j) ,$$

where $P_0, P_1, \ldots, P_n$ are homogeneous polynomials of degrees not higher than $k-1$. Since $p(l-k+1) > n$ then $T \in W_{p'}^{-l}(R^n)$.

We choose polynomials $P_0, P_1, \ldots, P_n$ so that (11.2.1/5) holds. Let $Q(\xi)$ and $R(\xi)$ be the sums of terms of degree not higher than k in the Taylor expansions of the Fourier transforms $\hat{T}(\xi)$ and $\hat{\psi}(\xi)$, respectively. We denote the homogeneous part of $R(\xi)$ of degree k by $r(\xi)$. It is clear that

$$\hat{T}(\xi) = P_0(\xi) + \sum_{j=1}^{n} P_j(\xi) \exp(-i\langle a_j, \xi\rangle),$$

$$Q(\xi) = \sum_{j=0}^{n} P_j(\xi) - i \sum_{j=1}^{n} \langle a_j, \xi\rangle P_j(\xi).$$

Since the forms $\langle a_j, \xi\rangle$ are independent, we can choose $P_1, \dots, P_n$ so that

$$-i \sum_{j=1}^{n} \langle a_j, \xi\rangle P_j(\xi) = r(\xi).$$

We define the polynomial P_0 by $P_0 = -(P_1 + \dots + P_n) + R - r$ (obviously, the degree of P_0 is less than k). Thus $Q(\xi) = R(\xi)$ which is equivalent to (11.2.1/5).

Necessity. Let $\mathring{L}_p^l(\Omega) \subset \mathscr{D}'(\Omega)$ and let $C\Omega \subset R^{n-1}$ (for definiteness we put $R^{n-1} = \{x: x_1 = 0\}$). We show that $C\Omega$ is not a $(p, n/p)$-polar set. By Lemma 11.2.1/2 for any $\psi \in \mathscr{D}(\Omega)$ there exists a distribution T with support in $C\Omega$ such that (11.2.1/3) holds. Since $C\Omega \subset R^{n-1}$ then

$$T = \sum_{j=0}^{l} \left(\frac{1}{i} \frac{\partial}{\partial x_1}\right)^j \delta(x_1) \times S_j(x_2, \dots, x_n) = \sum_{j=0}^{l} T_j$$

where $S_j \in \mathscr{D}'(R^{n-1})$, $\operatorname{supp} S_j \subset C\Omega$ (cf. Schwartz [224]). We show that $T_j \neq 0$ and $T_j \in W_{p'}^{-l}(R^n)$. We have

$$\hat{T}(\xi) = \sum_{j=0}^{l} \xi_1^j \hat{S}_j(\xi_2, \dots, \xi_n) = \sum_{j=0}^{l} \hat{T}_j(\xi).$$

Let $\beta_0, \dots, \beta_l$ be distinct numbers in $(0,1)$. According to the Lagrange interpolation formula there exist constants $\gamma_0, \dots, \gamma_l$ such that $a_k = \sum_{j=0}^{l} \gamma_j P(\beta_j)$ for any polynomial $P(t) = a_0 + a_1 t + \dots + a_l t^l$. In particular, if $P(t) = t^k$ then

$$1 = \sum_{j=0}^{l} \gamma_j \beta_j^k. \tag{2}$$

For the polynomial

$$\hat{T}(t\xi_1, \xi_2, \dots, \xi_n) = \sum_{j=0}^{l} \xi_1^j \hat{S}_j(\xi_2, \dots, \xi_n) t^j$$

we have

$$\xi_1^k \hat{S}_k(\xi_2, \dots, \xi_n) = \sum_{j=0}^{l} \gamma_j \hat{T}(\beta_j \xi_1, \xi_2, \dots, \xi_n).$$

Consequently,

$$T_k = \left(\frac{1}{i} \frac{\partial}{\partial x_1}\right)^k \delta(x_1) \times S_k(x_2, \dots, x_n)$$

$$= \sum_{j=0}^{l} \frac{\gamma_j}{\beta_j} T\left(\frac{x_1}{\beta_j}, x_2, \dots, x_n\right).$$

We define the function

(3) $$\psi_k = \sum_{j=0}^{l} \frac{\gamma_j}{\beta_j}\, \psi\left(\frac{x_1}{\beta_j}, x_2, \ldots, x_n\right).$$

Inequality (11.2.1/3) for $\psi - T$ implies

(4) $$|(u, \psi_k - T_k)| \leqslant K \|\nabla_l u\|_{L_p(R^n)}$$

for all $u \in \mathscr{D}(R^n)$. We may assume that the function $\psi \in \mathscr{D}(R^n)$ satisfies $(\psi, x_1^k) = 1$. This along with (2) and (3) yields $(\psi_k, x_1^k) = 1$. Suppose $T_k = 0$. Then for all $u \in \mathscr{D}(R^n)$

$$|(u, \psi_k)| \leqslant K \|\nabla_l u\|_{L_p(R^n)}.$$

Hence by this and Lemma 11.2.2 we obtain $(\psi_k, x_1^k) = 0$. Thus $T_k \neq 0$ or, equivalently, $S_k \neq 0$. Since $\varphi \in \mathscr{D}(R^n)$ then (4) implies $T_k \in W_{p'}^{-l}(R^n)$.

Next we show that $\delta(x_1) \times S_k \in W_{p'}^{k-l}(R^n)$. It is well known (see, for instance, Stein [237], § 4, Ch. 6) that for any collection of functions $g_j \in W_p^{l-j}(R^n)$ $(j = 0, 1, \ldots, l-1)$ there exists a function $\Phi \in W_p^l(R^n)$ such that $\partial^j \Phi / \partial x_j = g_j$ for $x \in R^{n-1}$ and

$$\|\Phi\|_{W_p^l(R^n)} \leqslant K \sum_{j=0}^{l-1} \|g_j\|_{W_p^{l-j}(R^n)}.$$

Let $g_j = 0$ for $j \neq k$ and $g_k = u$, where u is an arbitrary function in $W_p^{l-k}(R^n)$. Then

$$(u, \delta(x_1) \times S_k) = \left(\Phi, \left(\frac{1}{i}\frac{\partial}{\partial x_1}\right)^k \delta(x_1) \times S_k\right) = (\Phi, T_k).$$

Since $T_k \in W_{p'}^{-l}(R^n)$ then applying the above assertion we get

$$|(u, \delta(x_1) \times S_k)| \leqslant K \|\Phi\|_{W_p^l(R^n)} \leqslant K \|u\|_{W_p^{l-k}(R^n)}.$$

Thus $\delta(x_1) \times S_k \in W_{p'}^{-n/p}(R^n)$ and $C\Omega$ is not a $(p, n/p)$-polar set. The theorem is proved.

Thus, the proof of Theorem 11.2 is complete.

§ 11.3. The Imbedding $\overset{\circ}{L}{}_p^l(\Omega) \subset L_q(\Omega, \mathrm{loc})$

The following assertion shows that Theorem 11.2 contains necessary and sufficient conditions for the imbedding $\overset{\circ}{L}{}_p^l(\Omega) \subset L_q(\Omega, \mathrm{loc})$.

Theorem. *Let $n \leqslant pl$ for $p>1$ or $n<l$ for $p=1$. If the space $\mathring{L}_p^l(\Omega)$ is imbedded into $\mathscr{D}'(\Omega)$, then it is also imbedded into $L_q(\Omega, \mathrm{loc})$ for $n=pl$, where q is any positive number, and into $C(\Omega)$ for $n<pl$.*

Proof. Let G be a domain in R^n with compact closure and smooth boundary, $G \cap \Omega \neq \varnothing$. First we show that there exists a family of functions $\varphi_\alpha \in \mathscr{D}(G \cap \Omega)$, $|\alpha| = l-1$, such that the matrix $\|(\varphi_\alpha, x^\beta)\|$ is not degenerate. Let φ be any function in $\mathscr{D}(G \cap \Omega)$ with $(\varphi, 1) \neq 0$ and let $\varphi_\alpha = D^\alpha \varphi$. Obviously, for $\alpha > \beta$ we have

$$(\varphi_\alpha, x^\beta) = (-1)^{|\alpha|}(\varphi, D^\alpha x^\beta) = 0$$

and the matrix $\|(\varphi_\alpha, x^\beta)\|$ is triangular. Since the main diagonal terms are $(-1)^{|\alpha|}\alpha!(\varphi, 1) \neq 0$, the determinant is not zero and the existence of the functions φ_α follows.

Since $\mathring{L}_p^l(\Omega) \subset \mathscr{D}'(\Omega)$ then according to Corollary 11.2.1

$$|(\varphi_\alpha, u)| \leqslant K \| \nabla_l u \|_{L_p(\Omega)}, \tag{1}$$

where K is a constant that is independent of u. By virtue of the Sobolev imbedding theorem,

$$\|u\|_{L_q(G)} \leqslant K\left(\| \nabla_l u \|_{L_p(G)} + \sum_{|\alpha| = l-1} |(\varphi_\alpha, u)| \right)$$

for all $u \in \mathscr{D}(\Omega)$, which together with (1) yields

$$\|u\|_{L_q(G)} \leqslant K \| \nabla_l u \|_{L_p(\Omega)} .$$

In the same way as in § 11.1 we can prove that the mapping $\mathring{L}_p^l(\Omega) \ni u \to u \in L_q(\Omega, \mathrm{loc})$ is one to one. The theorem is proved.

Next we present two corollaries to Theorem 10.1.2 which complement the theorem of this section.

Corollary 1. *Let $n = pl$, $p>1$ and let Q_d be a cube for which*

$$\mathrm{Cap}(\bar{Q}_d \backslash \Omega, \mathring{L}_p^l(Q_{2d})) > 0 .$$

Then, for all $u \in \mathscr{D}(\Omega)$,

$$\|u\|_{L_q(Q_d)}^p \leqslant C \| \nabla_l u \|_{L_p(\Omega)}^p , \tag{2}$$

where $C \leqslant c d^{np/q} [\mathrm{Cap}(\bar{Q}_d \backslash \Omega, \mathring{L}_p^l(Q_{2d}))]^{-1}$.

Proof. According to Theorem 10.1.2,

$$\|u\|_{L_q(Q_d)}^p \leqslant c d^{np/q} [\mathrm{Cap}(\bar{Q}_d \backslash \Omega, \mathring{L}_p^l(Q_{2d}))]^{-1} |u|_{p,l,Q_{2d}}^p . \tag{3}$$

Since

$$\| \nabla_j u \|_{L_p(Q_{2d})} \leqslant c d^{l-j} \| \nabla_j u \|_{L_{q_j}(\Omega)} \leqslant c d^{l-j} \| \nabla_l u \|_{L_q(\Omega)}$$

for $j \geqslant 1$, $q_j = pn[n-p(l-j)]^{-1}$, then

$$\mathbf{|} u \mathbf{|}_{p,l,Q_{2d}} \leqslant c \| \nabla_l u \|_{L_p(\Omega)}$$

which together with (3) yields (2).

Corollary 2. 1) *If $pl > n$, n/p is an integer and* $\text{Cap}(\bar{Q}_d \setminus \Omega, \mathring{L}_p^{n/p}(Q_{2d})) > 0$, *then, for all $u \in \mathscr{D}(\Omega)$,*

$$\max_{\bar{Q}_d} |u|^p \leqslant C \| \nabla_l u \|_{L_p(\Omega)}^p, \tag{4}$$

where $C \leqslant c d^{lp-n} [\text{Cap}(\bar{Q}_d \setminus \Omega, \mathring{L}_p^{n/p}(Q_{2d}))]^{-1}$.

2) *If $pl > n$, n/p is not an integer and $\bar{Q}_d \setminus \Omega \neq \varnothing$, then (4) is valid for all $u \in \mathscr{D}(\Omega)$ with $C \leqslant c d^{lp-n}$.*

Proof. 1) Let $kp = n$, $q > n$. Using the Sobolev theorem, we obtain

$$\max_{\bar{Q}_d} |u| \leqslant c d^{l-k-1} \max_{\bar{Q}_d} |\nabla_{l-k-1} u| \leqslant c d^{l-k-n/q} \| \nabla_{l-k} u \|_{L_q(Q_d)}. \tag{5}$$

By virtue of (2) with l replaced by k and u replaced by $\nabla_{l-k} u$, we have

$$\| \nabla_{l-k} u \|_{L_p(Q_d)} \leqslant c d^{n/p} [\text{Cap}(\bar{Q}_d \setminus \Omega, \mathring{L}_p^k(Q_{2d}))]^{-1/p} \| \nabla_l u \|_{L_p(\Omega)}.$$

This and (5) imply (4).

2) Let j be an integer such that $l - p^{-1} n < j < l - p^{-1} n + 1$. Since $p(l-j) < n$, then

$$\| \nabla_j u \|_{L_q(\Omega)} \leqslant C \| \nabla_l u \|_{L_p(\Omega)}$$

where $q = pn[n-(l-j)p]^{-1}$. The condition $p(l-j+1) > n$ is equivalent to $q > n$. Therefore

$$\max_{\bar{Q}_d} |\nabla_{j-1} u| \leqslant c d^{1-q^{-1}n} \| \nabla_j u \|_{L_q(Q_d)} \leqslant c d^{-p^{-1}+l-j+1} \| \nabla_l u \|_{L_p(\Omega)}.$$

Hence from this and

$$\max_{\bar{Q}_d} |u| \leqslant c d^{j-1} \max_{\bar{Q}_d} |\nabla_{j-1} u|$$

we obtain (4). The corollary is proved.

§ 11.4. The Imbedding $\mathring{L}_p^l(\Omega) \subset L_q(\Omega)$ (The Case $p \leqslant q$)

In this section we find necessary and sufficient conditions for the validity of (11.1) where u is an arbitrary function in $\mathscr{D}(\Omega)$.

The results we present here can be deduced (although only for $p>1$) from the more general theorems proved in § 12.2 where the space $\mathring{L}_p^l(\Omega, \nu)$ is studied. However, the separate exposition seems reasonable because of the importance of this particular case, the possibility of including $p=1$ and the simpler statements.

11.4.1. A Condition in Terms of the (p, l)-inner Diameter

If we put $d=\infty$ in the proofs of Theorems 10.2.3/1 and 10.2.3/2, then we arrive at the following theorem.

Theorem. *Let q satisfy any one of the conditions:*
(i) $q \in [p, np(n-pl)^{-1}]$ *if* $p \geqslant 1, n>pl$;
(ii) $q \in [p, \infty)$ *if* $p>1, n=pl$;
(iii) $q \in [p, \infty]$ *if* $pl>n, p>1$ *or* $l=n, p=1$.
Then:
Inequality (11.1) *is valid if and only if*
(α) $D_{p,l}(\Omega)<\infty$ *for* $n>pl, p \geqslant 1$ *or* $n=pl, p>1$;
(β) $D(\Omega)<\infty$ *for* $n<pl, p>1$ *or* $n=l, p=1$.
The best constant C in (11.1) *satisfies*

$$C \sim \begin{cases} [D_{p,l}(\Omega)]^{l-n(p^{-1}-q^{-1})} & \text{in case } (\alpha); \\ [D(\Omega)]^{l-n(p^{-1}-q^{-1})} & \text{in case } (\beta). \end{cases} \tag{1}$$

11.4.2. A Condition in Terms of Capacity

By the Sobolev theorem inequality (11.1) is valid for any set Ω provided $q=pn(n-pl)^{-1}$, $n>pl$ or $q=\infty$, $p=1$, $l=n$. Therefore it remains to consider only the cases: $q<pn(n-pl)^{-1}$ for $n=pl$ and $q \leqslant \infty$ for $n<pl$, $p \geqslant 1$.

We present a necessary and sufficient condition for the validity of (11.1) stated in different terms and resulting from Theorem 10.1.2.

Theorem 1. *Let q be the same as in Theorem* 11.4.1. *Inequality* (11.1) *is valid if and only if*

$$\inf \operatorname{Cap}(\bar{Q}_d \backslash \Omega, \mathring{L}_p^l(Q_{2d}))>0 \tag{1}$$

for some $d>0$. Here the infimum is taken over all cubes Q_d with edge length d and with sides parallel to coordinate axes.

Proof. Sufficiency. We construct the cubic grid with edge length d. Suppose

$$d^{lp-n}\operatorname{Cap}(\bar{Q}_d \setminus \Omega, \mathring{L}_p^l(Q_{2d})) \geqslant \varkappa > 0$$

for any cube of the grid.

According to Theorem 10.1.2, we have

$$\|u\|^p_{L_p(Q_d)} \leqslant c\varkappa^{-1} \sum_{k=1}^{l} d^{pk} \|\nabla_k u\|^p_{L_p(Q_d)}.$$

Summing over all cubes of the grid, we obtain

$$\|u\|^p_{L_p(\Omega)} \leqslant c\varkappa^{-1} \sum_{k=1}^{l} d^{pk} \|\nabla_k u\|^p_{L_p(\Omega)}.$$

To estimate the right-hand side we use the inequality

(2) $$\|\nabla_k u\|_{L_p(\Omega)} \leqslant c \|\nabla_l u\|^{k/l}_{L_p(\Omega)} \|u\|^{1-k/l}_{L_p(\Omega)}.$$

Then

(3) $$\|u\|^p_{L_p(\Omega)} \leqslant c \sum_{k=1}^{l} (d^{pl}\varkappa^{-l/k} \|\nabla_l u\|^p_{L_p(\Omega)})^{k/l} \|u\|^{p(1-k/l)}_{L_p(\Omega)}.$$

Since

$$\operatorname{Cap}(\bar{Q}_d \setminus \Omega, \mathring{L}_p^l(Q_{2d})) \leqslant c d^{n-pl}$$

then $\varkappa \leqslant c$ and hence the right-hand side in (3) does not exceed

$$2^{-1}\|u\|^p_{L_p(\Omega)} + c d^{pl}\varkappa^{-l} \|\nabla_l u\|^p_{L_p(\Omega)}.$$

Thus

(4) $$\|u\|^p_{L_p(\Omega)} \leqslant c d^{pl}\varkappa^{-l} \|\nabla_l u\|^p_{L_p(\Omega)}.$$

We now prove (11.4.1/1) for $q > p$. By Theorem 10.1.2

$$\|u\|^p_{L_p(Q_d)} \leqslant c d^{np/q}\varkappa^{-1} \sum_{j=1}^{l} d^{pj-n} \int_{Q_d} |\nabla_j u|^p dx.$$

Summing over all cubes Q_d and using the inequality $\left(\sum_i a_i\right)^\varepsilon \leqslant \sum_i a_i^\varepsilon$ $(a_i \geqslant 0, 0 < \varepsilon \leqslant 1)$ we obtain

$$\|u\|^p_{L_q(\Omega)} \leqslant c\varkappa^{-1} d^{np/q} \sum_{j=1}^{l} d^{pj-n} \int_{\Omega} |\nabla_j u|^p dx.$$

Now inequality (2) yields

$$\|u\|^p_{L_q(\Omega)} \leqslant c\varkappa^{-1} d^{np/q} \sum_{j=1}^{l} d^{pj-n} \|\nabla_l u\|^{pj/l}_{L_p(\Omega)} \|u\|^{p(1-j/l)}_{L_p(\Omega)}.$$

Applying (4), we finally obtain

(5) $$\|u\|^p_{L_q(\Omega)} \leqslant c\varkappa^{-l} d^{np/q+pl-n} \|\nabla_l u\|^p_{L_p(\Omega)}.$$

Necessity. Let Q_d be an arbitrary cube with edge length d and let u be an arbitrary function in $C^\infty(\bar{Q}_d)$ such that $\operatorname{dist}(\bar{Q}_d\setminus\Omega, \operatorname{supp} u) > 0$. Replacing u by a function η in (11.1) where $\eta \in \mathscr{D}(Q_d)$, $\eta = 1$ on $Q_{d/2}$, $|\nabla_j \eta| \leqslant c d^{-j}$, we obtain

$$\|u\|_{L_p(Q_{d/2})} \leqslant C \|\nabla_l (u\eta)\|_{L_p(Q_d)}\,.$$

Hence

$$\|u\|_{L_q(Q_{d/2})} \leqslant cC \sum_{j=0}^{l} d^{j-l} \|\nabla_j u\|_{L_p(Q_d)}\,.$$

Applying the well-known inequality

$$\|u\|_{L_p(Q_d)} \leqslant cd \|\nabla u\|_{L_p(Q_d)} + c\|u\|_{L_p(Q_{d/2})}$$

and the Hölder inequality we obtain

$$\|u\|_{L_q(Q_{d/2})} \leqslant cC \sum_{j=1}^{l} d^{j-l} \|\nabla_j u\|_{L_p(Q_d)} + cCd^{-l+n(q-p)/pq} \|u\|_{L_q(Q_{d/2})}\,.$$

Thus for d so large that $2cCd^{-l+n(q-p)/pq} < 1$ we have

$$\|u\|_{L_q(Q_{d/2})} \leqslant cC \sum_{j=1}^{l} d^{j-l} \|\nabla_j u\|_{L_p(Q_d)}\,.$$

Since

$$\|u\|_{L_q(Q_d)} \leqslant cd^{n(p-q)/pq+1} \|\nabla u\|_{L_p(Q_d)} + c\|u\|_{L_q(Q_{d/2})}$$

then

$$\|u\|_{L_q(Q_d)} \leqslant c(C + d^{l+n(p-q)/pq}) \sum_{j=1}^{l} d^{j-l} \|\nabla_j u\|_{L_p(Q_d)}\,.$$

By the second part of Theorem 10.1.2, we have either

$$\operatorname{Cap}(\bar{Q}_d\setminus\Omega, \mathring{L}_p^l(Q_{2d})) \geqslant \gamma d^{n-pl},$$

where γ satisfies inequality (10.1.1/2), or

$$\operatorname{Cap}(\bar{Q}_d\setminus\Omega, \mathring{L}_p^l(Q_{2d})) \geqslant cd^{np/q}(C + d^{l+n(p-q)/pq})^{-p}\,.$$

The theorem is proved.

Theorem 1 can be rephrased as follows.

Theorem 2. *Any one of the following conditions is necessary and sufficient for the validity of inequality* (11.1).

1) *For some* $d > 0$,

$$\inf_{Q_d} \operatorname{Cap}(\bar{Q}_d\setminus\Omega, \mathring{L}_p^l(R^n)) > 0 \quad \textit{if } n > pl.$$

2) *For some* $d > 0$,

$$\inf_{Q_d} \operatorname{Cap}(\bar{Q}_d\setminus\Omega, \mathring{L}_p^l(Q_{2d})) > 0 \quad \textit{if } n = pl,\ p > 1.$$

3) *The domain Ω does not contain arbitrarily large cubes if* (i) $n<pl$, $p>1$, (ii) $n\leqslant l$, $p=1$, (iii) $n=pl$ *and* $C\Omega$ *is connected.*

Proof. Part 1) follows from Theorem 1 and Proposition 9.11/3, part 2) is contained in Theorem 1. For $n<pl$ the condition

$$\operatorname{Cap}(\bar{Q}_d\backslash\Omega, \mathring{L}_p^l(Q_{2d})) \geqslant c d^{n-pl}$$

is equivalent to $\bar{Q}_d\backslash\Omega \neq \varnothing$ which proves 3) for $n\neq pl$, $p>1$.

Let $n=pl$, $p>1$ and let $C\Omega$ be connected. If Ω contains arbitrarily large cubes, then, obviously, (1) does not hold. Suppose that cubes of arbitrary size can not be placed in Ω and that the number d_0 is so large that any cube Q_d with $d>d_0$ has a nonempty intersection with Ω. Then in $R^n\backslash\Omega$ there exists a continuum which contains points in Q_d and in $R^n\backslash Q_{2d}$. It remains to apply Proposition 9.1.2/1. This concludes the proof.

We present an example of an unbounded domain for which the hypotheses of Theorem are valid.

Example. In each cube $\mathcal{Q}_1^{(i)}$, $i\geqslant 1$, of the coordinate grid with edge length 1 we select a closed subset e_i lying in an s-dimensional plane, $s>n-pl\geqslant 0$. Let $\inf m_s e_i \geqslant \text{const}>0$.

We denote the complement of the set $\bigcup_i e_i$ by Ω. By Proposition 9.1.1/4, we have

$$\operatorname{Cap}(e_i, \mathring{L}_p^l(\mathcal{Q}_2^{(i)})) \geqslant \text{const}>0$$

for any cube $\mathcal{Q}_2^{(i)}$. Hence inequality (11.1) is fulfilled for Ω.

§ 11.5. The Imbedding $\mathring{L}_p^l(\Omega) \subset L_q(\Omega)$ (The Case $p>q\geqslant 1$)

11.5.1. Definitions and Lemmas

We continue the study of inequality (11.1). Here we obtain a necessary and sufficient condition for $q\in[1,p)$. Contrary to the case $q\geqslant p$ considered above, this condition does not depend on q. It means that up to a "small error" the set Ω is the union of cubes $\mathcal{Q}^{(i)}$ with a finite multiplicity of intersection and with edge lengths $\{d_i\}_{i\geqslant 1}$ satisfying

$$\sum_{i=1}^{\infty} d_i^{n+lpq/(p-q)} < \infty . \tag{1}$$

The "smallness" is described in terms of the capacity

$$\operatorname{Cap}_{l-1}(e, \mathring{L}_p^l(Q_{2d})) = \inf_{\Pi\in\mathbb{P}_{l-1}} \inf_{\{u\}} \int_{Q_{2d}} |\nabla_l u|^p dx$$

introduced in 10.3.4. We recall that $\mathbb{P}_{l-1}$ is the set of polynomials of degree not higher than $l-1$ normalized by the equality

$$d^{-n}\int_{Q_d}|\Pi|^p dx = 1$$

and $\{u\}$ is the set of functions in $\overset{\circ}{L}{}_p^l(Q_{2d})$ that are equal to polynomials $\Pi \in \mathbb{P}_{l-1}$ in a neighborhood of the compactum $e \subset \bar{Q}_d$.

We shall use the following assertion which is a particular case ($k = l-1$) of Corollary 10.3.4.

Lemma 1. 1) *Let e be a compact subset of the cube $\bar{Q}_d$ with* $\operatorname{Cap}_{l-1}(e, \overset{\circ}{L}{}_p^l(Q_{2d})) > 0$. *Then*

$$\|u\|_{L_q(Q_d)} \leqslant A \|\nabla_l u\|_{L_p(Q_d)}$$

for any function $u \in C^\infty(Q_d)$ that vanishes in a neighborhood of e. Here $1 \leqslant q \leqslant pn(n-pl)^{-1}$ for $n > pl$; $1 \leqslant q < \infty$ for $n = pl$, $1 \leqslant q \leqslant \infty$ for $n < pl$ and

$$A \leqslant c d^{n/q}[\operatorname{Cap}_{l-1}(e, \overset{\circ}{L}{}_p^l(Q_{2d}))]^{-1/p}.$$

2) *If* (11.1) *is valid for any function $u \in C^\infty(\bar{Q}_d)$ that vanishes in a neighborhood of the compactum $e \subset \bar{Q}_d$ and if*

$$\operatorname{Cap}_{l-1}(e, \overset{\circ}{L}{}_p^l(Q_{2d})) \leqslant c_0 d^{n-pl},$$

where c_0 is a small enough constant, then

$$A \geqslant c d^{n/q}[\operatorname{Cap}_{l-1}(e, \overset{\circ}{L}{}_p^l(Q_{2d}))]^{-1/p}.$$

Definition 1. Let γ be a sufficiently small constant depending only on n, p, l. A compact subset e of the cube $\bar{Q}_d$ is said to be $(p, l, l-1)$-*unessential* if

$$\operatorname{Cap}_{l-1}(e, \overset{\circ}{L}{}_p^l(Q_{2d})) < \gamma d^{n-pl}. \tag{2}$$

Otherwise e is called $(p, l, l-1)$-*essential*.

The collection of $(p, l, l-1)$-unessential subsets of the cube $\bar{Q}_d$ is denoted by $\mathcal{N}_{l-1}(Q_d)$.

Lemma 2. *Let $1 \leqslant q \leqslant p$ and let inequality* (11.1) *be valid for any $u \in C_0^\infty(\Omega)$. Then there exists a constant c that depends only on n, p, q, l and is such that $Q_d \backslash \Omega$ is a $(p, l, l-1)$-essential subset of Q_d for any cube Q_d with edge length d satisfying*

$$d \geqslant c C^{pq/(n(p-q)+lpq)}.$$

Proof. Consider a function $u \in C^\infty(\bar{Q}_d)$ with $\operatorname{dist}(\operatorname{supp} u, \bar{Q}_d \backslash \Omega) > 0$. Let $\eta \in C_0^\infty(Q_1)$, $\eta = 1$ on $Q_{1/2}$ and let $\eta_d(x) = \eta(x/d)$.

The insertion of the function $u\eta_d$ into (11.1) yields

$$\|u\|_{L_q(Q_{d/2})} \leqslant \|u\eta_d\|_{L_q(Q_d)} \leqslant C\|\nabla_l(u\eta_d)\|_{L_p(Q_d)}$$
$$\leqslant cC(\|\nabla_l u\|_{L_p(Q_d)} + d^{-l}\|u\|_{L_p(Q_d)}).$$

Hence from the inequality

(3) $$\|u\|_{L_p(Q_d)} \leqslant cd^l\|\nabla_l u\|_{L_p(Q_d)} + cd^{n(q-p)/pq}\|u\|_{L_q(Q_{d/2})}$$

(see, for instance, Lemma 1.1.11) we obtain

$$\|u\|_{L_q(Q_{d/2})} \leqslant c_0 C(\|\nabla_l u\|_{L_p(Q_d)} + d^{n(q-p)/pq-l}\|u\|_{L_q(Q_{d/2})}).$$

Consequently,

$$\|u\|_{L_q(Q_{d/2})} \leqslant 2c_0 C\|\nabla_l u\|_{L_p(Q_d)}$$

for $2c_0Cd^{n(q-p)/pq-l} < 1$. On the other hand, (3) and the Hölder inequality imply

$$\|u\|_{L_q(Q_d)} \leqslant d^{n(p-q)/pq}\|u\|_{L_p(Q_d)}$$
$$\leqslant c(d^{n(p-q)/pq+l}\|\nabla_l u\|_{L_p(Q_d)} + \|u\|_{L_q(Q_{d/2})}).$$

Therefore

$$\|u\|_{L_q(Q_d)} \leqslant c_1(d^{n(p-q)/pq+l} + C)\|\nabla_l u\|_{L_p(Q_d)}$$

for $2c_0Cd^{n(q-p)/pq-l} < 1$. Suppose, in addition, that $d^{n(p-q)/pq+l} > C$. Then

(4) $$\|u\|_{L_q(Q_d)} \leqslant 2c_1 d^{n(p-q)/pq+l}\|\nabla_l u\|_{L_p(Q_d)}.$$

If $\bar{Q}_d \backslash \Omega \notin \mathscr{N}_{l-1}(Q_d)$ then we have nothing to prove. Otherwise, according to part 2) of Lemma 1, inequality (4) implies

$$cd^{n/q}[\mathrm{Cap}_{l-1}(\bar{Q}_d\backslash\Omega, \mathring{L}_p^l(Q_{2d}))]^{-1/p} \leqslant 2c_1 d^{n(p-q)/pq+l}$$

or, equivalently,

$$\mathrm{Cap}_{l-1}(\bar{Q}_d\backslash\Omega, \mathring{L}_p^l(Q_{2d})) \geqslant (c/2c_1)^p d^{n-pl}.$$

We may always assume that $\gamma \leqslant (c/2c_1)^p$. Therefore $\bar{Q}_d\backslash\Omega \notin \mathscr{N}_{l-1}(Q_d)$. The result follows.

Definition 2. The cube $Q_D = Q_D(x)$ with center $x \in \Omega$ is called *critical* if

$$D = \sup\{d\colon \bar{Q}_d\backslash\Omega \in \mathscr{N}_{l-1}(Q_d)\}.$$

Lemma 2 implies the next corollary.

Corollary. *Let $1 \leqslant q < p$ and let (11.1) be valid for any $u \in C_0^\infty(\Omega)$. Then for any $x \in \Omega$ there exists a critical cube $Q_D(x)$.*

In what follows $\mathcal{Q}^{(i)}$ is an open cube with edges parallel to coordinate axes and with edge lengths d_i, $i = 1, 2, \ldots$. Further, let $c\,\mathcal{Q}^{(i)}$ be a concentric cube with edge length cd_i and with sides parallel to those of the cube $\mathcal{Q}^{(i)}$. Let μ denote a positive constant that depends only on n.

Definition 3. A covering $\{\mathcal{Q}^{(i)}\}_{i \geqslant 1}$ of the set Ω is in *the class* $C_{l,p,q}$ if:

1) $\overline{\mathcal{P}^{(i)}} \backslash \Omega \in \mathcal{N}_{l-1}(\mathcal{P}^{(i)})$, where $\mathcal{P}^{(i)} = \mu\,\mathcal{Q}^{(i)}$;
2) $\mathcal{P}^{(i)} \cap \mathcal{P}^{(j)} = \varnothing$ for $i \neq j$;
3) the multiplicity of the covering $\{\mathcal{Q}^{(i)}\}$ does not exceed a constant that depends only on n;
4) $\overline{\mathcal{Q}^{(i)}} \backslash \Omega \notin \mathcal{N}_{l-1}(\mathcal{Q}^{(i)})$;
5) the series (1) converges.

11.5.2. The Basic Result

Theorem. *Let $1 \leqslant q < p$. Inequality* (11.1) *is valid for all $u \in \mathring{L}_p^l(\Omega)$ if and only if there exists a covering of Ω in $C_{l,p,q}$.*

Proof. Necessity. Let $x \in \Omega$, $Q_d = Q_d(x)$ and let D be the edge length of the critical cube centered at x. We put

$$g(d) = d^{pl-n}\operatorname{Cap}_{l-1}(\bar{Q}_d \backslash \Omega, \mathring{L}_p^l(Q_{2d}))\,.$$

Let d denote a number in the interval $[D, 2D]$ such that $g(d) \geqslant \gamma$ where γ is the constant in (11.5.1/2). Further, let M be the collection of cubes $\{Q_d\}_{x \in \Omega}$.

We show that series (11.5.1/1) converges for any sequence $\{\mathcal{Q}^{(i)}\}$ of disjoint cubes in M.

By Lemma 11.5.1/1, given an arbitrary number $\varepsilon_i > 0$ there exists a function $v_i \in C^\infty(\overline{\mathcal{Q}^{(i)}})$ with $\operatorname{dist}(\operatorname{supp} v_i, \overline{\mathcal{Q}^{(i)}} \backslash \Omega) > 0$ such that

$$\int_{\mathcal{Q}^{(i)}} |\nabla_l v_i|^p dx \leqslant [c d_i^{-n} \operatorname{Cap}_{l-1}(\overline{\mathcal{Q}^{(i)}} \backslash \Omega, \mathring{L}_p^l(2\,\mathcal{Q}^{(i)})) + \varepsilon_i] \int_{\mathcal{Q}^{(i)}} |v_i|^p dx\,.$$

We assume that $\varepsilon_i = \gamma d_i^{-pl}$. Then by (11.5.1/2)

(1) $$\int_{\mathcal{Q}^{(i)}} |\nabla_l v_i|^p dx \leqslant c\gamma d_i^{-pl} \int_{\mathcal{Q}^{(i)}} |v_i|^p dx\,.$$

Estimating the right-hand side by virtue of the inequality

(2) $$\|v_i\|_{L_p(\mathcal{Q}^{(i)})} \leqslant c d_i^l \|\nabla_l v_i\|_{L_p(\mathcal{Q}^{(i)})} + c d_i^{n(p-q)/pq} \|v_i\|_{L_q(\frac{1}{2}\mathcal{Q}^{(i)})}$$

(see Lemma 1.1.11) and using the smallness of the constant γ we arrive at the estimate

(3) $$\int_{\mathcal{Q}^{(i)}} |\nabla_l v_i|^p dx \leqslant c d_i^{n(q-p)/q - pl} \|v_i\|^p_{L_q(\frac{1}{2}\mathcal{Q}^{(i)})}\,.$$

Let $\zeta_i \in \mathscr{D}(\mathscr{Q}^{(i)})$, $\zeta_i = 1$ in $\frac{1}{2}\mathscr{Q}^{(i)}$, $|\nabla_k \zeta_i| \leqslant c d_i^{-k}$, $k=1,2,\ldots$. We introduce the function $u_i = \zeta_i v_i$. It is clear that

$$\|\nabla_l u_i\|_{L_p(\mathscr{Q}^{(i)})} \leqslant c \sum_{k=0}^{l} d^{k-l} \|\nabla_k v_i\|_{L_p(\mathscr{Q}^{(i)})}$$

$$\leqslant c(\|\nabla_l v_i\|_{L_p(\mathscr{Q}^{(i)})} + d^{-l}\|v_i\|_{L_p(\mathscr{Q}^{(i)})}).$$

Applying (2) we obtain

$$\|\nabla_l u_i\|_{L_p(\mathscr{Q}^{(i)})} \leqslant c\|\nabla_l v_i\|_{L_p(\mathscr{Q}^{(i)})} + c d^{n(q-p)/pq - l}\|v_i\|_{L_p(\frac{1}{2}\mathscr{Q}^{(i)})}.$$

This and (3) imply

(4) $$\|\nabla_l u_i\|_{L_p(\mathscr{Q}^{(i)})} \leqslant c d_i^{n(q-p)/pq - l}\|u_i\|_{L_q(\mathscr{Q}^{(i)})}.$$

By the hypothesis of the theorem inequality (11.1) is valid for any $u \in \mathscr{D}(\Omega)$. We normalize u_i by

(5) $$\|u_i\|_{L_q(\mathscr{Q}^{(i)})} = d_i^{n/q - pl/(q-p)}$$

and put $u = \sum_{i=1}^{N} u_i$ into (11.1). Then

$$\left(\sum_{i=1}^{N} \|u_i\|_{L_q(\mathscr{Q}^{(i)})}^q\right)^{p/q} = \left(\int_\Omega |u|^q dx\right)^{p/q} \leqslant C^p \sum_{i=1}^{N} \int_{\mathscr{Q}^{(i)}} |\nabla_l u_i|^p dx.$$

By virtue of (4) we have

$$\left(\sum_{i=1}^{N} \|u_i\|_{L_q(\mathscr{Q}^{(i)})}^q\right)^{p/q} \leqslant c C^p \sum_{i=1}^{N} d_i^{n(q-p)/q - pl}\|u_i\|_{L_q(\mathscr{Q}^{(i)})}^p$$

which together with (5) yields

$$\left(\sum_{i=1}^{N} d_i^{n - plq/(q-p)}\right)^{(p-q)/q} \leqslant c C^p.$$

Thus series (11.5.1/1) converges.

According to Theorem 1.2.1 there exists a sequence of cubes $\{\mathscr{Q}^{(i)}\}_{i\geqslant 1} \subset M$ which forms a covering of Ω of finite multiplicity with $\mu\mathscr{Q}^{(i)} \cap \mu\mathscr{Q}^{(j)} = \varnothing$, $i \neq j$. The convergence of series (11.5.1/1) was proved above (the arguments should be applied to the sequence of mutually disjoint cubes $\mu\mathscr{Q}^{(i)}$). Therefore $\{\mathscr{Q}^{(i)}\}_{i\geqslant 1}$ is a covering in the class $C_{l,p,q}$.

Sufficiency. Let $u \in C_0^\infty(\Omega)$ and let $\{\mathscr{Q}^{(i)}\}_{i\geqslant 1}$ be a covering of Ω in the class $C_{l,p,q}$. Obviously,

$$\int_\Omega |u|^q dx \leqslant \sum_{i\geqslant 1} \lambda_i^{q/p} \lambda_i^{-q/p} \int_{\mathscr{Q}^{(i)}} |u|^q dx$$

where $\lambda_i = d_i^{-pn/q}\,\mathrm{Cap}_{l-1}(\overline{\mathscr{Q}^{(i)}}\setminus\Omega, \mathring{L}_p^l(2\mathscr{Q}^{(i)}))$. Applying the Hölder inequality we obtain

$$\int_\Omega |u|^q dx \leqslant \Big(\sum_{i\geqslant 1} \lambda_i^{q/(p-q)}\Big)^{(p-q)/q} \Big[\sum_{i\geqslant 1} \lambda_i \Big(\int_{\mathscr{Q}^{(i)}} |u|^q dx\Big)^{p/q}\Big]^{q/p}.$$

By Lemma 11.5.1/1

$$c\lambda_i \Big(\int_{\mathscr{Q}^{(i)}} |u|^q dx\Big)^{p/q} \leqslant \int_{\mathscr{Q}^{(i)}} |\nabla_l u|^p dx.$$

This implies

$$\int_\Omega |u|^q dx \leqslant c\Big(\sum_{i\geqslant 1} \lambda_i^{q/(p-q)}\Big)^{(p-q)/p} \Big(\int_\Omega |\nabla_l u|^p dx\Big)^{q/p}$$

and since $\overline{\mathscr{Q}^{(i)}}\setminus\Omega \notin \mathscr{N}(\mathscr{Q}^{(i)})$, then

$$\|u\|_{L_q(\Omega)} \leqslant c\Big(\sum_{i\geqslant 1} d_i^{n+lpq/(p-q)}\Big)^{(p-q)/pq} \|\nabla_l u\|_{L_p(\Omega)}. \tag{6}$$

This completes the proof.

In the proof of necessity we incidentally obtained the following necessary condition for the validity of inequality (11.1).

Proposition. *Let $\{\mathscr{Q}^{(i)}\}_{i\geqslant 1}$ be a sequence of disjoint cubes in Ω. Then the divergence of series* (11.5.1/1) *is necessary for the validity of* (11.1) *with $q<p$.*

11.5.3. The Imbedding $\mathring{L}_p^l(\Omega) \subset L_q(\Omega)$ for an "Infinite Funnel"

Example. Consider the domain

$$\Omega = \{x = (x', x_n) : x' = (x_1, \ldots, x_{n-1}),\ x_n > 0,\ |x'| < \varphi(x_n)\},$$

where φ is a bounded decreasing function.

We shall show that (11.1) with $p > q \geqslant 1$ holds if and only if

$$\int_0^\infty [\varphi(t)]^\alpha dt < \infty$$

where $\alpha = n-1+lpq/(p-q)$.

Proof. Let $\{a_i\}$ and $\{b_i\}$ be two number sequences defined as follows:

$$a_0 = 0; \quad a_{i+1} - a_i = 2\varphi(a_i), \qquad i\geqslant 1,$$

$$b_0 = 0; \quad b_{i+1} - b_i = \frac{2}{\sqrt{n-1}}\varphi(b_i), \qquad i\geqslant 1.$$

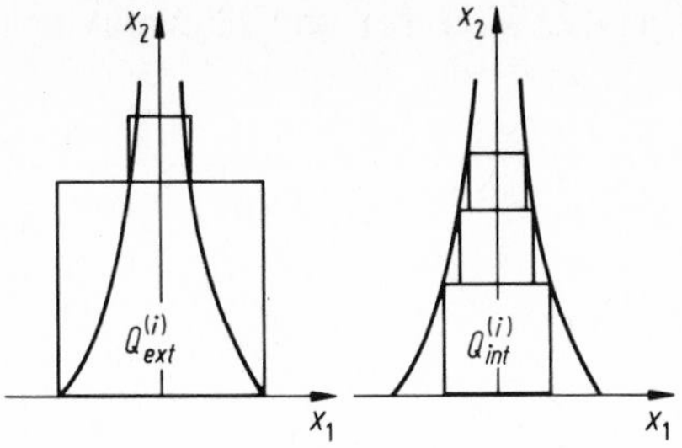

Fig. 25

Clearly $a_i, b_i \to 0$ as $i \to \infty$, and the differences $a_{i+1} - a_i$, $b_{i+1} - b_i$ decrease.

Define two sequences of cubes:

$$\mathscr{Q}_{\text{ext}}^{(i)} = \{a_i < x_n < a_{i+1},\ 2|x_\nu| < a_{i+1} - a_i,\ 1 \leqslant \nu \leqslant n-1\},$$

$$\mathscr{Q}_{\text{int}}^{(i)} = \{b_i < x_n < b_{i+1},\ 2|x_\nu| < b_{i+1} - b_i,\ 1 \leqslant \nu \leqslant n-1\}$$

(see Fig. 25). The cubes $\mathscr{Q}_{\text{ext}}^{(i)}$ cover Ω. All $(n-1)$-dimensional faces of $\mathscr{Q}_{\text{ext}}^{(i)}$ except two of them are contained in $R^n \setminus \Omega$ and

$$\operatorname{Cap}(\overline{\mathscr{Q}_{\text{ext}}^{(i)}} \setminus \Omega, \mathring{L}_p^1(2\,\mathscr{Q}_{\text{ext}}^{(i)})) \geqslant c(b_{i+1} - b_i)^{n-p}.$$

This along with Proposition 10.3.5 implies that $\mathscr{Q}_{\text{ext}}^{(i)} \setminus \Omega$ is a $(p, l, l-1)$-essential subset of $\mathscr{Q}_{\text{ext}}^{(i)}$.

We suppose that the integral (1) converges and show the convergence of series (11.5.1/1). In fact,

$$\sum_{i=0}^{\infty} (a_{i+1} - a_i)^{\alpha+1} \leqslant \sum_{i=1}^{\infty} (a_{i+1} - a_i)^{\alpha} (a_i - a_{i-1}) + a_1^{\alpha+1}$$

$$= \sum_{i=1}^{\infty} [\varphi(a_i)]^{\alpha} (a_i - a_{i-1}) + [\varphi(0)]^{\alpha+1}.$$

Since φ does not increase then

$$[\varphi(a_i)]^{\alpha} (a_i - a_{i-1}) \leqslant \int_{a_{i-1}}^{a_i} [\varphi(t)]^{\alpha} dt.$$

Hence

$$\sum_{i=0}^{\infty} (a_{i+1} - a_i)^{\alpha+1} \leqslant [\varphi(0)]^{\alpha+1} + \int_0^{\infty} [\varphi(t)]^{\alpha} dt$$

and the sufficient condition in Theorem 11.5.2 follows.

We prove the necessity of (1). Suppose

$$\int_0^{\infty} [\varphi(t)]^{\alpha} dt = \infty$$

and let series (11.5.1/1) converge for any sequence of disjoint cubes in Ω. By virtue of the monotonicity of φ we have

$$\sum_{i=1}^{\infty}(b_i-b_{i-1})^{\alpha+1} \geqslant \sum_{i=1}^{\infty}(b_i-b_{i-1})^{\alpha}(b_{i+1}-b_i)$$

$$= \sum_{i=1}^{\infty}[\varphi(b_i)]^{\alpha}(b_{i+1}-b_i)$$

$$\geqslant \sum_{i=1}^{\infty}\int_{b_i}^{b_{i+1}}[\varphi(t)]^{\alpha}dt.$$

Consequently series (11.5.1/1) diverges for the sequence of cubes $\mathcal{Q}_{\text{int}}^{(i)}$. Thus we arrived at a contradiction. It remains to apply the proposition of the present subsection.

§ 11.6. The Compactness of the Imbedding $\mathring{L}_p^l(\Omega) \subset L_q(\Omega)$

In this section we obtain necessary and sufficient conditions for the compactness of the imbedding operator of $\mathring{L}_p^l(\Omega)$ into $L_q(\Omega)$, $p, q \geqslant 1$.

11.6.1. The Case $p \leqslant q$

Theorem. *The set*

$$\mathfrak{F} = \{u \in \mathcal{D}(\Omega): \|\nabla_l u\|_{L_p(\Omega)} \leqslant 1\}$$

is relatively compact in $L_q(\Omega)$ if and only if any one of the following conditions holds:

1) *For any $d > 0$*

$$\lim_{\varrho\to\infty} \inf_{Q_d \subset R^n \setminus B_\varrho} \operatorname{Cap}(\bar{Q}_d \setminus \Omega, \mathring{L}_p^l(\Omega)) > k d^{n-pl} \tag{1}$$

if $n > pl$. Here k is a positive constant that is independent of d.

2) *For any $d > 0$*

$$\lim_{\varrho\to\infty} \inf_{Q_d \subset R^n \setminus B_\varrho} \operatorname{Cap}(\bar{Q}_d \setminus \Omega, \mathring{L}_p^l(Q_{2d})) > k \tag{2}$$

if $n = pl$.

3) *The set Ω does not contain an infinite sequence of disjoint cubes if $pl > n$ or $pl = n$ and the set $R^n \setminus \Omega$ is connected.*

Proof. Sufficiency. First we note that by Propositions 9.1.1/3, 9.1.2/1 and Corollary 9.1.1 the conditions of the theorem are equivalent to

(3) $$\lim_{\varrho\to\infty} \inf_{Q_d \subset R^n\setminus B_\varrho} \operatorname{Cap}(\bar{Q}_d\setminus\Omega, \mathring{L}_p^l(Q_{2d})) > k d^{n-pl}$$

(cf. the proof of Theorem 11.4.2/1). This and the first part of Theorem 11.4.2/1 imply (11.1) for all $u\in\mathscr{D}(\Omega)$ and hence the boundedness of $\mathfrak{F}$ in $W_p^l(\Omega)$.

Since any bounded subset of $W_p^l(\Omega)$ is compact in $L_q(\Omega\setminus B_\varrho)$, it suffices to prove the inequality

(4) $$\|u\|_{L_q(\Omega\setminus B_\varrho)} \leqslant \varepsilon \|u\|_{W_p^l(\Omega)}$$

with arbitrary positive ε and sufficiently large ϱ.

Let $\eta\in C^\infty(R^n)$, $\eta=0$ in $B_{1/2}$, $\eta=1$ outside B_1 and $\eta_\varrho(x)=\eta(x/\varrho)$. We denote by d a small number which depends on ε and which will be specified later. According to (3) there exists a sufficiently large radius $\varrho(d)$ such that

$$d^{pl-n}\operatorname{Cap}(\bar{Q}_d\setminus\Omega, \mathring{L}_p^l(Q_{2d})) > k d^{n-pl}$$

for $\varrho>\varrho(d)$ and for all cubes $Q_d\subset R^n\setminus B_{\varrho/4}$. Hence by inequality (11.1) with Ω replaced by $\Omega\setminus B_{\varrho/2}$ we have

$$\|u\eta_\varrho\|_{L_q(\Omega\setminus B_{\varrho/2})} \leqslant c k^{-l} d^{lp-n+np/q} \|\nabla_l(u\eta_\varrho)\|_{L_p(\Omega\setminus B_{\varrho/2})}.$$

We could choose d beforehand to satisfy

$$c k^{-l} d^{lp-n+np/q} < \varepsilon .$$

Then

$$\|u\|_{L_q(\Omega\setminus B_\varrho)} \leqslant c\varepsilon \sum_{j=0}^{l} \varrho^{j-l} \|\nabla_j u\|_{L_p(\Omega)} \leqslant c\varepsilon \|u\|_{W_p^l(\Omega)}$$

which completes the proof of the first part of the theorem.

Necessity. Let ε be any positive number. Suppose the set $\mathfrak{F}$ is relatively compact in $L_q(\Omega)$. Then there exists a number $\varrho=\varrho(\varepsilon)$ so large that

$$\|u\|_{L_q(\Omega)} \leqslant \varepsilon \|\nabla_l u\|_{L_p(\Omega)}$$

for all $u\in\mathscr{D}(\Omega\setminus\bar{B}_\varrho)$. Let Q_d denote any cube with edge length d situated outside the ball B_ϱ. In the proof of the second part of Theorem 11.4.2/1 it was shown that either

$$\operatorname{Cap}(\bar{Q}_d\setminus\Omega, \mathring{L}_p^l(Q_{2d})) \geqslant \gamma d^{n-pl},$$

where γ is a constant satisfying inequality (10.1.1/2), or

$$\operatorname{Cap}(\bar{Q}_d\setminus\Omega, \mathring{L}_p^l(Q_{2d})) \geqslant c d^{np/q}(\varepsilon + d^{l+n(p-q)/pq})^{-p}.$$

The theorem is proved.

11.6.2. The Case $p>q$

The following assertion shows that the imbedding operator of $\mathring{L}_p^l(\Omega)$ into $L_q(\Omega)$ is compact and continuous simultaneously for $p>q\geqslant 1$.

Theorem. *The set*

$$\mathfrak{F}=\{u\in\mathscr{D}(\Omega):\|\nabla_l u\|_{L_p(\Omega)}\leqslant 1\}$$

is relatively compact in $L_q(\Omega)$, $1\leqslant q<p$, if and only if there exists a covering of Ω in the class $C_{l,p,q}$.

Proof. The necessity follows immediately from Theorem 11.5.2. We prove the sufficiency. Let $\{\mathscr{Q}^{(i)}\}_{i\geqslant 1}$ be a covering of Ω in the class $C_{l,p,q}$, let d_i be the edge length of $\mathscr{Q}^{(i)}$, let ε be a positive number and let N be an integer so large that

$$\sum_{i\geqslant N+1} d_i^{n+lpq/(p-q)}<\varepsilon^{pq/(p-q)}. \tag{1}$$

We denote the radius of a ball $B_\varrho=\{x:|x|<\varrho\}$ such that $B_{\varrho/4}$ contains the cubes $\mathscr{Q}^{(1)},\dots,\mathscr{Q}^{(N)}$ by ϱ. By (11.5.2/6) we obtain

$$\|u\eta_\varrho\|_{L_q(\Omega\backslash B_{\varrho/2})}\leqslant c\left(\sum_{i\geqslant N+1} d_i^{n+lpq/(p-q)}\right)^{(p-q)/pq}\|\nabla_l(u\eta_\varrho)\|_{L_p(\Omega\backslash B_{\varrho/2})},$$

where η_ϱ is the same function as in the proof of Theorem 11.6.1. This and (1) immediately imply that

$$\|u\|_{L_q(\Omega\backslash B_\varrho)}\leqslant\varepsilon\|\nabla_l u\|_{L_p(\Omega)}+c(\varrho)\|u\|_{W_p^{l-1}(\Omega\cap(B_\varrho\backslash B_{\varrho/2}))}.$$

Now the result follows from the compactness of the imbedding of $\mathring{L}_p^l(\Omega)\cap L_q(\Omega)$ into $W_p^{l-1}(\Omega\cap(B_\varrho\backslash B_{\varrho/2}))$.

§ 11.7. Application to the Dirichlet Problem for a Strongly Elliptic Operator

Let l be a positive integer and let i, j be multi-indices of orders $|i|, |j|\leqslant l$. Let a_{ij} be bounded measurable functions in Ω such that $a_{ij}=\overline{a_{ij}}$ for any pair (i,j). Suppose

$$\sum_{|i|=|j|=l} a_{ij}(x)\zeta_i\bar{\zeta}_j\geqslant\gamma\sum_{|j|=l}|\zeta_j|^2,\qquad \gamma=\text{const}>0 \tag{1}$$

for all complex numbers ζ_i, $|i|=l$, and for almost all $x\in\Omega$.

We define the quadratic form

$$\mathfrak{A}(T,T)=\int_\Omega\sum_{|i|=|j|=l} a_{ij}D^iT\overline{D^jT}dx$$

on the space $L_2^l(\Omega)$. Obviously, the seminorms $\mathfrak{A}(T,T)^{1/2}$ and $\|\nabla_l T\|_{L_2(\Omega)}$ are equivalent.

Below we apply the results of previous sections to the study of the Dirichlet problem for the operator

$$Au = (-1)^l \sum_{|i|=|j|=l} D^j(a_{ij}D^i u).$$

11.7.1. The Dirichlet Problem with Nonhomogeneous Boundary Data

Lemma. *Let $\mathring{L}_2^l(\Omega)$ be a subspace of $\mathscr{D}'(\Omega)$. Then any function $T \in L_2^l(\Omega)$ can be expressed in the form*

(1) $$T = u + h,$$

where $u \in \mathring{L}_2^l(\Omega)$, $h \in L_2^l(\Omega)$ and $Ah = 0$ (in the sense of distributions).

Proof. We equip $\mathring{L}_2^l(\Omega)$ with the norm $[\mathfrak{A}(u,u)]^{1/2}$. Let $T = u_i + h_i\ (i=1,2)$ be two decompositions of the form (1). Since $A(h_1 - h_2) = 0$ and $(u_1 - u_2) \in \mathring{L}_2^l(\Omega)$ then $\mathfrak{A}(u_1 - u_2, h_1 - h_2) = 0$. Consequently, $\mathfrak{A}(u_1 - u_2, u_1 - u_2) = 0$ and $u_1 = u_2$. The uniqueness of the representation (1) is proved.

The space $L_2^l(\Omega)$ becomes the Hilbert space provided we equip it with any of the inner products

$$\mathfrak{A}_N(T,G) = \mathfrak{A}(T,G) + N^{-1}(T,G)_{L_2(\omega)}, \quad N = 1,2,\ldots,$$

where ω is a nonempty open bounded set, $\bar{\omega} \subset \Omega$. Let u_N denote the projection of the function $T \in L_2^l(\Omega)$ onto $\mathring{L}_2^l(\Omega)$ in the space $L_2^l(\Omega)$ with the norm $[\mathfrak{A}_N(G,G)]^{1/2}$ (by hypothesis, $\mathring{L}_2^l(\Omega)$ is a subspace of $L_2^l(\Omega)$). Then

(2) $$\mathfrak{A}_N(T - u_N, \varphi) = 0.$$

In § 11.3 we have noted that the imbedding $\mathring{L}_2^l(\Omega) \subset \mathscr{D}'(\Omega)$ implies the imbedding $\mathring{L}_2^l(\Omega) \subset L_2(\Omega, \mathrm{loc})$ and, hence, the estimate

$$\|u_N\|_{L_2(\omega)}^2 \leqslant C\mathfrak{A}(u_N, u_N),$$

where C is a constant that is independent of u_N. This and the obvious inequality $\mathfrak{A}(u_N,u_N) \leqslant \mathfrak{A}_N(T,T)$ show that the sequence u_N converges weakly in $\mathring{L}_2^l(\Omega)$ and in $L_2(\Omega)$ to some $u \in \mathring{L}_2^l(\Omega)$. Passing to the limit in (2) we obtain that $h = T - u$ satisfies $\mathfrak{A}(h,\varphi) = 0$, where φ is any function in $\mathring{L}_2^l(\Omega)$. The lemma is proved.

Representation (1) enables us to find the solution of the equation $Ah = 0$ which "has the same boundary values as T along with its derivatives of order up to $l-1$", i.e. to solve the Dirichlet problem for the equation $Ah = 0$. Therefore, the conditions for the imbedding $\mathring{L}_2^l(\Omega) \subset \mathscr{D}'(\Omega)$ in Theorem 11.2 imply criteria for the solvability of the Dirichlet problem formulated in terms of the $(2,l)$-capacity. Namely, we have the following theorem.

Theorem. *In order for any function $T \in L_2^l(\Omega)$ to be represented in the form* (1) *it is necessary and sufficient that any one of the following conditions be valid:* 1) $n > 2l$; 2) $C\Omega \neq \varnothing$ *for odd* n, $n < 2l$; 3) $C\Omega$ *is a set of the positive* $(2, n/2)$*-capacity for* $n = 2l$; 4) $C\Omega$ *is not contained in an* $(n-1)$*-dimensional hyperplane or is a set of positive* $(2, n/2)$*-capacity for even* $n < 2l$.

11.7.2. The Dirichlet Problem with Homogeneous Boundary Data

The results of §§ 11.4, 11.5 give conditions for the unique solvability in $\mathring{L}_2^l(\Omega)$ of the first boundary value problem for the equation $Au = f$ with $f \in L_r(\Omega)$.

We first formulate the problem. Let f be a given function in $L_{q'}(\Omega)$, $q' = q(q-1)^{-1}$, $1 < q \leqslant \infty$. We require a distribution $T \in \mathring{L}_2^l(\Omega)$ that satisfies $AT = f$.

The following fact is well known.

Lemma. *The Dirichlet problem is solvable for any* $f \in L_{q'}(\Omega)$ *if and only if*

$$\|u\|_{L_q(\Omega)} \leqslant C \|\nabla_l u\|_{L_2(\Omega)} \tag{1}$$

for all $u \in \mathscr{D}(\Omega)$.

Proof. Sufficiency. Since

$$|(f, u)| \leqslant \|f\|_{L_{q'}(\Omega)} \|u\|_{L_q(\Omega)} \leqslant C \|f\|_{L_{q'}(\Omega)} \|\nabla_l u\|_{L_2(\Omega)}$$

for all $u \in \mathscr{D}(\Omega)$, the functional (f, u) defined on the linear set $\mathscr{D}(\Omega)$, which is dense in $L_2^l(\Omega)$, is bounded in $\mathring{L}_2^l(\Omega)$. So by the Riesz theorem there exists $T \in \mathring{L}_2^l(\Omega)$ such that

$$(f, u) = \mathfrak{A}(T, u)$$

for all $u \in \mathscr{D}(\Omega)$. This is equivalent to $AT = f$.

Necessity. Any $u \in \mathscr{D}(\Omega)$ with $\|u\|_{L_2^l(\Omega)} = 1$ generates the functional (v, f), defined on $L_{q'}(\Omega)$. Since to any $f \in L_{q'}(\Omega)$ there corresponds a solution Tf of the Dirichlet problem then $|(v, f)| \leqslant \|\nabla_l Tf\|_{L_2(\Omega)}$. Consequently, the functionals (v, f) are bounded for any $f \in L_{q'}(\Omega)$. Hence the norms of (v, f) are totally bounded, which is equivalent to (1). The lemma is proved.

Inequality (1) can not be valid for all u with the same constant if either $q \geqslant 2n(n-2l)^{-1}$, $n > 2l$, or if $q = \infty$, $n = 2l$. On the other hand, for $q = 2n(n-2l)^{-1}$, $n > 2l$, inequality (1) is fulfilled for arbitrary domain Ω. The other cases were studied in §§ 11.4, 11.5. For $q \geqslant 2$, Theorem 11.4.2/1 together with the preceding lemma leads to the following theorem.

Theorem 1. *The Dirichlet problem is solvable in* $\mathring{L}_2^l(\Omega)$ *for all* $f \in L_{q'}(\Omega)$ $(2 \geqslant q' > 2n/(n+2l)$, $n \geqslant 2l$ *or for* $2 \geqslant q' \geqslant 1$, $n < 2l)$ *if and only if any one of the following conditions is valid:*

1) *there exists a constant $d>0$ such that*

$$\inf_{Q_d} \operatorname{Cap}(\bar{Q}_d \setminus \Omega, \mathring{L}_2^l) > 0 \quad \text{for } n>2l,$$

2) *there exists a constant $d>0$ such that*

$$\inf_{Q_d} \operatorname{Cap}(\bar{Q}_d \setminus \Omega, \mathring{L}_2^l(Q_{2d})) > 0 \quad \text{for } n=2l,$$

3) *the domain Ω does not contain arbitrarily large cubes if $n<2l$ or if $n=2l$ and $R^n \setminus \Omega$ is connected.*

For $q<2$, Theorems 11.5.2 and Lemma imply the following theorem.

Theorem 2. *The Dirichlet problem for the equation $AT=f$ is solvable in $\mathring{L}_2^l(\Omega)$ for all $f \in L_{q'}(\Omega)$, $1<q<2$, if and only if there exists a covering of the set Ω belonging to the class $C_{l,2,q}$ and having a finite multiplicity.*

11.7.3. The Discreteness of the Spectrum of the Dirichlet Problem

The quadratic form $\mathfrak{A}(u,u)$ generates a selfadjoint operator A in $L_2(\Omega)$. By the well-known Rellich theorem, a necessary and sufficient condition for the discreteness of the spectrum of this operator is the compactness of the imbedding $\mathring{L}_2^l(\Omega) \subset L_2(\Omega)$. So Theorem 11.6.1 implies the following criterion for the discreteness of the spectrum of A stated in terms of the $(2,l)$-capacity.

Theorem. *The spectrum of the operator A is discrete if and only if any one of the following conditions is valid:*

1) *For any constant $d>0$*

$$\lim_{\varrho\to\infty} \inf_{Q_d \subset R^n \setminus B_\varrho} \operatorname{Cap}(\bar{Q}_d \setminus \Omega, L_2^l) > k d^{n-2l}$$

if $n>2l$.

Here and in what follows k is a positive number which does not exceed d.

2) *For any $d>0$*

$$\lim_{\varrho\to\infty} \inf_{Q_d \subset R^n \setminus B_\varrho} \operatorname{Cap}(\bar{Q}_d \setminus \Omega, \mathring{L}_2^l(Q_{2d})) > k$$

if $n=2l$.

3) *The domain Ω does not contain an infinite sequence of disjoint congruent cubes if $n<2l$, or if $n=2l$ and $R^n \setminus \Omega$ is connected.*

11.7.4. The Dirichlet Problem for a Nonselfadjoint Operator

Consider the quadratic form

$$\mathfrak{B}(u,u) = \int_\Omega \sum_{|i|,|j|\leq l} a_{ij}(x) D^i u \overline{D^j u}\, dx$$

(where i, j are n-dimensional multi-indices).

We state the Dirichlet problem with homogeneous boundary data for the operator

$$Bu = \sum_{|i|, |j| \leqslant l} (-1)^{|j|} D^j (a_{ij}(x) D^i u)$$

in the following way. Let f be a continuous functional on $\mathring{W}_2^l(\Omega)$. We require an element in $\mathring{W}_2^l(\Omega)$ such that

$$\mathfrak{B}(u, \varphi) = (\varphi, f), \tag{1}$$

where the function $\varphi \in \mathring{W}_2^l(\Omega)$ is arbitrary.

The next assertion is a particular case of a well-known theorem of Hilbert space theory (see, for instance, Lions and Magenes [132], Chapter 2, § 9.1).

Lemma. *If*

$$\| \varphi \|^2_{W_2^l(\Omega)} \leqslant C | \mathfrak{B}(\varphi, \varphi) |$$

for all $\varphi \in \mathring{W}_2^l(\Omega)$ *then the Dirichlet problem* (1) *is uniquely solvable.*

Let Γ denote a positive constant such that

$$\operatorname{Re} \sum_{\substack{|i|, |j| \leqslant l, \\ |i| + |j| < 2l}} a_{ij}(x) \zeta_i \overline{\zeta_j} \geqslant -\Gamma \Big(\sum_{|i| \leqslant l} |\zeta_i|^2 \Big)^{1/2} \Big(\sum_{|j| < l} |\zeta_j|^2 \Big)^{1/2}$$

for all complex numbers ζ_i, $|i| \leqslant l$, and introduce the set function

$$\lambda_\Omega = \inf \{ \| \nabla_l u \|^2_{L_2(\Omega)} : \| u \|_{L_2(\Omega)} = 1, u \in \mathring{L}_2^l(\Omega) \}.$$

Theorem. *Let*

$$\delta_{2,l}(\Omega) < c_0 \gamma / \Gamma \quad \text{if } n \geqslant 2l,$$

$$\delta(\Omega) < c_0 \gamma / \Gamma \quad \text{if } n < 2l,$$

where $\delta_{2,l}(\Omega)$ *is the* $(2, l)$*-inner diameter of* Ω, $\delta(\Omega)$ *is the inner diameter of* Ω, γ *is the constant in* (11.7/1) *and* c_0 *is a constant that depends only on* n, l. *Then the Dirichlet problem is uniquely solvable.*

Proof. Obviously,

$$\mathfrak{A}(u, u) - \operatorname{Re} \mathfrak{B}(u, u) \leqslant \Gamma \Big(\sum_{k=0}^{l} \| \nabla_k u \|^2_{L_2(\Omega)} \Big)^{1/2} \Big(\sum_{k=0}^{l-1} \| \nabla_k u \|^2_{L_2(\Omega)} \Big)^{1/2}.$$

Using the inequality

$$\| \nabla_k u \|_{L_2(\Omega)} \leqslant c \| \nabla_l u \|^{k/l}_{L_2(\Omega)} \| u \|^{1-k/l}_{L_2(\Omega)}, \quad u \in \mathring{L}_2^l(\Omega),$$

we obtain

$$\mathfrak{A}(u, u) - \operatorname{Re} \mathfrak{B}(u, u) \leqslant \frac{\gamma}{2} \| \nabla_l u \|^2_{L_2(\Omega)} + \frac{c\Gamma^{2l}}{\gamma^{2l-1}} \| u \|^2_{L_2(\Omega)}.$$

Consequently,

$$\text{(2)} \qquad \operatorname{Re}\mathfrak{B}(u,u) \geqslant \frac{\gamma}{4}\|\nabla u\|^2_{L_2(\Omega)} + \left(\lambda_\Omega \frac{\gamma}{4} - \frac{c\Gamma^{2l}}{\gamma^{2l-1}}\right)\|u\|^2_{L_2(\Omega)}.$$

It remains to note that by Theorem 11.4.1

$$\lambda_\Omega \sim \begin{cases} \delta_{2,l}(\Omega)^{-2l} & \text{if } n \geqslant 2l, \\ \delta(\Omega)^{-2l} & \text{if } n < 2l. \end{cases}$$

The theorem is proved.

Thus *the Dirichlet problem is uniquely solvable for domains with small $(2,l)$-inner diameter for $n \geqslant 2l$ or with small inner diameter for $n < 2l$.*

§ 11.8. Comments to Chapter 11

§ 11.1, 11.2. In [51] Deny and Lions studied the orthogonal projection method with respect to the Dirichlet problem for the Laplace operator. In particular, they gave the following description of the sets Ω satisfying $\mathring{L}_2^1(\Omega) \subset \mathscr{D}'(\Omega)$. This imbedding occurs for $n \geqslant 3$ for arbitrary set Ω, for $n = 2$ if the Wiener capacity of $C\Omega$ is positive and for $n = 1$ if $C\Omega \neq \varnothing$. The proof by Deny and Lions uses the thin potential theory.

For any integer l the problem of the imbedding $\mathring{L}_2^l(\Omega) \subset \mathscr{D}'(\Omega)$ was solved by Hörmander and Lions [100] using a different approach. Their result is formulated in terms of $(2,l)$-polarity. In the author's paper [147] it was noted that the conditions of the Hörmander and Lions theorem can be restated in terms of the l-harmonic capacity.

The proof of Theorem 11.2 is a modification of the approach due to Hörmander and Lions [100]. In the main, our presentation follows the paper by Hvoles and the author [174], where the next result is obtained.

Let $p > 1$, $l > 0$ and let $\mathring{h}_p^l(\Omega)$ be the completion of $\mathscr{D}(\Omega)$ with respect to the norm $\|(-\Delta)^{l/2}u\|_{L_p(R^n)}$ (in particular, $\mathring{h}_p^l(\Omega) = \mathring{L}_p^l(\Omega)$ for integer l).

Theorem. *The space $\mathring{h}_p^l(\Omega)$ is imbedded into $\mathscr{D}'(\Omega)$ if and only if any one of the following conditions is valid:*

1) $n > pl$; 2) $\operatorname{cap}(C\Omega, H_p^l) > 0$, *if* $n = pl$; 3) $C\Omega \neq \varnothing$ *if* $n < pl$ *and* $l - n/p$ *is fractional;* 4) *either* $\operatorname{cap}(C\Omega, H_p^{n/p}) > 0$ *or* $C\Omega$ *does not lie in a* $(n-1)$*-dimensional hyperplane, if* $n < pl$, $l - n/p$ *is fractional.*

§§ 11.3 – 11.6. The results of these sections are due to the author [156, 158, 161].

§ 11.7. The presented scheme of applications of integral inequalities to boundary value problems in variational form is well known (see, for instance, Deny and Lions [51], Lions and Magenes [132]).

The criterion for the discreteness of the spectrum of the Dirichlet problem for the Laplace operator (Theorem 11.7.3 for $l = 1$) was found by Molčanov [189]. For any integer l, Theorem 11.7.3 was proved by the author [145]. Similar results for more general operators are presented in § 12.3.

The unique solvability of the Dirichlet problem for the operator B (see 11.7.4) in domains with small $(2, l)$-inner diameter (which is understood in a sense different from ours) was shown by Kondrat'ev [115, 116] (see Comments to § 10.2). Among other applications of results of Chapter 10 to the theory of elliptic equations we list the following: theorems of Phragmèn-Lindelöf type for elliptic equations of arbitrary order (see Landis [124]), estimates for eigenvalues of the operator of the Dirichlet problem in an unbounded domain (see Rosenbljum [221] and Otelbaev [207, 208]), conditions for the Wiener regularity of a boundary point with respect to the polyharmonic equation (see Maz'ja [164], Maz'ja and Dončev [169]).

Theorems proved in 11.7.2 are also valid for quasilinear elliptic equations. Here is an example of such a generalization (see Maz'ja [154]).

Consider the equation

$$Au \equiv (-1)^l D^\alpha(a_\alpha(x, \nabla_l u)) = f(x)\,, \qquad x \in \Omega\,,$$

where f is summable in Ω, α is a multi-index of order l, $D^\alpha = \partial^l/\partial x_1^{\alpha_1} \dots \partial x_n^{\alpha_n}$. We take the sum over identical indices. All the functions are real.

Suppose the functions a_α are continuous for almost all $x \in \Omega$ with respect to the totality of all other variables and let them be measurable in x for any values of these variables. Besides, we assume that

$$a_\alpha(x, v)\, v_\alpha \geqslant |v|^p\,, \qquad \sum_\alpha |a_\alpha(x, v)| \leqslant \lambda\, |v|^{p-1}$$

for any vector $v = \{v_\alpha\}$ and some $p > 1$. We assume that the "monotonicity" condition

$$[a_\alpha(x, v) - a_\alpha(x, w)]\,(v_\alpha - w_\alpha) > 0$$

is fulfilled for $w \neq v$.

A function $u \in \mathring{L}_p^l(\Omega) \cap L(\Omega, \mathrm{loc})$ is called a solution of the Dirichlet problem

$$Au = f \quad \text{in } \Omega\,, \qquad u = 0 \quad \text{on } \partial\Omega$$

if

$$\int_\Omega a_\alpha(x, \nabla_l u)\, D^\alpha \varphi\, dx = \int_\Omega f \varphi\, dx$$

for all $\varphi \in \mathscr{D}(\Omega)$.

By virtue of the Leray and Lions theorem [127], we can show that this problem is solvable for any $f \in L_{q'}(\Omega)$, $1 \leqslant q' < \infty$, $1/q + 1/q' = 1$ if and only if $\mathring{L}_p^l(\Omega) \subset L_q(\Omega)$. Clearly this result and the theorems in §§ 11.4, 11.5 imply explicit necessary and sufficient conditions for the solvability of this problem.

Chapter 12. The Imbedding $\overset{\circ}{L}{}_p^l(\Omega, \nu) \subset W_r^m(\Omega)$

In this chapter we denote by $\overset{\circ}{L}{}_p^l(\Omega, \nu)$ the completion of $\mathscr{D}(\Omega)$ with respect to the metric

$$\| \nabla_l u \|_{L_p(\Omega)} + \| u \|_{L_p(\Omega, \nu)} ,$$

where $p > 1$, Ω is an open set in R^n and ν is a measure in Ω.

For instance, in § 12.2 we show that the space $\mathscr{D}(\Omega)$ equipped with the norm $\overset{\circ}{L}{}_p^l(R^n, \nu)$ is continuously imbedded into $L_p(R^n)$ if and only if

$$\inf_{\{e\}} \nu(Q_d \backslash e) \geqslant \text{const} > 0 \tag{1}$$

for any cube Q_d with sufficiently large edge length d. Here $\{e\}$ is the collection of all subsets of the cube Q_d with small enough capacity $\operatorname{cap}(e, \overset{\circ}{L}{}_p^l(Q_{2d}))$. The corresponding imbedding operator is compact if and only if condition (1) holds and $\inf_{\{e\}} \nu(Q_d \backslash e)$ tends to infinity as the cube Q_d tends to infinity (§ 12.3).

In § 12.4 we study the closability of certain imbedding operators. One of the theorems in that section asserts that the identity operator defined on $\mathscr{D}(\Omega)$ and acting from $L_p(\Omega)$ into $\overset{\circ}{L}{}_p^l(\Omega)$ is closable if and only if the measure ν is absolutely continuous with respect to the (p, l)-capacity. In § 12.5 the previously proved criteria are reformulated for $p = 2$ as necessary and sufficient conditions for the positive definiteness and for the discreteness of the spectrum of the selfadjoint elliptic operator generated by the quadratic form

$$\int_\Omega \sum_{|\alpha| = |\beta| = l} a_{\alpha\beta}(x) D^\alpha u \overline{D^\beta u}\, dx + \int_\Omega |u|^2 d\nu , \qquad u \in \mathscr{D}(\Omega) .$$

§ 12.1. Auxiliary Assertions

Lemma 1. *For any* $u \in C^\infty(\bar{Q}_d)$ *we have*

$$\|u\|^p_{L_p(Q_d)} \leqslant c\gamma^{-1} d^{pl} |u|^p_{p,l,Q_d} + \frac{c d^n}{\inf \nu(Q_d \backslash e)} \|u\|^p_{L_p(Q_d, \nu)} , \tag{1}$$

where ν *is a measure in* Q_d, *the infimum is taken over all compacta* $e \subset \bar{Q}_d$ *with* $\operatorname{cap}(e, \overset{\circ}{L}{}_p^l(Q_{2d})) \leqslant \lambda d^{n-pl}$ *(*λ *is an arbitrary constant) and the seminorm* $|\cdot|_{p,l,Q_d}$ *is that introduced in* 10.1.2.

Proof. We assume that the average value $\bar{u}_{Q_d}$ of the function u in Q_d is nonnegative and put

$$2\tau = d^{-n/p} \| u \|_{L_p(Q_d)}, \; e_\tau = \{x \in \bar{Q}_d \colon u(x) \leqslant \tau\}.$$

Obviously

$$\| u \|_{L_p(Q_d)} \leqslant \| u - \tau \|_{L_p(Q_d)} + \tau d^{n/p}$$

and hence

$$\| u \|_{L_p(Q_d)} \leqslant 2 \| u - \tau \|_{L_p(Q_d)}. \tag{2}$$

First consider the case $\operatorname{cap}(e_\tau, \mathring{L}_p^l(Q_{2d})) > \lambda d^{n-pl}$. If $\bar{u}_{Q_d} \geqslant \tau$, then applying Theorem 10.1.3 to the function $u - \tau$ and using (2) we deduce the estimate

$$\| u \|^p_{L_p(Q_d)} \leqslant c \lambda^{-1} d^{pl} | u |^p_{p, l, Q_d}. \tag{3}$$

On the other hand, if $\bar{u}_{Q_d} < \tau$, then by virtue of the inequality

$$\| u - \bar{u}_{Q_d} \|_{L_p(Q_d)} \leqslant c d \| \nabla u \|_{L_p(Q_d)}$$

we obtain

$$\| u \|_{L_p(Q_d)} \leqslant 2 (\| u \|_{L_p(Q_d)} - \bar{u}_{Q_d} d^{n/p}) \leqslant 2 c d \| \nabla u \|_{L_p(Q_d)}.$$

(Here we used the fact that $\bar{u}_{Q_d} \geqslant 0$.) So, for $\operatorname{cap}(e_\tau, \mathring{L}_p^l(Q_{2d})) > \lambda d^{n-pl}$ the estimate (3) is valid. In the case $\operatorname{cap}(e_\tau, \mathring{L}_p^l(Q_{2d})) \leqslant \lambda d^{n-pl}$ we have

$$\| u \|^p_{L_p(Q_d)} = 2^p d^n \tau^p \leqslant \frac{2^p d^n}{\nu(Q_d \backslash e_\tau)} \int_{Q_d \backslash e_\tau} | u |^p d\nu \leqslant \frac{2^p d^n}{\inf \nu(Q_d \backslash e)} \| u \|^p_{L_p(Q_d, \nu)}.$$

This and (3) imply (1).

Lemma 2. *Let E be a compact subset of $\bar{Q}_d$ with*

$$\operatorname{cap}(E, \mathring{L}_p^l(Q_{2d})) < \mu d^{n-pl}, \tag{4}$$

where μ is a sufficiently small positive constant which depends only on n, p, l. Then

$$\inf_{u \in C_0^\infty(Q_d \backslash e)} \frac{\| u \|_{\mathring{L}_p^l(R^n, \nu)}}{\| u \|_{L_p(R^n)}} \leqslant c (d^{-l} + d^{n/p} \nu(Q_d \backslash e)^{1/p}). \tag{5}$$

Proof. Clearly, it suffices to consider the case $d = 1$. By Remark 9.3.2 there exists a $\varphi \in \mathfrak{M}(e, Q_2)$ such that $0 \leqslant \varphi \leqslant 1$ and

$$\| \nabla_l \varphi \|_{L_p(R^n)} \leqslant c_0 \mu^{1/p}. \tag{6}$$

Let ω be an arbitrary function in $C_0^\infty(Q_1)$ that is equal to unity on $Q_{1/2}$ and satisfies $0 \leqslant \omega \leqslant 1$. For the function $u = \omega(1 - \varphi)$ which is obviously in $C_0^\infty(Q_1 \backslash E)$ we obtain

(7) $$\int_{Q_1} |u|^p d\nu \leqslant \nu(Q_1 \backslash E)\,,$$

(8) $$\begin{aligned}\|\nabla_l u\|_{L_p(R^n)} &\leqslant c(\|\nabla_l \omega\|_{L_p(R^n)} + \|\nabla_l(\omega\varphi)\|_{L_p(R^n)})\\ &\leqslant c_1 + c_2\|\nabla_l \varphi\|_{L_p(R^n)} \leqslant c_1 + c_0 c_2 \mu^{1/p}\,.\end{aligned}$$

We obtain the following lower bound for the norm of u in L_p:

$$\|u\|_{L_p(R^n)} \geqslant \|\omega\|_{L_p(R^n)} - \|\varphi\|_{L_p(R^n)} \geqslant 2^{-n/p} - \|\nabla_l \varphi\|_{L_p(R^n)} \sup_{u \in C_0^\infty(Q_2)} \frac{\|u\|_{L_p(R^n)}}{\|\nabla_l u\|_{L_p(R^n)}}\,.$$

This and (6) along with the smallness of μ imply $\|u\|_{L_p(R^n)} \geqslant 2^{-1-n/p}$. Combining this estimate with (7) and (8) we arrive at (5). The lemma is proved.

From the proof of Lemma 2 it follows that μ can be subjected to the inequality

(9) $$\mu \leqslant 2^{-n-p} c_0^{-p} \inf_{u \in C_0^\infty(Q_2)} \frac{\|\nabla_l u\|_{L_p(R^n)}}{\|u\|^p_{L_p(R^n)}}\,,$$

where c_0 is the constant in (6).

In what follows, the subsets of Q_d that satisfy the inequality

$$\operatorname{Cap}(e, \overset{\circ}{L}{}_p^l(Q_{2d})) \leqslant \gamma d^{n-pl}\,,$$

where $n \geqslant pl$, $\gamma = \mu c_*^{-1}$, c_* is the constant in (9.3.2/5), will be called (p, l)-unessential (cf. Definition 10.1.1). As before, for $pl > n$, by definition, the only (p, l)-unessential set is the empty one.

As before, the collection of all (p, l)-unessential closed subsets of the cube $\bar{Q}_d$ will be denoted by $\mathcal{N}(Q_d)$.

§ 12.2. The Continuity of the Imbedding Operator $\overset{\circ}{L}{}_p^l(\Omega, \nu) \to W_r^m(\Omega)$

Let Ω be an arbitrary open set in R^n and let ν be a measure in Ω. We denote by F_Ω the set of all cubes $\bar{Q}_d$ whose intersections with $R^n \backslash \Omega$ are (p, l)-unessential.

We introduce the number

(1) $$D = D_{p,l}(\nu, \Omega) = \sup_{\bar{Q}_d \in F_\Omega} \left\{ d : d^{n-pl} \geqslant \inf_{e \in \mathcal{N}(Q_d)} \nu(\bar{Q}_d \backslash e) \right\}.$$

Obviously, D is a nondecreasing function of the set Ω. For $\nu = 0$ the number D coincides with the (p, l)-inner diameter of the set Ω, introduced in § 10.2.

Theorem 1. *Let* $0 \leqslant m \leqslant l$, $p \leqslant r < \infty$, $l - m > n/p - n/r$. *Then:*

a) *The inequality*

$$\|u\|_{W_r^m(R^n)} \leqslant C \|u\|_{\mathring{L}_p^l(\Omega, \nu)} \tag{2}$$

is valid for all $u \in C_0^\infty(\Omega)$ *if and only if there exist positive constants d and k such that*

$$\nu(\bar{Q}_d \backslash E) \geqslant k \tag{3}$$

for all cubes $\bar{Q}_d$ *in* F_Ω *and for all compacta E in* $\mathcal{N}(Q_d)$.

b) *The best constant in* (2) *satisfies the estimates*

$$c^{-1} C \leqslant D^{l - n(1/p - 1/r)} \max\{D^{-m}, 1\} \leqslant cC. \tag{4}$$

Proof. We begin with the right inequality in (4) and with the necessity of condition (3). From the definition of D it follows that for any $\varepsilon > 0$ there exists a cube $\bar{Q}_d \in F_\Omega$ with

$$d^{n-pl} \geqslant \inf_{e \in \mathcal{N}(Q_d)} \nu(\bar{Q}_d \backslash e)$$

and with $D \geqslant d \geqslant D - \varepsilon$ if $D < \infty$, $d > \varepsilon^{-1}$ if $D = \infty$.

Let $e \in \mathcal{N}(Q_d)$. According to Corollary 9.3.2/2 the set $E = e \cup (\bar{Q}_d \backslash \Omega)$ satisfies (12.1/4). By Lemma 12.1/2 we can find a function $u \in C_0^\infty(Q_d \backslash E)$ such that

$$\|u\|_{\mathring{L}_p^l(\Omega, \nu)} \leqslant c_1 (d^{-pl} + d^{-n} \nu(\bar{Q}_d \backslash E))^{1/p} \|u\|_{L_p(Q_d)} \leqslant c_2 d^{-l} \|u\|_{L_p(Q_d)}. \tag{5}$$

Making use of the obvious inequalities

$$\begin{aligned} \|u\|_{L_p(Q_d)} &\leqslant c_3 \min\{d^{n/p - n/r} \|u\|_{L_r(Q_d)}, d^{n/p - n/r + m} \|\nabla_m u\|_{L_r(R^n)}\} \\ &\leqslant c_4 d^{n/p - n/r} \min\{1, d^m\} \|u\|_{W_r^m(R^n)} \end{aligned}$$

from (5) we obtain

$$\|u\|_{\mathring{L}_p^l(\Omega, \nu)} \leqslant c_5 d^{-l + n/p - n/r} \min\{1, d^m\} \|u\|_{W_r^m(R^n)}.$$

Since ε is arbitrarily small, the right inequality in (4) is proved.

If (2) holds then the right-hand side of (4) together with $l > n/p - n/r$ imply $D < \infty$. In this case, for $d = 2D$ and $k = d^{n-pl}$ we have (3).

Now we shall prove the sufficiency of (3) and the left inequality in (4). Cover R^n by the cubic grid $\{\bar{Q}_d\}$ where d is chosen to satisfy (3). If the cube Q_d has a (p, l)-essential intersection with $R^n \backslash \Omega$ then, by Theorem 10.1.2,

$$\|u\|_{L_p(Q_d)}^p \leqslant c d^{pl} |u|_{p, l, Q_d}^p.$$

On the other hand, if $\bar{Q}_d \backslash \Omega \notin \mathcal{N}(Q_d)$ then by virtue of Lemma 12.1/1

$$\|u\|_{L_p(Q_d)}^p \leqslant c d^{pl} |u|_{p,l,Q_d}^p + c k^{-1} d^n \|u\|_{L_p(Q_d,\nu)}^p . \tag{6}$$

Summing over all cubes of the grid, we obtain

$$\|u\|_{L_p(\Omega)}^p \leqslant c \sum_{j=1}^{l} d^{pj} \|\nabla_j u\|_{L_p(\Omega)}^p + c k^{-1} d^n \|u\|_{L_p(\Omega,\nu)}^p . \tag{7}$$

Applying (11.4.2/2) and Hölder's inequality, from (7) we obtain

$$\|u\|_{L_p(\Omega)}^p \leqslant c d^{pl} \|\nabla_l u\|_{L_p(\Omega)}^p + c k^{-1} d^n \|u\|_{L_p(\Omega,\nu)}^p . \tag{8}$$

Since the imbedding operator of W_p^l into W_r^m is continuous, the sufficiency of (3) is proved.

Let

$$R = \max\{d, (d^n k^{-1})^{1/pl}\} .$$

Then by (8) we have

$$\|u\|_{L_p} \leqslant c R^l \|u\|_{\overset{\circ}{L}{}_p^l(\Omega,\nu)} ,$$

which implies the following estimate for the best constant C in (2):

$$C \leqslant c \sup_{u \in \mathscr{D}} \frac{\|\nabla_m u\|_{L_r} + \|u\|_{L_r}}{\|\nabla_l u\|_{L_p} + R^{-l} \|u\|_{L_p}} .$$

Replace $u(x/R)$ by u. Then

$$\begin{aligned} C &\leqslant c \sup_{u \in \mathscr{D}} \frac{R^{-m+n/r} \|\nabla_m u\|_{L_r} + R^{n/r} \|u\|_{L_r}}{R^{n/p-l} (\|\nabla_l u\|_{L_p} + \|u\|_{L_p})} \\ &\leqslant c R^{l-n/p+n/r} \max\{R^{-m}, 1\} \sup_{u \in \mathscr{D}} \frac{\|u\|_{W_r^m}}{\|u\|_{W_p^l}} . \end{aligned} \tag{9}$$

We may assume that $D < \infty$. The definition of D implies the validity of (3) for $d = 2D$, $k = d^{n-pl}$. Inserting $\lambda = 2D$ into (9) we arrive at the left inequality in (4). The theorem is proved.

Since for $pl > n$ the only unessential set is the empty set, Theorem 1 can, in this case, be restated in the following equivalent formulation without the notion of capacity.

Theorem 2. *Let $pl > n$, $0 \leqslant m \leqslant l$, $p \leqslant r < \infty$, $l - m > n/p - n/r$. Then:*

a) *Inequality* (2) *holds for all $u \in \mathscr{D}(\Omega)$ if and only if the estimate $\nu(Q_d) > k$ is valid for some $d > 0$, $k > 0$ for all cubes Q_d with $\bar{Q}_d \subset \Omega$.*

b) *The best constant C in* (2) *satisfies* (4) *with*

$$D = D_{p,l}(\nu, \Omega) = \sup_{\bar{Q}_d \subset \Omega} \{d \colon d^{n-pl} \geqslant \nu(\bar{Q}_d)\} . \tag{10}$$

Part a) of Theorem 1 can also be simplified for $pl = n$ when $R^n \backslash \Omega$ is connected.

Theorem 3. *Let $pl = n$ and let $R^n \backslash \Omega$ be connected. Inequality* (2) *is valid for all $u \in \mathscr{D}(\Omega)$ if and only if there exist constants $d > 0$, $k > 0$ such that* (3) *holds for all cubes Q_d with $\bar{Q}_d \subset \Omega$ and for all (p, l)-unessential compacta $F \subset \bar{Q}_d$.*

Proof. We need only establish the sufficiency since the necessity is contained in Theorem 1.

Let $\bar{Q}_d$ be a cube of the coordinate grid having a nonempty intersection with $R^n \backslash \Omega$. Then Q_{2d} contains a continuum in $R^n \backslash \Omega$ with length not less than d. So according to Proposition 9.1.2/2 we have

$$\operatorname{cap}(\bar{Q}_{2d} \backslash \Omega, \mathring{L}_p^l(Q_{4d})) \geqslant c .$$

This and Theorem 10.1.2 imply

$$\|u\|_{L_p(Q_d)}^p \leqslant c d^{pl} |u|_{p,l,Q_d}^p , \quad u \in \mathscr{D}(\Omega) . \tag{11}$$

The latter estimate, applied to each cube $\bar{Q}_d$ that intersects $R^n \backslash \Omega$, together with inequality (6) for cubes $\bar{Q}_d \subset \Omega$ leads to (7). The further arguments are just the same as in the proof of the sufficiency of condition (3) in Theorem 1. The theorem is proved.

§ 12.3. The Compactness of the Imbedding Operator $\mathring{L}_p^l(\Omega, \nu) \to W_r^m(\Omega)$

12.3.1. The Essential Norm of the Imbedding Operator

Let E be the identity mapping of the space $C_0^\infty(\Omega)$ considered as an operator from $\mathring{L}_p^l(\Omega, \nu)$ into $W_r^m(R^n)$.

With E we associate its essential norm, i.e. the value

$$\varrho = \varrho_{p,l,m} = \inf_{\{T\}} \|E - T\| , \tag{1}$$

where $\{T\}$ is the set of all compact operators

$$\mathring{L}_p^l(\Omega, \nu) \to W_r^m(R^n) .$$

Theorem. *Let $0 \leqslant m < l$, $p \leqslant r < \infty$, $l - m > n/p - n/r$. Then:*

a) *$\varrho < \infty$ if and only if $D = D_{p,l}(\nu, \Omega) < \infty$,*

b) *there exists a constant $c > 1$ such that*

$$c^{-1} \varrho \leqslant \overset{\infty}{D}{}^{l-n/p+n/r} \max\{\overset{\infty}{D}{}^{-m}, 1\} \leqslant c\varrho \tag{2}$$

with

(3) $$\overset{\infty}{D} = \overset{\infty}{D}_{p,l}(\nu, \Omega) = \lim_{N\to\infty} D_{p,l}(\nu, \Omega\backslash\bar{Q}_N),$$

where Q_N is a cube with center 0 *and edge length N.*

Proof. Part a) follows from Theorem 12.2/1. We prove the left-hand side of (2). Let T_N be the operator of multiplication by $\eta(N^{-1}x)$, $N=1,2,\dots$, where $\eta\in C_0^\infty(Q_2)$, $\eta=1$ on Q_1. By virtue of Theorem 12.2/1, for any $u\in C_0^\infty(Q_2)$ we have

(4) $$c^{-1}\|u\|_{\mathring{L}_p^l(\Omega,\nu)} \leqslant \|\nabla_l u\|_{L_p} + D^{-l}\|u\|_{L_p} + \|u\|_{L_p(\Omega,\nu)} \leqslant c\|u\|_{\mathring{L}_p^l(\Omega,\nu)}.$$

Hence if $N \geqslant D$ then

(5) $$\|T_N\|_{\mathring{L}_p^l(\Omega,\nu)\to\mathring{L}_p^l(\Omega,\nu)} \leqslant c.$$

From (4) and the well-known compactness theorem it follows that the mapping T_N: $\mathring{L}_p^l(\Omega,\nu)\to W_r^m$ is compact. Applying Theorem 12.2/1 to the set $\Omega\backslash\bar{Q}_N$ we obtain for any $u\in C_0^\infty(\Omega)$ that

$$\|(E-T_N)\|_{W_r^m} \leqslant cD_N^{l-n/p+n/r}\max\{D_N^{-m},1\}\|(E-T_N)u\|_{\mathring{L}_p^l(\Omega,\nu)},$$

where $D_N = D_{p,l}(\nu, \Omega\backslash\bar{Q}_N)$. Hence, using (5) and passing to the limit as $N\to\infty$ we arrive at the left inequality in (2).

We prove the right inequality in (2). We may assume that $\overset{\infty}{D} \neq 0$. Obviously $D_1 \geqslant D_2 \geqslant \dots \geqslant \overset{\infty}{D}$. Using the same arguments as in the proof of the right inequality (12.2/4), for any large enough number N we construct a function $u_N \in C_0^\infty(\Omega\backslash\bar{Q}_N)$ with diameter of the support not exceeding $2\overset{\infty}{D}$ and such that

(6) $$\|u_N\|_{\mathring{L}_p^l(\Omega,\nu)} \leqslant c\overset{\infty}{D}{}^{-l}, \quad \|u_N\|_{L_p} = 1.$$

Obviously,

(7) $$\|u_N\|_{L_p} = \overset{\infty}{D}{}^{n/p}\|G_{\overset{\infty}{D}}u_N\|_{L_p} \leqslant c_1\overset{\infty}{D}{}^{n/p}\min\{\|G_{\overset{\infty}{D}}u_N\|_{L_r}, \|\nabla_m G_{\overset{\infty}{D}}u_N\|_{L_r}\},$$

where G_a is the operator defined by $(G_a u)(x) = u(ax)$. We choose a sequence $\{N_i\}_{i\geqslant 1}$ so that the distance between the supports of u_{N_i} and u_{N_j} $(i \neq j)$ is more than $2\sqrt{n}\,\overset{\infty}{D}$. From (6) and (7) we obtain

(8) $$1 \leqslant c_2\overset{\infty}{D}{}^{n/p}\min\{\|G_{\overset{\infty}{D}}(u_{N_j}-u_{N_i})\|_{L_r}, \|\nabla_m G_{\overset{\infty}{D}}(u_{N_i}-u_{N_j})\|_{L_r}\}$$
$$\leqslant c_3\overset{\infty}{D}{}^{n/p-n/r}\min\{\overset{\infty}{D}{}^m, 1\}\|u_{N_i}-u_{N_j}\|_{W_r^m}.$$

We denote an arbitrary compact operator by T: $\mathring{L}_p^l(\Omega,\nu)\to W_r^m$. Passing, if necessary, to a subsequence we may assume that the sequence $\{Tu_{N_i}\}$ converges in W_r^m. Further,

$$\|(E-T)(u_{N_i}-u_{N_j})\|_{W_r^m} \geqslant \|u_{N_i}-u_{N_j}\|_{W_r^m} - \|T(u_{N_i}-u_{N_j})\|_{W_r^m},$$

which along with (8) shows

$$c_5 \limsup_{N_i, N_j \to \infty} \|(E-T)(u_{N_i}-u_{N_j})\|_{W_r^m} \geqslant \overset{\infty}{D}{}^{l-n/p+n/r} \max\{\overset{\infty}{D}{}^{-m}, 1\}.$$

This and (6) imply

$$c_6 \|E-T\|_{\mathring{L}_p^l(\Omega,\nu) \to W_r^m} \geqslant \overset{\infty}{D}{}^{l-n/p+n/r} \max\{\overset{\infty}{D}{}^{-m}, 1\}.$$

The proof is complete.

12.3.2. Criteria for Compactness

From Theorem 12.3 we immediately obtain the following theorem.

Theorem 1. *Let* $0 \leqslant m \leqslant l$, $p \leqslant r < \infty$, $l-m > n(p^{-1}-r^{-1})$. *Then the set*

$$\mathfrak{F} = \{u \in \mathscr{D}(\Omega) : \|u\|_{\mathring{L}_p^l(\Omega,\nu)} \leqslant 1\}$$

is relatively compact in W_r^m *if and only if* $D = D_{p,l}(\nu, \Omega) < \infty$ *and*

$$\lim_{N \to \infty} D_{p,l}(\nu, \Omega \backslash \bar{Q}_N) = 0.$$

The preceding theorem admits the following equivalent formulation.

Theorem 2. *Let* $0 \leqslant m \leqslant l$, $p \leqslant r < \infty$, $l-m > n(p^{-1}-r^{-1})$. *Then the set* $\mathfrak{F}$ *is relatively compact in* W_r^m *if and only if:*

a) *there exist positive constants* d_0 *and* k *such that inequality* (12.2/3) *is valid for any cube* Q_{d_0} *with* $\bar{Q}_{d_0} \subset F_\Omega$ *and for any compactum* $E \in \mathscr{N}(Q_{d_0})$;

b) *we have*

(1)
$$\inf_{e \in \mathscr{N}(Q_d)} \nu(\bar{Q}_d \backslash e) \to \infty$$

as the cube Q_d, $\bar{Q}_d \subset F_\Omega$ *tends to infinity where* d *is an arbitrary positive number.*

Proof. Necessity. Inequality (12.2/3) follows from Theorem 12.2/1. If (1) is not valid then there exists a sequence of cubes $\{\mathscr{Q}^{(i)}\}_{i \geqslant 1}$, with limit point at infinity and satisfying the conditions: (i) the set $\{d_i\}$ of edge lengths of the cubes $\mathscr{Q}^{(i)}$ is bounded, (ii) the inequality

$$\inf_{e \in \mathscr{N}(\mathscr{Q}^{(i)})} \nu(\overline{\mathscr{Q}^{(i)}} \backslash e) < c_0$$

holds. This and Lemma 12.1/2 imply that we can find a sequence of functions $\{u_i\}_{i \geqslant 1}$ in $\mathscr{D}(\Omega)$ with

$$\operatorname{diam} \operatorname{supp} u_i \leqslant c\,, \qquad \operatorname{dist}(\operatorname{supp} u_i, \operatorname{supp} u_j) \geqslant c > 0\,, \qquad i \neq j\,;$$

$$\|u_i\|_{\mathring{L}_p^l(\Omega, \nu)} \leqslant c\,, \qquad \|u_i\|_{W_r^m} \geqslant c_1\,, \qquad \|u_i\|_{L_p} \geqslant c_2 > 0\,.$$

Sufficiency. Let conditions (12.2/3) and (1) be valid. By Theorem 12.2/1 and (12.2/3) the value $D_{p,l}(\nu, \Omega)$ is finite. Now (1) and (12.2/8) yield

$$\lim_{N \to \infty} \sup_{u \in C_0^\infty(\Omega \setminus \bar{Q}_N)} \|u\|_{W_r^m} / \|u\|_{\mathring{L}_p^l(\Omega, \nu)} = 0\,.$$

This and the right inequality (12.2/4) applied to $\Omega \setminus \bar{Q}_N$ imply

$$\lim_{N \to \infty} D_{p,l}(\nu, \Omega \setminus \bar{Q}_N) = 0\,.$$

Hence, $\mathfrak{F}$ is relatively compact in W_r^m by virtue of Theorem 1. The proof is complete.

Clearly, in the case $pl > n$ Theorem 2 can be stated as follows.

Theorem 3. *Let $pl > n$, $0 \leqslant m < l$, $p \leqslant r < \infty$, $l - m > n/p - n/r$. The set $\mathfrak{F}$ is relatively compact in W_r^m if and only if the condition of Theorem* 12.2/1 *holds and if*

(2) $$\nu(Q_d) \to \infty$$

as the cube Q_d with $\bar{Q}_d \subset \Omega$ tends to infinity.

In the case $pl = n$ under the hypothesis of the connectedness of $R^n \setminus \Omega$ the statement of Theorem 2 can be simplified in the following way.

Theorem 4. *Let $pl = n$, $0 \leqslant m < l$, $p \leqslant r < \infty$, $m < n/r$ and suppose the complement of Ω is connected. Then $\mathfrak{F}$ is relatively compact in W_r^m if and only if the condition of Theorem* 12.2/3 *holds and* (1) *is valid as the cube Q_d, $\bar{Q}_d \subset \Omega$, tends to infinity.*

Proof. Taking into account Theorem 2 we can limit ourselves to proving sufficiency. According to the Gagliardo-Nirenberg theorem (see Theorem 1.4.7),

$$\|\nabla_k u\|_{L_r} \leqslant c\, \|\nabla_l u\|_{L_p}^{\beta}\, \|u\|_{L_p}^{1-\beta}\,,$$

where $0 \leqslant k \leqslant l$ and $\beta = l^{-1}(n/p - n/r + k)$. Hence, it suffices to obtain the relative compactness of $\mathfrak{F}$ in L_p. By Theorem 12.2/3, $\mathfrak{F}$ is bounded in $W_p^l(R^n)$ and consequently it is relatively compact in $L_p(B_\varrho)$ for any $\varrho \in (0, \infty)$. It remains to show that for any ε we can find a $\varrho = \varrho(\varepsilon)$ such that

(3) $$\|u\|_{L_p(R^n \setminus B_\varrho)} \leqslant \varepsilon\,.$$

Put $d^l = \varepsilon$ in (12.1/1) and choose $\varrho = \varrho(\varepsilon)$ so that for any cube $\bar{Q}_d \subset \Omega$ that intersects $R^n \setminus B_\varrho$ we have

$$\inf_{e \in \mathcal{N}(Q_d)} \nu(\bar{Q}_d \backslash e) \geqslant \varepsilon^{-p} d^n .$$

Then for such cubes

$$\|u\|_{L_p(Q_d)} \leqslant c\varepsilon(|u|_{p,l,Q_d} + \|u\|_{L_p(Q_d,\nu)}) . \tag{4}$$

For all $\bar{Q}_d$ which intersect both $R^n \backslash \Omega$ and $R^n \backslash B_\varrho$ the estimate

$$\|u\|_{L_p(Q_d)} \leqslant c\varepsilon |u|_{p,l,Q_d} \tag{5}$$

holds by (12.2/11). We take the p-th power of (4) and of (5) and then sum them over all cubes of the coordinate grid with the edge length d which have a nonempty intersection with $R^n \backslash B_\varrho$. This implies (3). The theorem is proved.

§ 12.4. On the Closability of Imbedding Operators

Let ν be a measure in R^n. We call it *(p, l)-absolutely continuous* if the equality $\operatorname{cap}(B, W_p^l) = 0$, where B is a Borel set, implies $\nu(B) = 0$.

For instance, by Proposition 7.2.3/2 the Hausdorff φ-measure is (p, l)-absolutely continuous provided the integral (7.2.3/4) converges.

Let $\mathscr{E}$ be the identity operator defined on $\mathscr{D}(\Omega)$ which maps $L_p(\Omega)$ into $\overset{\circ}{L}{}_p^l(\Omega, \nu)$.

Theorem 1. *Let $n \geqslant pl$, $p > 1$. The operator $\mathscr{E}$ is closable if and only if the measure ν is (p, l)-absolutely continuous.*

Proof. Sufficiency. Suppose a sequence of functions $\{u_k\}_{k \geqslant 1}$ in $\mathscr{D}(\Omega)$ converges to zero in $L_p(\Omega)$ and that it is a Cauchy sequence in $\overset{\circ}{L}{}_p^l(\Omega, \nu)$. Further, let $D^\alpha u_k \to v_\alpha$ in $L_p(\Omega)$ for any multi-index α with $|\alpha| = l$. Then for all $\varphi \in \mathscr{D}(\Omega)$

$$(-1)^{|\alpha|} \int_\Omega v_\alpha \varphi \, dx = \lim_{k \to \infty} \int_\Omega u_k D^\alpha \varphi \, dx = 0$$

and $v_\alpha = 0$ almost everywhere in Ω. Consequently, $u_k \to 0$ in $\overset{\circ}{W}{}_p^l(\Omega)$. The sequence $\{u_k\}$ contains a subsequence $\{w_k\}$ that converges to zero (p, l)-quasi everywhere (see 7.2.4). The (p, l)-absolute continuity of the measure ν implies $w_k \to 0$ ν-almost everywhere. Since $\{u_k\}$ is a Cauchy sequence in $L_p(\Omega, \nu)$ then $u_k \to 0$ in the same space.

Necessity. Suppose there exists a Borel set $B \subset \Omega$ with $\operatorname{cap}(B, W_p^l) = 0$ and $\nu(B) > 0$. Let F denote a compact subset of B satisfying $2\nu(F) > \nu(B)$. Further let $\{\omega_k\}_{k \geqslant 0}$ be a sequence of open sets with the properties: 1) $F \subset \bar{\omega}_{k+1} \subset \omega_k \subset \Omega$, 2) $\operatorname{cap}(\bar{\omega}_k, W_p^l) \to 0$, and 3) $\nu(\omega_k) \to \nu(F)$. We introduce the capacitary measure μ_k and the capacitary Bessel potential $w_k = V_{p,l}\mu_k$ of the set $\bar{\omega}_k$ (see Proposition 7.2.2/2).

We show that $w_k \to 0$ in the space $C(e)$ where e is any compactum disjoint with F. Let $\delta = \operatorname{dist}(e, F)$ and let k be a number satisfying $2\operatorname{dist}(e, \bar{\omega}_k) > \delta$. We set

$$g_k(y) = [\int G_l(y-z)\, d\mu_k(z)]^{1/(p-1)}$$

(see the definition of the Bessel potential in 7.1.2). If $4|x-y| < \delta$ then $4|z-y| \geqslant \delta$ for all $z \in \bar{\omega}_k$ and consequently

$$g_k(y) \leqslant c(\delta)\, [\mu_k(\bar{\omega}_k)]^{1/(p-1)} = c(\delta)\, [\operatorname{cap}(\bar{\omega}_k, W_p^l)]^{1/(p-1)}.$$

Therefore,

$$\int_{4|x-y| \leqslant \delta} G_l(x-y)\, g_k(y)\, dy \leqslant c_1(\delta)\, [\operatorname{cap}(\bar{\omega}_k, W_p^l)]^{1/(p-1)}.$$

On the other hand,

$$\int_{4|x-y| > \delta} G_l(x-y)\, g_k(y)\, dy \leqslant c_2(\delta)\, \|g_k\|_{L_p} = c_2(\delta)\, [\operatorname{cap}(\bar{\omega}_k, W_p^l)]^{1/(p-1)}.$$

These estimates and the equality

$$w_k(x) = \int G_l(x-y)\, g_k(y)\, dy$$

imply $w_k \to 0$ in $C(e)$.

The arguments used in the proof of Theorem 9.3.2/1 show that the functions $v_k = 1 - [(1 - w_k)_+]^l$ satisfy

(1) $$\|v_k\|_{W_p^l} \leqslant c\, \|w_k\|_{W_p^l}.$$

Moreover, it is clear that $v_k = 1$ in a neighborhood of F, $0 \leqslant v_k \leqslant 1$ in R^n and that the sequence $\{v_k\}$ converges uniformly to zero on any compactum disjoint with F.

Let u_k denote a mollification of v_k with small enough radius. Using the equality $\lim \operatorname{cap}(\bar{\omega}_k, W_p^l) = 0$ and the estimate (1) we obtain $\|u_k\|_{W_p^l} \to 0$. Let η be any function in $\mathfrak{M}(F, \Omega)$ with support S. Clearly, $\eta u_k = 1$ in a neighborhood of F and $\|\eta u_k\|_{W_p^l} \to 0$. We show that ηu_k is a Cauchy sequence in $L_p(\Omega, \nu)$. Let ε be an arbitrary positive number and let M be so large that $\nu(\omega_M \backslash F) < \varepsilon$. We choose an integer N to satisfy

$$|u_k(x)|^p \leqslant \varepsilon / \nu(S), \quad x \in S \backslash \omega_M,$$

for $k > N$. Hence, for any $k, l > N$, we obtain

$$\int_\Omega |\eta(u_k - u_l)|^p d\nu \leqslant c\Big(\int_{S \backslash \omega_M} |u_k - u_l|^p d\nu + \int_{\omega_M \backslash F} |u_k - u_l|^p d\nu\Big) < c\varepsilon.$$

Therefore ηu_k is a Cauchy sequence in $L_p(\Omega, \nu)$. Since $u_k = 1$ on F then

$$\|\eta u_k\|^p_{L_p(\Omega, \nu)} \geqslant \nu(F) > 0 .$$

The existence of such a sequence contradicts the closability of the operator $\mathscr{E}$. The theorem is proved.

In the case $pl > n$ the operator $\mathscr{E}$ is always closable, which trivially follows from the Sobolev theorem on the imbedding $W_p^l(\Omega) \subset C(\Omega)$.

Theorem 2. *The identity operator defined on $\mathscr{D}(\Omega)$ which maps $\overset{\circ}{W}{}_p^l(\Omega)$ into $L_p(\Omega, \nu)$ is closable if and only if the measure ν is (p, l)-absolutely continuous.*

Proof. Sufficiency. Let $\{u_k\}_{k \geqslant 1}$, $u_k \in \mathscr{D}(\Omega)$ be a Cauchy sequence in $L_p(\Omega, \nu)$ that converges to zero in $\overset{\circ}{W}{}_p^l(\Omega)$. Then it converges to zero in $L_p(\Omega, \nu)$ by the previous theorem.

Necessity. Suppose there exists a Borel set B with $\operatorname{cap}(B, W_p^l) = 0$ and $\nu(B) > 0$. Under this condition, in Theorem 1 we constructed a sequence of functions $u_k \in \mathscr{D}(\Omega)$ which is a Cauchy sequence in $L_p(\Omega, \nu)$ that converges to zero in $\overset{\circ}{W}{}_p^l(\Omega)$, and does not converge to zero in $L_p(\Omega, \nu)$. The result follows.

Theorem 3. 1) *The identity operator defined on $\mathscr{D}(\Omega)$, which maps $\overset{\circ}{L}{}_p^l(\Omega)$ into $L_p(\Omega, \nu)$ $(lp < n)$, is closable if and only if the measure ν is (p, l)-absolutely continuous.*

2) *The same is valid for $n = pl$ provided $R^n \backslash \Omega$ is a set of positive (p, l)-capacity.*

Proof. 1) *Sufficiency.* Let a sequence of functions u_k in $\mathscr{D}(\Omega)$ be a Cauchy sequence in $L_p(\Omega, \nu)$ that converges to zero in $\overset{\circ}{L}{}_p^l(\Omega)$. Since $lp < n$, then $\overset{\circ}{L}{}_p^l(\Omega) \subset L_q(\Omega)$, $q = pn(n - pl)^{-1}$ and hence $\{u_k\}$ converges to zero in n-dimensional Lebesgue measure. Further, using the same approach as in the proof of sufficiency in Theorem 1, from $\{u_k\}$ we can select a subsequence $\{w_k\}$ that converges to zero ν-almost everywhere.

Necessity follows from Theorem 2.

2) The case $n = pl$ is considered in the same way, making use of the imbedding $\overset{\circ}{L}{}_p^l(\Omega) \subset L_q(\Omega, \mathrm{loc})$ (see § 11.3).

§ 12.5. Application: Positive Definiteness and Discreteness of the Spectrum of a Strongly Elliptic Operator

We define two quadratic forms

$$\mathfrak{A}(u, u) = \sum_{|\alpha| = |\beta| = l} \int_\Omega a_{\alpha\beta}(x) D^\alpha u D^\beta \bar{u}\, dx ,$$

$$\mathfrak{B}(u, u) = \mathfrak{A}(u, u) + \int_\Omega |u|^2 d\nu ,$$

where $u \in \mathscr{D}(\Omega)$, $a_{\alpha\beta}$ are measurable functions and ν is a measure in Ω. Suppose

$$\varkappa_1 \| \nabla_l u \|^2_{L_2(\Omega)} \leqslant \mathfrak{A}(u, u) \leqslant \varkappa_2 \| \nabla_l u \|^2_{L_2(\Omega)}$$

for all $u \in \mathscr{D}(\Omega)$.

By definition the form $\mathfrak{B}$ is closable in $L_2(\Omega)$ if any Cauchy sequence $u_m \in \mathscr{D}(\Omega)$ that converges to zero in $L_2(\Omega)$ in the norm $(\mathfrak{B}(u, u))^{1/2}$ converges to zero in the norm $(\mathfrak{B}(u, u))^{1/2}$.

This condition implies the existence of the unique selfadjoint operator B in $L_2(\Omega)$ with

$$(u, Bv) = \mathfrak{B}(u, v) \qquad \text{for all } u, v \in \mathscr{D}(\Omega)\,.$$

Clearly, the closability of the form $\mathfrak{B}$ is necessary for the existence of B.

By Theorem 12.4/1, $\mathfrak{B}$ is closable in $L_2(\Omega)$ if and only if the measure ν is (p, l)-absolutely continuous. We shall assume that ν has this property.

The next assertion is a particular case of Theorem 12.2/1.

Theorem 1. 1) *The operator B is positive definite if and only if*

$$\nu(Q_d \backslash F) \geqslant k \tag{1}$$

for all cubes $\bar{Q}_d$ having $(2, l)$-unessential intersection with $R^n \backslash \Omega$ and for all $(2, l)$-unessential compacta $F \subset \bar{Q}_d$ with certain $d > 0$, $k > 0$.

2) *The lower bound Λ of the spectrum of the operator B satisfies*

$$c_1 \varkappa_1 D^{-2l} \leqslant \Lambda \leqslant c_2 \varkappa_2 D^{-2l}\,, \tag{2}$$

where c_1, c_2 are constants that depend only on n, l and D is defined by (12.2/1) *with $p = 2$.*

Corollary 1. 1) *For $2l > n$ a necessary and sufficient condition for the positive definiteness of B is the inequality $\nu(Q_d) \geqslant k$, where d and k are certain positive constants and $\bar{Q}_d$ is any cube in Ω.*

2) *The lower bound Λ of the spectrum of B satisfies* (2) *with D defined by* (12.2/10) *for $p = 2$.*

Corollary 2. *If $2l = n$ and the set $R^n \backslash \Omega$ is connected, then a necessary and sufficient condition for the positive definiteness of B is the validity of* (1) *for all cubes $\bar{Q}_d \subset \Omega$ and for all $(2, n/2)$-unessential compacta $F \subset \bar{Q}_d$ with certain $d > 0$, $k > 0$.*

This corollary is a special case of Theorem 12.2/3.

Theorem 2. *The lower bound Γ of points of condensation of the spectrum of B satisfies*

$$c_1 \varkappa_1 \overset{\infty}{D}{}^{-2l} \leqslant \Gamma \leqslant c_2 \varkappa_2 \overset{\infty}{D}{}^{-2l}\,, \tag{3}$$

where $\overset{\infty}{D}$ is defined by (12.3.1/3) *with $p = 2$.*

Proof. Let ϱ be the number defined by (12.3.1/1) for $p=2$. By virtue of Theorem 12.3.1 it suffices to prove that $\Gamma = \varrho^{-2}$. From Theorems 12.3.1 and 1 it follows that $\Gamma = 0$ if and only if $\varrho = \infty$. So we may suppose $\Gamma \neq 0$ and $\varrho \neq \infty$.

We introduce the family $\{E_\lambda\}$ of orthogonal projective operators that form a resolution of the identity generated by the selfadjoint operator B in $L_2(\Omega)$. Then

$$\lambda^{-1}\mathfrak{B}(u,u) \geqslant \|(E-E_\lambda)u\|^2_{L_2(\Omega)}\,. \tag{4}$$

Since the projective operator E_λ is finite-dimensional for $\lambda < \Gamma$, then (4) and the definition of ϱ imply $\Gamma \leqslant \varrho^{-2}$.

For any ε, $0<\varepsilon<\Gamma$, in $L_2(\Omega)$ there exists an orthogonal and normalized infinite sequence of functions $\{\varphi_i\}_{i\geqslant 1}$ such that $(B\varphi_i, \varphi_j) = 0$ for $i \neq j$ and $\Gamma - \varepsilon \leqslant (B\varphi_i, \varphi_j) \leqslant \Gamma + \varepsilon$.

Let T be an arbitrary compact operator mapping $\mathring{L}_2^l(\Omega, \nu)$ into $L_2(\Omega)$. We have that

$$\begin{aligned}
\frac{\|(E-T)(\varphi_i-\varphi_j)\|_{L_2(\Omega)}}{\|\varphi_i-\varphi_j\|_{\mathring{L}_2^l(\Omega,\nu)}} &\geqslant \frac{\|\varphi_i-\varphi_j\|_{L_2(\Omega)} - \|T(\varphi_i-\varphi_j)\|_{L_2(\Omega)}}{(B(\varphi_i-\varphi_j),\, \varphi_i-\varphi_j)^{1/2}} \\
&= \frac{(\|\varphi_i\|^2_{L_2(\Omega)} + \|\varphi_j\|^2_{L_2(\Omega)})^{1/2} - \|T(\varphi_i-\varphi_j)\|_{L_2(\Omega)}}{[(B\varphi_i,\varphi_i)+(B\varphi_j,\varphi_j)]^{1/2}} \\
&\geqslant (\Gamma+\varepsilon)^{-1/2} - 2^{-1/2}(\Gamma-\varepsilon)^{-1/2}\|T(\varphi_i-\varphi_j)\|_{L_2(\Omega)}\,.
\end{aligned}$$

The upper limit of the right-hand side as $i, j \to \infty$ equals $(\Gamma+\varepsilon)^{-1/2}$. So by the arbitrariness of ε and the definition of ϱ we obtain $\varrho^2 \geqslant \Gamma^{-1}$. The theorem is proved.

The preceding result implies the next theorem.

Theorem 3. *The spectrum of the operator B is discrete if and only if $\overset{\infty}{D} = 0$.*

This theorem is equivalent to the following assertion.

Theorem 4. *The spectrum of the operator B is discrete if and only if*

$$\inf_{F\in\mathcal{N}(Q_d)} \nu(\bar{Q}_d \backslash F) \to \infty \tag{5}$$

as the cube $\bar{Q}_d$ (d is an arbitrary positive number), having a $(2,l)$-unessential intersection with $R^n \backslash \Omega$, tends to infinity.

For $2l > n$ this criterion can be reformulated as follows.

Theorem 5. *Let $2l>n$. The operator B has a discrete spectrum if and only if*

$$\nu(\bar{Q}_d) \to \infty$$

as the cube $\bar{Q}_d \subset \Omega$, where $d>0$, tends to infinity.

Theorem 12.3.2/4 implies the following result.

Theorem 6. *Let* $2l = n$ *and let* $R^n \backslash \Omega$ *be connected. The operator* B *has a discrete spectrum if and only if* (5) *holds as the cube* $\bar{Q}_d \subset \Omega$, *where* $d > 0$, *tends to infinity.*

§ 12.6. Comments to Chapter 12

The results of this chapter develop in a certain sense the paper by Molčanov [189] which contains a necessary and sufficient condition for the discreteness of the spectrum of the Dirichlet problem for the Schrödinger operator $-\Delta + v$ (v is an absolutely continuous measure) or, equivalently, a condition for the compactness of the imbedding $\mathring{L}_2^1(\Omega, v) \subset L_2(\Omega)$. Such criteria were obtained for the space $\mathring{L}_2^l(\Omega, v)$ with $2l > n$ (when there is no need for a capacity) by Birman and Pavlov [31]. In the case $q \geqslant p > 1$, $l = 1, 2, \ldots$, necessary and sufficient conditions for the boundedness and compactness of the imbedding operator of $\mathring{L}_p^l(\Omega, v)$ into $L_q(\Omega)$ were established by the author [156]. Two-sided estimates for the norm and for the essential norm of this operator are due to the author and Otelbaev [175], where the space with the norm

$$\|(-\Delta)^{l/2} u\|_{L_p(\Omega)} + \|u\|_{L_p(\Omega, v)}$$

is considered (l is any positive number). The imbedding theorems for more general spaces with weighted norms were obtained by Oleinik and Pavlov [205], Lizorkin and Otelbaev [139] and by Otelbaev [208]. The function

$$D_{p,l}(x) = \sup \{d \colon d^{n-pl} \geqslant \inf_{e \in \mathcal{N}(Q_d(x))} v(Q_d(x) \backslash e)\}$$

(compare with (12.2/1)) was used by Otelbaev [207] in the derivation of bounds for the Kolmogorov diameter of a unit ball in $\mathring{L}_p^l(\Omega, v)$ measured in $L_p(\Omega)$. We present his result.

The *Kolmogorov diameter* of a set M in a Banach space B is defined to be the number

$$d_k(M, B) = \begin{cases} \inf\limits_{\{L_k\}} \sup\limits_{f \in M} \inf\limits_{g \in L_k} \|f - g\|_B, & k = 1, 2, \ldots, \\ \sup\limits_{f \in M} \|f\|_B, & k = 0, \end{cases}$$

where $\{L_k\}$ is the set of subspaces of B with $\dim L_k \leqslant k$.

Theorem (Otelbaev [207]). *Let* M *be the unit ball in the space* $\mathring{L}_p^l(\Omega, v)$ *and let* $N(\lambda)$ *be the number of Kolmogorov diameters of* M *in* $L_p(\Omega)$ *which exceed* λ^{-1}, $\lambda > 0$. *Then*

$$c^{-1}N(c\lambda) \leqslant \lambda^{-n/l} m_n\{x: D_{p,l}(x) \geqslant \lambda^{1/l}\} \leqslant cN(c^{-1}\lambda),$$

where c does not depend on Ω, ν, λ.

By definition, the imbedding operator of $\overset{\circ}{L}{}_p^l(\Omega, \nu)$ into $L_p(\Omega)$ is in *the class* l_θ if

$$\sum_{k=0}^{\infty} [d_k(M, L_p(\Omega))]^\theta < \infty .$$

The Otelbaev theorem just stated shows that *the imbedding operator under consideration is in the class* l_θ *if and only if* $\theta l > n$ *and*

$$\int_\Omega [D_{p,l}(x)]^{l\theta - n} dx < \infty .$$

An immediate application of these results are two-sided estimates for the eigenvalues of the Dirichlet problem for the operator $(-\Delta)^{l/2} + \nu$ and the conditions for the nuclearity of the resolvent of this operator.

References

1. Adams, D.R.: Traces of potentials arising from translation invariant operators. Ann. Sc. Norm. Super. Pisa. 25 (1971) 203 – 217.
2. Adams, D.R.: A trace inequality for generalized potentials. Stud. Math. 48 (1973) 99 – 105.
3. Adams, D.R.: Traces of potentials II. Indiana Univ. Math. J. 22 (1973) 907 – 918.
4. Adams, D.R.: On the exceptional sets for spaces of potentials. Pac. J. Math. 52 (1974) 1 – 5.
5. Adams, D.R.: On the existence of capacitary strong type estimates in R^n. Ark. Mat. 14 (1976) 125 – 140.
6. Adams, D.R.: Sets and functions of finite L^p-capacity. Indiana Univ. Math. J. 27 (1978) 611 – 627.
7. Adams, D.R.: Lectures on L^p-potential theory. Dept. of Math., Univ. of Umeå. Preprint No. 2 (1981) 1 – 74.
8. Adams, D.R., Hedberg, L.I.: Inclusion relations among fine topologies in non-linear potential theory. Reports Dept. of Math., Univ. of Stockholm. No. 10 (1982) 1 – 15.
9. Adams, D.R., Meyers, N.G.: Thinness and Wiener criteria for non-linear potentials. Indiana Univ. Math. J. 22 (1972) 139 – 158.
10. Adams, D.R., Meyers, N.G.: Bessel potentials. Inclusion relations among classes of exceptional sets. Indiana Univ. Math. J. 22 (1973) 873 – 905.
11. Adams, D.R., Polking, J.C.: The equivalence of two definitions of capacity. Proc. Am. Math. Soc. 37 (1973) 529 – 534.
12. Adams, R.A.: Sobolev spaces. New York-San Francisco-London: Academic Press, 1975.
13. Ahlfors, L.: Lectures on quasiconformal mappings. Toronto-New York-London: Van Nostrand, 1966.
14. Amick, C.J.: Some remarks on Rellich's theorem and the Poincaré inequality. J. Lond. Math. Soc., II. Ser. 18 (1978) 81 – 93.
15. Andersson, R.: Unbounded Soboleff regions. Math. Scand. 13 (1963) 75 – 89.
16. Andersson, R.: The type set of a generalized Sobolev operator. Meddelanden från Lunds Universitets Matem. Semin. 19 (1972) 1 – 101.
17. Aronszajn, N.: On coercive integro-differential quadratic forms. Conference on Partial Differential Equations. Univ. of Kansas, Report No. 14 (1954) 94 – 106.
18. Aronszajn, N., Mulla, P., Szeptycki, P.: On spaces of potentials connected with L^p-classes. Ann. Inst. Fourier 13 (1963) 211 – 306.
19. Aubin, T.: Problèmes isopérimetriques et espaces de Sobolev. C. R. Acad. Sci., Paris. 280 (1975) 279 – 281.
20. Babič, V.M.: On the extension of functions. Usp. Mat. Nauk, 8 (1953) 111 – 113 (Russian).
21. Babič, V.M., Slobodeckiĭ, L.N.: On the boundedness of the Dirichlet integral. Dokl. Akad. Nauk SSSR, 106 (1956) 604 – 607 (Russian).
22. Bagby, T.: Approximation in the mean by solutions of elliptic equations. Trans. Am. Math. Soc. 281 (1984) 761 – 784.
23. Bagby, T., Ziemer, W. P.: Pointwise differentiability and absolute continuity. Trans. Am. Math. Soc. 191 (1974) 129 – 148.
24. Besicovitch, A.S.: A general form of the covering principle and relative differentiation of additive functions. Proc. Cambridge Philos. Soc. I. 41 (1945) 103 – 110; II. 42 (1946) 1 – 10.

25. Besov, O.V.: Investigation of a family of function spaces in connection with imbedding and extension theorems. Trudy Mat. Inst. Steklova, Akad. Nauk SSSR, 60 (1961) 42 – 81 (Russian). English translation: Amer. Math. Soc. Transl. 40 (1964) 85 – 126.
26. Besov, O.V., Il'in, V.P., Kudrjavcev, L.D., Lizorkin, P.I., Nikol'skiĭ, S.M.: Imbedding theory for classes of differentiable functions of several variables. In the book: Partial Differential Equations, 38 – 63. Moscow: Nauka 1970 (Russian).
27. Besov, O.V., Il'in, V.P., Nikol'skiĭ, S.M.: Integral representations of functions and imbedding theorems. Moscow: Nauka, 1975 (Russian). English edition: V.H. Winston and Sons, Washington, D.C., vol. I, 1978; vol. II, 1979.
28. Beurling, A.: Ensembles exceptionnels. Acta Math. 72 (1939) 1 – 13.
29. Birman, M.Š.: Perturbation of quadratic forms and the spectrum of singular boundary value problems. Dokl. Akad. Nauk SSSR 125 (1959) 471 – 474 (Russian).
30. Birman, M.Š.: On the spectrum of boundary value problems. Mat. Sb. 55 (1961) 125 – 174 (Russian).
31. Birman, M.Š., Pavlov, B.S.: On the complete continuity of certain imbedding operators. Vestn. Leningr. Univ., Mat. Mekh. Astron., No. 1 (1961) 61 – 74 (Russian).
32. Björup, K.: On inequalities of Poincaré's type. Math. Scand. 8 (1960) 157 – 160.
33. Bokowski, J., Sperner, E.: Zerlegung konvexer Körper durch minimale Trennflächen. J. Reine Angew. Math. 311/312 (1979) 80 – 100.
34. Bourbaki, N.: Espaces vectoriels topologiques. Paris: Hermann, 1953.
35. Burago, Ju.D., Zalgaller, V.A.: Geometric inequalities. Leningrad: Nauka, 1980 (Russian). English edition: in preparation, Berlin-Heidelberg: Springer-Verlag.
36. Burago, Ju.D., Maz'ja, V.G.: Some questions of potential theory and function theory for domains with non-regular boundaries. Zap. Nauchn. Semin. Leningr. Otd. Mat. Inst. Steklova, 3 (1967) 1 – 152 (Russian). English translation: Seminars in Math., V.A. Steklov Math. Inst., Leningrad 3 (1969) 1 – 68. Consultants Bureau, New York.
37. Burenkov, V.I.: On imbedding theorems for the domain $R_k = \{\alpha_i h < x_i^{k_i} < \beta_i h;\ 0 < h < 1\}$. Mat. Sb. 75 (1968) 496 – 501 (Russian). English translation: Math. USSR-Sb., 4 (1968) 457 – 462.
38. Burenkov, V.I.: On the additivity of the spaces W_p^r and B_p^r and imbedding theorems for regions of a general kind. Tr. Mat. Inst. Steklova, 105 (1969) 30 – 45 (Russian). English translation: Proc. Steklov Inst. Math. 105 (1969) 35 – 53.
39. Caccioppoli, R.: Misure e integrazione sugli insiemi dimensionalmente orientati. Rend. Accad. Naz. dei Lincei. 12 (1952) 3 – 11.
40. Caccioppoli, R.: Misure e integrazione sugli insiemi dimensionalmente orientati. Rend. Accad. Naz. dei Lincei. 12 (1952) 137 – 146.
41. Calderón, A.P.: Lebesgue spaces of differentiable functions and distributions. In: Proc. Symp. Pure Math., Vol. IV (1961) 33 – 49.
42. Campanato, S.: Il teoreme di immersione di Sobolev per una classe di aperti non dotati della proprietà di cono. Ric. Mat. 11 (1962) 103 – 122.
43. Carleson, L.: Selected problems on exceptional sets. Toronto-London-Melbourne: Van Nostrand Co., 1967.
44. Cartan, H.: Sur les systèmes de fonctions holomorphes à variétés linéaires et leurs applications. Ann. École Norm. Sup. 3 (1928) 255 – 346.
45. Choquet, G.: Theory of capacities. Ann. Inst. Fourier. 5 (1955) 131 – 395.
46. Coifman, R., Fefferman, C.: Weighted norm inequalities for maximal functions and singular integrals. Stud. Math. 5 (1974) 241 – 250.
47. Courant, R., Hilbert, D.: Methoden der mathematischen Physik. Berlin: Springer, 1937. English edition: Methods of mathematical physics. New York: Interscience, 1953, 1962.
48. Dahlberg, B.E.J.: Regularity properties of Riesz potentials. Indiana Univ. Math. J. 28 (1979) 257 – 268.
49. De Giorgi, E.: Su una teoria generale della misure $(r-l)$-dimensionale in uno spazio ad r dimensioni. Ann. Mat. Pura Appl., IV. Ser., 36 (1954) 191 – 213.
50. De Giorgi, E.: Nuovi teoremi relative alle misure $(r-l)$-dimensionale in spazio ad r dimensioni. Ric. Mat. 4 (1955) 95 – 113.

51. Deny, J., Lions, J.-L.: Les espaces du type de Beppo Levi. Ann. Inst. Fourier, 5 (1953–1954) 305–370.
52. Donoghue, W.F., Jr.: A coerciveness inequality. Ann. Sc. Norm. Super. Pisa. Cl. Sci. 20 (1966) 589–593.
53. Douglas, J.: Solution of the problem of Plateau. Trans. Am. Math. Soc. 33 (1931) 263–321.
54. Dunford, N., Schwartz, J.: Linear operators I. New York-London: Interscience, 1958.
55. Edmunds, D.E.: Embeddings of Sobolev spaces, Nonlinear Analysis, Function Spaces and Applications. In: Proc. of a Spring School held in Horni Bradlo, 1978, 38–58. Leipzig: Teubner-Texte zur Math. 1979.
56. Ehrling, G.: On a type of eigenvalue problem for certain elliptic differential operators. Math. Scand. 2 (1954) 267–285.
57. Faddeev, D.K.: On representations of summable functions by singular integrals at Lebesgue points. Mat. Sb. 1 (1936) 352–368 (Russian).
58. Federer, H.: A note on the Gauss-Green theorem. Proc. Am. Math. Soc. 9 (1958) 447–451.
59. Federer, H.: Curvature measures. Trans. Am. Math. Soc. 93 (1959) 418–491.
60. Federer, H.: The area of nonparametric surfaces. Proc. Am. Math. Soc. 11 (1960) 436–439.
61. Federer, H.: Geometric measure theory. Berlin-Heidelberg-New York: Springer, 1969.
62. Federer, H.: A minimizing property of extremal submanifolds. Arch. Ration. Mech. Anal. 9 (1975) 207–217.
63. Federer, H., Fleming, W.H.: Normal and integral currents. Ann. Math. 72 (1960) 458–520.
64. Fleming, W.H.: Functions whose partial derivatives are measures. Ill. J. Math. 4 (1960) 452–478.
65. Fleming, W.H., Rishel, R.W.: An integral formula for total gradient variation. Arch. Math. 11 (1960) 218–222.
66. Fraenkel, L.E.: On regularity of the boundary in the theory of Sobolev spaces. Proc. Lond. Math. Soc. 39 (1979) 385–427.
67. Freud, G., Králik, D.: Über die Anwendbarkeit des Dirichletschen Prinzips für den Kreis. Acta Math. Hung. 7 (1956) 411–418.
68. Friedrichs, K.: Spektraltheorie halbbeschränkter Operatoren und Anwendung auf die Spektralzerlegung von Differentialoperatoren. Math. Ann. 109 (1934) 465–487, 685–713.
69. Gagliardo, E.: Caratterizzazioni delle tracce sulla frontiera relative ad alcune classi di funzioni in piu variabili. Rend. Semin. Mat. Univ. Padova. 27 (1957) 284–305.
70. Gagliardo, E.: Proprieta di alcune classi di funzioni in piu variabili. Ric. Mat. 7 (1958) 102–137.
71. Gagliardo, E.: Ulteriori proprieta di alcune classi di funzioni in piu variabili. Ric. Mat. 8 (1959) 24–51.
72. Gel'fand, I.M., Šilov, G.E.: Spaces of fundamental and generalized functions. Moscow: Nauka, 1958 (Russian). English edition: New York-London: Academic Press, 1968.
73. Gel'man, I.V., Maz'ja, V.G.: Abschätzungen für Differentialoperatoren im Halbraum. Berlin: Akademie Verlag, 1981.
74. Glazman, I.M.: Direct methods of qualitative spectral analysis of singular differential operators. Moscow: Nauka, 1963 (Russian).
75. Globenko, I.G.: Some questions of imbedding theory for domains with singularities on the boundary. Mat. Sb. 57 (1962) 201–224 (Russian).
76. Gluško, V.P.: On regions which are star-like with respect to a sphere. Dokl. Akad. Nauk SSSR, 144 (1962) 1215–1216 (Russian). English translation: Soviet Math. Dokl. 3 (1962) 878–879.
77. Gol'dsteĭn, V.M.: Extension of functions with first generalized derivatives from planar domains. Dokl. Akad. Nauk SSSR, 257 (1981) 268–271 (Russian). English translation: Soviet Math. Dokl. 23 (1981) 255–258.
78. Gol'dsteĭn, V.M., Vodopjanov, S.K.: Prolongement des fonctions de classe L_p^l et applications quasi conformes. C. R. Acad. Sci., Paris. 290 (1980) 453–456.
79. Golovkin, K.K.: Imbedding theorems for fractional spaces. Tr. Mat. Inst. Steklova 70 (1964) 38–46 (Russian). English translation: Amer. Math. Soc. Transl. 91 (1970) 57–67.

80. Golovkin, K.K.: Parametric-normed spaces and normed massives. Tr. Mat. Inst. Steklova 106 (1969) 1–135 (Russian). English translation: Proc. Steklov Inst. Math. 106 (1969) 1–121.
81. Golovkin, K.K., Solonnikov, V.A.: Imbedding theorems for fractional spaces. Dokl. Akad. Nauk SSSR, 143 (1962) 767–770 (Russian). English translation: Soviet Math. Dokl. 3 (1962) 468–471.
82. Grušin, V.V.: A problem for the entire space for a certain class of partial differential equations. Dokl. Akad. Nauk SSSR, 146 (1962) 1251–1254 (Russian). English translation: Soviet Math. Dokl. 3 (1962) 1467–1470.
83. Gustin, W.: Boxing inequalities. J. Math. Mech. 9 (1960) 229–239.
84. Guzman, M.: Differentiation of integrals in R^n. Lect. Notes Math. 481. Berlin-Heidelberg-New York: Springer, 1975.
85. Hadwiger, H.: Vorlesungen über Inhalt, Oberfläche und Isoperimetrie. Berlin-Göttingen-Heidelberg: Springer, 1957.
86. Hahn, H., Rosenthal, A.: Set functions. The Univ. of New Mexico Press, Albuquerque, N.M., 1948.
87. Hansson, K.: On a maximal imbedding theorem of Sobolev type and spectra of Schrödinger operators. Linköping Studies in Science and Technology. Dissertation. Linköping, 1978.
88. Hansson, K.: Imbedding theorems of Sobolev type in potential theory. Math. Scand. 45 (1979) 77–102.
89. Hansson, K.: Continuity and compactness of certain convolution operators. Inst. Mittag-Leffler, Report No. 9 (1982) 1–12.
90. Hardy, G.H., Littlewood, J.E., Pólya, G.: Some simple inequalities satisfied by convex functions. Messenger of Math. 58 (1929) 145–152.
91. Hardy, G.H., Littlewood, J.E., Pólya, G.: Inequalities. Cambridge: Cambridge Univ. Press, 1934. Russian edition: Moscow: IL, 1948.
92. Hayman, W.K.: Multivalent functions. Cambridge: Cambridge Univ. Press, 1958.
93. Hedberg, L.I.: On certain convolution inequalities. Proc. Am. Math. Soc. 36 (1972) 505–510.
94. Hedberg, L.I.: Two approximation problems in function spaces. Ark. Mat. 16 (1978) 51–81.
95. Hedberg, L.I.: Spectral synthesis in Sobolov spaces and uniqueness of solutions of the Dirichlet problem. Acta Math. 147 (1981) 237–264.
96. Hedberg, L.I., Wolff, T.H.: Thin sets in nonlinear potential theory. Ann. Inst. Fourier, 33:4 (1983) 161–187.
97. Hestenes, M.R.: Extension of the range of differentiable function. Duke Math. J. 8 (1941) 183–192.
98. Hoffmann, D., Spruck, J.: Sobolev and isoperimetric inequalities for Riemannian submanifolds. I. Commun. Pure Appl. Math. 27 (1974) 715–727; II. Commun. Pure Appl. Math. 28 (1975) 765–766.
99. Hörmander, L.: Linear partial differential operators. Berlin-Heidelberg-New York: Springer, 1963.
100. Hörmander, L., Lions, J.-L.: Sur la complétion par rapport à une intégrale de Dirichlet. Math. Scand. 4 (1956) 259–270.
101. Hurd, A.E.: Boundary regularity in the Sobolev imbedding theorems. Can. J. Math. 18 (1966) 350–356.
102. Il'in, V.P.: Some inequalities in function spaces and their application to the investigation of the convergence of variational processes. Dissertation. Leningrad, LGU, 1951 (Russian).
103. Il'in, V.P.: On a imbedding theorem for a limiting exponent. Dokl. Akad. Nauk SSSR, 96 (1954) 905–908 (Russian).
104. Il'in, V.P.: Some integral inequalities and their application to the theory of differentiable functions of many variables. Mat. Sb. 54 (1961) 331–380 (Russian).
105. Il'in, V.P.: Integral representations of differentiable functions and their application to questions of the extension of functions of the class $W_p^l(G)$. Sib. Mat. Zh. 8 (1967) 573–586 (Russian). English translation: Siberian Math. J. 8 (1967) 421–432.

106. Il'in, V.P.: Integral representations of functions of the class $L_p^l(G)$ and imbedding theorems. Zap. Nauchn. Semin. Leningr. Otd. Mat. Inst. Steklova, 19 (1970) 95–155 (Russian).
107. Jones, P.W.: Quasiconformal mappings and extendability of functions in Sobolev spaces. Acta Math. 147 (1981) 71–88.
108. Jonsson, A., Wallin, H.: A Whitney extension theorem in L^p and Besov spaces. Ann. Inst. Fourier, 28 (1978) 139–192.
109. Klimov, V.S.: Imbedding theorems for Orlicz spaces and their application to boundary value problems. Sib. Mat. Zh. 13 (1972) 334–348 (Russian). English translation: Siberian Math. J. 13 (1972) 231–240.
110. Klimov, V.S.: Isoperimetric inequalities and imbedding theorems. Dokl. Akad. Nauk SSSR, 217 (1974) 272–275 (Russian). English translation: Soviet Math. Dokl. 15 (1974) 1047–1051.
111. Klimov, V.S.: Imbedding theorems and geometric inequalities. Izv. Akad. Nauk SSSR, 40 (1976) 645–671 (Russian). English translation: Math. USSR-Izv. 10 (1976) 615–638.
112. Kokilašvili, V.M.: On Hardy inequalities in weighted spaces. Soobshch. Gruz. Akad. Nauk SSR, 96 (1979) 37–40 (Russian).
113. Kolsrud, T.: Approximation by smooth functions in Sobolev spaces. A counterexample. Bull. Lond. Math. Soc. 13 (1981) 167–169.
114. Kondrašov, V.I.: On some properties of functions from the space L_p. Dokl. Akad. Nauk SSSR, 48 (1945) 563–566 (Russian).
115. Kondrat'ev, V.A.: On the solvability of the first boundary value problem for elliptic equations. Dokl. Akad. Nauk SSSR, 136 (1961) 771–774 (Russian). English translation: Soviet Math. Dokl. 2 (1961) 127–130.
116. Kondrat'ev, V.A.: Boundary problems for elliptic equations in domains with conical or angular points. Tr. Mosk. Mat. O-va, 16 (1967) 209–292 (Russian). English translation: Trans. Moscow Math. Soc. 16 (1967) 227–313.
117. Krasnosel'skiĭ, M.A., Rutickiĭ, Ja.B.: Convex functions and Orlicz spaces. Moscow: Nauka, 1958. English edition: Groningen: Noordhoff, 1961.
118. Krickeberg, K.: Distributionen, Funktionen beschränkter Variation und Lebesguescher Inhalt nichtparametrischer Flächen. Ann. Mat. Pura Appl., IV Ser., 44 (1957) 105–134.
119. Kronrod, A.S.: On functions of two variables. Usp. Mat. Nauk, 5 (1950) 24–134 (Russian).
120. Kudrjavcev, L.D.: Direct and inverse imbedding theorems. Applications to the solution of elliptic equations by the variational method. Tr. Mat. Inst. Steklova, 55 (1959) 1–181 (Russian). English translation: Amer. Math. Soc. Transl. 42 (1974).
121. Kufner, A.: Weighted Sobolev spaces. Leipzig: Teubner-Texte zur Math. 1980.
122. Ladyženskaja, O.A.: Mathematical questions of the dynamics of a viscous incompressible fluid. Moscow: Nauka, 1970 (Russian).
123. Landis, E.M.: Second order equations of elliptic and parabolic types. Moscow: Nauka, 1971 (Russian).
124. Landis, E.M.: On the behavior of solutions of higher-order elliptic equations in unbounded domains. Tr. Mosk. Mat. O-va, 31 (1974) 35–58 (Russian). English translation: Trans. Moscow Math. Soc. 31 (1974) 30–54.
125. Landkof, N.S.: Foundations of modern potential theory. Moscow: Nauka, 1966 (Russian). English edition: Berlin-Heidelberg-New York: Springer, 1972.
126. Laptev, S.A.: Closure in the metric of a generalized Dirichlet integral. Differ. Uravn. 7 (1971) 727–736 (Russian). English translation: Differential Equations. 7 (1971) 557–564
127. Leray, J., Lions, J.-L.: Quelques résultats de Višik sur les problèmes elliptiques non linéaires par les méthodes de Minty-Browder. Bull. Soc. Math. Fr. 93 (1965) 97–107.
128. Levi, B.: Sul prinzipio di Dirichlet. Rend. Palermo, 22 (1906) 293–359.
129. Levin, V.I.: Exact constants in inequalities of the Carlson type. Dokl. Akad. Nauk SSSR, 59 (1948) 635–639 (Russian).
130. Lichtenstein, L.: Eine elementare Bemerkung zur reellen Analysis. Math. Z. 30 (1929) 794–795.
131. Lions, J.-L.: Ouverts *m*-réguliers. Rev. Union Mat. Argent. 17 (1955) 103–116.

132. Lions, J.-L., Magenes, B.: Problèmes aux limites non homogènes et applications, v. 1. Paris: Dunod, 1968. English edition: Non-homogeneous limit problems and applications, Berlin-Heidelberg-New York: Springer, 1972.
133. Littman, W.: A connection between α-capacity and (m,p)-polarity. Bull. Am. Math. Soc. 73 (1967) 862–866.
134. Littman, W.: Polar sets and removable singularities of partial differential equations. Ark. Math. 7 (1967) 1–9.
135. Lizorkin, P. I.: Boundary properties of functions from "weight classes". Dokl. Akad. Nauk SSSR, 132 (1960) 514–517 (Russian). English translation: Soviet Math. Dokl. 1 (1960) 589–593.
136. Lizorkin, P. I.: Generalized Liouville differentiation and the function spaces $L_p^r(E_n)$. Imbedding theorems. Mat. Sb. 60 (1963) 325–353 (Russian).
137. Lizorkin, P. I.: Generalized Hölder spaces $B_{p,\theta}^r$ and their relations to the S. L. Sobolev spaces L_p^r. Sib. Mat. Zh. 9 (1968) 1127–1152 (Russian). English translation: Siberian Math. J. 9 (1968) 837–858.
138. Lizorkin, P. I.: Estimates of integrals of potential type in norms with difference relations. In the book: Theory of cubature formulas and applications of functional analysis to some problems of mathematical physics, 94–109, Novosibirsk, 1975 (Russian).
139. Lizorkin, P. I., Otelbaev, M.: Imbedding theorems and compactness for spaces of Sobolev type with weights. I. Mat. Sb. 108 (1979) 358–377; II. Mat. Sb. 112 (1980) 56–85 (Russian). English translation: Math. USSR-Sb., 36 (1980) 331–349; 40 (1981) 51–77.
140. Ljusternik, L. A.: Brunn-Minkowski inequality for arbitrary sets. Dokl. Akad. Nauk SSSR, 3 (1935) 55–58 (Russian).
141. Maz'ja, V. G.: Classes of regions and imbedding theorems for function spaces. Dokl. Akad. Nauk SSSR, 133 (1960) 527–530 (Russian). English translation: Soviet Math. Dokl. 1 (1960) 882–885.
142. Maz'ja, V. G.: The p-conductivity and theorems on imbedding certain function spaces into a C-space. Dokl. Akad. Nauk SSSR, 140 (1961) 299–302 (Russian). English translation: Soviet Math. Dokl. 2 (1961) 1200–1203.
143. Maz'ja, V. G.: Classes of sets and imbedding theorems for function spaces. Dissertation. Moscow: MGU, 1962 (Russian).
144. Maz'ja, V. G.: The negative spectrum of the n-dimensional Schrödinger operator. Dokl. Akad. Nauk SSSR, 144 (1962) 721–722 (Russian). English translation: Soviet Math. Dokl. 3 (1962) 808–810.
145. Maz'ja, V. G.: The Dirichlet problem for elliptic equations of arbitrary order in unbounded regions. Dokl. Akad. Nauk SSSR, 150 (1963) 1221–1224 (Russian). English translation: Soviet Math. Dokl. 4 (1963) 860–863.
146. Maz'ja, V. G.: On the theory of the multidimensional Schrödinger operator. Izv. Akad. Nauk SSSR, 28 (1964) 1145–1172 (Russian).
147. Maz'ja, V. G.: Polyharmonic capacity in the theory of the first boundary value problem. Sib. Mat. Zh. 6 (1965) 127–148 (Russian).
148. Maz'ja, V. G.: On closure in the metric of the generalized Dirichlet integral. Zap. Nauchn. Semin. Leningr. Otd. Mat. Inst. Steklova, 5 (1967) 192–195 (Russian).
149. Maz'ja, V. G.: On Neumann's problem in domains with nonregular boundaries. Sib. Mat. Zh. 9 (1968) 1322–1350 (Russian). English translation: Siberian Math. J. 9 (1968) 990–1012.
150. Maz'ja, V. G.: On weak solutions of the Dirichlet and Neumann problems. Tr. Mosk. Mat. O-va, 20 (1969) 137–172 (Russian). English translation: Trans. Moscow Math. Soc. 20 (1969) 135–172.
151. Maz'ja, V. G.: Classes of sets and measures connected with imbedding theorems. In the book: Imbedding theorems and their applications. (Trudy simpoziuma po teoremam vloženija, Baku, 1966), 142–159. Moscow: Nauka, 1970 (Russian).
152. Maz'ja, V. G.: On some integral inequalities for functions of many variables. In the book: Problems in mathematical analysis. Leningrad: LGU, No. 3, 33–68 (1972) (Russian). English translation: J. Soviet Math. 1 (1973) 205–234.

153. Maz'ja, V. G.: Removable singularities of bounded solutions of quasilinear elliptic equations of any order. Zap. Nauchn. Semin. Leningr. Otd. Mat. Inst. Steklova, 26 (1972) 116–130 (Russian). English translation: J. Soviet Math. 3 (1975) 480–492.
154. Maz'ja, V. G.: Applications of some integral inequalities to the theory of quasilinear elliptic equations. Comment. Math. Univ. Carolinae, 13 (1972) 535–552 (Russian).
155. Maz'ja, V. G.: On a degenerating problem with directional derivative. Mat. Sb. 87 (1972) 417–454 (Russian). English translation: Math. USSR-Sb., 16 (1972) 429–469.
156. Maz'ja, V. G.: On (p, l)-capacity, imbedding theorems and the spectrum of a selfadjoint elliptic operator. Izv. Akad. Nauk SSSR, Ser. Mat. 37 (1973) 356–385 (Russian). English translation: Math. USSR-Izv., 7 (1973) 357–387.
157. Maz'ja, V. G.: On the continuity and boundedness of functions from Sobolev spaces. In the book: Problems in Mathematical Analysis. Leningrad: LGU, No. 4 (1973) 46–77 (Russian).
158. Maz'ja, V. G.: On the connection between two kinds of capacity. Vestn. Leningr. Univ., Mat. Mekh. Astron. 7 (1974) 33–40 (Russian). English translation: Vestnik Leningrad Univ. Math. 7 (1974) 135–145.
159. Maz'ja, V. G.: On the summability of functions in S. L. Sobolev spaces. In the book: Problems in Mathematical Analysis. Leningrad: LGU, 5 (1975) 66–98 (Russian).
160. Maz'ja, V. G.: Capacity-estimates for "fractional" norms. Zap. Nauchn. Semin. Leningr. Otd. Mat. Inst. Steklova, 70 (1977) 161–168 (Russian). English translation: J. Soviet Math. 23 (1983) 1997–2003.
161. Maz'ja, V. G.: On an integral inequality. Seminar instituta prikladnoi matematiki. Doklady. Tbilisskiĭ universitet, 12–13 (1978) 33–36 (Russian).
162. Maz'ja, V. G.: Multipliers in S. L. Sobolev spaces. In the book: Application of function theory and functional analysis methods to problems of mathematical physics. Pjatoe Sovetsko-Čehoslovackoe Soveščanie, 181–189. Novosibirsk, 1978 (Russian).
163. Maz'ja, V. G.: On summability with respect to an arbitrary measure of functions in S. L. Sobolev-L. N. Slobodeckiĭ spaces. Zap. Nauchn. Semin. Leningr. Otd. Mat. Inst. Steklova, 92 (1979) 192–202 (Russian). English translation: J. Soviet Math.: in preparation.
164. Maz'ja, V. G.: Behaviour of solutions to the Dirichlet problem for the biharmonic operator at a boundary point. Equadiff IV. Prague 1977. Lect. Notes Math. 703 (1979) 250–262.
165. Maz'ja, V. G.: Einbettungssätze für Sobolewsche Räume. Leipzig: Teubner-Texte zur Math. Teil 1, 1979; Teil 2, 1980.
166. Maz'ja, V. G.: Zur Theorie Sobolewscher Räume. Leipzig: Teubner-Texte zur Math. 1981.
167. Maz'ja, V. G.: Integral representation of functions satisfying homogeneous boundary conditions and its applications. Izv. Vyssh. Uchebn. Zaved., Mat., 2 (1980) 34–44 (Russian). English translation: Sov. Math. 24 (1980) 35–44.
168. Maz'ja, V. G.: On an imbedding theorem and multipliers in pairs of S. L. Sobolev spaces. Tr. Tbilis. Mat. Inst. Razmadze, 66 (1980) 59–69 (Russian).
169. Maz'ja, V. G., Dončev, T.: On the Wiener regularity of a boundary point for a polyharmonic operator. Dokl. Bolgarskoĭ Akad. Nauk, 36 (1983) 177–179 (Russian).
170. Maz'ja, V. G., Havin, V. P.: A nonlinear analogue of the Newton potential and metric properties of the (p, l)-capacity. Dokl. Akad. Nauk SSSR, 194 (1970) 770–773 (Russian). English translation: Soviet Math. Dokl. 11 (1970) 1294–1298.
171. Maz'ja, V. G., Havin, V. P.: Nonlinear potential theory. Usp. Mat. Nauk, 27 (1972) 67–138 (Russian). English translation: Russian Math. Surveys, 27 (1972) 71–148..
172. Maz'ja, V. G., Havin, V. P.: On approximation in the mean by analytic functions. Vestn. Leningr. Univ., 23 (1968) 62–74 (Russian). English translation: Vestnik Leningrad Univ. Math. 1 (1974) 231–245.
173. Maz'ja, V. G., Havin, V. P.: Use of (p, l)-capacity in problems of the theory of exceptional sets. Mat. Sb. 90 (1973) 558–591 (Russian). English translation: Math. USSR-Sb., 19 (1973) 547–580.
174. Maz'ja, V. G., Hvoles, A. A.: On imbedding the space $\mathring{L}_p^l(\Omega)$ into the space of generalized functions. Tr. Tbilis. Mat. Inst. Razmadze, 66 (1981) 70–83 (Russian).

175. Maz'ja, V.G., Otelbaev, M.: Imbedding theorems and the spectrum of a pseudodifferential operator. Sib. Mat. Zh. 18 (1977) 1073–1087 (Russian). English translation: Siberian Math. J. 18 (1977) 758–769.
176. Maz'ja, V.G., Preobraženskiĭ, S.P.: On estimates of (p, l)-capacity and traces of potentials. Wissenschaftliche Informationen. Technische Hochschule, Karl-Marx-Stadt, Sektion Mathematik, No. 28 (1981) 1–38 (Russian).
177. Maz'ja, V.G., Šapošnikova, T.O.: On multipliers in Sobolev spaces. Vestn. Leningr. Univ. 7 (1979) 33–40 (Russian). English translation: Vestnik Leningrad Univ. Math. 12 (1980) 125–134.
178. Maz'ja, V.G., Šapošnikova, T.O.: Multipliers in spaces of differentiable functions. In the book: Theory of cubature formulas and application of functional analysis to problems of mathematical physics. Tr. Semin. S.L. Soboleva, Novosibirsk, No. 1 (1979) 37–90 (Russian).
179. Maz'ja, V.G., Šapošnikova, T.O.: Multipliers in pairs of potential spaces. Math. Nachr. 99 (1980) 363–379.
180. Maz'ja, V.G., Šapošnikova, T.O.: Change of variable as an operator in a pair of S.L. Sobolev spaces. Vestn. Leningr. Univ. 1 (1982) 43–48 (Russian). English translation: Vestn. Leningr. Univ., Math. 15 (1983) 53–58.
181. Maz'ja, V.G., Šapošnikova, T.O.: Multipliers in pairs of spaces of differentiable functions. Tr. Mosk. Mat. O-va, 43 (1981) 37–80 (Russian). English translation: Trans. Moscow Math. Soc. 43 (1981) 39–85.
182. Meyers, N.G.: A theory of capacities for potentials of functions in Lebesgue classes. Math. Scand. 26 (1970) 255–292.
183. Meyers, N.G.: Continuity of Bessel potentials. Isr. J. Math. 11 (1972) 271–283.
184. Meyers, N.G.: Integral inequalities of Poincaré and Wirtinger type. Arch. Ration. Mech. Anal. 68 (1978) 113–120.
185. Meyers, N.G., Serrin, J.: H = W. Proc. Nat. Acad. Sci. USA. 51 (1964) 1055–1056.
186. Michael, J.H., Simon, L.M.: Sobolev and mean-value inequalities on generalized submanifolds of R^n. Commun. Pure Appl. Math. 26 (1973) 362–379.
187. Mihlin, S.G.: Multidimensional singular integrals and integral equations. Moscow: Nauka, 1962 (Russian).
188. Miranda, M.: Disuguaglianze di Sobolev sulle ipersuperfici minimali. Rend. Semin. Mat. Univ. Padova. 38 (1967) 69–79.
189. Molčanov, A.M.: On conditions for discreteness of the spectrum of selfadjoint differential equations of the second order. Tr. Mosk. Mat. O-va. 2 (1953) 169–200 (Russian).
190. Morrey, C.B.: Functions of several variables and absolute continuity II. Duke Math. J. 6 (1940) 187–215.
191. Morrey, C.B.: Multiple integrals in the calculus of variations. Berlin-Heidelberg-New York: Springer, 1966.
192. Morse, A.P.: The behavior of a function on its critical set. Ann. Math. 40 (1939) 62–70.
193. Morse, A.P.: A theory of covering and differentiation. Trans. Am. Math. Soc. 55 (1944) 205–235.
194. Muckenhoupt, B.: Hardy's inequality with weights. Stud. Math. 44 (1972) 31–38.
195. Muckenhoupt, B.: Weighted norm inequalities for the Hardy maximal function. Trans. Am. Math. Soc. 165 (1972) 207–226.
196. Natanson, I.P.: Theory of functions of a real variable. Moscow: Nauka 1974 (Russian). English edition: New York: Ungar, 1955. German edition: Berlin: Akademie-Verlag, 1981.
197. Nečas, J.: Les méthodes directes en théorie des equations elliptiques. Prague: Academia, 1967.
198. Nevanlinna, R.: Eindeutige analytische Funktionen. Berlin: Springer, 1936. Russian edition: Single-valued analytic functions. GTTI, Moscow-Leningrad, 1941.
199. Nikodým, O.: Sur une classe de fonctions considérées dans le problème de Dirichlet. Fundam. Math. 21 (1933) 129–150.
200. Nikol'skiĭ, S.M.: Inequalities for entire functions of exponential type and their application to the theory of differentiable functions of several variables. Tr. Mat. Inst. Steklova, 38

(1951) 244 – 278 (Russian). English translation: Amer. Math. Soc. Transl. 80 (1969) 1 – 38.
201. Nikol'skiĭ, S.M.: Properties of certain classes of functions of several variables on differentiable manifolds. Mat. Sb. 33 (1953) 261 – 326 (Russian).
202. Nikol'skiĭ, S.M.: Approximation of functions of several variables and imbedding theorems. Moscow: Nauka, 1977 (Russian).
203. Nirenberg, L.: On elliptic partial differential equations (Lecture II). Ann. Sc. Norm. Super. Pisa, S. 3, 13 (1959) 115 – 162.
204. Nirenberg, L.: An extended interpolation inequality. Ann. Sc. Norm. Super. Pisa, Sci. fis. e mat. 20 (1966) 733 – 737.
205. Oleĭnik, V.L., Pavlov, B.S.: On criteria for boundedness and complete continuity of certain imbedding operators. In the book: Problems in mathematical physics, 4 (1970) 112 – 116 (Russian).
206. Osserman, R.: The isoperimetric inequality. Bull. Am. Math. Soc. 84 (1978) 1182 – 1238.
207. Otelbaev, M.: Two-sided estimates for diameters and applications. Dokl. Akad. Nauk SSSR, 231 (1976) 810 – 813 (Russian). English translation: Soviet Math. Dokl. 17 (1976) 1655 – 1659.
208. Otelbaev, M.: Imbedding theorems for weighted spaces and their applications in the study of the spectrum of the Schrödinger operator. Tr. Mat. Inst. Steklova, 150 (1979) 265 – 305 (Russian). English translation: Proc. Steklov Inst. Math. 150 (1981) 281 – 321.
209. Otsuki, T.: A remark on the Sobolev inequality for Riemannian submanifolds. Proc. Jap. Acad. 51 (1975) 785 – 789.
210. Peetre, J.: New thoughts on Besov spaces. Duke Univ. Math. Series I, Durham, 1976.
211. Pfaltzgraff, J.A.: Radial symmetrization and capacities in space. Duke Math. J. 34 (1967) 747 – 755.
212. Polking, J.C.: Approximation in L^p by solutions of elliptic partial differential equations. Am. J. Math. 94 (1972) 1231 – 1244.
213. Pólya, G., Szegö, G.: Isoperimetric inequalities in mathematical physics. Ann. Math. Stud. 27, Princeton Univ. Press, Princeton, 1951.
214. Pólya, G., Szegö, G.: Inequalities for the capacity of a condenser. Am. J. Math. 67 (1945) 1 – 32.
215. Rellich, F.: Ein Satz über mittlere Konvergenz. Math. Nachr. 31 (1930) 30 – 35.
216. Rešetnjak, Ju.G.: On the concept of capacity in the theory of functions with generalized derivatives. Sib. Mat. Zh. 10 (1969) 1109 – 1138 (Russian). English translation: Siberian Math. J. 10 (1969) 818 – 842.
217. Rešetnjak, Ju.G.: Some integral representations of differentiable functions. Sib. Mat. Zh. 12 (1971) 420 – 432 (Russian). English translation: Siberian Math. J. 12 (1971) 299 – 307.
218. Rešetnjak, Ju.G.: Spatial transformations with bounded distortion. Novosibirsk: Nauka, 1982 (Russian).
219. Rickman, S.: Characterization of quasiconformal arcs. Ann. Acad. Sci. Fenn. Ser. AI-395 (1966) 7 – 30.
220. Rosen, G.: Minimum value for C in the Sobolev inequality $\|\varphi^3\| < C\|\text{grad } \varphi\|^3$. SIAM J. Appl. Math. 21 (1971) 30 – 33.
221. Rosenbljum, G.V.: On estimates of the spectrum of the Schrödinger operator. In the book: Problems in mathematical analysis. Leningrad 5 (1975) 152 – 165 (Russian).
222. Šapošnikova, T.O.: Equivalent norms in spaces of functions with fractional or functional smoothness. Sib. Mat. Zh. 21 (1980) 184 – 196 (Russian). English translation: Siberian Math. J. 21 (1980) 450 – 460.
223. Schmidt, E.: Über das isoperimetrische Problem im Raum von n Dimensionen. Math. Z. 44 (1939) 689 – 788.
224. Schwartz, L.: Théorie des distributions. Paris: Hermann, 1973.
225. Sjödin, T.: Capacities of compact sets in linear subspaces of R^n. Pac. J. Math. 78 (1978) 261 – 266.

226. Slobodeckiĭ, L.N.: Generalized S.L. Sobolev spaces and their application to boundary value problems for partial differential equations. Uch. Zap. Lening. pedagogicheskogo Inst. Gercena, 197 (1958) 54–112 (Russian).
227. Smirnov, V.I.: Course in higher mathematics, Vol. 5. Moscow: Nauka, 1959 (Russian). German edition: Lehrgang der höheren Mathematik. Berlin: Deutscher Verlag der Wissenschaften, 1960.
228. Smith, K.T.: Inequalities for formally positive integro-differential forms. Bull. Am. Math. Soc. 67 (1961) 368–370.
229. Sobolev, S.L.: On some estimates relating to families of functions having derivatives that are square integrable. Dokl. Akad. Nauk SSSR. 1 (1936) 267–270 (Russian).
230. Sobolev, S.L.: On a theorem in functional analysis. Math. Sb. 4 (1938) 471–497 (Russian). English translation: Am. Math. Soc. Translations, vol. (2) 34 (1963) 39–68.
231. Sobolev, S.L.: Applications of functional analysis in mathematical physics. Leningrad: Izd. LGU im. A.A. Ždanova, 1950 (Russian). English translation: Am. Math. Soc. Translations, vol. 7 (1963).
232. Sobolev, S.L.: Introduction to the theory of cubature formulas. Moscow: Nauka, 1974 (Russian).
233. Solonnikov, V.A.: On certain properties of $\mathscr{W}_p^l$ spaces of fractional order. Dokl. Akad. Nauk SSSR, 134 (1960) 282–285 (Russian). English translation: Soviet Math. Dokl. 1 (1960) 1071–1074.
234. Solonnikov, V.A.: Inequalities for functions of the classes $W_p^m(R^n)$. Zap. Nauchn. Semin. Leningr. Otd. Mat. Inst. Steklova. 27 (1972) 194–210 (Russian). English translation: J. Soviet Math. 3 (1975) 549–564.
235. Souček, J.: Spaces of functions on the domain Ω whose k-th derivatives are measures defined on $\bar{\Omega}$. Čas. Pestovani Mat. 97 (1972) 10–46, 94.
236. Stampacchia, G.: Problemi al contorno ellittici, con dati discontinui, dotati di soluzioni hölderiane. Ann. Mat. Pura Appl. IV. Ser. 51 (1958) 1–38.
237. Stein, E.M.: Singular integrals and differentiability properties of functions. Princeton, N.J.: Princeton Univ. Press, 1970.
238. Strichartz, R.S.: Multipliers on fractional Sobolev spaces. J. Math. and Mech. 16 (1967) 1031–1060.
239. Taibleson, M.H.: Lipschitz classes of functions and distributions in E_n. Bull. Am. Math. Soc. 69 (1963) 487–493.
240. Taibleson, M.H.: On the theory of Lipschitz spaces of distributions on Euclidean n-space. I Principal properties. J. Math. and Mech. 13 (1964) 407–479.
241. Talenti, G.: Best constant in Sobolev inequality. Ann. Mat. Pura Appl. IV. Ser. 110 (1976) 353–372.
242. Taščijan, G.M.: The classical formula of the asymptotic behavior of the spectrum of elliptic equations that are degenerate on the boundary of the domain. Mat. Zametki, 30 (1981) 871–880 (Russian). English translation: Math. Notes 30 (1981), No. 5–6, (1982) 937–942.
243. Tonelli, L.: L'estremo assoluto degli integrali doppi. Ann. Sc. Norm Super. Pisa, 2 (1933) 89–130.
244. Triebel, H.: Spaces of Besov-Hardy-Sobolev type. Leipzig: Teubner-Texte zur Math., 1978.
245. Triebel, H.: Interpolation theory, function spaces, differential operators. Berlin: VEB Deutscher Verlag der Wissenschaften, 1978.
246. Ural'ceva, N.N.: On the non-selfadjointness in $L_2(R^n)$ of an elliptic operator with rapidly growing coefficients. Zap. Nauchn. Semin. Leningr. Otd. Mat. Inst. Steklova, 14 (1969) 288–294 (Russian).
247. Uspenskiĭ, S.V.: Properties of the W_p^r classes with a fractional derivative on differentiable manifolds. Dokl. Akad. Nauk SSSR, 132 (1960) 60–62 (Russian). English translation: Soviet Math. Dokl. 1 (1960) 495–497.
248. Uspenskiĭ, S.V.: Imbedding theorems for classes with weights. Tr. Mat. Inst. Steklova 60 (1961) 282–303 (Russian). English translation: Amer. Math. Soc. Transl. 87 (1970) 121–145.

249. Vodopjanov, S.K., Gol'dsteĭn, V.M., Latfullin, T.G.: Criteria for extension of functions of the class L_2^1 from unbounded plane domains. Sib. Mat. Zh. 20 (1979) 416–419 (Russian). English translation: Siberian Math. J. 20 (1979) 298–301.

250. Vodopjanov, S.K., Gol'dsteĭn, V.M., Rešetnjak, Ju.G.: On geometric properties of functions with generalized first derivatives. Usp. Mat. Nauk, 34 (1979) 17–65 (Russian). English translation: Russian Math. Surveys 34 (1979) 19–74.

251. Volevič, L.R., Panejakh, B.P.: Certain spaces of generalized functions and embedding theorems. Usp. Mat. Nauk, 20 (1965) 3–74 (Russian). English translation: Russian Math. Surveys 20 (1965) 1–73.

252. Vol'pert, A.I.: The spaces BV and quasi-linear equations. Mat. Sb. 73 (1967) 255–302 (Russian). English translation: Math. USSR-Sb., 2 (1967) 225–267.

253. Whitney, H.: A function not constant on a connected set of critical points. Duke Math. J. 1 (1935) 514–517.

List of Symbols

Function Spaces

Subsets of R^n

Classes of Sets in R^n

Set Functions

m_n, $\mathrm{dist}(E, F)$ ... 1.1.1
H_d ... 1.1.5
μ ... 1.4.1
s, $\sigma(\partial g)$ ... 2.1.1
(p, Φ)-cap(e, Ω), p-cap(e, Ω) 2.2.1
$\pi_{p,M}(F, \Omega)$, $\pi(F, \Omega)$ ... 2.4.1
$\mathfrak{A}_G^{(\alpha)}$, $\mathfrak{A}^{(\alpha)}$ ... 3.2.3
$c_p(K)$ ... 4.1.1
$\mathfrak{A}_G^{(p,\alpha)}$ ... 4.2
$\mathfrak{B}_G^{(p,\alpha)}$ ... 4.4.1
$\tilde{c}_p(K)$ ... 4.11.1
$c_{p,l}(G \backslash F)$ ... 5.6.1
$P_\Omega(\mathscr{E})$, $P(\mathscr{E})$, $P_{C\Omega}$ ... 6.1.1
$\tau_\Omega(\mathscr{E})$ ... 6.3
$|\Omega|$, A_Ω ... 6.3.4
$\zeta_{\mathscr{A}}^{(\alpha)}$ ... 6.5.3
$\mathrm{cap}(e, S_p^l)$, $\mathrm{cap}(E, S_p^l)$, $\overline{\mathrm{cap}}(E, S_p^l)$ ... 7.2.1
μ_E ... 7.2.2
$H(E, \varphi)$ ... 7.2.3
$\mathrm{cap}^+(e, \mathring{L}_p^2(\Omega))$ ... 8.2.1
$\mathrm{Cap}(e, \mathring{L}_p^l(\Omega))$ ... 9.1.1
$\lambda_{p,q}^l(G)$ ... 10.2.1
$D_{p,l}(G, Q_d)$, $D_{p,l}(G)$, $D(G)$. 10.2.2
$\mathrm{Cap}_k(e, \mathring{L}_p^l(Q_{2d}))$ ... 10.3.4
$D_{p,l}(\nu, \Omega)$ ... 12.2
$\varrho = \varrho_{p,l,m}$, $\overset{\infty}{D} = \overset{\infty}{D}_{p,l}(\nu, \Omega)$ ... 12.3.1

Operators

D^α, ∇_l, $\nabla = \nabla_1$ ... 1.1.1
$\mathscr{M}_\varepsilon$ ... 1.1.5
I_l ... 1.4.1; 7.1.2
$\mathring{\mathscr{E}}$ ... 1.5.3
∇_Ω ... 6.1.1
$Fu = \hat{u}$, J_l, $\mathscr{D}_{\{l\}}$ ... 7.1.2
$U_{p,l}\mu$, $V_{p,l}\mu$, $W_{p,l}\mu$, $S_{p,l}\mu$ ... 7.2.2
T ... 8.2.2

Constants

$c, c_1, c_2, \ldots, v_n$ ... 1.1.1
p' ... 1.1.14
ω_n ... 2.1.1
$\mathfrak{M}$ ... 7.2.2

Functions

$N(x)$ ... 2.1.1
u^-, u^+ ... 3.1.1
$\mathfrak{A}_\alpha(M)$ ... 3.2.1
λ_M, λ ... 3.2.4
$\mathfrak{A}_{p,\alpha}(M)$ ... 4.3.1
$v_{M,p}$ ... 4.3.4
$\mathfrak{B}_{p,\alpha}(M)$ ... 4.4.2
$\overset{\infty}{\mathfrak{A}}_{p,\alpha}(M)$, $\overset{\infty}{\mathfrak{A}}_{1,\alpha}(M)$ ... 4.7.1
σ_p ... 4.11.1
γ_p, $\overset{\infty}{\gamma}_p$ ... 5.1.1
$u^*(x)$ ... 6.5.1
$\zeta_\alpha(S)$ ... 6.5.3
$\bar{u}(x)$, $\underline{u}(x)$ ... 6.6.1
η_d ... 10.3.2

Other Symbols

Author Index

Subject Index